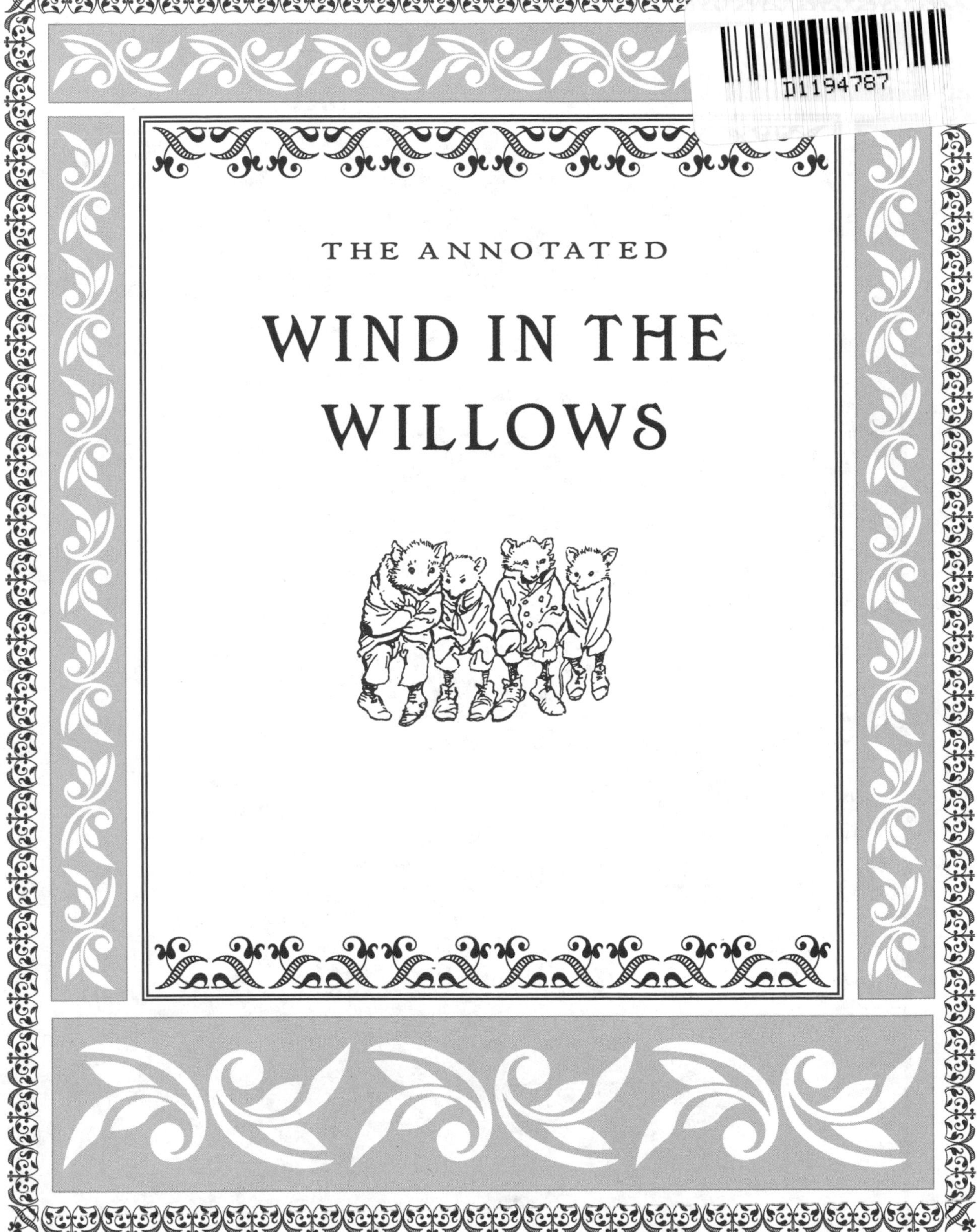

THE ANNOTATED

WIND IN THE WILLOWS

A MAP OF THE WILD WOOD

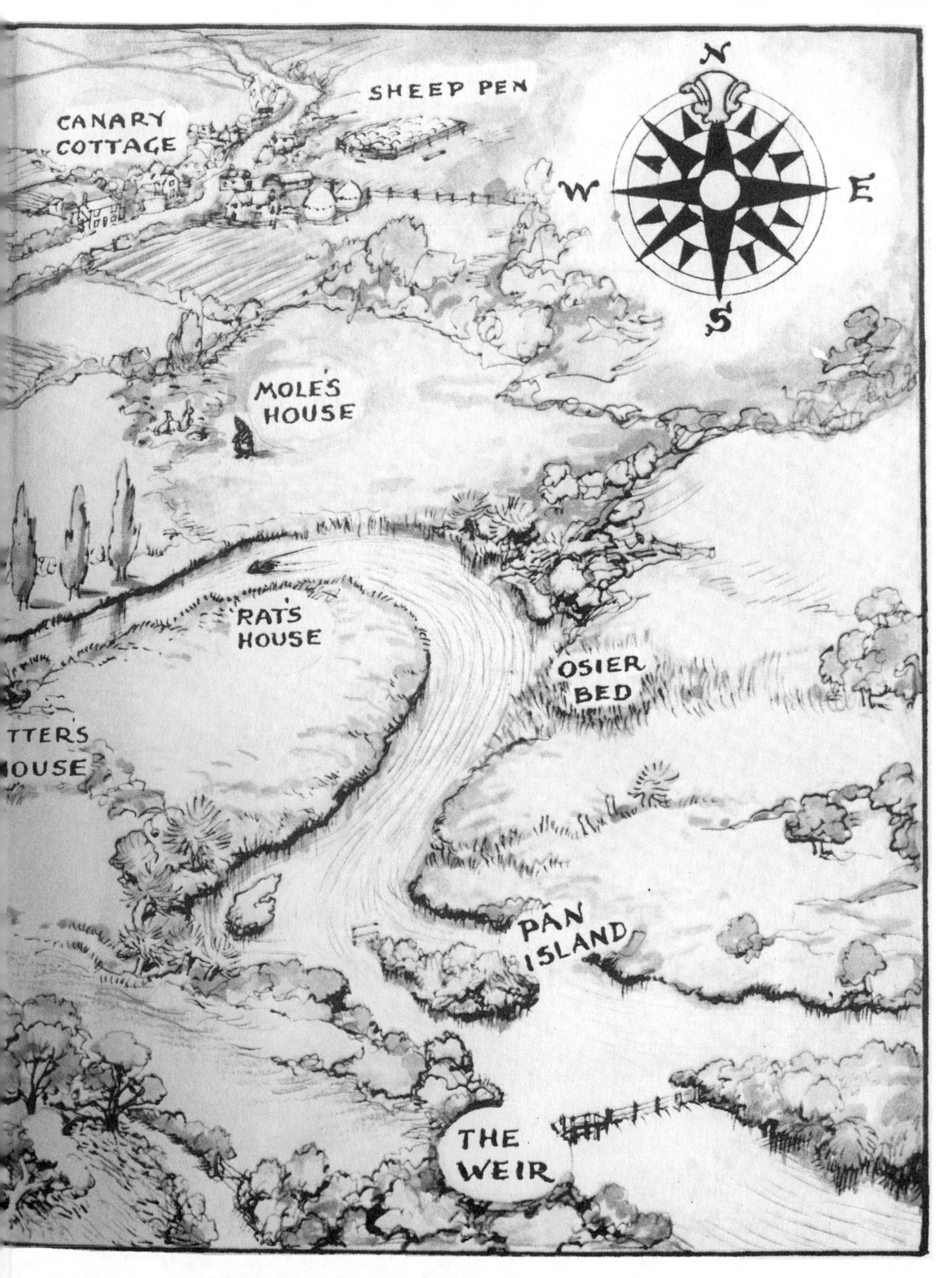

AND SURROUNDING COUNTRY

OTHER ANNOTATED BOOKS FROM W. W. NORTON & COMPANY

The Annotated Alice
by Lewis Carroll, edited with an introduction
and notes by Martin Gardner

The Annotated Wizard of Oz
by L. Frank Baum, edited with an introduction
and notes by Michael Patrick Hearn

The Annotated Huckleberry Finn
by Mark Twain, edited with an introduction
and notes by Michael Patrick Hearn

The Annotated Christmas Carol
by Charles Dickens, edited with an introduction
and notes by Michael Patrick Hearn

The New Annotated Sherlock Holmes, Volumes I, II, and III
by Sir Arthur Conan Doyle, edited with an
introduction and notes by Leslie Klinger

The Annotated Classic Fairy Tales
edited with an introduction and notes by Maria Tatar

The Annotated Brothers Grimm
by Jacob and Wilhelm Grimm, with an introduction by A. S. Byatt,
edited with a preface and notes by Maria Tatar

The Annotated Hunting of the Snark
by Lewis Carroll, with an introduction by Adam Gopnik,
edited with notes by Martin Gardner

The Annotated Uncle Tom's Cabin
by Harriet Beecher Stowe, edited with an introduction
and notes by Henry Louis Gates Jr. and Hollis Robbins

The Annotated Hans Christian Andersen
translated by Maria Tatar and Julie Allen, with an introduction
and notes by Maria Tatar

The Annotated Secret Garden
by Frances Hodgson Burnett, edited with an introduction
and notes by Gretchen Holbrook Gerzina

The New Annotated Dracula
by Bram Stoker, with an introduction by Neil Gaiman,
edited with a preface and notes by Leslie S. Klinger

KENNETH GRAHAME

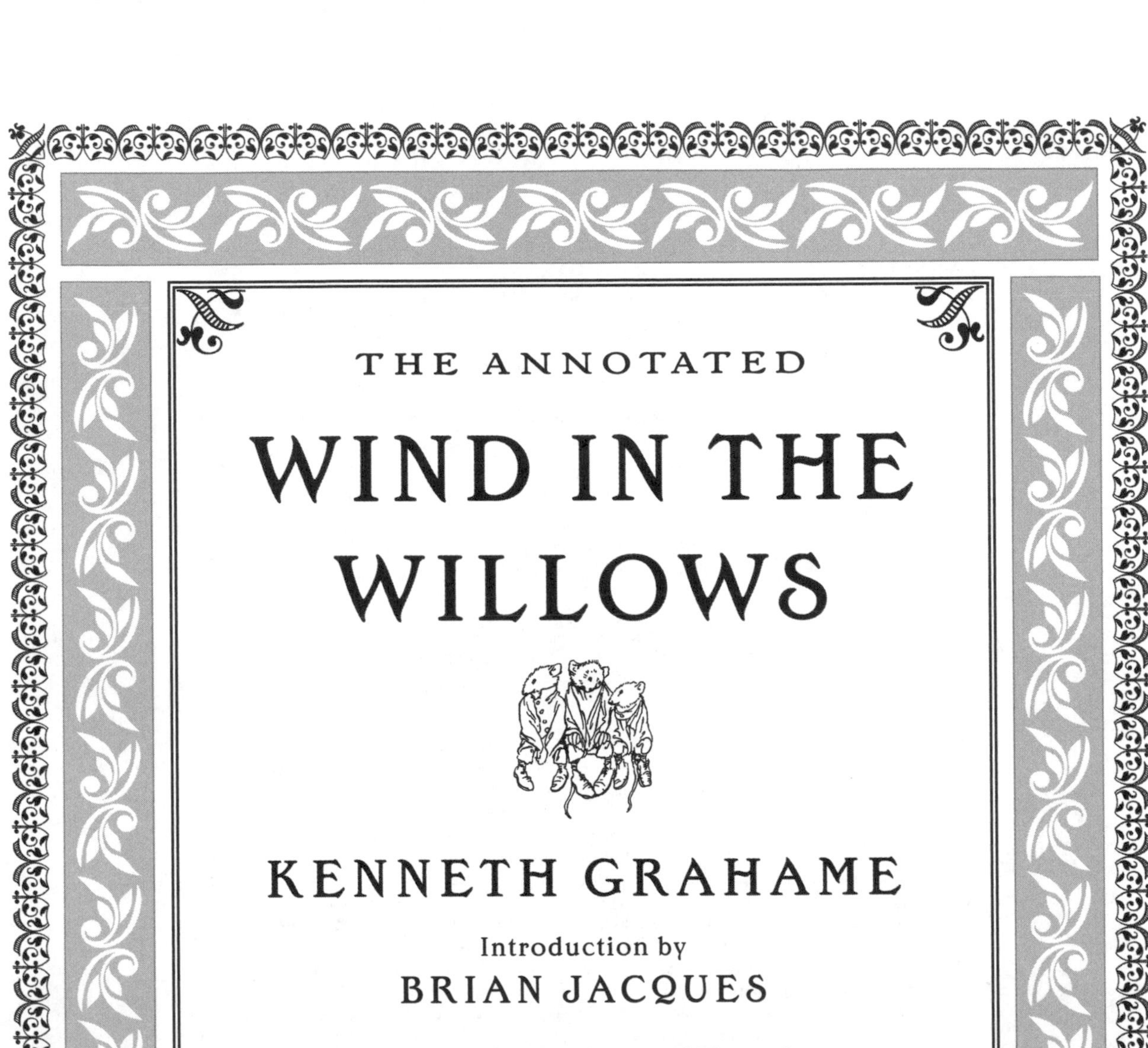

THE ANNOTATED

WIND IN THE WILLOWS

KENNETH GRAHAME

Introduction by

BRIAN JACQUES

Edited with a Preface and Notes by

ANNIE GAUGER

W. W. NORTON & COMPANY

New York London

Printed in the United States of America

Book design by JAM design
Production manager: Julia Druskin

ISBN 978-1-61523-529-2

W. W. Norton & Company, Inc.
500 Fifth Avenue, New York, N.Y. 10110

W. W. Norton & Company Ltd.
Castle House, 75/76 Wells Street, London W1T 3QT

Frontispiece: Original pen-and-ink portrait of Kenneth Grahame. Unsigned but attributed to Herbert Cole (1867–1930). Courtesy of the David J. Holmes Collection. Illustrations by Ernest H. Shepard reprinted with the permission of Athaneum Books for Young Readers, an imprint of Simon & Schuster Children's Publishing Division, from *The Wind in the Willows* by Kenneth Grahame, illustrated by Ernest H. Shepard. Copyright 1933, 1953 Charles Scribner's Sons. Copyright renewed © 1961 Ernest H. Shepard. Copyright renewed © 1981 Charles Scribner's Sons and Mary Eleanor Jessie Knox. Illustrations by E. H. Shepard © Estate of E. H. Shepard, reproduced by permission of Curtis Brown Group Ltd., London. The Arthur Rackham pictures are reproduced with the kind permission of his family and The Bridgeman Art Library. Material from the Archives of Charles Scribner's Sons is published with the permission of the Princeton University Library. Illustrations by Alastair Grahame, letters by his governess, Naomi Stott, from Peter M. Green's archive, have been reprinted with the permission of The Harry Ransom Humanities Research Center at the University of Texas at Austin. The text of Kenneth Grahame's "My Dearest Mouse" letters from 1907, as well as various other letters and manuscripts are reprinted with the permission of The Oxford University Chest. Photograph of Arthur Quiller-Couch reprinted with the permission of the President and Fellows of Trinity College, Oxford. Photographs by Nigel McMorris reproduced with the permission of the Kenneth Grahame Society. Photographs, ephemera, and letters are included by the kind courtesy of collectors David J. Holmes and Roger A. Oakes. Facts on File publishing grants permission to reprint certain images from Peter M. Green's *Beyond the Wild Wood: The World of Kenneth Grahame*.

FOR THE GIRLS

Mackenzie Remarkable August Gauger
Cynthia Beatrice Mackenzie

and let's not forget L.L.G.

Contents

Introduction

by Brian Jacques

A vast quantity of water has flowed down the river since October 8, 1908, Methuen's original publication date. However, I wager the current is that same "sleek, sinuous, full-bodied animal, chasing and chuckling, gripping things. . . ." Aye, gripping the imagination and captivating young and old for generations. Kenneth Grahame's tale of an enchanted bygone era. *The Wind in the Willows.*

My first encounter with Mr. Grahame's masterpiece was in the Stanley Road Library. This was situated between the Grosvenor Cinema and a steam laundry, close to the docklands, in my hometown of Liverpool, England. Even as a ten year old, I could not resist the lure of libraries. Hushed rooms, wood block flooring, tightly packed shelves, and the aroma of books, old and new, indescribable, fascinating! My *Wind in the Willows* was a plain little book, green cloth bound, with no brightly illustrated dust jacket. Its muted sage green cover, contrasting with the slim spine, which through exposure to window sunlight had faded to *eau de nil*. I was charmed from the start. "The Mole had been working very hard all the morning, spring-cleaning his little home." And why not? Why shouldn't moles whitewash ceilings, rats paddle boats, badgers sit snoozing in armchairs, and toads have hilarious escapades on various forms of transport?

Fie upon those dullards who scorn anthropomorphic animals, a plague upon their houses, say I! This became doubly clear to me in adult years, when being interviewed about my own first major novel. A lady (seemingly well educated) asked me how a mouse, tending to an injured fox, could lift up the unconscious fox's head? I told her, in no uncertain terms, that she should read *Wind in the Willows* and discover how a toad drives a horse and caravan!

Kenneth Grahame (stout fellow) never had any qualms about mixing animals with humankind. In front of me is a *Willows* edition, with a full-page illustration of Toad, at a railway station booking office. He is disguised as a washerwoman, mob cap, apron, billowing skirts, and cape, in a roomful of people, all in Victorian costume. Soldiers, nursemaids, children and their parents, porters, a ticket clerk, etc. Nobody there seems the least taken aback, or pays much attention, to a feminine-clad amphibian. Bear in mind, this is a stroke of good luck for him, as a nearby fellow is reading a copy of *The Times*, but he is ignoring the banner headline, "Toad Escapes!" Still, we often tend to miss things, don't we. It only struck me, when I was twelve years old, that I knew the words of "Ducks' Ditty," the music also. I learned it at age six, in Miss Taggart's class, at St. John's Infant School (Kirkdale, Liverpool). When I read the book, at age ten, I must have glossed over the piece, in my initial hasty foray into the *Willows*. Two years later, I recall rereading the work, more diligently (slowed down, no doubt, by the weight of years). Imagine my delight at finding a verse that I was familiar with.

Everyone for what he likes!
We like to be
Heads down, tails up,
Dabbling free!

Picture Ratty, with a foaming tankard in one paw, leaning against an upright piano, surrounded by his friends at some riverbank inn, singing lustily. I like to think that, somewhere among the notes in Kenneth Grahame's manuscripts, there exist music sheets to accompany the libretti of the verses. Toad's compositions are particularly enjoyable, outrageously conceited, but jolly good fun, notably his snub to academic scions.

The clever men at Oxford,
Know all there is to be knowed,
But none of them know one half as much
As intelligent Mr. Toad!

Which, as Mr. Grahame assures us, was among the milder verses. Music has always played a major part in my life. (I mean real music, not the efforts of certain callow youths, who sound as though they are bent upon destorying a drainpipe with a shovel.)

Sometimes, when on a country ramble, I'll linger beside a tranquil lake or woodland stream, picturing *Willow* scenes muscially. Pond weed drifting idly on green-tinted water, patrolled by caddisfly and banded demoiselle, whilst Debussy's *Afternoon of a Faun* plays in the background of my mind. Can you picture it, inhabited by Mole and Ratty. Two small animals, taking their ease in the little blue and white boat, with not a care in their world, apart from the best spot to put in for a picnic. Drifting out of the trees, onto the open country, meandering with the flow, through meadow and field. Distant church spires, framed by aspen, poplar, and silver birch. Now a wonderful orchestral arrangement of Vaughan Williams's *Fantasia on "Greensleeves"* swells out over the terrain. I know that later, when twilight falls, that same small boat, with our friends in it, will be bound homeward, with maybe a twinkling lantern on the stern, drifting into the sun's last crimson rays. And what more fitting accompaniment to wend them on their way than Mascagni's Intermezzo from *Cavalleria Rusticana*. Though as I recall, on that first trip, they ended up at Ratty's cottage. The Mole was grateful to be there, though as the tale progresses he is often homesick, longing for his humble abode.

Aye, dear little humdrum Mole, my music for him is "The Old Castle" from Mussorgsky's *Pictures at an Exhibition*. Solitary with few light passages, in keeping with the moleish feeling. He is by no means as dashing as his companions, Ratty or Toad, neither is he much of a fashion icon. I often wonder is Ratty merely being kind when he comments on Mole's attire. "I like your clothes awfully, old chap. I'm going to get a black velvet smoking suit myself some day, as soon as I can afford it."

Mole however, is oblivious to such remarks, more entralled by the experiences a burgeoning newfound world has to offer, counting himself fortunate to be taken under the wing of such a top-hole chap as Ratty. He is every child basically, curious, questioning, obedient, and ever willing to learn. Throughout the *Willows* narration, Mole grows in confidence and ability, emerging as a fully fledged hero. I find myself touched by the results of his transformation when, on the final page, mother weasels pointed out to their young ones: "And yonder comes the famous Mr. Mole, of whom you so often have heard your father tell!" Praise indeed, from a vermin matriarch. Mole could be any growing child learning life's lessons, from Pinocchio to Oliver Twist.

From the illustrations by E. H. Shepard (which he enhanced with color in 1953), I see the rat is brown. *Rattus norvegicus*, often seen swimming in the water, hence the title of Water Rat. Now you will pardon me for mentioning, but are rats not described widely as pests? Vermin that foul, and gnaw on, food stores. Usually at home in sewers, liable to contract, and transmit, diseases. Why then did the good Mr. Grahame choose a rat as one of his heroes? However, reason led me to deduce that this was no run-of-the-mill slinking scabrous beast, this is Ratty. Made more palatable by the inclusion of two letters to his name. Yes, Ratty! A good egg and a stout fellow. See him as Mole first does: "A little brown face, with whiskers. A grave round face, with the same twinkle in its eye that had first attracted his notice. Small neat ears and thick silky hair. It was the Water Rat!" Added to which, he was wearing lace-up plimsolls, white shirt, and white trousers, supported by a decidedly sporty red belt. For the space of a single illustration we see Ratty in a rather fetching white hat, probably of the type worn by coves who like messing about in boats. How could both we, and Mole, not take an instant shine to him? Ratty, the debonair chum, at once impeccably mannered and suitably attired. He could have sprung from the pages of some Victorian school novel, the popular and good-natured Head Boy, a sympathetic paw around the shoulders of some bewildered new pupil. My musical signature for Ratty would be something light, jolly, but precise. The Eton boating song would fit the bill admirably. In some ways I like to think that Ratty is a protégé of the Badger. Good old Badger, the paternal host, pillar of sagacity, upholder of woodland lore and law. Unswervingly loyal and continually helpful, there is not the slightest doubt who rules the roost in the Wild Wood. Badger!

> "Who is it at *this* time, disturbing people on such a night? Speak up!"
>
> "Oh, Badger," cried the rat, "let us in, please. It's me, Rat, and my friend Mole, and we've lost our way in the snow."
>
> "What, Ratty, my dear little man!" exclaimed the Badger, in quite a different voice. "Come along in, both of you, at once. Why, you must be perished. Well I never! Lost in the snow! And in the Wild Wood, too, and at this time of night! But come in with you."

Notice, there is no mention of beasts, animals, or creatures here. Kenneth Grahame has Badger referring to himself as "people," and Ratty as a "little man." The Wild Wood is a somewhat murky, downmarket neighborhood, populated mainly by weasels, yet Badger chooses to live there, by and large for the good of that area. Noble fellow! What do you think his musical endorsement should be? Blake's *New Jerusalem*, or perhaps Bizet's duet from *The Pearl Fishers*, "Au fond du temple saint," an affirmation of comradeship.

So now we are gathered in Badger's comfortable home, to enjoy a hearty repast in front of a roaring fire, sheltered from the dark forest, safe from the snowstorm. They chat amiably, discussing this and that. Until the dreaded subject confronts them . . . Toad! Need I say more? Toad! The harum-scarum, devil-may-care flouter of all convention and manners. Toad! The original rich, spoiled, self-willed naughty boy, whom we have all at some point in life encountered. Toad, with money to burn and indulge his many whims, with not the least thought to consequences, either to himself or others. And what pray is the scallywag up to now? Why, smashing up motor-cars, to be sure.

> "How many has he had?" inquired the Badger gloomily.
>
> "Smashes, or machines?" asked the Rat. "Oh, well, after all, it's the same thing—with Toad. This is the seventh. As for the others—you know that coach-house of his? Well, it's piled up—literally piled up to the roof—with fragments of motor-cars, none of them bigger than your hat! That accounts for the other six—so far as they can be accounted for."
>
> "He's been in hospital three times," put in the Mole; "and as for the fines he's had to pay, it's simply awful to think of."

In those long-ago pre-television days, young lads like myself would listen to radio (or "the wireless," as it was known). Nightly we would gather round to hear the latest escapades of a serial hero named Dick Barton, Special Agent! The signature tune to this was a rousing piece by one Charles Williams, entitled "Devil's Gallop," just the stuff that would have suited Toad. That and a whole mishmash of Tchaikovsky's *1812 Overture*, Offenbach's "Can Can," Suppe's "Light Cavalry," Gayaneh's "Sabre Dance" . . . the list is endless. Anarchic arias for an absurd amphibian! Toad is Frank Richards's Billy Bunter, Richmal Crompton's Just William, Peck's Bad Boy, and the comic mainstay of *Wind in the Willows*. Witness his first hypnotic meeting with the motorcar.

> Toad sat straight down in the middle of the dusty road, his legs stretched out before him, and stared fixedly in the direction of the disappearing motor-car. He breathed short, his face wore a placid, satisifed expression, and at intervals he faintly murmured "Poop-poop!"

In those two simple words we have the fate of Toad sealed. The adventure then for him is all blood and thunder. Toad goes from motorcar theft to magistrate's court; from prison escape, in the guise of a washerwoman, to a hair-raising chase on a steam railway engine. As if that is not sufficient drama, he is drubbed soundly by a lady bargee, and flung into the river. Undaunted, he takes his revenge by stealing her barge horse. Toad sells the horse for six shillings and six pence (plus a plate of hot stew) to a gypsy. Gobbling down the stew, which contains partridge, pheasant, chicken, hares, rabbits, peahens, guinea fowls, and one or two other things, and which probably would have slain any self-respecting vegetarian (pish tush to them, and good health to ravenous Toad), he sets off refreshed, with money in his apron pocket, giving voice to an outrageously conceited song, made up on the spur of the moment.

> *The world has held great Heroes,*
> *As history-books have showed,*
> *But never a name to go down to fame*
> *Compared with that of Toad!*

As stated earlier, together with other bizarre stanzas, this was one of the milder verses. Continuing his criminal career, Toad, still in washerwoman costume, through trickery and shameless blubbering manages to obtain a lift in yet another motorcar, from two charitable gentlemen. He repays their kindness by commandeering the driver's seat, accelerating furiously, and sending the vehicle hurtling into a pond, along with its two gentlemen! He is away again, singing and chortling happily.

The motor-car went Poop-poop-poop,
as it raced along the road.
Who was it steered it into a pond?
Ingenious Mr. Toad!

But he is spotted, by a uniformed chauffeur and two hefty rural policemen. Yet again Toad has to flee.

Escaping his pursuers, the rascally Toad lands up on Ratty's front doorstep. There he learns, to his dismay, that his ancestral home, Toad Hall, has fallen into the clutches of vermin. Savage stoats, wily weasels, and furtive ferrets, the real villains of the piece. What to do? That's when one finds who his true friends are! Badger, Ratty, and Mole, despite Toad's previous reprehensible behavior, rally to his aid.

Badger, wise chap that he is, has a plan. This involves a secret tunnel (oh joy) that leads into Toad Hall and comes up, through the squeaky floorboard, into the butler's pantry. Suitably armed with swords, clubs, and pistols, several sets of handcuffs, some bandages and sticking plaster, and a flask and sandwich case. What equipment! But cease and desist, hold hard! My brain reels, it's all become too exciting for words!!!

Suffice it to say, dear friend, that our comrades carry all before them. The day is won, Toad Hall recaptured, and those dreadful vermin get the drubbing they so richly deserve. A fitting finale to a splendid epic, with Badger, Ratty, Mole, and Toad taking their place in Wild Woods annals as legendary warriors. And happily, we find that the owner of Toad Hall leaves behind his wayward seasons, finally succumbing to the genteel life of a country squire. As the author assures us . . . "He was indeed an altered Toad!" (Cue Sir

Edward Elgar's "Land of Hope and Glory," with perhaps a *soupçon* of the "Knightsbridge March.")

I have glossed over many parts of *Willows*, giving mere thumbnail sketches of the main characters, and the taste of childish delight I felt at the escapades of Toad. There is, however, one section of Kenneth Grahame's story that enthralled my imagination, so mystical, enigmatic, so magical.

The Piper at the Gates of Dawn!

Ratty and Mole find themselves in the presence of a demigod, the great Pan! Suddenly the forest daybreak is suffused with, to my mind, *Morning*, from Edvard Grieg's *Peer Gynt*. The hooved creature, with powerful hirsute lower limbs, horns sprouting from between his curled locks, hook-nosed, smiling eyes, and goatee beard, playing his pipes melodically. The lost baby otter sleeping peacefully in front of him. This is an image that will stay with me all my life.

Kenneth Grahame (1859–1932) was a gentleman who, from my brief knowledge of his circumstances, did not have a particularly happy life. Denied his desire for a university education, he worked as a bank clerk, lost a son to suicide, and suffered much ill health. Sir, how in the midst of all this did you find and create such a wondrous fable? Did you find solace and friendship in Mole, Ratty, Badger, and the irrepressible Mr. Toad? It is my earnest hope that somewhere, in some serene wooded backwater, you are spending many halcyon days with your beloved companions, taking picnics with sangwiches. I love Ratty's word "sangwich." I had many such boyhood sangwiches; they tasted so much better than correctly spelled sandwiches. I will leave you, with Puccini's Humming Chorus, from *Madama Butterfly*, in peace. Finally, I commend *The Wind in the Willows* to all the generations, both bygone and yet to come, who have shared, and will share, your beautiful tale. Thank you, Kenneth.

DR. BRIAN JACQUES, PHD L HC
Liverpool, October 2007

Preface

by Annie Gauger

Kenneth Grahame was born on March 8, 1859, to James Cunningham Grahame and Bessie Ingles. They lived at 32 Castle Street in Edinburgh, Scotland, across the road from the last home of novelist Sir Walter Scott. Self-described as a "mid-Victorian" and thought of as the quintessentially "English" author, Grahame was actually the third of four children born into a solid Scottish family of accountants and advocates.

In April of 1864, shortly after giving birth to Kenneth's younger brother, Roland, Bessie Grahame contracted scarlet fever. On the day she died, Kenneth also came down with the disease. Though he eventually recovered, the boy was to be plagued by respiratory ailments for the rest of his life. Their mother dead and their father paralyzed by grief, the four Grahame children were sent to live in southern England with their maternal grandmother. Unable to keep close tabs on four energetic children, Granny Ingles, as she was known, allowed the Grahame children free rein around The Mount, the large house where they lived in the small town of Cookham Dean, a picturesque, Thames-side town thirty-five miles from London.

The Cookham adventures of the Grahame children, Helen, Willie, Kenneth, and Roland, would later serve as inspiration for Grahame's best-selling books of the 1890s. *The Golden Age,* published in 1895, and *Dream Days*, published in 1898, featured children much like the Grahames "without the proper equipment of parents."[1]

After two years at The Mount, one of Kenneth's uncles convinced Granny Ingles to shutter her large and unmanageable house. Just before Christmas of 1865, one of the chimneys toppled over in a gale, leaving the structure in questionable condition. Granny Ingles and the children all moved to a small cottage in Cranbourne, where they lived in tight quarters until Grahame's father came to collect his children. When James Cunningham Grahame brought his children back to Scotland it seemed that he had pulled himself together. He had gained a respectable post as sheriff-substitute of Argyllshire in Inveraray and had every intention of supporting his family. But it soon became clear that he never recovered from his wife's death. Within three years he resigned from his post and sent his children back to relatives in England. He eventually retired to Le Havre, France, where he would die of complications related to alcoholism twenty years later.

When they returned to England, Kenneth and Willie were sent to St. Edward's, a new boarding school founded in 1863 on New Inn Hall Street in the heart of Oxford. Willie was forced to withdraw by 1871 due to a chronic bronchial condition, but Kenneth remained and thrived there until his graduation in 1875. Compared to other schools at the time, St. Edward's had few restrictions on what its students could do in their free time. As in Cookham Dean, Grahame was allowed to explore the riverbanks of Oxford and the surrounding town.

With its medieval cobbled streets and crowds of pedestrians, Oxford in the 1870s was a throwback to the days before bicycles and the automobile. Populated by men in subfusc,[2] the town reveled in academic ritual and pageantry. Though Oxford was a happy place for Kenneth—he was allowed to explore the different colleges in the company of the intellectual and social

1. Kenneth Grahame, *The Golden Age* (John Lane / The Bodley Head, 1895), 3. Grahame's books were so popular in the 1890s that other publishers sought out authors who could produce similar works. Grahame's satirical collections about children and childhood from an adult perspective served as inspiration for E. Nesbit, whose books also chronicle the lives of children. Nesbit's most well-known books with similar themes are *The Story of the Treasure-Seekers* (1898), *The Wouldbegoods* (1899), *Five Children and It* (1902), *The Phoenix and the Carpet* (1904), *The Story of the Amulet* (1905), and *The Railway Children* (1906).

2. The academic garb required at Oxford and Cambridge for formal occasions and exams.

elite—his life was soon to be marked by tragedy and disappointment. On New Year's Eve of 1874, the winter before Kenneth's graduation, his brother Willie died unexpectedly of a pulmonary inflammation. Compounding his grief, John Grahame, Kenneth's uncle, informed him that he would not be allowed to attend Oxford University upon graduation from St. Edward's. An Oxford education was a rite of passage for the English upper classes—the company Kenneth had become accustomed to keeping. Grahame and his uncle, however, were of the Scottish middle class. Though the family could afford to send him, Uncle John told Kenneth that Oxford was out of the question, and he sent Kenneth to London, where he became a clerk in his uncle's Westminster firm of Grahame, Currie, and Spens.

Two years later, as a newly minted clerk for the Bank of England—a position gained through family connections—Grahame made the acquaintance of scholar Frederick James Furnivall while dining alone one night in Soho. Furnivall edited scholarly editions of classic literary works, and he had been instrumental in founding the New Shakespere [*sic*] Society and the Early English Text Society. He was also a rowing enthusiast who ran a working man's rowing club on the Thames. Though he never learned to swim, Furnivall was a champion rower and even had a wager boat designed especially for him. According to Peter Green, one of several Grahame biographers, it was Furnivall who taught Grahame how to row. Soon after befriending Furnivall, Grahame became secretary to the New Shakespere Society, keeping the minutes and the ledgers for their meetings. During this period, as Grahame began to write essays and poems, he shared his lodgings with his younger brother, Roland, who over the years would borrow large sums of money from him. Though the two worked together at the Bank, they gradually became estranged. Roland disappeared after Kenneth lent him £200 in 1912, a debt that was never repaid. Only Helen Grahame, Kenneth's older sister, knew of his death in October 1929.

In 1884 Grahame visited the Lizard Peninsula, in Cornwall, the southernmost tip of England. His traveling companion was his older sister, Helen. Two years later they traveled to Italy together, visiting their cousin Annie and staying with their aunt, Georgina Grahame, in Villino Landau, near Florence.[3]

3. In 1902, Georgina Grahame, Kenneth's aunt, published *In a Tuscan Garden* with John Lane. The book gives no author credit, but in the John Lane archives (Harry Ransom Humanities Research Center, The University of Texas at Austin) the readers' notes reveal that the manuscript was clearly sub-

Both places enchanted Kenneth, making him long for southern Europe and warmer climes, themes that would recur in his writing. In 1888, Grahame's first published work, "By a Northern Furrow," appeared in the *St. James Gazette*. A year later, as he began to contribute regularly to both the *St. James Gazette* and the *National Observer*, Kenneth was transferred to the Secretary's Office of the Bank of England. Now more affluent, Grahame was able to travel more often. In 1890, at the age of thirty-one, he visited Venice for the first time. Venice would find its way into his essays, and of course, years later, into chapter IX of *The Wind in the Willows*. Each of Grahame's travels inspired more articles. In three years he had enough essays for a book, *The Pagan Papers*, which received mixed reviews upon its publication by John Lane in 1893.

In 1894 Grahame set up house at 5 Kensington Crescent with a barrister named Tom Greg. In July of that year he published his first essay in *The Yellow Book*, a literary quarterly that ran for thirteen installments from 1894 to 1897. The essay "The Roman Road" was reprinted the following February in his second collection, *The Golden Age*, which received rave reviews. With the money from these publications, Kenneth Grahame took a spring vacation to Alassio, Italy—a location he would later draw on when composing the detailed description of Mole End in chapter V of *The Wind in the Willows*.

Late in 1897, Grahame met his future wife, Elspeth Thomson. Like Kenneth, Elspeth had been born in Edinburgh.[4] Her father, an inventor, died when she was ten. He had taken out patents on the pneumatic tire and a glass-nib pen, among other items, which included the first floating dock and, most significantly, the first steam-driven road vehicle—the ancestor to the motorcar. Elspeth's mother, who was wealthy, then married a man named John Fletcher Moulton, a London barrister, who later went into politics. Elspeth lived with Moulton, who had used Elspeth's mother's fortune to rise to the role of Lord of Appeal. Other than writing a penny novelette called *Amelia Jane's Ambition*, published in 1888 under the pseudonym Clarence Onslow, Elspeth had done little except, as Grahame's second biographer has put it, "feed on the personalities of artistic celebrities, and use their genius as a prop

mitted by Mrs. Grahame. According to the readers' reports at the HRC, Lane declined to publish a later book because the author proved too temperamental to work with.

4. Born on January 3, 1862, she was the second of four children.

for her own lack of creative talent" (Peter Green, *Kenneth Grahame: A Biography* [Cleveland and New York: Cleveland World Publishers, 1959], 202).

Green speculates that the couple met when Grahame paid a visit to Fletcher Moulton on behalf of the Bank of England. Kenneth would have been greeted by Elspeth, then thirty-five. The gainfully employed and erudite Grahame was three years her senior. The following year, at the age of thirty-nine, he would be appointed Secretary of the Bank of England—one of the youngest Secretaries on record. Grahame seemed to be the perfect bachelor. He had a solid position, yet he was also artistic and had gained significant notoriety for his writing. In December of 1898 he published his third collection of essays, *Dream Days.* Except for "A Departure" and "The Reluctant Dragon," all of the essays had already been published in magazines. The book was praised by critics and proved popular among readers. It was his second major literary success.[5] In one of the essays, "A Saga of the Seas," Grahame describes a fantasy princess he comes to rescue: a no-nonsense encounter that may have been a description of Elspeth, written with characteristic emotional aloofness:

> I came upon her at last in the big state-cabin in the stern; and she wore a holland pinafore over her Princess-clothes, and she had brown wavy hair, hanging down her back, just like—well, never mind, she had brown wavy hair. When gentle-folk meet, courtesies pass; and I will not weary other people with relating all the compliments and counter-compliments that we exchanged, all in the most approved manner. Occasions like this, when tongues wagged smoothly and speech flowed free, were always especially pleasing to me, who am naturally inclined to be tongue-tied with women. But at last ceremony was over, and we sat on the table and swung our legs and agreed to be fast friends. And I showed her my latest knife—one-bladed, horn-handled, terrific, hung round my neck with string; and she showed me the chiefest treasures the ship contained, hidden away in a most private and particular locker—a musical box with a glass top that let you see the works, and a railway train with real lines and a real tunnel, and a tin iron-clad that followed a magnet,

5. According to Peter Green, the *Athenaeum* "decided that *Dream Days* was not so much a children's book as a collection of stories about children for grown-up people" (*Kenneth Grahame: A Biography*, 171).

> and was ever so much handier in many respects than the real full-sized thing that still lay and applauded in the offing. (*Dream Days* [London: John Lane / The Bodley Head, 1898, 168–69)

With the new book a success, Grahame was at his peak both in his professional career and as a writer. On April 3, 1899, however, he fell ill with pneumonia and empyema.[6]

Kenneth went to Cornwall with his sister, Helen, to convalesce, all the while corresponding with Elspeth. Grahame's letters from this period, written in a sort of baby-talk gibberish, are unlike the rest of his correspondence. They are written in pencil and, as biographer Alison Prince points out, they were sometimes written in secret. In one letter, Grahame wrote, "this is a smuggled line—for I am not supposed to sit up writing letters yet" (Bodleian MS. eng. misc. e 480). All of Grahame's penciled notes survive, while Elspeth's responses do not. In a time when written correspondence was central to all relationships, the lack of letters from Elspeth is curious. One wonders if Grahame disposed of them, or if they got lost in a move, or if Elspeth destroyed them as part of her later campaign to control Kenneth Grahame's legacy.

During the convalescence Helen and Kenneth stopped in Torquay for ten days, and then went on to Fowey, a harborside town in Cornwall. Fowey, like Cookham Dean, was littered with boats. The mouth of the Fowey River was near enough to the ocean to bring interesting, seaworthy vessels into the harbor and upriver. When he was able, every day, if he could, Grahame was up and exploring the shorelines. He often kept the company of Arthur Quiller-Couch, an academic who had retired to Fowey in order to write full time and boat.

Another companion was Edward Atkinson, or Atky, the commodore of the Fowey Yacht Club and the owner of over thirty boats.[7] Vivid memories of the friendships Grahame forged among boating partners, and on the riverbanks of Fowey, were to find their way into *The Wind in the Willows* eight years later. By the time summer rolled around, Grahame had recovered from his illness and seemed ready to get on with his life. On July 1, 1899, there was a public

6. Not to be confused with emphysema, empyema is an affliction of the pleural space outside of the lungs, often a complication of pneumonia.

7. Atkinson's family made a fortune manufacturing lavender water and perfume. The company's most popular product was Atkinson's Essence of White Rose.

announcement in the London *Morning Post* that Kenneth and Elspeth were to be married. The engagement brought about a rift between Kenneth and his sister, who did not care for Elspeth. When Helen saw the announcement, she asked her brother if he really intended to marry Elspeth. His despondent reply was, "I suppose so; I suppose so."[8] Helen left Fowey and moved permanently to the Lizard Peninsula. Kenneth and Elspeth were married on July 22.

Photograph of "Q," Arthur Quiller-Couch, as an older man in his captain's hat. *Courtesy of Trinity College Oxford Archives.*

Elspeth had many literary friends and acquaintances. Shortly after the ceremony she wrote to Emma (Mrs. Thomas) Hardy to express her dismay that Kenneth continued to spend a great deal of time with his boating companions. She seemed shocked that he preferred the company of his male peers to her own. Mrs. Hardy replied, "hundreds of wives go through a phase of disillusionment." Grahame's sister wasn't the only woman who had been alienated by the new union. When he returned to London, Grahame found that his housekeeper at 5 Kensington Crescent, Sarah Bath, was not interested in remaining in his employ. According to Prince's meticulously researched biography, Bath, "who specialized in bachelors," ". . . had not forgiven Elspeth for the impropriety of forcing her way, unchaperoned, into Kenneth's presence, thus, in Sarah's view, deliberately compromising his honor and forcing him to marry her" (*Kenneth Grahame: An Innocent in the Wild Wood* [London: Allison & Busby Ltd, 1994], 171).

Grahame accepted the estrangement from Helen, left 5 Kensington Crescent, leased 16 Durham Villas in Campden Hill (London), and moved there with his new wife. It was at this new house that the Grahames were to raise their only child, Alastair, and where, only a few years later, Grahame began to tell Alastair a series of nightly bedtime stories that much later would become *The Wind in the Willows.*

Born May 12, 1900, less than ten months after their wedding in Fowey,

8. Personal information to Peter Green, from Barbara Euphan Todd (Green, *Kenneth Grahame: A Biography*, 215).

Photograph of 16 Durham Villas, in Campden Hill, London, where Grahame wrote much of *The Wind in the Willows* in 1908. *Photo by Nigel McMorris. Courtesy of the Kenneth Grahame Society.*

Alastair, or Mouse, as he was nicknamed, was to be Kenneth and Elspeth's only child. Alastair's parents were on the eve of middle age—Elspeth was thirty-seven and Kenneth, forty-one. Kenneth, endowed with generous resources from his previous books and his position at the Bank, and Elspeth, with an inheritance of her own, could afford to hire a succession of housekeepers and nurses as they needed them. Elspeth, who had a difficult time postpartum, came under the care of three different physicians who treated her for nervous ailments. It seems she had been traumatized by the birth of Alastair, and it appears that she did not want another child. There is a letter in the Grahame archives prescribing a contraceptive—a topic that was rarely discussed openly in Edwardian England—and instructing Elspeth on its application.[9]

As Alastair grew, it became clear that he could not focus his eyes properly. When he was eighteen months old the Grahames took him to an ophthalmologist, who prescribed glasses and diagnosed him with a congenital cataract in his right eye. In a letter written to Dr. William Collins[10] on November 18, 1901, Kenneth Grahame reports that according to Dr. Tweedy (one of the other eye specialists the Grahames consulted), the cataract was possibly "progressive" and likely to worsen. In addition, the boy's left eye was diagnosed as "oversighted" (see chapter I, note 9).

The Grahames did not cope well with the idea that their child might be handicapped. In an undated letter likely from late November 1903,[11] Kenneth Grahame writes at length about his day spent with Alastair in the

9. Some of Elspeth's contraceptive concoction still exists, wrapped in tin foil in Peter Green's papers at the Harry Ransom Humanities Research Center, The University of Texas at Austin.

10. Dr. William Collins was later knighted for his expertise in ophthalmology. Letter courtesy of the David J. Holmes Collection.

11. This letter is placed next to the note describing the shooting at the Bank of England, dated November 24. The two letters are from the Bodleian Library (MS. Eng. misc e. 481), dated 1903–1905.

gardens and on the steps of the Albert Memorial, where they "watched & criticized motors." The letter is written in the same baby talk Grahame used when he was courting Elspeth from Fowey. At this time Alastair would have been around three and a half, still small enough to be in a pram. The letter has the germ of what was to become the "My Dearest Mouse" letters of 1907, which were to be revised into *The Wind in the Willows* a year later.

> Once e ad got is mouf well stuffed wif brednbutter ee sed softly "now tell me about the mole!" So the ole of the time I ad ter [s]pin out mole [s]tories. Eeee is cummin on tremenjus both in ideas & language, & missus nuffin—there was atory in which a mole, a beever a badjer & a water rat was characters & I got them terribly mixed up as I went along but ee always stratened em out & remembered wich was wich.

With Elspeth too weak to participate fully in raising Alastair, Kenneth included her by writing her notes and letters describing the growth of their son. In the same letter as above, Grahame mentions their nanny, whom they referred to as "D" or "Dutchy":

> I erd i[m] telling D arterwards "And do you no Nanny, the Mole saved up al is money & went & bought a motor car! gave hundreds of pounds for it! fancy, *an animal*, Nanny![")
>
> You will perceive by this that Mr Mole has been goin the pace since he first went [on] his simple boatin spedishin wif the Water Rat. Arter that he ran races on the grass. Poor little fellow!

Life at Durham Villas revolved around Alastair, and it seems that Kenneth lost all interest in writing. His stream of stories and essays—a total of sixty-nine since 1888—simply dried up. Grahame's letters, the only thing he was writing at this time, are all in baby talk. After the banner year of 1898, when Grahame published *Dream Days* and a long story called *The Headswoman*, he wrote nothing but a few essays: a preface to Eugene Field's *Lullaby Land* in 1898 and, in 1899, an introduction to P. J. Billinghurst's *A Hundred Fables of Aesop.* In 1899 an essay, "The Fabric of the Fairy Tale," was published in a review of children's books in the *Daily Mail*. Through it all, Grahame kept his job at the Bank. Artistically he thought of himself "as a spring, not a pump."[12] In the collection of Grahame's letters in the Bodleian Library (e. 481), an urgent note dated November 24, 1903, on Bank of England stationery, might help explain why Grahame's spring of artistic creativity went dry between the years of 1903 and 1908:

> Darling M.—Just a line to tell you not to be alarmed at any rumours or statements on posters & c. There was a lunatic in here this morning, "shooting free" with a revolver, but *nobody* got hurt at all, except the lunatic, who was secured after some trouble.

The shooting was one of the odder episodes in Grahame's professional life. At about 11:00 in the morning on November 24, a respectably dressed gentleman by the name of George F. Robinson came to call on the governor of the Bank. Robinson was a socialist turned radical anarchist and seemed intent on making a scene. The governor was not in that day, so Grahame, the acting Secretary, invited Robinson into his office, upon which the stranger produced two scrolls of rolled-up papers, one tied with a white ribbon and the other with black. Robinson asked Grahame to choose one; Grahame grew irritated and refused, so Robinson pulled out a service revolver and started shooting. Grahame got out of the room, escaping harm, but his nerves were tried.[13] When the public heard of the incident Grahame's fans were outraged. Hundreds of notes of sympathy and support were sent to him at the bank.

The Robinson affair seems to have had a formative impact on Grahame's view of class and its effect on culture. Though solidly in the upper class himself, Grahame had met people who had amassed great wealth, through family ties or industry. His friend Atkinson from Fowey was just such a person, with a riverside house and over thirty boats moored in the current. On the other side of the spectrum were those who wanted land and tax reform—demands that ultimately imperiled the way of life that Grahame championed in *The Wind in the Willows*. Grahame was a conservative by nature—after all, he worked in a bank—and every day he witnessed how the wealthiest used

12. See Elspeth Grahame's *First Whisper of "The Wind in the Willows"* (Philadelphia and New York: J. P. Lippincott, 1945), 4.

13. Robinson was later committed to Broadmoor, a hospital for the criminally insane in Berkshire.

their fortunes. In a story called "A Falling Out" in *The Golden Age*, Grahame describes where he worked: "and the window of the bank, wherein gold was thought so little of that it was dealt about in shovels" (220). Yet Grahame was also a witness to the Pall Mall riots of 1886, wherein two rival leftist organizations gathered and clashed, smashing the shops of Piccadilly. That so much of *The Wind in the Willows* dwells on avoiding the dangers of the Wide World, specifically the danger posed by the "lower-class" stoats and weasels, seems to have been inspired at least in part by the anxiety that arose after the Robinson affair.

After the shooting Grahame withdrew from the public eye. He filled Durham Villas with extravagant toys—toys that his neighbor and confidant Graham Robertson blames for Grahame's lack of literary output. In the gap between the shooting in 1903 and the publication of *The Wind in the Willows* in October of 1908, Grahame published only one item, a short poem titled "The Mountain Stream" in the *Hull Weekly News* on October 15, 1905. Rather than writing, Grahame focused his energies on Alastair, retreating with him from the Wide World. It was in the nursery at bedtime that the stories of the Mole, the Rat, the Badger, and the Toad began to take form. The tales were of a world devoid of human troubles where an installment was revised every night.

In August 1905, while the family was staying in a hotel on vacation in Inveraray, a fellow guest anxiously asked to meet Kenneth Grahame.[14] Arriving late at the hotel, the guest was directed to the night nursery, where he listened from outside the door. Kenneth was telling a story that was punctuated with Alastair's interruptions, questions, and comments. It sounded, to the visitor, as if they were writing the story together.

After the New Year, in early 1904, Kenneth Grahame started looking for a new house. After almost thirty years in London, he hoped to move to a more rural location, commuting to and from the city by train. He and Elspeth rented a house called Woodside in South Ascot for short-term visits but decided not to stay there when they discovered that a new vicarage was being built at one end of the property.

14. Green, *Kenneth Grahame: A Biography*, 236. Green identifies the letter as one from Kenneth Grahame to Arthur Quiller-Couch, dated December 29, 1905.

Elspeth at this time had her own troubles. Her younger brother Courtauld Thomson[15] began to investigate the inheritance that their father had left their mother when he died in 1888. Clara Thomson had been a wealthy woman, and she owned the patents from her first husband's inventions. At the time of their mother's death, the income was left to the four Thomson children in a trust that was to be administered by their stepfather, John Fletcher Moulton. Fletcher Moulton, however, was the sole trustee—having had Clara sign a will that he had written by hand.[16] Upon marriage, Elspeth should have received a settlement of approximately £5,000 or an allowance of £300 per annum. Instead, Elspeth was only granted a one-time payout of £250.

> Elspeth realised for the first time that during the years of living in her stepfather's house and managing his social programme on a scant allowance which left her nothing for her own clothes and expenses, she should have been receiving £300 a year from her mother's bequest. Her marriage did not invalidate the allowance . . . she was owed a lot of money. (Prince, *Kenneth Grahame: An Innocent in the Wild Wood*, 197)

On behalf of his sisters, Elspeth and Winnifred, Courtauld brought a civil action against their stepfather. In the time between Kenneth's shooting in 1903 and when the case came to a public trial in April 1905, Elspeth spent much of her time under the care of her physicians at Woodhall Spa. Courtauld calculated that Fletcher Moulton owed his step-daughters £10,000. After a court battle, Moulton capitulated and settled the case, drawing a sum of £6,069 and dividing it between the two sisters. Unfortunately for Elspeth, nearly a third of that money went to pay the solicitors.

After the close of the trial, but before a family vacation together to Scotland in August of 1905, Alastair's nanny Dutchy was replaced by a governess named Naomi Stott. While "D" left no written record of her time with Alastair and the Grahames, Stott was a prolific letter writer. She left a vibrant history of the family, and her correspondence provides crucial insight into

15. He was to become a baron. His name was expanded by deed poll in February 1944 to Sir Courtauld Greenwood Courtauld-Thomson. His barony became extinct upon his death in 1954.

16. See Prince, *Kenneth Grahame: An Innocent in the Wild Wood*, 197.

the relationship between Grahame and his son. Stott is even credited with having saved Kenneth Grahame's "My Dearest Mouse" letters from the trash—for it was she who received them and read them aloud to Alastair when they were away together.

In many ways, Stott became a surrogate parent for Alastair. In 1907, Kenneth and Elspeth took their summer vacation without their son. Though they could have afforded to travel together, even bringing Stott along, the boy remained at home in Cookham Dean with his governess, later staying in the seaside town of Littlehampton while his parents went off to Cornwall. Peter Green describes the significance of the vacations spent apart in 1907, shortly after Alastair's seventh birthday:

> In May of 1907 Alastair went with his governess, Miss Stott, on a seven weeks' holiday to Littlehampton. At the same time his parents left for the West Country. They spent a few days in Falmouth and then returned to . . . Fowey. Half-way through June Elspeth returned to Cookham Dene [*sic*] to be with Alastair, but Kenneth went to London—the house

Kenneth Grahame's view from the Fowey Hotel. It was here that he spent his time convalescing in 1907. The large yellow house down the hill is Arthur Quiller-Couch's The Haven. To the left is the Whitehouse and the steps leading down to the harbor where they kept their boats waiting. *Photo by B. W. Goold. Daphne du Maurier Literary Centre, Fowey.*

> in Durham Villas had been kept as a *pied-à-terre*—and [Kenneth Grahame] remained there at least till September, occasionally coming down to Cookham Dene for week-ends. (*Kenneth Grahame: A Biography*, 266)

From May 10 to September 1907, Kenneth tried to make up for missing the nightly bedtime storytelling installments by writing a series of letters describing the most recent adventures of Mr. Toad. Stott had become privy to the bedtime stories when she joined the Grahames, not realizing that when they all relocated to Cookham Dean in 1906, she would be responsible for keeping up Alastair's end of the narrative when his parents were away. It was during this period that the major outline of the novel took shape. But it would never have become a book had Grahame not been coaxed into developing the story into a full novel.

In late August of 1907, Constance Smedley, a suffragist, visited the Grahames under the pretense that she was related to the fictional maid, Miss Smedley, in Grahame's *The Golden Age* (1895). Smedley had helped to found the International Lyceum Club[17] in 1903, and she lived nearby in the Thames-side town of Bray. Smedley also worked as a literary scout for the American magazine *Everybody's*. She had secretly been sent by her editor, John O'Hara Cosgrave, to see if she could coax Grahame into writing a new book. The subject of the book was unimportant, he said, and he promised to pay handsomely. Cosgrave, a native New Zealander, had admired Grahame's previous three collections and was hoping the reclusive writer might produce a new volume. At the very least, Cosgrave thought a piece by Kenneth Grahame would bring British notoriety to the magazine. *Everybody's* was popular in the United States but was virtually unknown in England at the time.

What Smedley and Cosgrave didn't know was that in 1906, Paul Revere Reynolds, Esq., who holds the distinction of being the first American literary agent, had somehow gotten Kenneth Grahame to agree to write a new book. Though he dealt with publishers and other agents in London, Reynolds lived

17. To this day, the club is described as being "for women interested in the arts, sciences, social concerns, and in the pursuit of lifelong learning."

and worked in New York. So long as Grahame's new work was "along the same lines"[18] as *The Golden Age* and *Dream Days*, Grahame would be advanced $3,000 upon delivery of the manuscript, and paid a 20 percent royalty by his new American publisher, Charles Scribner's Sons. In January 1907 Reynolds promised Scribners that Grahame was "just starting work on the book." When Smedley came to visit that August, however, Grahame hadn't written a word.

Constance Smedley around the time she met the Grahames (Smedley, *Crusaders: Reminiscences of Constance Smedley* [London: Duckworth, 1929], 72).

Constance Smedley was also a novelist. When she wrote to the Grahames requesting a meeting, she was stunned, not only by their immediate response, but by the fact that Grahame said he had read her novel *An April Princess*, published four years before, in 1903. Grahame initially declined Cosgrave's request. "He hated writing; it was physical torture. Why should he undergo it?" wrote Smedley in *Crusaders* (150). Grahame's days as Secretary to the Bank of England were full, and his home close to the river was his retreat from the world. Smedley recounts their first meeting in *Crusaders*:

> . . . I remember the sloe gin poured into tiny cordial glasses . . . the ceremony of the salad, served in a great basket with herbs and flasks of condiments and solemnly prepared by Mr. Grahame; the rows of tear bottles of Bristol glass, the peasant toys from all countries, the wonderful collections of old glass and china used, not only looked at. One night I remember. . . . Some very tall glasses with a curious convoluted edge . . . through which one saw everything as through the wrong end of an opera glass. . . . Mr. and Mrs. Grahame appeared like animated toys miles away across a miniature dinner table. When I left the housekeeper was waiting in the hall with one of these glasses most beautifully packed up and tied. "It is the custom," said Mr. Grahame, "to give your guest the cup he has drunk from." (Ibid., 152)

18. Letter dated December 28, 1906. Scribner Archives, Princeton University.

Smedley's first visit that August of 1907 coincided with the period in which Grahame was composing the "My Dearest Mouse" letters. She was received warmly despite her feminist politics and the fact that she arrived unescorted in a motor car—two details that would have put Grahame off. From his correspondence and other writings, it appears that Grahame did not consider the sexes equal. One of his poems indicates that he didn't support women's suffrage. And his apparent unconcern about an incident in which Alastair slapped a little girl in Kensington Gardens says a lot about his regard for women. More tellingly, the female characters in *The Wind in the Willows* are a minor lot, treated dismissively. Smedley was forthright and confident, however, and she made an impression on Grahame. In fact, once she learned of the father-son storytelling sessions, she knew she had found a topic for Grahame's next work. Smedley recalled:

> . . . I made friends with Mouse on this first visit. He was an unusually attractive child, with very beautiful thick dark hair cut straight across his forehead and bright calm eyes. . . . Every evening Mr. Grahame told Mouse an unending story, dealing with the adventures of the little animals whom they met in their river journeys. This story was known to him and Mouse alone and was related in a bedtime visit of extreme secrecy.

When Smedley broached the subject of revising the letters and the nightly stories into a book, the boy was delighted by the idea: "He [Mouse] was the only person who could have persuaded Mr. Grahame into so hated a task. The adventures of Rat and Mole and Badger slowly became chronicled. Mouse's own tendency to exult in his exploits was gently satirized in Mr. Toad" (*Crusaders,* 151). Once Smedley had talked Kenneth Grahame into writing a new book, she convinced Elspeth to write her an introduction to the even more reclusive Thomas Hardy, Elspeth's friend. Having corresponded with the Hardys for years, Elspeth was glad to comply, and gave Smedley several of her most recent poems to be hand delivered.

Grahame finished a draft of the first two chapters in December 1907[19] and

19. Based on the dates of correspondence from Paul Revere Reynolds, Scribner Archives, Princeton Archives.

sent it to Cosgrave. The new chapters were so completely different from *The Golden Age* and *Dream Days* that it constituted an entirely different project than the book Reynolds had originally proposed in 1906. The new book was titled *The Mole and the Water Rat*, and though the editor was pleased, the owners of the magazine rejected the manuscript. They felt that the book was out of character with the style of the magazine. In her memoir, Smedley comments that "their readers had been led to look to them for drama and exposure of evil in high places." No matter how beguiling Grahame's animal tale was, *Everybody's* wanted a sentimental follow-up to *The Golden Age* and *Dream Days*.

Photograph of Mouse with a cricket bat, early 1908. Taken by governess Naomi Stott. *Courtesy of the Harry Ransom Humanities Research Center, The University of Texas at Austin.*

Her letters around this time reveal that she felt terribly guilty for encouraging Grahame to write a book that the intended publisher declined. Smedley was aware that there was a great demand for Grahame's work in America, so she introduced the author to the American literary agent Curtis Brown. Though Brown had a New York office, he preferred to live and work in London. The agency represented some of the finest writers of the day, such as George Bernard Shaw and D. H. Lawrence, but Brown still had a difficult time placing the manuscript. Rather than being a book written for adults about the lives of children like his previous works, *The Mole and the Water Rat* was a book written for children that parodied the lives of adults. It was initially sent to publishers without even a proper title. Grahame's British publisher, John Lane, who had made a fortune with Grahame's books in the 1890s, was baffled by the manuscript and decided to pass. In his 1935 memoir, *Contacts,* Curtis Brown recounts how he convinced the English publisher Algernon Methuen to accept the book on Grahame's previous publishing merits: "He didn't believe in the book enough to pay a guaranteed advance on it; but, on the other hand, he agreed to excellent rising royalties, just in case the book *should* fulfil my dreams." Methuen thought that it would initially sell as a curiosity and then go out of print soon thereafter.

If finding an English publisher had been challenging, Grahame had to struggle even harder to secure a home for the book in the United States. Curtis Brown sent the manuscript back to Paul Reynolds,[20] who then submitted the first two chapters—"The River Bank" and "The Open Road"—to Charles Scribner. In correspondence dated Dec. 3, 1907, Reynolds writes: "There is a plan in England to have Clayton Colthrop [*sic*] make the illustrations under the author's directions." The illustrator, who spelled his name "Calthrap," was known in his day for his somewhat comic paintings of English women's costumes. One look at his watercolors and it is easy to imagine how he would render Mr. Toad dressed in his washerwoman's ensemble. Charles Scribner's reply was surprisingly unreceptive:

> Dear Mr. Reynolds:
>
> We have read the two stories by Kenneth Grahame which you sent last week but it is with regret that I must write that they prove very disappointing to us and that we should prefer not to carry out our provisional arrangement for this book. You will remember that the book suggested was to be along the same lines as Mr. Grahame's other books but this is very different in character and altogether lacking in human interest. There have been so many of these animal stories lately that I think the public is tired of them and the outlook for a new book not particularly inviting. All this is very disappointing to me as well as to you and shows again the dangers of making arrangements in advance of more definite knowledge. (December 16, 1907, Scribner Archives, Princeton University)

The manuscript was returned to Reynolds on December 24, 1907. At that point, Reynolds seems to have given up on or lost interest in the project. Then, in February of 1908, Curtis Brown countered the rejection with the following letter, addressed to Scribners:

> Dear Sirs:
>
> I have just been having a long talk with Mr. Kenneth Grahame about his new book, and [he] says he would much prefer to have the book published by the house of Scribner than by any other firm. He has received

20. Paul Revere Reynolds (1864–1944) also had a son, Paul Revere Reynolds Jr. (b. 1904), who joined his father's firm in 1923 and later became president of the agency.

> two offers for the American rights at $2000 advance on 20%, but would rather take one of $1500 advance on 20% from you, if you really care about the book. As I understand it, your first offer . . . was withdrawn on the ground that you thought "Mr. Toad" (as the new book will probably be called) was not likely to have a similar sale. . . . But as Mr. Grahame would so much rather you have the book than anyone else, it seems best to lay this offer before you—especially as the later chapters contain more and more of human interest and humour and aimiable [*sic*] satire on modern social conditions.

Around the time that Scribners was considering the book, Grahame received word from Theodore Roosevelt, the sitting president of the United States. Knowing that Roosevelt had greatly enjoyed his previous books, the author had sent the president a typed manuscript. According to Curtis Brown: "Theodore Roosevelt had read the MS., saying that he heard the book had been submitted, and that it was such a beautiful thing that Scribner *must* publish it" (Brown, *Contacts* [New York: Charles Scribner's Sons, 1934], 60). The president's support must have swayed Scribner, because Curtis Brown closed the deal with the following arrangement:

> Presumably this letter will reach you by Thursday February 27th, and it would be a courtesy greatly appreciated by Mr. Grahame if, in case you care for the book, you would on receipt of this letter cable me to BROWNCURT: LONDON the word "GRAHAME" signifying that you will accept his offer . . . or the word "KENNETH", signifying that you would rather not undertake the book. I am sending a copy of this letter to Mr. Reynolds, as, after he had kindly approached you on the subject, it would be hardly fair to him to write to you direct about it without letting him know what I had said. (February 18, 1908, Scribner Archives, Princeton University)

On March 2, 1908, a cable was returned from Scribners with "GRAHAME" written in the center. Kenneth Grahame's contract with Scribners, dated March 28, 1908, lists the book's title as "MR. TOAD."

Though Methuen didn't expect *The Wind in the Willows* to be a blockbuster, Curtis Brown wrote to Charles Scribner that "Mr. Methuen proposes to take infinite pains in illustrating the book." Initially, Arthur Rackham was asked if he would illustrate the first edition. At the time, any book illustrated by Rackham was assured to be popular. Grahame was a best-selling author, and therefore merited illustrations by the sought-after artist. Rackham, however, was constantly being approached by writers, publishers, and agents, and at the time was busy illustrating *A Midsummer Night's Dream*, a project that had no fewer than seventy illustrations. He was in the prime of his career; the previous year, he had illustrated *Alice's Adventures in Wonderland*, with twenty-seven color plates, and in 1906, *Peter Pan in Kensington Gardens*, with fifty color plates. Each of these books was to become a classic. Rackham was booked for years in advance and had to turn down Grahame's new book—something he later regretted.[21]

Methuen eventually published *The Wind in the Willows* primarily as a text, providing only a minimum of decoration at a time when most books for children were lavishly produced. Children's literary historian Peter Hunt writes:

> The period from 1890 to 1914 was unquestionably the golden age of children's book illustration, when colour printing reached new standards of accuracy. The bright, sometimes sticky process of lithography pioneered by Ernest Nistor [in Germany] was now replaced by the more expensive four-colour process which reproduced watercolor painting particularly effectively. . . . Using this technique publishers created luxurious gift books, often heavily illustrated with line drawings, colour plates, and decorative end papers.[22]

Despite these trends, Methuen was a conservative press. The house relied heavily on its backlist for profits. Between October 8, 1908—when *The Wind in the Willows* was first published in England—and March of 1909, Methuen's advertisements in the *Times Literary Supplement*[23] appeared exactly half as often as Macmillan and Company's, one of Methuen's more innovative competitors. Methuen's edition of *The Wind in the Willows* carried only a black-and-white frontispiece and a stamped decoration on the cover and

21. Derek Hudson, *Arthur Rackham, His Life and Work* (New York: Charles Scribner's Sons, 1960), 168–69.

22. Peter Hunt, *Children's Literature: An Illustrated History* (Oxford: Oxford University Press, 1994), 182.

23. They ran from October 8, 1908, through February 11, 1909.

spine of the book. The first British edition is printed on inexpensive paper. The cover is also lackluster—nothing compared to the spectacular editions that would follow. According to the Methuen ledgers, kept at the University of Indiana in Bloomington, the company initially printed 1,500 copies. On October 9, the day after the British release, Algernon Methuen wrote to Grahame: "I congratulate you on your charming book—so full of grace & insight. I hope you like the outside. I like the inside. . . . I telegraphed to you yesterday that we shall want a 2d edition at once."[24]

The Wind in the Willows was published in America and England almost simultaneously, producing very different-looking books. According to Iona and Peter Opie, major collectors of primarily English children's books and ephemera,[25] the first edition of *The Wind in the Willows* was American, not English. Alastair Grahame's reading copy, inscribed "To / Alastair Grahame / from his affectionate father / Kenneth Grahame / Cookham Dean, / Oct. 1908," is the Scribner edition, not Methuen. [26] Brian Alderson and the Opies speculate that Kenneth Grahame, a "fastidious bookman," possibly thought that the American edition was more elegant than the book produced by Methuen. However, the first Scribner edition lacks the cover illustration of Pan, Mole, and Rat in their skiff, as well as the drawing of Toad in his motoring togs that appears on the spine of the book. The cover of the Scribner edition is lime-green and has only the title pressed onto the boards. It leaves much to be desired, and if compared, it is doubtful that Grahame would have preferred the Scribner—because Graham Robertson contributed the first three illustrations to the Methuen edition.

According to the Scribner archives at Princeton University, Scribners printed 4,700 copies of the book. The archives indicate that, by October 10, half of the original stock was sold. A second printing of 3,125 copies was issued on December 8, and another 3,340 copies were printed on February 7, 1909. Now popular on both sides of the Atlantic, the humble stories told to Alastair by his father had become an international success.

24. Letter courtesy of the David J. Holmes Collection.

25. Iona Opie, Robert Opie, and Brian Alderson, *The Treasures of Childhood: Books, Toys, and Games from the Opie Collection* (New York: Arcade, 1989), 29.

26. Alastair Grahame's reading copy is part of the Opie Collection in the Bodleian Library.

Alastair Grahame and *The Merry Thought*

The letters that became *The Wind in the Willows* are reprinted in full in this edition. Mostly addressed to "My Dearest Mouse," they form the basis for chapters VI, VIII, X, XI, and XII. The original documents—saved, as noted earlier, by Naomi Stott—are now kept in the Bodleian Library in Oxford. Filed next to the letters is Grahame's first draft of the manuscript, written in his beautifully neat handwriting. The next draft is a typed manuscript—the final draft before Methuen eventually took it to press. The story, from the letters, to the manuscript, and then to the typed draft—grew in size with each successive round. Each of these documents has been consulted by a steady stream of Grahame scholars over the years. The annotations for this edition include the variants from Grahame's successive manuscripts, listed as d. 281, e. 247, and e. 248.

What has not been addressed up until now, however, is another significant body of work that Alastair and Naomi Stott produced in response to the letters from Grahame. During early 1908, when Kenneth Grahame was in London revising his correspondence and composing the chapters not outlined in the letters, Alastair and Stott were left to themselves in Cookham Dean. Elspeth was also away, taking another cure. The absence of his parents left a void in Alastair's life. To fill the time, Stott encouraged Mouse to begin his own literary magazine. *The Merry Thought,* as they called it, resembles a scrapbook, with each installment including cut-outs from postcards, drawings by Alastair, and contributions by the Grahames and other writers[1] and artists of the day. One copy of each edition came out every month from February 1908 to February 1909. One of the more famous pieces included was "Bertie's Escapade," one of Kenneth Grahame's short stories. Besides its appearance in *The Merry Thought,* this story was never published in Grahame's lifetime, only appearing posthumously. Over the course of its thirteen issues, the magazine forms a sort of diary. *The Merry Thought* is a record of the Grahames' lives told in Alastair's drawings, ephemera cut from scraps—newspapers, cards, letters, snapshots—and stories dictated by Alastair in the governess's handwriting. Alastair and Naomi Stott painstakingly put together all thirteen editions of the magazine. Each was then passed around Mayfield, the Grahames' grand country house,[2] and among the Grahames' closest friends in Cookham Dean.

The Merry Thought was composed on thick construction paper and bound by a single brass tack. For many years the only copy of each edition remained in the possession of Peter Green. The magazine is full of recurring episodes of stories with titles such as "The History of Fairyland," which stars gnomes and trolls drawn by Alastair. "Adventures of Punn's Athletic Club" and "Sphinx Island, Leaves from a Pirate Diary" were both regular serials, the latter being Alastair's version of a shipwrecked adventure fantasy—a genre he obviously enjoyed, because his nursery library was stocked with such books. "The Witch of the Old Tree" is about a witch on Winter Hill[3] who takes Alastair to her playground deep under the river, reached by a secret underground passage. As we will see, underground spaces fascinated Kenneth Grahame, and they seem to have also been a passion for Alastair. "The Windsor Passenger's Train," "The Useful Nail at the Ramsgate Hotel," and "A Reminder of Littlehampton" explore some of the locations that Alastair and Naomi Stott visited in their travels together. "Letter from Benjy" and "The Rabbits Farewell on Fair Day" are poems about Alastair's pet rabbits, named after Beatrix Potter characters.

1. Including such notable people as May Sinclair, and a teenage painter who would become Sir Stanley Spencer.

2. The house is now the Herries Preparatory School in Cookham Dean.

3. Winter Hill is a great hill in Cookham Dean. It overlooks the Thames.

The women's suffrage movement was also covered in the pages of *The Merry Thought.* Kenneth Grahame's poem "This pussy is wanting the votes" and Alastair's "Suffragette Ode" appear among the pages.[4]

Quirky advertisements run throughout, such as this recipe for "'Delicious Cake': 1 lb flour. ½ butter ½ sugar 2 eggs ½ oz. candied peel, baking powder or gunpowder + mix. Then run away as fast as you can, when that cake goes into the oven." An advertisement for Dr. Brown the Dentist reads: "Go to him for gas—when your tooth torments you. Pockets searched when under gas—especially when millionaires call." A distant relative took advertising space: "*Grahame Lawyer* Go to him for all arguments. No talk will tire his tongue."

Another trove of materials besides Grahame's well-known letters to Alastair and *The Merry Thought* is a set of unpublished letters written by Naomi Stott and addressed to Elspeth Grahame.[5] Written in the late winter and early spring of 1908,[6] while Elspeth was convalescing yet again, the letters reveal previously unknown details about the Grahames' lives. Contrary to Peter Green and Alison Prince, who characterize Alastair as an *enfant terrible* with overly permissive parents, Stott portrays a boy with an easy nature who is loving and precociously creative. Nevertheless, Alastair Grahame was deeply troubled. He had been evicted from Kensington Gardens for biting and kicking other children. Kenneth Grahame writes to Elspeth in baby talk about Alastair's penchant for slapping little girls: "he splane that ee 'wanted to' & I ad no argument set up gainst that" (Prince, 195). As his governess, Naomi Stott seems to have provided a calming influence. While Grahame records that the former nanny, "D," was accustomed to being slapped by Alastair, Stott records no such behavior. In fact, Alastair seemed to flourish under her influence. His drawings of Stott are benevolent. The two of them come off as buddies, yet Stott is clearly in charge.

Alastair's tantrums remained in check when he was with Stott. Beyond

4. Kenneth Grahame's poem "This pussy is wanting the votes" appears in print for the first time in chapter X, note 11.

5. The magazine, along with the letters, are included in the papers donated by Peter Green to the Harry Ransom Humanities Research Center, The University of Texas at Austin.

6. Dated February 26 through May 16, 1908, at the same time Kenneth Grahame was revising his letters from the previous summer into the text of *The Wind in the Willows*.

Cover illustration for *The Merry Thought*, May 1908, by Alastair Grahame. *Courtesy of the Harry Ransom Humanities Research Center, The University of Texas at Austin.*

reporting about the boy, Stott provides a bucolic narrative of what the days were like in and around Mayfield, Cookham Dean.

> At/ Mayfield, Cookham Dean, Berks
> March 5th 1908
>
> Dear Mrs: Grahame,
>
> I hope that you are feeling better. Mouse has had a satisfactory day. It was such lovely weather. We started for a drive at 10:30, + got to Hurley. It was so pretty going along through the woods. On our return, we had time for some football. After dinner we got out as soon as we could to make the most of the sunshine, + with our faithful friend the "pram" we went to Cookham. I left some of my boots at the cobbler's at Cookham Rise, where you once visited him in his little

"Miss Stott teaching Mouse to drill + to endure . . ." *Courtesy of the Harry Ransom Humanities Research Center, The University of Texas at Austin.*

glass house. A woman at the cottage asked after you. We are hoping to get our magazine ready by Sunday. Mitey [Sullivan] has not contributed much this time. She is such a mopey child at times, but Mouse never notices it, + rattles along in his own cheery way. She likes singing, but will not join in, + once when Kathleen was at tea too, Mitey was quite silent, from a sort of shyness, + Mouse did his best to rouse her.

Friday

Mouse is quite well + having a cantor on firefly.

Yours Sincerely, N. Stott

Mitey was a neighbor who became close friends with Alastair. Her father, an artist who lived in Cookham, contributed a beautiful pencil

Photo titled "Mouse and Peggy," with rabbit named Benjamin. It is possible that Peggy is Mitey, the child whom Stott mentions in her letters to Mrs. Grahame in 1908. *Courtesy of the David J. Holmes Collection.*

March 12, 1908: "Mouse had his hoop out for a run." Photo by Naomi Stott. *Courtesy of the Harry Ransom Humanities Research Center, The University of Texas at Austin.*

drawing of their dog, Neb, to the February 1908 issue of *The Merry Thought*. Elspeth Grahame mentions the girl's father only as S. Sullivan in *First Whisper of "The Wind in the Willows"* and credits him as contributing the cover decoration for the first edition of *The Merry Thought*. The woods were the Quarry Wood, Grahame's model for the Wild Wood of chapter III, and Firefly was Alastair's pony, which lived in the paddock in close proximity to Bertie, a black pig that became Alastair's pet. Indeed, the house was full of pets. In April 1908 Stott reveals that Kenneth Grahame gave Alastair a pair of rabbits for Easter that the boy named Benjamin and Peter—as noted, after Beatrix Potter's popular new *Peter Rabbit* series.

Over the course of this correspondence, Stott provided such a prolific amount of material for her employers that one wonders if she had literary aspirations. Many of Stott's observations have parallels in Grahame's final manuscript. That's not to say Grahame plagiarized or borrowed from the governess—far from it, for no one could write like Grahame—but whether she is reporting local events to Elspeth, or contributing to *The Merry Thought,* in pieces such as "Nature Notes" and "Notes here + there," Stott provides a running commentary on all strata of life in and around Cookham Dean. It is easy to see how Kenneth Grahame would have been influenced by her exacting descriptions and the slightly comic take on the condition of the creatures around them.

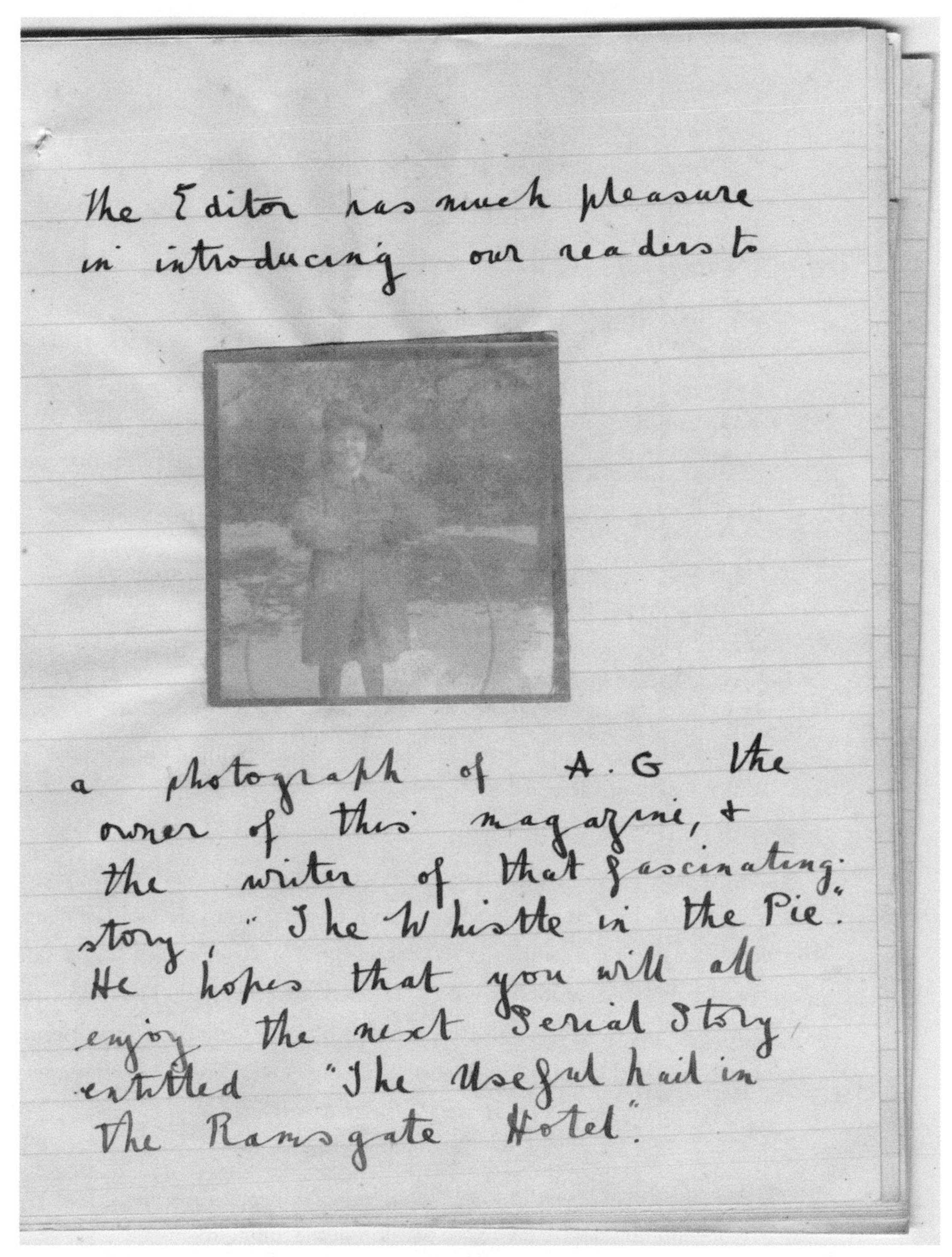

The Editor has much pleasure
in introducing our readers to

a photograph of A. G the
owner of this magazine, &
the writer of that fascinating
story, "The Whistle in the Pie".
He hopes that you will all
enjoy the next Serial Story,
entitled "The Useful Nail in
the Ramsgate Hotel".

Stott was responsible for the few snapshots of Alastair Grahame, taken in 1908. Some of them were included in the magazine—such as with this masthead or title page from the May 1908 issue of *The Merry Thought*. *Courtesy of the Harry Ransom Humanities Research Center, The University of Texas at Austin.*

> Notes here + there
>
> - - - - - - N.S.
>
> Our favorite haunt has been the garden, + no wonder for flowers and birds have made it a gay world.
>
> Often Peter + Benjamin have a gambol on the tennis lawn, + we sit + watch them + interfere only when they go trespassing, or try to escape to the unknown, or when it is time for bed.
>
> - - - - - -
>
> The birds complain that a yellow ~~most~~ monster has come to the house. A week ago the London Puss arrived in a hamper, + he climbs trees, + investigates bushes, + gives many a black bird good reason to scold him. Puss remarks that a country cat has far more liberty than a London cat, + he hopes that there will be no town house taken for his benefit.
>
> - - - - - -
>
> Somebody new has come to the Pig Sty, + that is a pig. The last occupant used it in the day time only. The Pig will be ready for callers night or day, as he intends to reside there permanently, + has no intention of having a second residence.
>
> - - - - - -
>
> [an advertisement] Kitty the Mayfield pony is willing to collect sugar. All lumps accepted

The pig was Bertie, who actually got loose on occasion and would prove the inspiration for Grahame's short story "Bertie's Escapade." Often these reminiscences bear a resemblance to passages in *The Wind in the Willows*. The "escapade" included not only a mole but a Mrs. Mole as well. The following Christmas report by Stott sounds very much like the Christmas activities of chapter V, "Dulce Domum," in the finished book. Of course, the account also reflects how many people celebrated Christmas at the time.

> The Christmas time of 1908 must have been a happy time for A. G. Twice mummers were invited to perform in the dining rooms, & songs were sung delightful to the mind of A. G. On *the day* there was an enormous stocking of blue and silver, adorned with pictures of the giver, + full of toys, for him to see before breakfast. Parcels + cards abounded at

breakfast time; the morning was spent *indoors* & not out, dinner was in the dining Room, + the chief features were turkey + dessert, + crackers, + there was a Daddy & Mummy to share the fun. After dinner there was a short visit to Mrs. Luke, & on our return such a splendid Christmas tree was on view in the hall, + many were made happy with presents. Visitors brought more presents after tea, the visitors being Daddy & Mummy, + the last treat in the day was that the choir came to sing carols, + stood in the dark with lanterns outside the study windows, + sang "Good King Wesceslas." The tree was lighted up, + the last carol was sung in the hall in view of the tree + soon after A. G. had given his bottles of sweets to little choir boys, he was got to bed.

Before ~~Christ~~ Christmas, A.G. went to a play at His Majesty's called "Pinkie and the Fairies", + now he knows a lot about acting. + theatres after Christmas he went to a Pantomime in Cookham, called "King Kitchen of Ballyrot, + now he can write a Pantomime to be acted at Drury Lane.

Alastair was obviously fond of Stott, sketching her often, with the two of them at play. Most of the drawings are given titles or have commentary written in the governess's recognizable hand. The portrait of Mouse and Naomi lifting bar bells titled "Miss Stott teaching Mouse to drill + to endure . . ." (see page xlv) gives one the sense that Alastair was actually clever in his own right and that he and Stott were a comic duo: she the straight man to his reactive clown.

Portrait of governess Naomi Stott by Alastair Grahame. This portrait finds Stott in the blooming garden they had planted together down near Bertie's pigsty. *Courtesy of the Harry Ransom Humanities Research Center, The University of Texas at Austin.*

Once Alastair went off to boarding school, however, his drawings and writing lost their edge. His schoolwork became robotic and repetitive. Alastair was not cut out for English public schools. Born with a congenital defect that that gave him very limited vision, he was not athletic, which made it hard for him in the culture of the public school, where the sportiest boys were the top boys. He attended Rugby and then Eton but had to be removed from both schools due to emotional problems. On top of the social challenges, Alastair had a difficult time with required exams, passing them only after several attempts. He eventually went up to Oxford in 1818 and was a member of Christ Church. Still, he didn't fit with university life, which was a great disappointment for his father, who had so dearly wanted to attend Oxford himself. Alastair was unfortunate to arrive at university when there was an influx of young men returning from World War I. Oxford was seemingly inundated with what was left of the best and the brightest of England—peers against whom Alastair could not compete.

On May 7, 1920, after dining at college, Alastair asked for a glass of port wine—the wine drunk at the high table and on social occasions in college. He then walked to Port Meadow, outside Oxford, next to the fields where Kenneth Grahame had played cricket as a boy. There are numerous train tracks and exchanges coming into and out of Oxford. At some point during the night, Alastair was struck by a train and died. It's easy to see how, as his father pointed out in a letter to Arthur Quiller-Couch, the boy might have become disoriented due to his limited vision. Yet his autopsy report was consistent with a person who had lain down on the tracks and waited for a train to strike him. Though he had been decapitated and all four limbs had been run over, his death was ruled an accident.

Alastair's untimely passing devastated Kenneth and Elspeth. A month later the Grahames sold off many of their possessions, including all of Alastair's clothes, in a Blewbury jumble sale. They divested themselves of reminders of how their lives had been before his death. In August of that year, Grahame played host to the five Purves brothers, who came to visit Oxford from Philadelphia.[7] Though deeply grieved, Grahame booked rooms for the Purveses and showed them every turn and detail of Oxford as he had known and loved it. Shortly thereafter, the Grahames leased Bohams, their house in Blewbury, and left for Italy. They stayed abroad for almost four

7. Austin Purves, their father, had been a close friend of Kenneth's. They met in Fowey in the summer of 1907, while Alastair and Naomi Stott were in Littlehampton. Though Grahame wrote the letters to his son, the Purves family has always said that *The Wind in the Willows* was partially inspired by a boat trip that they took with Grahame "to the little town of Golant" that summer. Austin Purves died unexpectedly in 1915. The boys had not been back to England since before the war.

years,[8] returning to England only after they managed to sell Bohams. They settled in Pangbourne, another Thames-side town, in a large house called Church Cottage. It was there that they would both live until their deaths. Kenneth was able to walk about as always, looking at the "pretty boats."

Alastair had been an enigma for his father—tempestuous but creative, smart and funny, yet handicapped. Grahame had been a talented young man, a successful banker, and one of the most iconic literary figures of the day, while Alastair has been regarded by Grahame's later biographers as a great disappointment. By reprinting pages of *The Merry Thought*, and Naomi Stott's correspondence, I hope, with this annotated edition of Grahame's beloved classic, to reaffirm Alastair's importance to the novel. A proper bedtime story is created not only by the teller but by the listener. *The Wind in the Willows* owes as much to Alastair Grahame, its first editor and coauthor, as it does to his father, the man who first whispered the adventures of Mole, Rat, Toad, Otter, and Badger to his son over one hundred years ago.

Photo of Mouse taken by governess Naomi Stott on May 1, 1908. *Courtesy of the David J. Holmes Collection.*

8. On September 1, 1923, Kenneth Grahame wrote to A. A. Milne and offered to lease him their house. According to Green, the offer fell through because the Milnes were looking for a house to buy, not rent.

The Illustrators, Their Editions, and Other Depictions of *The Wind in the Willows*

Think of illustrating 'The Wind in the Willows'!
You might as well try to whistle at the Taj Mahal.

—illustrator Maxfield Parrish to children's librarian Anne Carroll Moore, February 23, 1934
(Courtesy of the New York Public Library)

W. GRAHAM ROBERTSON AND THE FIRST THREE ILLUSTRATIONS

The first edition of *The Wind in the Willows* contained three illustrations by W. Graham Robertson, a confidant of Kenneth Grahame's. He had gone to Eton, and he wrote and illustrated a series of books about a baby girl nicknamed Binky that were published by John Lane. Robertson was also an artist and a playwright, the author of a children's play called *Pinkie and the Fairies* that was well received when it was produced in December 1908. Robertson is probably best remembered, however, for his collection of manuscripts and drawings by William Blake. His holdings were so significant that in 1952 Faber published a book called *The Blake Collection of W. Graham Robertson—Described by the Collector*. The 140 items in the catalogue contain Robertson's own descriptions of the Blake materials as well as the full particulars of how their previous owners, the Butts family, came to own the material. Robertson was obviously influenced by Blake—his own work is full of similar visionary and otherworldly figures.

Grahame and Robertson had been neighbors in London and continued to write once Grahame moved to Cookham. Unfortunately, Robertson later destroyed all of their correspondence to prevent Grahame's letters from being published posthumously. He wrote to Grahame's widow, Elspeth: "Some months ago I nearly set the house on fire by burning a pretty brisk correspondence extending over 40 years. The publication of the Shaw letters showed me that executors are not to be relied upon" (Bodleian, MS. Eng. misc. d. 529, pp. 39–40). Fortunately, Elspeth Grahame not only kept all of her husband's letters but also sought out copies of them. After he died she placed advertisements in the papers requesting readers to hand copy any correspondence and send it to her. Over time, a slew of transcribed letters arrived. Graham Robertson's letters from the summer of 1908 leave a record of several details about the first edition of *The Wind in the Willows*. Most notable is the fact that Robertson was an early reader of the manuscript:

> That title! I should like to call the book "Down Stream"—I suppose because it is quite irrelevant and has certainly been used before as a title. "With the Stream"—"Among the Sedges"—"The Garden of Pan"—no good. (Bodleian, MS. Eng. misc. d. 529, pp. 7, 8)

Though Kenneth Grahame did not accept his friend's advice on the title, it is clear that the two continued to share ideas. At various times Robertson suggested other titles, including "*The Lapping of the Stream*, *The Babble of the Stream*, '*By Pleasant Streams*' (Blake), '*By Waters Fair*' (Blake), *The Whispering Reeds, In the Sedges, Under the Alders, Reeds and Rushes, Reeds of the River, River Folk*" (Patrick R. Chalmers, *Kenneth Grahame* [London: Methuen, 1933], 126). In America, the manuscript also went through several titles: *Mr. Mole and his Mates, Worldlings of the Soil,* and *Mr. Toad.* Kenneth Grahame and Charles Scribner finally settled on *The Wind in the Reeds* in mid-July of 1908. However, it was soon pointed out to Algernon Methuen that the poet William Butler Yeats had published a collection of poems called *The Wind Among the Reeds* in 1899. In a letter dated September 2, 1908, only five weeks before publication, Methuen wrote to Grahame: "It is a pity about the title but I

Autographed photo of Graham Robertson as an older man with Richard, one of his Old English Bobtail Sheepdogs. Robertson had a succession of four sheepdogs: Bob, Portly, Ben, and Richard. His second dog, Portly, was the inspiration for Grahame's baby Otter in chapter VII. *Photo courtesy of Roger Oakes.*

Poster of Richard, one of Robertson's sheepdogs, as the Pageant Pup. Robertson designed this poster for the Chiddingfold Pageant Players.

think that *The Wind in the Willows* has a charming & wet sound, & if you don't write to the contrary, we will adopt it."[1]

Robertson and Grahame were so close that Kenneth chose to name the Otter's baby, Portly, after one of Robertson's beloved dogs. Portly was a large, fat, black-and-white puppy, and the center of attention in Robertson's house. Robertson recounts those days when he and Grahame were neighbors:

> He was then in Durham Villas, Campden Hill and I in Argyll Road, just around the corner; a two-minutes' walk lay between us and the path soon became well worn. . . . His special room in number 16 was most characteristic; it looked like a nursery. Books there were certainly, but they were out numbered by toys—intriguing, fascinating toys which could hardly have been conducive to study and may have accounted to some extent for their owner's very occasional literary output. As his house was full of toys so was mine full of dogs, and we found the other's surroundings quite normal and satisfactory. (Chalmers, *Kenneth Grahame*, 97)

Most of Robertson's letters to Grahame give accounts of the dogs, for the beasts were very much the heart of the home. After Grahame's death in 1933, Robertson wrote to Elspeth, "I'm so glad [Portly's] name remains enshrined in *The Wind in the Willows*."

Very few of Robertson's letters are dated, so we don't know exactly when he contributed the cover illustration, frontispiece, or spine illustration. There is a letter from Robertson, however, persuading Grahame to accept his illustration:

> I am glad the cover design found favor. Of course Methuen won't like it—but I don't mind that. But if by any strange chance he *does* adopt it I

1. Letter courtesy of the David J. Holmes Collection.

had perhaps better see a proof. Printers have curious and original ideas which sometimes clash with mine.

I cannot break them of the habit (when given a design in—say—grey and yellow) of submitting various "frills" in living violet and shrimp pink, also in orange and sky blue, likewise in liver brown and scarlet—for me to *choose* from. (Bodleian, MS. Eng. misc. d. 529, p. 11)

Robertson, who was familiar with the reproduction of illustrations in books at the time,[2] had considerable influence on Grahame. Once the author had accepted the cover design, Robertson made a pitch to contribute a frontispiece:

Frontispiece by Graham Robertson. *Photo by Rich Grant. Courtesy of the David J. Holmes Collection.*

I am sending you a little design which might—or might *not*—do for the "half-title" page of the book—slightly reduced.

If you think well of it—will you submit it? If not, have not further "tuck" with it.

And I daresay there is now no time to form it even if it were worth-while.

I expect it is purely asinine. In fact I'm *sure* it is. Still I send it.

Sincerely Graham Robertson

(Bodleian, MS. Eng. misc. d. 529, p. 12)

The frontispiece depicts three nude babies in the company of a water rat and an otter at a waterfall. The caption quotes the first part of Genesis 2:10: "And a River went out from Eden." Robertson and Grahame both recognized the connection to Milton, who alludes to the line in book 4, line 223, of *Paradise Lost*: "Southward through Eden went a river large." There are no

2. See bibliography for some of Robertson's illustrated books.

Photograph of Graham Robertson with parrot, taken around the time he and Kenneth Grahame were neighbors. Dated 17/4/1907. *Courtesy of the David J. Holmes Collection.*

children in *The Wind in the Willows,* so the babies are an anomaly added by the illustrator.

In a 1933 interview with Patrick R. Chalmers, Kenneth Grahame's first biographer, Robertson expressed joy about his initial illustrations:

> I well remember my joyful enthusiasm when I first read the MSS. It was wonderful to be allowed to witness and even, in a tiny way, to assist at so happy a birth. There was then some talk of my providing illustrations, but time was lacking and, moreover, I mistrusted my powers, for I could not number an otter or a water-rat among my acquaintances. . . . Yet I could not altogether forgo the honour of lending a hand, so I drew, hastily and very badly. (Chalmers, *Kenneth Grahame*, 126)

When Algernon Methuen accepted the illustrations, Robertson, naturally, was pleased and promptly wrote to Grahame:

> . . . I am inflated to bursting point with pride that the "Eden" drawing should be in the book. It is not worthy—but I'm very glad, all the same. It's nice of Methuen to say it's charming when I'm sure he hates it. Pub-

Robertson often painted children, including this nude that resembles the children in his frontispiece. *Courtesy of the David J. Holmes Collection.*

lishers don't like my children—they prefer this kind [sentimental drawing of angelic child]. Perhaps one day, when the book attains to an edition of Donne we might rig up some more illustrations. I see now that it could be done by a series of landscapes (rather in the style of Blake's portrayals) with a merest suggestion of beasts creeping in and out of them. But now the *first* edition is the thing. I hope the cover will be "in time." (Bodleian, MS. Eng. misc, d. 529, pp. 13–14)

Pen-and-ink illustration from Robertson's *The Baby's Day Book, For A Woman of Four.* Titled "Sea Pinks," both drawing and painting resemble the frontispiece he contributed to Grahame's first edition.

The three Robertson illustrations appeared in each of the first seven Methuen editions but have not been published with Grahame's text since October 1913. In America, Scribners didn't publish Robertson's cover in the first edition, but they did include the frontispiece. As noted before, except for the Robertson illustrations, *The Wind in the Willows* remained a work of text alone. Readers on both continents contented themselves with Grahame's language and the power of his descriptions. By the time Paul Bransom illustrated the eighth edition in 1913, the characters and scenes had long been fixed in the public imagination. Perhaps that is why the work of subsequent illustrators started to morph from naturalistic animals to cartoonish animals in foppish clothing who lived in human homes.

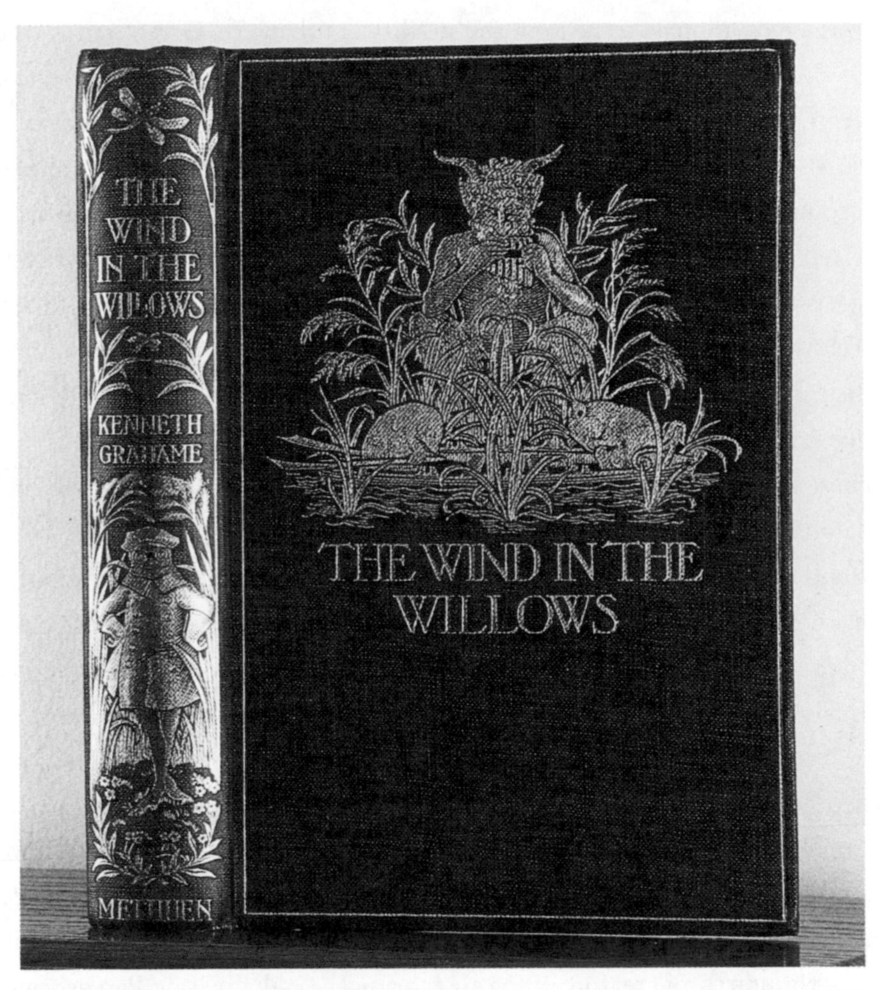

Cover and spine of the first Methuen edition, with illustration by Graham Robertson, 1908.
Courtesy of the David J. Holmes Collection.

As the book was given treatments by different illustrators, and then even developed into a stage play, *Toad of Toad Hall*, by A. A. Milne (1929), *The Wind in the Willows* gradually came to be as much associated with its illustrations as with its language. Robertson's and Bransom's first illustrations are significant, then, because they reflect Grahame's preoccupation with animals in the steadily disappearing natural world, the cult of perpetual youth, and the Edwardian and late Victorian preoccupation with the neo-pagan deity Pan—all sensibilities that faded from popular culture after World War I.

Both Grahame and Robertson shared this latter fascination, and they created works that tended to valorize the natural world. Peter Green argues that Grahame and Robertson lived in London during a period when industry and commerce had overpowered the rhythms of nature. Their hobby of weekend rambles arose as a recreational escape from the sterility of urban life. Green writes "they saw a deep split developing between man's working life and his recreation, between what he had to do and what he wanted to do" (*Kenneth Grahame: A Biography*, 119). Artists, aesthetes, and writers, therefore, turned to cultivate "the countries of the mind"—or they turned to alcohol and drugs. Grahame preferred weekend walking with his friends to inebriation. Writers like Aleister Crowley—magician, occultist, poet, and writer—reveled in excess and self-destructive behavior. In 1922, long after *The Wind in the Willows* was originally published, Crowley finally published his *Diary of a Drug Fiend* (1922), describing his extended experience with heroin, cocaine, and cannabis.

These new movements began to form in the 1880s and 1890s, in the literary salons of London, where writers and artists who contributed to *The Yellow Book* and the *National Observer* met. Both publications and their contributors were known for their rejection of social conventions. Besides a permissive attitude toward drugs, neo-pagans also honored the idea of Pan. Though we see many versions of Pan in the literature and art of the late Victorians, the deity has a long history. In Greek mythology, he is the son of Hermes, a horned god of herds and flocks of sheep with the legs of a goat and the body of a man. The Romans later adopted Pan as the god of nature. The most famous Pan-like character is Shakespeare's Puck in *A Midsummer Night's Dream.* While many of the neo-pagans worshiped Pan as half-man, half-beast—the startling creature who causes panic—Grahame saw Pan as a wild but benevolent force.

Illustrations and references to Pan were common up into the 1920s. Pan appears in a story by Saki (H. H. Munro), "The Music on the Hill" (1911), and in E. M. Forster's "The Story of a Panic" (1902). J. M. Barrie's children's play, *Peter Pan,* was first performed in 1904, and his novelization of the stage play, *Peter and Wendy*, was published in 1911. Barrie's first sketch for Peter Pan appears in his 1902 novel *The Little White Bird.* The American poet Robert Frost included a poem titled "Pan with Us" in his first collection, *A Boy's Will* (1914).

In *The Wind in the Willows*, Pan makes his appearance as a divine figure in chapter VII, when he rescues baby Portly after he goes missing. Whenever the book has been abridged, the "Piper at the Gates of Dawn" chapter is usually the first to be cut. After Algernon Methuen's death in 1924, Methuen started a series of abridged books from their backlist. Their aim was to corner the market in class readers for elementary schools. Grahame, however, had very different ideas about abridgment.[3] But Pan has his place in the history of the book even now, long after the Disney treatments have erased neopaganism from *The Wind in the Willows* and other children's literature. Indeed, when modern readers think of *The Wind in the Willows*, they imagine the pastoral country, not a pagan deity. For Grahame, one evoked the other; they were interchangeable. The first Methuen cover, featuring Graham Robertson's depiction of Pan, might have been better served with an illustration of the famous picnic on the grassy riverbank—a central scene drawn by almost every illustrator since Paul Bransom's 1913 endpapers.

And yet many of Grahame's early readers would have immediately made the connection to Pan as Graham Robertson drew him. For Grahame and his audience, Pan represented a return to the wilderness and a state of nature.

Grahame biographer Patrick Chalmers observed that "whether the reviewers praised Mr. Grahame's new book or regretted it, they were united in naming it an allegory and almost united in prophesying that, to be successful, *The Wind in the Willows* wanted an illustrator" (Chalmers, *Kenneth Grahame*, 137). But how was an artist to portray the animals of *The Wind in the Willows*? As the riverbankers Mole, Rat, Otter, Badger, and Toad appear in the

3. See page 365 for Eleanor Graham's essay on Kenneth Grahame's sentiments about abridgment. Chapter IX, "Wayfarers All," is usually the second chapter to be cut. Also see Maureen Duffy, *A Thousand Capricious Chances / A History of the Methuen List* (London: Methuen, 1989), 89.

Paul Bransom's 1913 endpapers mimic Claude Monet's painting *Le Déjeuner sur l'herbe*.

text of the first chapter, the reader notices that they are all about the same size, say as a group of friends who vary only slightly—in height a few inches and in weight, a few pounds. "The two animals looked at each other and laughed," Grahame writes of the Otter and the Rat, as they look at Toad rowing his wager boat in the distance. A real otter and a real badger are closer in size to a small-to-medium dog—weighing twenty to twenty-five pounds—while a water rat is considerably smaller, four pounds at most. A mole and a toad are closer to each other in size, weighing only ounces. While Grahame gives his characters their natural habitat and attributes very much like *wild* animals, they are all nearly the same size. Badger and Mole can use the same furniture in chapter IV. Mr. Toad's Gypsy caravan is the same size as a motorcar built by human beings. Likewise, Toad is able to steal a horse and, on two occasions, a motorcar. Toad is also able to interact with an engineer of a train, and to shovel coal into the steam engine. Is Mr. Toad really a toad? Yes and no. The size of each animal is relative to the surroundings, and the size of each character shifts to fit the needs of the setting and the scene. As Peter Green discovered, Grahame was well aware of the inconsistencies: "When asked specifically (apropos the escape on the railway train) whether Toad was life sized or train sized, he answered that he was both and neither:

the Toad was train-size, the train was Toad-size, and therefore there should be no illustrations" (Green, *Kenneth Grahame: A Biography*, 285).[4]

PAUL BRANSOM, 1913

The first person to fully illustrate *The Wind in the Willows* was an American. Paul Bransom contributed ten full-color paintings that were reproduced through chromolithography in 1913.[5] Bransom was a self-taught artist who learned his craft by drawing animals at the Washington National Zoo. He illustrated Jack London's *Call of the Wild* in 1910 and Kipling's *Just So Stories* in 1932. In retrospect, Bransom's interpretation of the riverbankers is unique because his animals often appear in their natural habitats. Rat's "bijoux riverside residence" is truly a hole, rather than an elaborate house. Only the Sea Rat in chapter IX is dressed in human clothing. In comparison with later editions by other artists, Bransom's animals are primitive. Toad *is* a toad—there is nothing eccentric about him. He wears no clothing, nor does he look able to ride a horse, let alone steal a car from a party of human beings. When published, Bransom was criticized: ". . . in depicting the various characters with so much fidelity to nature . . . the artist seems to us to have entirely missed the spirit of this delightful romance."[6]

Bransom's decorative cover for the Scribner edition lacks Grahame's comical characters. Instead, the cover recalls the arts and crafts movement with a five-color stamp on the cloth cover.[7] The illustration also parallels Monet's 1896 series *Matinée sur la Seine*. Willow branches hang to the water from the top of the image, neatly tying in the title of the book, while in the distance,

4. See Green, *Kenneth Grahame: A Biography*, 372, p. 40: "Personal information, Mr. Spencer Curtis Brown."

5. Chromolithography involves producing multicolored prints from lithographic stones. As many as twenty stones were used at a time. After the illustration was drawn, each stone was inked in a different color or shade. Then the print paper was passed from stone to stone to pick up the colors.

6. Quoted from *The Studio,* vol. 60 (249), listed in Simon Houfe, *The Dictionary of British Book Illustrators and Caricaturists, 1800–1914* (Woodridge, Suffolk, England: Antique Collectors Club, 1996), 242.

7. The arts and crafts movement was founded in England by John Ruskin during the Industrial Revolution. Ruskin believed that the working man should be surrounded with the beauty of nature, and well-designed utilitarian objects. Bransom's cover reflects the incorporation of nature motifs—possibly contrived—into manufactured objects. The movement existed from (approximately) 1880 to 1910.

Paul Bransom's illustration from *The Last of the Sea Otters*, by Harold McCracken, 1942.

the water reflects the trees above on the opposite riverbank. The only place where this cover hints at its contents is the small toad head that appears below the author's name. The head is so small and stylized that it's barely noticeable. The small toad on the cover is a cartoon, whereas the toad of the illustrations is scientifically correct. Bransom's cover is a variation of a popular technique pioneered within his generation in which high art of the era—the arts and crafts style—was translated into a recognizable motif to help sell manufactured products. When Kenneth Grahame was sent a copy of Bransom's illustrated edition, he wrote back to Curtis Brown, his agent:

> I was much relieved to find no bowler hats or plaid waistcoats. And I like the drawings, too, very much. They have charm and dignity and good taste, and I should think the book will have a satisfactory sale. (October 17, 1913, Scribner Archives, Princeton University)

Paul Bransom's Scribners cover, 1913.

On October 5, 1913, the *New York Times* ran the following copy in a display advertisement, placed by Scribners, for new publications. *The Wind in the Willows* was being released by both Methuen and Scribners in time for the holiday season:

> KENNETH GRAHAME'S MOST BEAUTIFUL BOOK
>
> *The Wind in the Willows*
>
> Illustrated in full colors by Paul Bransom.
>
> No more difficult work to illustrate could be found than "The Wind in the Willows," for there humor, tenderness, satire, romance, whimsicality, and exquisite lyrical poetry—if prose can be that—are inseparably mixed. But the little bright eyed mole, the gray wandering sea rat, the rotund jolly Mr. Toad with his craze for motoring, and the Great God Pan, piping at the Gates of Dawn, are here pictured by Paul Bransom, an artist who, seeing not the humor nor any other quality alone, but all the complementary qualities as one, commands the subtle, graceful skill to blend them into unity.
>
> *$2.00 net; postage extra*

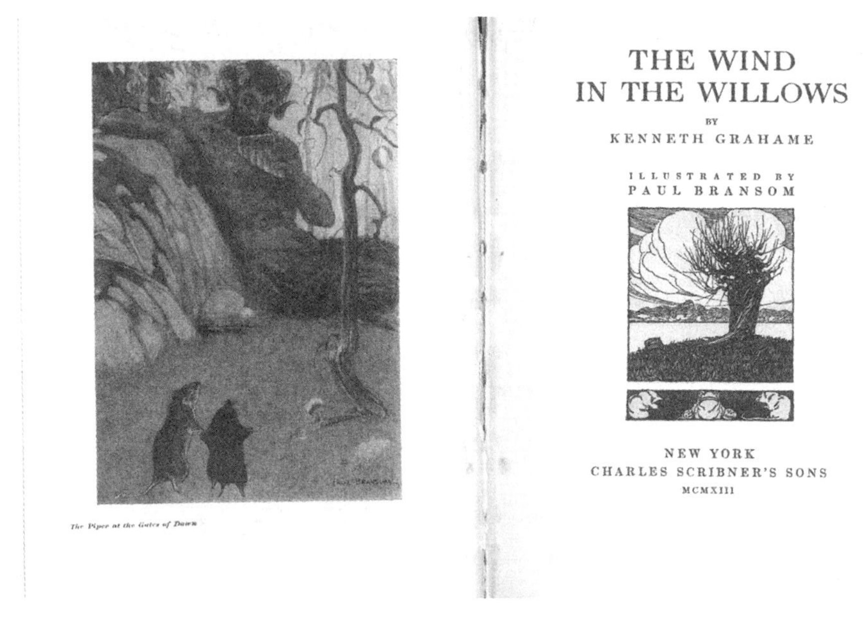
THE WIND
IN THE WILLOWS
BY
KENNETH GRAHAME
ILLUSTRATED BY
PAUL BRANSOM
NEW YORK
CHARLES SCRIBNER'S SONS
MCMXIII

Bransom's title page and frontispiece, 1913.

In keeping with Graham Robertson, Bransom's pipe-playing Pan appears on the frontispiece. In successive editions, Pan became less prominent.[8]

NANCY BARNHART, 1922

Nancy Barnhart, the second illustrator, was also an American. Her edition was published in both the United States and England. Very little has been written about Barnhart, and her professional output was so small that it is hard to piece together where she lived and worked.[9] In her brief biography in the *Horn Book's Illustrators of Children's Books* (1945), she is mistakenly identified as the first illustrator of the book. Bransom, as we know, had that honor. Barnhart says the following about her favorite book: "It was really a testi-

8. According to Michael Patrick Hearn, Paul Bransom's original paintings resurfaced in a Scribners storage closet at the publisher's Fifth Avenue offices in the 1980s before the company was bought by Simon & Schuster.

9. Other books Nancy Barnhart illustrated include her own *The Lord Is My Shepherd; Stories from the Bible* (New York: Charles Scribner & Sons, 1949); Mildred Criss McGuckin, *Little Cabbages* (New York: Doubleday, Doran, 1928); and Lucy Thacher and Marguerite Wilkinson, *Listening Child* (New York: Macmillan and Company, 1924).

mony to the unity of English and American culture that I should have illustrated *The Wind in the Willows*. . . . what a joy in later years to have my drawings accepted." In 1933 Methuen released an edition of the book that included only a frontispiece by Barnhart, and a now scarcely seen jacket by Edith Morris. The rest of the book lacks decoration.

Rare Edith Morris dust jacket published by Methuen in 1933, wrapped around an inexpensive edition that boasted: "With a frontispiece in colour by Nancy Barnhart." *Courtesy of Roger A. Oakes.*

According to Maureen Duffy's *A Thousand Capricious Chances,* the 1989 book on the hundred-year history of Methuen Publishers, the dust jacket on the Edith Morris / Nancy Barnhart edition had a price mark of 5 shillings, which is one shilling less than the first edition of 1908. It is possible that the cheaper edition was published after the death of Algernon Methuen in 1924, when numerous backlisted titles were abridged for classroom use in England. This later edition lacks Barnhart's blue cloth cover with the single black stamp of Rat sitting under a tree reading a book. Barnhart's cover is juvenile compared to Bransom's, and unlike his primitive animals, Barnhart's Rat is wearing a blazer and sitting cross-legged like a man. In the five editions after Bransom's primitive paintings, the riverbankers became steadily more human.

WYNDHAM PAYNE, 1927

Wyndham Payne was a young man when he illustrated *The Wind in the Willows* in 1927. Payne was a book decorator and illustrator who worked for C. W. Beaumont, who was both an author and a publisher. His books include *A Burmese Fire at Wembley* (1924) and *The Mysterious Toyshop* (1924). Very little has been written about Payne apart from the fact that he illustrated several obscure children's books in the 1920s. Despite his drawings depicting the riverbankers as bowler-hat-wearing dandies—the sort of illustrations Grahame was eager to avoid—Grahame responded to Payne's request for an auto-

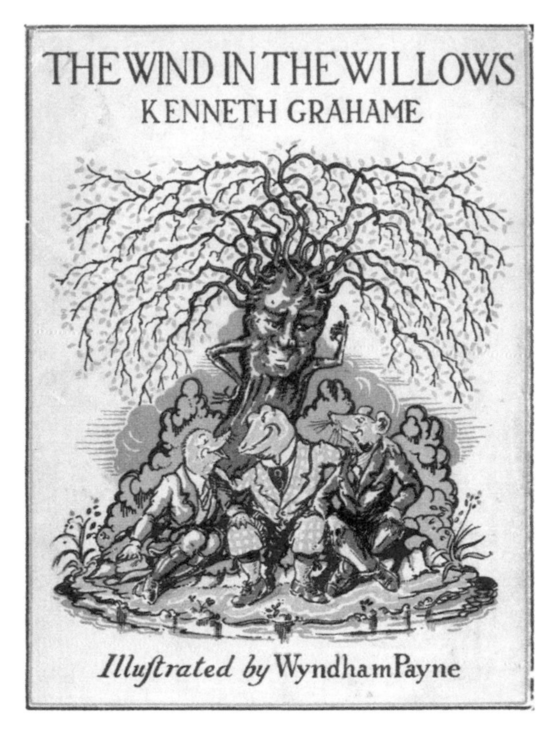

Wyndham Payne's cover, 1927.

graphed copy on October 26, 1927: "I was greatly amused by your spirited little drawings, and expect the edition will be a great success. I see it displayed in every window" (Bodleian, MS. Eng. misc. d. 527, p. 148).

The twenty-fifth edition includes a white book jacket with a drawing of Mole, Toad, and Rat sitting on what appears to be a small island. Mr. Toad sits between Mole and Rat. The three of them are fully dressed, in casual blazers and neckties. With his arms around the others, Toad is the central riverbanker in the image. Above Toad is a tree with a face—an image that Arthur Rackham was to repeat in his chapter headings in 1940. The branches of the tree act as a large head of hair. Like Robertson's Pan on the cover of the first edition, the anthropomorphized tree is misleading with regard to the content of the book. There are no talking trees in *The Wind in the Willows*, and the tree—a character in its own right—appears only on the cover.

In Rackham's edition, talking trees appear as headings in chapters I, III, VIII, X, and XI. Payne's and Rackham's trees add a new dimension to the work—as though the trees of the natural world, beyond Grahame's animals, are capable of feeling and action. Both artists drew trees as animated as any of the riverbankers. The idea has origins in a poem by Tennyson, "The Talking Oak," and in the seventeenth-century book *Tableaux du Temple des Muses.* In an engraving, three trees appear to take the form of women.

When Payne learned of Kenneth Grahame's death, he wrote to Elspeth:

> April 20th 1933
> Dear Madam,
>
> I have just returned from abroad to find your letter of the 7th just redirected to me here + with much pleasure I hasten to comply with your request for a copy of the letter to which you refer. I need hardly say how

Rackham. Dancing trees. Heading for chapter I.

very much I appreciated your late husband's kindness in writing to me, + the copy of "The Wind in the Willows" which he autographed is a most treasured possession.

Yours Sincerely
Wyndham Payne
(Harry Ransom Humanities Research Center,
The University of Texas at Austin)

ERNEST SHEPARD, 1931, 1933, 1953

The illustrations most readily associated with *The Wind in the Willows* are Ernest Shepard's primarily pen-and-ink drawings, published in London in the thirty-eighth edition of 1931. Charles Scribner's Sons published the American edition in 1933. When Methuen & Company offered Shepard the job, he had already achieved notoriety as the illustrator of several works by A. A. Milne, including *When We Were Very Young* (1924), *Winnie-the-Pooh* (1926), *Now We Are Six* (1927), and *The House at Pooh Corner* (1928).

Shepard had steady work as an illustrator with *Punch* and was reluctant, at first, to illustrate Grahame's classic. He writes in the preface to the 1953 anniversary edition: "There are certain books that should never be illustrated . . . and I had felt that *The Wind in the Willows* was one of these. Perhaps if it had not already been done, I should not have given way to the desire to do it myself, but it so happened that when the opportunity was offered me, I seized upon it gladly."

Shepard had been paid a flat fee and no royalties for his acclaimed work on the *Winnie-the-Pooh* books, but he had recently been widowed and left with two children to raise. When he was offered *The Wind in the Willows*, he agreed to illustrate the book on the condition that he receive one third of the royalties, terms that Grahame accepted. The agreement was a boon to Shepard and his children, yet the project was daunting because *The Wind in the Willows* had been a best-selling favorite for children for twenty-two years. Shepard went to visit the author at Church Cottage in Pangbourne in the early fall of 1930 and described his meeting with the elderly Kenneth Grahame:

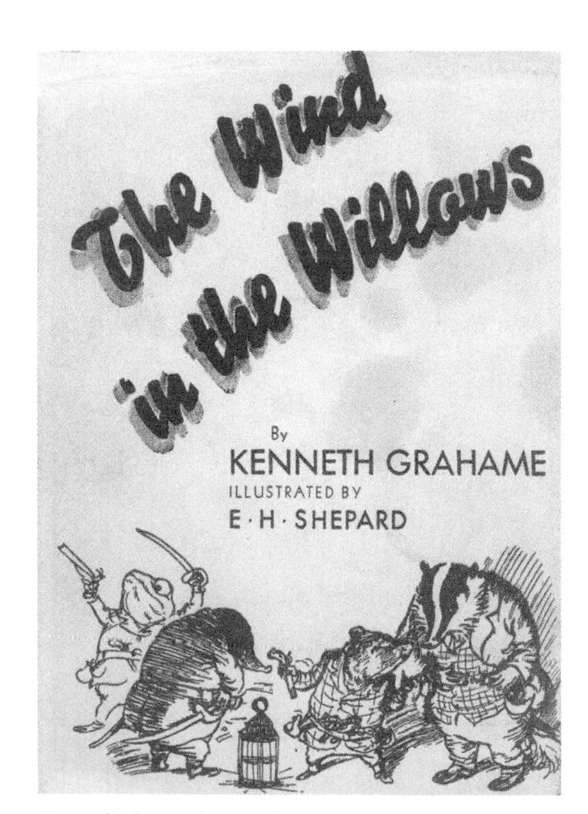

Shepard's dust jacket. Scribners, 1933.

> Not sure about this new illustrator of his book, he listened patiently while I told him what I hoped to do. Then he said 'I love these little people, be kind to them.' Just that; but sitting forward in his chair, resting upon the arms, his fine handsome head turned aside, looking like some ancient Viking, warming, he told me of the river nearby, of the meadows where Mole broke ground that spring morning, of the banks where Rat had his house, of the pools where Otter hid, and of the Wild Wood way up on the hill above the river . . . ("Illustrating 'The Wind in the Willows,' " *The Wind in the Willows* [New York: Charles Scribner's Sons, 1953])

Shepard was to visit Grahame one more time, when he had a portfolio of drawings.

Grahame was critical but finally said: "I'm glad to see you've made them real." Grahame passed away before the book was published; he never saw the Shepard edition.

Charles Scribner IV wrote, in a preface to the twentieth anniversary of Shepard's edition:

> Shepard's edition went through numerous printings, and the plates being worn, my father, Charles Scribner, III decided to bring out a new edition, completely reset, and to ask the artist to contribute six new drawings. It turns out that Shepard had kept the notebook he used in first illustrating the book, and on the basis of the material it contained, much of it unused in his first edition, he has produced what we believe are some of his very finest illustrations. (Preface, ibid.)

Most reissues of the Shepard edition now include eight color plates, a full-color cover, and several pen-and-ink drawings that were not used until 1953.

Shepard's 1933 American edition came with a dust jacket that resembled a bold and splashy newspaper cartoon of the riverbankers preparing to retake Toad Hall. The earlier Methuen edition was more conservative, with the illustration of the Gypsy cart from chapter II on the cover. The first American Shepard edition sold for $1.50, with all illustrations being black and white. When Shepard was asked to make color illustrations in 1953, he added a full-color dust jacket that exudes the essence of *The Wind in the Willows*. Even so, the image is not from a particular scene in the book but rather looks like a movie poster because of the way it incorporates an amalgam of different scenes.

One of Shepard's more famous illustrations is of Mole and Rat reclining on the riverbank, the picnic spread between them. Rackham's full-color treatment of the same subject includes the river and both sides of the bank beyond. Rackham's surroundings are a country paradise, with Mole and Rat at the center. Paul Bransom included endpapers with the same scene. Many of the illustrations of the picnic scenes resemble Monet's early painting *Le Déjeuner sur l'herbe* (1865). Monet was desperately poor when he painted this giant canvas. He was trying to make paintings that would appeal to the bourgeoisie who, like Grahame and his peers, fled the cities on weekends. Grahame's characters as ren-

Arthur Rackham's picnic, 1940.

Ernest Shepard's picnic, 1931.

dered by the early illustrators and Monet's subjects are dressed in the finest clothing. Monet's women are fashion plates, while Rackham's reclining Rat wears the light-colored clothing of the leisured classes.

The image of the sophisticated urbanite in a tranquil country setting has long been a tradition in painting. Monet himself intended to improve Lancret's 1740 painting *Le Collation après la Chasse*. The scene of the picnic in *The Wind in the Willows* is composed of the same elements: The riverbank is crowded with weekend boaters—so much so that, in Grahame's text, Badger flees when he sees the number of people. The picnic cloth is spread with all the trimmings, and surrounding the scene are naturally-growing trees. Bransom meticulously renders Grahame's characters as the animals that they are.

Shepard draws willows at the edge of the illustration. In one of Grahame's more pastoral moments, he refers to Pan's abode as "that willow-fringed island"—an image of Nature as fecund, filling every space. Monet and Grahame were contemporaries, and they shared an obsession with water and the need to be surrounded by flora and fauna. As industrialization encroached, Monet in France and Grahame in England did everything to retreat from the demands of the modern world.[10] Artist and writer focused

10. In 1891, Monet diverted the Epte River to flow into his sculpted water-lily pond at Giverny. Though his paintings leave out details of modern life, train tracks separated

on specific images—Monet, the lilies in his pond, and Grahame, the riverbank. Both were influenced by Ruskin's idea that the common man should have a place outside the metropolis, overgrown with vegetation and near water.

Shepard's Mole with picnic basket.

In 1908, as Grahame wrote *The Wind in the Willows,* Monet was beginning his second round of paintings that focused on the reflections off the water's surface. Grahame's illustrators picked up on his preoccupation with water and water images, and they drew inspiration from the subtle compositions of famous paintings. Monet's 1903 canvas is one of his earliest lily paintings. He added the willows to show that the painting was not an abstraction but a painting of the water's surface. The willow fringe adds context to the composition.

ARTHUR RACKHAM, 1940

Arthur Rackham was the most sought-after British illustrator of his day, his work adorning and enhancing books by dozens of authors.[11] He also kept up a lively correspondence with his admirers, many of whom were children. In a letter written on October 26, 1909, Rackham revealed that he was a fan of Grahame's book:

> My dear Betty, Joan & Gilbert
>
> Very many thanks for your kind letter   I was most pleased that you thought of me when you were reading the 'Wind in the Willows
>
> Curiously enough I very nearly did illustrate it. The publishers asked

the pond and gardens from the main house where the artist and his family lived. Monet crossed the tracks whenever he went out to paint and was well aware of the train that steamed through his property four times a day.

11. Rackham was in great demand when *The Wind in the Willows* was published. The major works he illustrated at the time are: *Fairy Tales of the Brothers Grimm* (1900), *Rip van Winkle* (1905), *Peter Pan in Kensington Gardens* (1906), *Alice's Adventures in Wonderland* (1907), *A Midsummer Night's Dream* (1908), and *Undine* (1909).

me to, but at the time it would have had to be done, I was too busy illustrating the Midsummer Night Dream.

But its a splendid book, isn't it! The little field mice singing carols are among the jollier things in it. I especially like when they toasted their chilblains till they tingled—(but perhaps you've never had chilblains? Well, *don't*!)

And Toad is grand, isn't he!

I suppose you know that the frontispiece is by the same clever man who wrote the play 'Pinkie & the Fairies.' Which you saw or will see.

In the summer of 1936 George Macy visited Arthur Rackham on behalf of the Limited Editions Club of New York. The club offered Rackham a job illustrating a book called *A Crock of Gold.* Rackham, then elderly, had nothing lined up afterward, so he asked for a second project. When Macy suggested *The Wind in the Willows*, he saw that Rackham was moved: "He explained that for years he had ardently wished to illustrate the book, and had always regretted that he had refused the invitation of Kenneth Grahame and his publishers nearly thirty years before."[12] Rackham, in declining health, decided to illustrate *The Wind in the Willows* first.

Grahame's classic was Rackham's final work—he did not live to see publication—and it was a labor of love on the part of all parties involved. Apparently Rackham needed quite a lot of prodding by George Macy to finish his illustrations. Six months after he agreed to the project and had met with Elspeth Grahame in Pangborne, Rackham wrote:

Stilegate/Limpsfield/Surrey

11 July 37

Dear Mr Macy

Do forgive me for not having written before. And do also please forgive me if I say I would rather not show *any* body, yet, what I am doing for The Wind in the Willows.

I am deep in it—but too experimental to want to show my work. I have not *finished* much yet. And I am not sure that I may not scrap what I have done. This is no unusual thing for me—I get stuck or experimen-

12. Hudson, *Arthur Rackham*, 144.

> tal or off on false lines—and I know by experience that I may be in what seems a muddle + then get going like a house a fire.
>
> I have been down by the River Thames—and out and about in the woods. And discovering canal barges + all the rest of "stuff" that the book talks of.
>
> I don't know how long you'll be over here. But perhaps before you go, I shall be able to report visible progress. If not, I am sure to, by the time by our next visit comes.
>
> But you mustn't think things are going badly.

According to his letters to Macy, Rackham was ill by August. He was "in the doctor's hands for more than one complaint" during the year and had a difficult time working, let alone finishing the illustrations. In the end, Rackham completed all of his line drawings—the chapter headers—from his bed, with the idea that upon completion of the *Wind in the Willows* illustrations, he would have another project. On April 14, 1939, Macy wrote the following:

> The truth is that I am not able at this time intelligently to discuss the whole question of publication. This is because the Limited Editions Club follows the system of publishing its books in annual series, one each month. Because the illustrations for The Wind in the Willows were promised to us a year ago, we had announced the book for publication last year. When you were unable to deliver the pictures to us, we had to send out an announcement of postponement, and we substituted another book in that series.
>
> Our catalog for the coming year does not include The Wind in the Willows. It may therefore be two years before we are able to announce and publish the book. So I am not able to say definitely by what process the plates can be made, or who can make them, or when they can be made.
>
> This indefiniteness will of course make it impossible for me at this time to discuss the making of yet another book with you.

By the time the book was eventually ready to go to press, it was already sold out. A total of 2,020 hardcover copies were to be manufactured by the

Walpole Printing Company. A less expensive edition manufactured by The Heritage Illustrated Bookshelf was later released.[13]

DISNEY TO TERRY JONES, A. A. MILNE, THE POOH CONNECTION, AND *TOAD OF TOAD HALL*

In the generation after Grahame, A. A. Milne, a long-time fan of *The Wind in the Willows*, became England's greatest children's-book author. Well known as a West End playwright in his early career, he is remembered today for *Winnie-the-Pooh,* a fact he came to regret in the late 1920s. In 1921 Grahame's literary agent, Curtis Brown, approached Milne about dramatizing *The Wind in the Willows.* Milne wrote the play in 1921, but because the staging is complicated by the size of the riverbankers in relation to their world, it took years to find a producer willing to stage Milne's dramatization. However, after a seven-year search for a producer, Milne's play, *Toad of Toad Hall,* was produced in Liverpool, England. A decade later, Milne wrote in the introduction of the Rackham Heritage edition: "For years I have been talking about this book, quoting it, recommending it. In one of my early panegyrics I said: 'I feel sometimes that it was I who wrote it and recommended it to Kenneth Grahame.' "

The first full production of *Toad of Toad Hall* opened on Saturday, December 21, 1929, at the Liverpool Playhouse. A review appeared in the *New York Times* two days later:

> MILNE PLAY WITH ANIMAL ROLES
> DELIGHTS CHILDREN IN ENGLAND
>
> Dec. 22.—A new play by A.A. Milne . . . was produced here last night for the first time on any stage. It is a fanciful children's play built from Kenneth Graeme's [*sic*] book . . . and has more in common with Mr. Milnes verse, "When We Were Very Young," than with his detective thrillers.

13. Files of the George Macy Co., Inc., Harry Ransom Humanities Research Center, The University of Texas at Austin, box 109, folders 22–33.

Photograph of an early production of *Toad of Toad Hall*, no date. *Courtesy of Peter Green via the Harry Ransom Humanities Research Center, The University of Texas at Austin.*

> All the characters are animals—a toad, a mole, a rat and badgers—and the play is unfolded so clearly that even the youngest children in last night's audience were able to follow its whimsicality without strain.

According to Peter Green's manuscript notes, kept at the Harry Ransom Humanities Resarch Center, a production was next mounted "at the Lyric (with Wendy Toye, Frederich Bartwell, Richard Goolden & Nor Bamiard)." Richard Goolden (1894–1981) went on to play the role of Mole in numerous productions over a span of fifty years. *Toad of Toad Hall* also played at the "Savoy (with Nova Pilbeam); & at the Royalty (Dec. 1934)" and was later produced by the Reading Repertory Co. (December 31, 1945). It was in the program for this performance that the Savoy Theatre thanked Ernest H. Shepard and Methuen & Co. for letting them lower a copy of the map from the endpapers during intermissions. The play has since become a West End London tradition, running in numerous matinees for children every Christmastime.

When Disney decided to produce an animated version, they bought the rights for both *The Wind in the Willows* and *Toad of Toad Hall*. In a letter from Curtis Brown to Charles Scribner's Sons dated March 13, 1939, Brown's lawyer asks Scribner's lawyer to have the first illustrator, Paul Bransom, sign a waiver giving Disney permission to reproduce the original pictures in the animated film (Scribner Archives, Princeton University). The illustrator was located in upstate New York, a waiver was reluctantly signed, and a decade later Disney released a film called *The Adventures of Ichabod and Mr. Toad* (1949). Originally titled *Two Fabulous Characters*, the two animated shorts looked nothing like any of the illustrated editions. *Ichabod and Mr. Toad* was one of Disney's "package films" made during the war, when several short ideas were strung together to make a feature-length film. In classic Disney style, creative license is taken with the texts of Kenneth Grahame, A. A. Milne, and Washington Irving. Names are changed: In *Mr. Toad,* Angus MacBadger tells Ratty and Mole that something must be done about the spendthrift ways of J. Thaddeus Toad. Apparently this was a dig at Roy Disney, who often complained to the animators about the money spent by his brother Walt. Rat dubs Toad's obsession with cars Motor Mania, a term used as the title for a seven-minute Goofy cartoon one year later.

Other commercial productions appeared. Three years before Disney's package film, a television adaptation of *Toad of Toad Hall* was made for the BBC. Written by Michael Barry and directed by Brian Bell, *Toad of Toad Hall* was released December 29, 1946. The TV show was ninety minutes long and done, like all television shows at this time, in black and white.

During his first foray into professional theater, Sir Ian McKellen played the role of Chief Weasel in a 1961 production of *Toad of Toad Hall* at the Belgrade Theatre in Coventry. Like most Christmastime productions, the show ran from December 23 to January 12. On his official Web page, Sir Ian reminisces about this time:

> I was disappointed not to be playing Mole or Water Rat, which went to more experienced actors who were also favourites with the Belgrade audiences. I was contracted to "play as cast" and don't remember being confident enough to ever complain. I was still ecstatic to be earning my living as a professional.

> As Chief Weasel (my first stage villain) the national newspaper, The Guardian, reported that mine was one of "the most engaged performances" and the Coventry Evening Telegraph that I was "a perfectly hateful Weasel"—Kind Critics!

In Orlando, Florida, the Disney World attraction Mr. Toad's Wild Ride opened on October 1, 1971. In the October 22, 1997, edition of the *Orlando Sentinel,* Walt Disney World sources revealed plans to close the ride in favor of a trip through the Hundred Acre Woods with Pooh and his friends. For an entire year, Mr. Toad's Wild Ride fans staged "Toad Ins" to protest the impending action and launched a Web site, savetoad.com. Alas, despite the fans' efforts and outpouring of love, the brass at Disney would not budge: The theme park ride was closed on September 7, 1998, replaced by The Many Adventures of Winnie the Pooh.

One of the more memorable film adaptations is Terry Jones's satirical 1996 treatment, released in the United States as *Mr. Toad's Wild Ride,* or *Go Wild in the Country!* Starring Eric Idle (as Rat) and Terry Jones (as Toad), of Monty Python's Flying Circus fame, the production veers away from the original text to further explore the evolving technology of Grahame's era. Mole is evicted from his underground home by the weasels, who have bought the land from the wealthy Mr. Toad. Mole and Rat wage a war to regain his home and way of life. Shot in bucolic Sussex, the production ends with Mr. Toad taking up an airplane—a technological advance that would have been even more uncommon than a motor car in southern England in 1908. Nevertheless, we now know that the imaginative Alastair was dreaming of flying machines while his father was writing *The Wind in the Willows*. In the final edition of *The Merry Thought*, he wrote extensively about the air ship and the circumstances under which it would come into existence:

> See . . . the engine room of the airship of Mr: Thomas Thompson. He['s] from the time of 19__ [and] had a craving for airships, though he did not know how to make one. His father was a rich man but would not give him the money for it. When the father died Mr. Thomas Thompson inherited the father's money, + paid Mr. Wood to make the airship for him. He took in Mr: Wood for chief engineer, + he married a wife, + had a boy + a girl, + took the lot of his butler Samuel Crate, + his cook

+ housekeeper up in the airship which was as big as a house with lots of bedrooms, + a drawing room + a kitchen in it. The housepart was slung below the engine room, + they were fastened together by iron bars. Mr: Samuel Crate sometimes relieved the engineer, when he wanted to get a nap or a meal.

A Note on the Text

There are four major biographies of Kenneth Grahame:

Chalmers, Patrick. *Kenneth Grahame*. London: Methuen, 1933.

Green, Peter. *Kenneth Grahame: A Biography*. Cleveland: World Publishing, 1959.

Green, Peter. *Beyond the Wild Wood: The World of Kenneth Grahame*. New York: Facts on File, 1983.

Prince, Alison. *Kenneth Grahame: An Innocent in the Wild Wood*. London: Allison & Busby Ltd, 1994.

These books are given a full citation in their initial encounter and thereafter a shortened citation.

Two comrades-in-arms have contributed significantly to the text. James Jayo has kindly contributed either the material for the notes or the text of the notes themselves in the following cases: chapter I, note 10; chapter II, note 70; chapter III, note 8; chapter V, notes 1, 15, and 16; chapter VII, notes 12, 16, and 17; chapter VIII, note 22, chapter IX, note 55; and chapter XII, note 10. These notes are also marked with the initials "J. J." In addition, Professor Mary Shaner of the University of Massachusetts, Boston, contributed the essence of note 18 in chapter IV, on the lax manners at Badger's house.

Contrary to printed British editions of *The Wind in the Willows*, Grahame always used double quotation marks in his holograph and typed manuscripts. This edition restores the double quotation marks and Grahame's original punctuation, and lists significant textual variants from the four early manuscripts. These manuscripts are housed along with a substantial amount of material on Kenneth Grahame at the Bodleian Library at Oxford, which catalogues them as follows:

MS. Eng. misc. d. 281	The Dear Mouse letters to Alastair Grahame, 1907
MS. Eng. misc. d. 247	Holograph manuscript, The Mole + ~~the~~ Water Rat
MS. Eng. misc. d. 248	Holograph manuscript, The Mole + the Water Rat
MS. Eng. misc. d. 524	Typescript from holograph
MS. Eng. misc. d. 282	Letters and holograph ms. "Bertie's Escapade"

The Bodleian requires a full citation whenever letters are cited. However, for the sake of brevity, I have referred to the holograph manuscripts as e. 247 and e. 248.

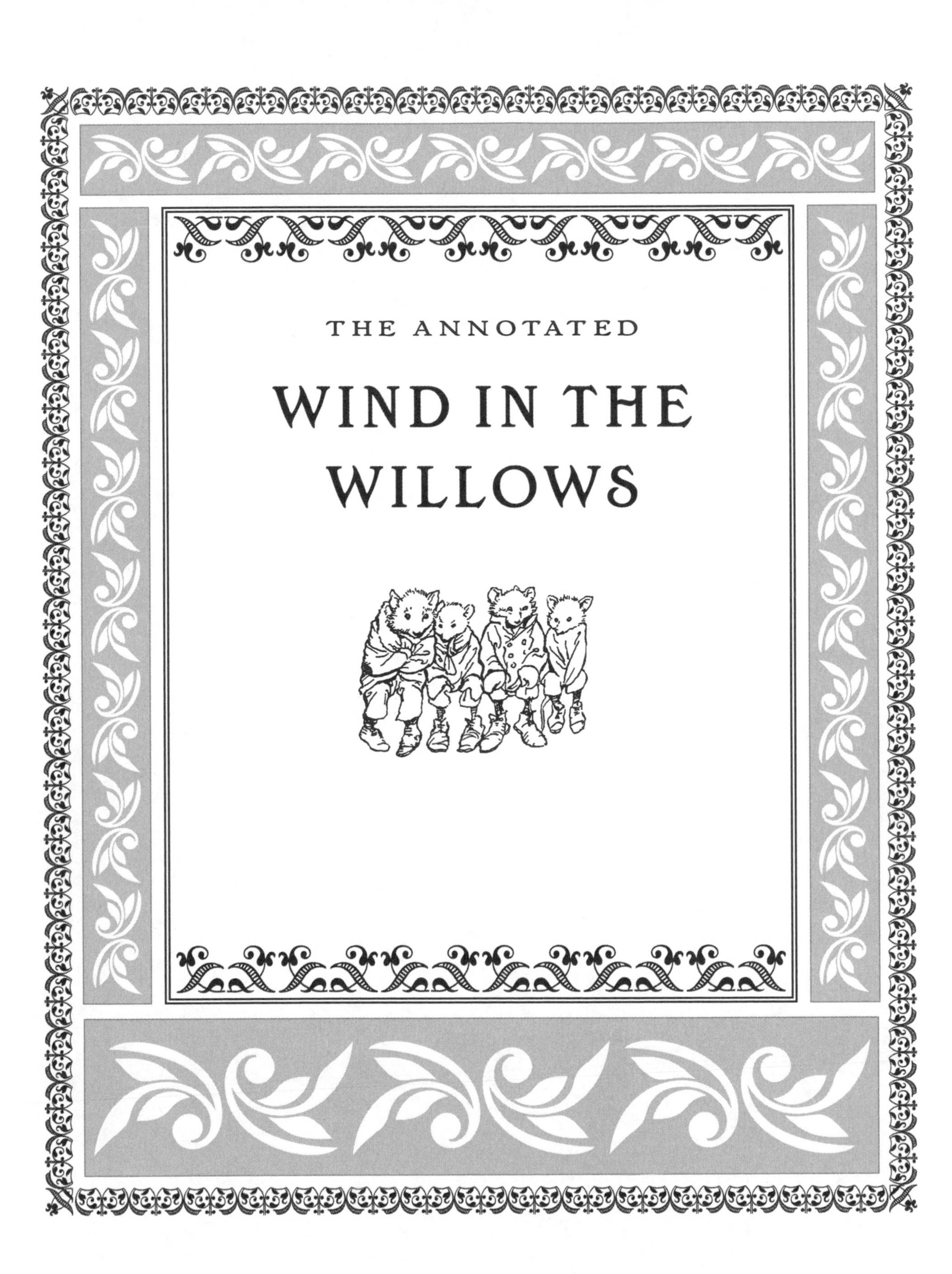
THE ANNOTATED
WIND IN THE
WILLOWS

I

The River Bank

The Mole had been working very hard all the morning,[1] spring-cleaning his little home. First with brooms, then with dusters; then on ladders and steps and chairs, with a brush and a pail of whitewash; till he had dust in his throat and eyes, and splashes of whitewash all over his black fur, and an aching back and weary arms. Spring was moving in the air above and in the earth below and around him, penetrating even his dark and lowly little house with its spirit of divine discontent[2] and longing. It was small wonder, then, that he suddenly flung down his brush on the floor, said "Bother!" and "O blow!" and also "Hang spring-cleaning!" and bolted out of the house without even waiting to put on his coat. Something up above was calling him imperiously, and he made for the steep little tunnel which answered in his case to the gravelled carriage-drive owned by animals whose residences are nearer to the sun and air. So he scraped and scratched and scrabbled and scrooged and then he scrooged again and scrabbled and scratched and scraped, working busily with his little paws and muttering to himself, "Up we go! Up we go!" till at last, pop! his snout came out into the sunlight, and he found himself rolling in the warm grass of a great meadow.[3]

Shepard's illustration of Mole whitewashing.

1. *The Mole had been working very hard all the morning.* Mole is working when chapter I begins. There is no servant or wife to do his spring cleaning for him. A wealthier male, such as Grahame himself, would probably hire someone to whitewash for him. The issue of who works and who does

not in *The Wind in the Willows* reflects class and changing class structure in 1908.

In "Bertie's Escapade," a story Grahame wrote for *The Merry Thought*, Mr. Mole has a Mrs. Mole. In Grahame's attempt to keep *The Wind in the Willows* "clean of the clash of sex"—as he wrote in a descriptive paragraph for the Methuen announcement list—he gave none of his riverbankers wives.

2. *divine discontent.* Mole's longing for spring mirrors Grahame's longing to escape from his London job as Secretary of the Bank of England. Grahame had spent the happiest days of his early childhood in the quaint riverside town of Cookham Dean, and he later returned to live there with his wife and young son.

In a letter to John Lane, publisher of his 1890s collections *Pagan Papers* (1893), *The Golden Age* (1895), and *Dream Days* (1898), Grahame wrote:

> We have just got back from three weeks' holiday at Cookham Dean, where I have taken a cottage for some little time. We have left the small boy + his governess there, + hope to get back ourselves when the days get longer, + to spend a good deal of the year there.
>
> Meantime, my 'Deputy' has just left me again, for three months' voyage southwards, which it is hoped will completely restore him to health. During that time I must sit tight + take up my white man's burden, short-handed, + with busy days ahead.
>
> All this means that I have if possible even less spare time than before to attend to my own affairs, + forces me to husband what leisure I have left more carefully. (January 8, 1908; Bodleian, MS. don. e. 27, pp. 43, 44)

The line "take up my white man's burden" is from a Rudyard Kipling poem. Written in 1899, the poem was published in *McClure's* magazine two months after the United States Senate ratified the Treaty of Paris, which ended the Spanish American War and brought the Philippines, Guam, and Puerto Rico under the control of the United States. The poem focuses on the exhausting responsibilities of imperialism. Though Grahame was not personally involved in the politics of the Philippines, his work for the Bank of England tied him to the imperialism of nineteenth- and twentieth-century British society. Below is the first of the poem's seven eight-line stanzas:

> *Take up the White Man's burden—*
> *Send forth the best ye breed—*
> *Go bind your sons to exile*
> *To serve your captives' need;*
> *To wait, in heavy harness,*
> *On fluttered folk and wild—*
> *Your new-caught sullen peoples,*
> *Half-devil and half-child.*
> ("The White Man's Burden," *McClure's*, February 12, 1899)

The arrival of spring is also a "reverdie," the regreening part of the year when, after surviving another winter, one begins anew through such rituals as spring cleaning.

3. *So he scraped and scratched and scrabbled and scrooged and then he scrooged again.* Grahame wrote about the Mole with urban Londoners in mind—the very people who were trapped in the city by their jobs. During the late Victorian period London had become highly polluted by both industrial fires and the soot from domestic, bituminous coal-burning stoves. Mole is literally digging himself out of his own domestic soot.

Rackham's illustration from the 1940 Heritage edition.

"This is fine!" he said to himself. "This is better than whitewashing!" The sunshine struck hot on his fur,[4] soft breezes caressed his heated brow, and after the seclusion of the cellarage he had lived in so long[5] the carol of happy birds fell on his dulled hearing almost like a shout. Jumping off all his four legs at once, in the joy of living and the delight of spring without its cleaning, he pursued his way across the meadow till he reached the hedge on the further side.[6]

"Hold up!" said an elderly rabbit at the gap.[7] "Sixpence for the privilege of passing by the private road!" He was bowled over in an instant by the impatient and contemptuous Mole, who trotted along the side of the hedge chaffing the other rabbits as they peeped hurriedly from their holes to see what the row was about. "Onion-sauce! Onion-sauce!"[8] he remarked jeeringly, and was gone before they could think of a thoroughly satisfactory reply. Then they all started grumbling at each other. "How *stupid* you are! Why didn't you tell

4. *The sunshine struck hot on his fur.* In *The Wind in the Willows: A Fragmented Arcadia* (New York: Wayne Publishers, 1994), Peter Hunt points out that Mole's emergence into the sunlight is reminiscent of the beginning of Wordsworth's *The Prelude.*

O there is blessing in this gentle breeze,
A visitant that while it fans my cheek
Doth seem half-conscious of the joy it brings
From the green fields, and from yon azure sky.

Grahame starts with Mole in his "lowly" home and moves us, via Mole's point of view, up from his familiar underground. For Mole and Toad *The Wind in the Willows* is a bildungsroman: a novel about the moral and psychological growth of the main character. Mole begins at home, leaves, and is initiated into a new life, yet he will return home in the company of the

Water Rat and be transformed throughout the twelve chapters.

5. *after the seclusion of the cellarage he had lived in so long.* The word *cellarage* came into use in 1602 in Shakespeare's *Hamlet* (act 1, scene 5, line 151). Cellarage means cellar space, used especially for storage.

Mole, like Hamlet heeding the voice of the ghost, is listening to the language of the earth. Mole does what a Londoner with moderate means would like to do—he quits in favor of a lush meadow.

6. *he pursued his way across the meadow till he reached the hedge on the further side.* In 1919, G. T. Hill, a professor of botany at London University and a friend of Graham Robertson's, wrote to Kenneth Grahame asking who looked after Mole End while Mole was away. In a letter in Elspeth Grahame's handwriting, dated September 24, 1919, Grahame responded:

> Mole, though unmarried and evidently in rather poor circumstances . . . could probably have afforded some outside assistance say twice a week or so. . . . He probably then had a char-mouse in for a few hours and her dinner on certain days, and the animal would have cleaned up his whitewashing mess in a perfunctory sort of way; then, finding that her weekly pittance was no longer forthcoming, quite naturally and properly would have taken her services elsewhere, though from kindness of heart she might have continued to give an occasional eye to the goldfish. (Bodleian, MS. Eng. misc. d. 529, p. 43)

As for the Grahames' perspectives on class, servants, and the difference between the Mole and the Water Rat:

> The presence of certain characters may be indicated in or required by the story, but if the author has no immediate use for them, he simply ignores their existence. Take this very question of domestic service—however narrow poor Mole's means may have been, it is evident that Rat was comfortably off—indeed I strongly suspect him of a butler-valet and cook-housekeeper. Toad Hall, again, must have been simply crawling with idle servants eating their heads off. (Ibid.)

After Alastair Grahame's suicide in May of 1920, Grahame either typed his letters or had Elspeth Grahame write them for him. At the time of Alastair's death Grahame's hand developed an uncontrollable tremor. "Forgive the typed letter—my hand has given out," he wrote to Arthur Quiller-Couch, on May 15, 1920 (Trinity College, Oxford, Archive, DD36). Because so many of the later letters by Grahame are in Elspeth's hand, we cannot be certain who actually composed them.

7. *"Hold up!" said an elderly rabbit at the gap.* Rackham is the only early artist to render Mole's interaction with the rabbits. The illustration is appropriate as a frontispiece because the scene occurs within the first page of Grahame's text. The caption, "'Onion-Sauce! Onion-Sauce!' he remarked jeeringly, and was gone before they could think of a reply," is abridged from the text. The words "thoroughly satisfactory" before "reply" have been omitted. Captions are necessary for Rackham's edition because the illustrations are unfortunately inconsistent with Grahame's text.

8. *"Onion-sauce! Onion-sauce!"* Mole is threatening the rabbits and making a joke at their expense. Onion sauce was always served with baked rabbit. Grahame consistently portrays the rabbits as dimwits—a theme that A. A. Milne was to pick up in the *Pooh* books, published in the 1920s. The dialogue, as Eeyore floats downstream

him———" "Well, why didn't *you* say———" "You might have reminded him———" and so on, in the usual way; but, of course, it was then much too late, as is always the case.

It all seemed too good to be true. Hither and thither through the meadows he rambled busily, along the hedgerows, across the copses, finding everywhere birds building, flowers budding, leaves thrusting—everything happy, and progressive, and occu-

Wyndham Payne's illustration with caption: *The best part of a holiday perhaps . . . to see all the other fellows busy working* (Payne edition, 1927, 3). The line parallels one in Jerome K. Jerome's *Idle Thoughts of an Idle Fellow*: "It is impossible to enjoy idling thoroughly unless one has plenty of work to do" ([New York and Boston: H. M. Caldwell Co., 1890], 53).

in *The House at Pooh Corner*, is indicative of Rabbit's stupidity:

> "Eeyore, what *are* you doing there?" said Rabbit.
>
> "I'll give you three guesses, Rabbit. Digging holes in the ground? Wrong. Leaping from branch to branch of a young oak-tree? Wrong. Waiting for somebody to help me out of the river? Right. Give rabbit time, and he'll always get the answer." (New York: Puffin Books, 1992, 97)

Wyndham Payne illustrated the 25th Methuen edition, which was published in 1927 and, in 1930, as the 33rd edition. Payne's illustration for the first chapter does not accurately depict the text: Mole is reclining on the ground, admiring the birds in a birdhouse above him. In Grahame's text, Mole is running "hither and thither . . . busily through the meadows." He has just dashed by the toll-collecting rabbits. Though the Dickensian theme of a bird in a cage appears three times in *The Wind in the Willows*—in chapters II, V, and VIII—Payne added a birdhouse in the first chapter.

In a fan letter dated December 17, 1931, Margaret Stewart writes to Grahame to complain about the new Shepard edition: "Since my earliest childhood I have wondered why artists do not *read* the books they illustrate," to which a letter in Elspeth's handwriting replies, "Yes—it is exasperating. These artists are very tiresome fellows—and they all do it!" (MS. Eng. misc. d. 531, pp. 186–88).

pied. And instead of having an uneasy conscience pricking him and whispering "whitewash!" he somehow could only feel how jolly it was to be the only idle dog among all these busy citizens. After all, the best part of a holiday is perhaps not so much to be resting yourself, as to see all the other fellows busy working.

He thought his happiness was complete when, as he meandered aimlessly along, suddenly he stood by the edge of a full-fed river. Never in his life had he seen a river before—this sleek, sinuous, full-bodied animal,[9] chasing and chuckling, gripping things with a gurgle and leaving them with a laugh, to fling itself on fresh playmates that shook themselves free, and were caught and held again.[10] All was a-shake and a-shiver—glints and gleams and sparkles, rustle and swirl, chatter and bubble. The Mole was bewitched, entranced, fascinated.[11] By the side of the river he trotted as one trots, when very small, by the side of a man who holds one spell-bound by exciting stories; and when tired at last, he sat on the bank, while the river still chattered on to him, a babbling procession of the best stories in the world, sent from the heart of the earth to be told at last to the insatiable sea.[12]

As he sat on the grass and looked across the river, a dark hole in the bank opposite, just above the water's edge,[13] caught his eye, and dreamily he fell to considering what a nice snug dwelling-place it would make for an animal with few wants and fond of a bijou[14] riverside residence, above flood level and remote from noise and dust. As he gazed, something bright and small seemed to twinkle down in the heart of it, vanished, then twinkled once more like a tiny star. But it could hardly be a star in such an unlikely situation; and it was too glittering and small for a glow-worm. Then, as he looked, it winked at him, and so declared itself to be an eye; and a small face began gradually to grow up round it, like a frame round a picture.

A brown little face, with whiskers.

A grave round face, with the same twinkle in its eye that had first attracted his notice.[15]

9. *Never in his life had he seen a river before—this sleek, sinuous, full-bodied animal.* It is odd that the fresh and exciting river is first glimpsed from Mole's point of view, because moles, for the most part, are blind. Defined as burrowing insectivores, they have minute eyes and concealed ears and survive primarily by their sense of smell and touch. According to the Oxford English Dictionary moles usually have "very poor (or no) vision, velvety fur that can be brushed in any direction, and short strong forelimbs with broad clawed toes adapted for digging."

In a letter to Dr. William Collins on November 18, 1901, Grahame reported that according to Dr. Tweedy (one of the eye specialists the Grahames consulted), the cataract in Alastair's eye was possibly "progressive" and likely to worsen. The boy's left eye was diagnosed as " 'over-sighted' . . . and unable to focus objects near at hand without such a strain on the focusing mechanism" (courtesy of the David J. Holmes Collection). Glasses were prescribed for the eighteen-month-old boy, because he could not see objects near to him and squinted at objects in the distance. In a letter dated April 11, 1908, the Grahames' governess, Naomi Stott, comments on Alastair's sight: "He has shown a blinking tendency again. The hair is not quite long enough to need tying back, but it is a worry to him indoors. Out of doors his cap helps to keep it out of his eyes" (Peter Green Papers, Harry Ransom Humanities Research Center, The University of Texas at Austin).

Alastair Grahame was, in effect, as blind as a mole. In December 2002, Peter Green speculated that Alastair's congenital defect was due to inherited syphilis. Alison Prince writes about how the Grahames coped with his disability in her 1994 biography of Kenneth Grahame:

> Typically, the disaster [of his blindness] was one which the Grahames would

> not face. Elspeth in particular denied the distress . . . declaring that Mouse was the perfect child, not only normal, but talented to a breathtaking degree. . . . He was, for her . . . a brilliant, beautiful boy who could only have been created by genius parents. Kenneth, too, had no way of coming to terms with his son's disability. (*Kenneth Grahame: An Innocent in the Wild Wood*, 187)

In "At the Back of *The Wind in the Willows*: An Experiment in Biographical and Autobiographical Interpretation," Michael Steig suggests that Alastair Grahame was a model for both the well-mannered Mr. Mole as well as for the "Dr. Jekyll and Mr. Hyde" persona of Mr. Toad. Steig suggests that the Grahames refused to acknowledge their son's disability, proposing that by giving Mole sight Grahame was ignoring Alastair's near blindness.

> Apart from the fact that Alistair's nickname was "Mouse" during his early years, he was blind in one eye and had poor vision in the other, which is suggestive when one considers that the mole, an animal which in real life is virtually blind, seems to have no trouble with his sight. This is purely speculative, but Green makes a persuasive case that the Grahames attempted to deny to themselves and to Alistair that he was in any way abnormal. Giving sight to a mole certainly sounds like a symbolic form of denial. (*Victorian Studies* 24, no. 3 [Spring 1981]: 322 n. 27)

Kenneth Grahame's letter to Dr. Collins reveals how involved he was in his son's care at that early part of his life. Perhaps sight was bestowed on Mr. Mole not out of denial but out of the deep wish for Alastair to gain full sight.

10. *to fling itself on fresh playmates that shook themselves free, and were caught and held again.* The river is a crucial character in the narrative, and here Grahame gives it a personality. Other great English novels that use a river as a character are *The Mill on the Floss* (1860), by George Eliot, and *Our Mutual Friend* (1865), by Charles Dickens.

In Greek mythology, spirits—usually female, called nymphs—inhabit all forms of nature. River nymphs, like the playmates Grahame describes here, are called naiads.

—J. J.

11. *The Mole was bewitched, entranced, fascinated.* The rivers Thames—called the Isis where it runs through Oxford—and Cherwell are deep and narrow waterways. As a schoolboy at St. Edward's School on New Inn Hall Street, in the heart of Oxford in the 1870s, Grahame had enough unsupervised time to pass long hours playing along the riverbanks. To this day the Cherwell and Isis are used both for swimming and for the navigation of small, self-propelled boats such as punts, sculls, and canoes. The rivers are also tame enough not to seem threatening to swimmers. Grahame said of his boyhood in Oxford:

> The two influences which most soaked into me there, and have remained with me ever since, were the good grey Gothic on the one hand and, on the other, the

Illustration by E. W. Haslehust of punters on the Cherwell River, Oxford (from F. D. How, *Beautiful England: Oxford* [London: Blackie and Son, Ltd, 1910], 21).

Photo of Folly Bridge. *Courtesy of Nigel McMorris, the Kenneth Grahame Society.*

> cool secluded reaches of the Thames—the "stripling Thames," remote and dragonfly haunted, before it attains to the noise, ribbons, and flannels of Folly Bridge. . . . But these elements, the classics, the Gothic, the primeval Thames, fostered in me, perhaps, the pagan germ . . . ("Oxford Through a Boy's Eyes," in Chalmers, *Kenneth Grahame*, 21)

12. *sent from the heart of the earth to be told at last to the insatiable sea.* The setting for this river is also quite possibly the River Fowey in Cornwall, which begins in the Bodmin Moor watershed and eventually meets the ocean water around the town of Lostwithiel.

13. *a dark hole in the bank opposite, just above the water's edge.* Paul Bransom created the first fully illustrated edition of *The Wind in the Willows* in 1913 and remains the artist who stayed closest to Grahame's text. In this illustration for chapter I (see page 12), the first glimpse of the Water Rat from across the river shows him emerging from a dirt hole. Grahame's text says nothing about a house—he describes Rat's home as a "bijou riverside residence" and nothing more. In Bransom's rendering of the scene, Rat looks like vermin, and his hole is surrounded by leaves and snakelike roots.

With each successive illustrator, Rat's riverside residence gradually became more like a doll's house than a rat's hole.

In Shepard's less menacing illustration of the emergence of the Water Rat, the creature's tiny face appears in a square doorway, not a hole. On his right, there is a small window complete with four panes of glass.

Rackham revised Rat's house further in his 1940 edition. Instead of roots, Rat has a dock, complete with posts driven into the riverbank.

Though a variation, Rackham's illustration is virtually identical to Shepard's famous 1931 pen-and-ink composition. This is the last illustration Rackham ever made. He was very ill as he finished it, and when his daughter pointed out that he had forgotten to include oars, he went back and added them in opaque white paint. The oars

Shepard's 1931 version of the Rat's house.

sit in the boat, exactly like Shepard's. Rackham died before the edition was published.

14. *bijou.* A small, dainty, highly prized piece of workmanship; "jewel" in French. Used loosely as an adjective to describe houses, the *OED* defines it as "small, elegant, and luxurious." In George Washburn Smally and Thomas Hay Sweet Escott's Edwardian *Society in the New Reign* (London: T. F. Unwin, 1904), the term is used as follows: "The London *pied-à-terre* consisted . . . of a bijou residence in Mayfair" (73). Rat's hole is a desirable place to live, and without a second thought, Mole will move right in and become part of the household.

15. *A grave round face, with the same twinkle in its eye that had first attracted his notice.* In 1876, at the end of his first year in London, Grahame befriended the scholar Frederick Furnivall. Furnivall had many interests and filled an intellectual void in Grahame's life, introducing him to Christian Socialism and the world of literary scholarship. Furnivall was also wild about boats and sculling. Jessie Currie, who lived near him, gave the following account: "Let me introduce you to Dr. Furnivall. He will ask you if you can scull. If you say 'No' he will take you up the river to teach you. If you say 'Yes' he will take you up the river to keep you in prac-

Rackham, 1940. The passing of the luncheon basket. Caption: "'Shove that under your feet,' he observed to the Mole, as he passed it down into the boat."

Shepard's passing of the basket, 1931.

tice. He will take you anyhow" (Green, *Kenneth Grahame: A Biography*, 65).

At the time, Grahame was like a mole in London who at last had met a proper playmate. Furnivall may very well have been one of Grahame's inspirations for the Water Rat. The other possible model for the Rat is Grahame's friend Edward Atkinson. A bachelor of private means, Atkinson owned over thirty boats, lived in a beautiful riverside house on the Fowey estuary in Cornwall, was the commodore of the Fowey Yacht Club, and kept drawers full of mechanical toys.

In a letter to Peter Green in 1957, Dale Purves wrote of his boyhood impression of Atky, as he was known to friends:

> Mr. Atkinson had a lovely year-round house up the Fowey River. It was set right on the river bank and was called "Rosebank." Mr. Atkinson led a life of highly civilized seclusion. I think he had a house keeper but I am sure he was a bachelor, perhaps a widower. In any event, the house was set right at the water's edge and the interior was thoroughly fascinating. As I recall it, a ship's ladder led to the upper floor and it was strictly a man's retreat. I can well imagine, and therefore do imagine, that Mr.

Photo of Edward Atkinson and his cousin and housekeeper, Miss Marston (Green, *Beyond the Wild Wood*, 128).

Atkinson played "Rat" to Kenneth Grahame's "Mole." I would not want to send you on a wild goose chase for it is quite possible that "WW" is strictly unadulterated Thamesside, but it could very well have been Fowey for the Fowey river, stretching back beyond Fowey Harbour, is pure "WW" country. You ought to go there some time. . . . Fowey is a place of boat houses and river bends. (Letter to Peter Green, Harry Ransom Humanities Research Center, The University of Texas at Austin)

16. *"Would you like to come over?" enquired the Rat presently.*

"Oh, it's all very well to talk*," said the Mole, rather pettishly.* Mole and Rat's exchange is a call and response. The words "presently" and "pettishly" in the two lines form a slant rhyme.

There is also an immediate class distinction between Mole and Rat in this introduction. Rat, who represents the bourgeois riverbanker, graciously introduces himself out of a sense of noblesse oblige. Mole is a stranger to the ways of the riverbank; he puts himself at odds with Rat's social position when he behaves "pettishly."

Paul Bransom's 1913 illustration: Rat's hole across the river.

Small neat ears and thick silky hair.

It was the Water Rat!

Then the two animals stood and regarded each other cautiously.

"Hullo, Mole!" said the Water Rat.

"Hullo, Rat!" said the Mole.

"Would you like to come over?" enquired the Rat presently.

"Oh, its all very well to *talk*," said the Mole, rather pettishly,[16] he being new to a river and riverside life and its ways.

The Rat said nothing, but stooped and unfastened a rope and hauled on it; then lightly stepped into a little boat which the Mole had not observed. It was painted blue outside and white within, and was just the size for two animals;[17] and the Mole's whole heart went out to it at once, even though he did not yet fully understand its uses.

The Rat sculled smartly across and made fast.[18] Then he held up his forepaw as the Mole stepped gingerly down. "Lean on that!" he said. "Now then, step lively!" and the Mole to his surprise and rapture found himself actually seated in the stern of a real boat.

"This has been a wonderful day!" said he, as the Rat shoved off and took to the sculls again. "Do you know, I've never been in a boat before in all my life."

"What?" cried the Rat, open-mouthed: "Never been in a—you never—well I—what have you been doing, then?"

"Is it so nice as all that?" asked the Mole shyly, though he was quite prepared to believe it as he leant back in his seat and surveyed the cushions, the oars, the rowlocks, and all the fascinating fittings, and felt the boat sway lightly under him.

"Nice? It's the *only* thing," said the Water Rat solemnly, as he leant forward for his stroke. "Believe me, my young friend, there is *nothing*—absolute nothing—half so much worth doing as simply messing about in boats.[19] Simply messing," he went on dreamily: "messing—about—in—boats; messing———"

"Look ahead, Rat!" cried the Mole suddenly.

It was too late. The boat struck the bank full tilt.[20] The dreamer, the joyous oarsman, lay on his back at the bottom of the boat, his heels in the air.

"—about in boats—or *with* boats," the Rat went on composedly, picking himself up with a pleasant laugh. "In or out of 'em, it doesn't matter. Nothing seems really to matter, that's the charm of it. Whether you get away, or whether you don't; whether you arrive at your destination or whether you reach somewhere else, or whether you never get anywhere at all, you're

17. *It was painted blue outside and white within, and was just the size for two animals.* Here Grahame introduces what will become a familiar theme: the ambivalence of size. Rat moves like a human, yet what size is he? Who made his boat? Grahame says the boat "was just the size for two animals." Are the animals human-sized or are they rat-sized? At first they appear animal-sized—yet later Mr. Toad will ride in a gypsy caravan, steal horses and cars, try to buy railway tickets, and converse with human beings as if they were the same size.

18. *The Rat sculled smartly across and made fast.* Sculled means rowed. Rat is a natural on the water.

19. *"simply messing about in boats."* One of the most-quoted lines from *The Wind in the Willows*, and all of English literature.

20. *The boat struck the bank full tilt.* Wyndham Payne's second illustration in chapter

Drawing of Furnivall (Peter Green, *Beyond the Wild Wood: The World of Kenneth Grahame* [New York: Facts on File, 1984], 54).

I is of Rat and Mole rowing, a topic Shepard took up with an image of them in the boat as well as capsizing. Payne, however, mistakenly drew a dragonfly. Grahame's text calls for a mayfly, which is a very different kind of insect. A mayfly is a short-lived insect that is used as an angler in fishing. Otter also eats a mayfly in the first-chapter picnic. Shepard, too, drew a dragonfly instead of a mayfly.

While the Grahames were in the town of Fowey, Cornwall, in the summer of 1907, they met an American family from Philadelphia by the name of Purves. The five Purves boys later told Peter Green, Grahame's 1959 biographer, that the setting for the riverbank had to be the Fowey they recollected, and that the picnic of chapter I was inspired by a trip they took upriver "to a little village called Golant" (Green, *Kenneth Grahame: A Biography*, 268).

But Kenneth Grahame was no stranger to Fowey. In his courtship letters to Elspeth—beginning on May 21, 1899, and continuing up to their wedding, held at St. Fimbarrus Church in Fowey on July 22—he describes his fascination with the town and the river. Grahame had gone to Fowey to recover from pneumonia. Free of the pressures and society of London, his letters—written in a sort of baby talk crossed with the local dialect—recount the pleasures of that summer. Elspeth, who was a London socialite, actively pursued Grahame, later becoming his caretaker. The letters chronicle Grahame's time in Cornwall. He rested—sleeping nine to ten hours a day—and spent afternoons boating.

> Fowey Hotel—Fursday—my darlin own Ki-Wi (which was the name o the little steemer wot ustertake me over paignton tother wun wos called ethel)
>
> I like this place *orfly* s'far's I've gorn. As the river mouth came in view larst night with the boats and the little grey town I felt summow's if I was coming *ome,*—from boardin-school at Torquay! Ain't bin out splorin yet, but the view from ere is lovely. (Bodleian, MS. Eng. misc. e. 480, p. 35)

Grahame's passion for boating, which was to find its way into *The Wind in the Willows*, comes through in these letters:

> We ad a fine sale yesterday, bote a layin over proper. . . . In the mornin terday I got aboard the R. & E. [a boat called the *Richard and Elizabeth*] at 11, & padoled er up the river & drifted back wif the tide—ad it ort to myself & a lovely mornin. Probbly goin to paddle er out again bout 5 if the wind falls away & its a fine evnin. But wind seems rer be gettin up & it blows my tub about too much. . . . Wensdy—. . . Yestdy ad a paddle in R. & E. went out to Arbermouf were there was a nice sea coming in, & spored some caves & enns back on the tide. (Ibid., 62, 63)

Elspeth came to resent Grahame's friend Q, or Arthur Quiller-Couch, because soon after they were married she discovered that Grahame preferred his company to hers. Most of the letters mention Q: "Now I must say good bye . . . cos

Golant on the River Fowey (Green, *Beyond the Wild Wood*, 165).

Picture postcards of Fowey, Cornwall, circa 1908. *Courtesy of the David J. Holmes Collection.*

Mr. 'Q' as just curled, to arst me to come a salin . . ." (ibid., 52). Like Mr. Rat, Grahame's idea of the perfect day involved nonstop boating.

In a 1930 letter to a fan Grahame writes, "I'm so glad you like the books, and I hope you recognize the 'Fowey' bit in *The Wind in the Willows*" (Bodleian, MS. Eng. misc. d. 531, p. 172).

Austin Purves, a friend of the Grahames, visiting Bohams in Blewbury, circa 1911.

Photo of Sir Arthur Quiller-Couch (Green, *Beyond the Wild Wood*, 125).

21. *He looped the painter through a ring in his landing-stage.* A painter is a line used for towing or securing a boat.

Wyndham Payne's illustration with caption: "The boat struck the bank full tilt."

always busy, and you never do anything in particular; and when you've done it there's always something else to do, and you can do it if you like, but you'd much better not. Look here! If you've really nothing else on hand this morning, supposing we drop down the river together, and have a long day of it?"

The Mole waggled his toes from sheer happiness, spread his chest with a sigh of full contentment, and leaned back blissfully into the soft cushions. "*What* a day I'm having!" he said. "Let us start at once!"

"Hold hard a minute, then!" said the Rat. He looped the painter through a ring in his landing-stage,[21] climbed up into his hole above, and after a short interval reappeared staggering under a fat, wicker luncheon-basket.

"Shove that under your feet," he observed to the Mole, as he passed it down into the boat. Then he untied the painter and took the sculls again.

"What's inside it?" asked the Mole, wriggling with curiosity.

"There's cold chicken inside it," replied the Rat briefly; "coldtonguecoldhamcoldbeefpickledgherkinssaladfrenchrolls cresssandwichespottedmeatgingerbeerlemonadesodawa-ter———"[22]

"O stop, stop," cried the Mole in ecstacies: "This is too much!"

"Do you really think so?" enquired the Rat seriously. "It's only what I always take on these little excursions; and the other animals are always telling me that I'm a mean beast and cut it *very* fine!"

The Mole never heard a word he was saying. Absorbed in the new life he was entering upon, intoxicated with the sparkle, the ripple, the scents and the sounds and the sunlight, he trailed a paw in the water and dreamed long waking dreams. The Water Rat, like the good little fellow he was, sculled steadily on and forebore to disturb him.

"I like your clothes awfully, old chap,"[23] he remarked after some half an hour or so had passed. "I'm going to get a black velvet smoking-suit myself some day, as soon as I can afford it."

"I beg your pardon," said the Mole, pulling himself together with an effort. "You must think me very rude; but all this is so new to me. So—this—is—a—River!"

"*The* River," corrected the Rat.

"And you really live by the river? What a jolly life!"

"By it and with it and on it and in it," said the Rat. "It's brother and sister to me, and aunts,[24] and company, and food and drink, and (naturally) washing. It's my world, and I don't want any other. What it hasn't got is not worth having, and

22. *"There's cold chicken inside it,' replied the Rat briefly; "coldtonguecoldhamcoldbeefpickledgherkinssaladfrenchrollscresssandwichespottedmeatgingerbeerlemonadesodawater."* The list of foods is a parody of the epic catalogue, much like John Milton's fallen angels in *Paradise Lost* or Homer's warriors in *The Iliad.*

Authors of children's literature have often been required, or have wished, to leave sex and violence out of their books. Peter Hunt notes that food is what's left after sex and violence have been removed. Hunt has proposed that Grahame was unable to express adult emotions and "punctuated" his fantasy world "at every important point by food" ("Fantastic Food in the Books of Kenneth Grahame," *Journal of the Fantastic in the Arts*, 7, no. 1 [1996]: 5–22). Grahame, it seems, had been planning this particular feast for some time. In "Bertie's Escapade," he drafts an early version of it: Bertie the pig plans to break into the Grahames' house to raid the kitchen: "Put your trust in me, and you shall have cold chicken, tongue, pressed beef, jellies, trifle, *and* champagne—at least; perhaps more" (Bodleian, MS. Eng. Misc. d. 282).

23. *"I like your clothes awfully, old chap."* The term "little gentleman in black velvet" has political and historical implications. In 1702, William III's horse stumbled over a molehill at Hampton Court Park, throwing the king to his death. William's enemies, the Jacobites, thereafter toasted the mole as that "little gentleman in black velvet."

In *First Whisper of "The Wind in the Willows,"* Elspeth Grahame tells of the origins of Mr. Mole in their lives at Cookham Dean:

> Here is the earliest known instance of the coming together of Kenneth and Mole. He, Kenneth was changing for

dinner one evening (the Mole being a gentleman always "in velvet" is already attired for his late dinner) when, glancing from the window towards the sunsetting sky, behind a group of trees at the far end of the lawn, he perceived beneath them some sort of flurry or disturbance going on. . . . in a flash he was down the stairs, out of the door, and on the scene where the startling drama was being enacted, namely a vital contest between a robin and a mole for the possession of a seven course dinner, in the shape of a very large worm.

Kenneth Grahame kept the mole, but upon its escape it was later captured and killed by the Grahames' housekeeper, Mrs. Blunt, who "sought to make up for her tragic mistake by saying to Kenneth: 'Oh, but, sir, couldn't you just make the mole into a story for Master Alastair?' " (*First Whisper of "The Wind in the Willows,"* 7–10).

24. *"It's brother and sister to me, and aunts."* See chapter VIII, note 17, for Grahame's attitude toward aunts.

Illustration of the mole from "Bertie's Escapade" by E. H. Shepard. *Courtesy of the David J. Holmes Collection.*

what it doesn't know is not worth knowing. Lord! the times we've had together! Whether in winter or summer, spring or autumn, it's always got its fun and its excitements. When the floods are on in February, and my cellars and basement are brimming with drink that's no good to me, and the brown water runs by my best bedroom window; or again when it all drops away and shows patches of mud that smells like plum-cake, and the rushes and weed clog the channels, and I can potter about dry shod over most of the bed of it and find fresh food to eat, and things careless people have dropped out of boats!"

"But isn't it a bit dull at times?" the Mole ventured to ask. "Just you and the river, and no one else to pass a word with?"

"No one else to—well, I mustn't be hard on you," said the

Rat with forbearance. "You're new to it, and of course you don't know. The bank is so crowded nowadays that many people are moving away[25] altogether: O no, it isn't what it used to be, at all. Otters, kingfishers, dabchicks, moorhens, all of them about all day long and always wanting you to *do* something—as if a fellow had no business of his own to attend to!"

"What lies over *there?*" asked the Mole, waving a paw towards a background of woodland that darkly framed the water-meadows on one side of the river.

"That? O, that's just the Wild Wood," said the Rat shortly. "We don't go there very much, we river-bankers."

"Aren't they—aren't they very *nice* people in there?" said the Mole, a trifle nervously.

"W-e-ll," replied the Rat, "let me see. The squirrels are all right. *And* the rabbits—some of 'em, but rabbits are a mixed lot.[26] And then there's Badger, of course. He lives right in the heart of it; wouldn't live anywhere else, either, if you paid him to do it. Dear old Badger! Nobody interferes with *him*. They'd better not," he added significantly.

"Why, who *should* interfere with him?" asked the Mole.

"Well, of course—there—are others," explained the Rat in a hesitating sort of way. "Weasels—and stoats—and foxes—and so on. They're all right in a way—I'm very good friends with them—pass the time of day when we meet, and all that—but they break out sometimes, there's no denying, it, and then—well, you can't really trust them, and that's the fact."[27]

The Mole knew well that it is quite against animal-etiquette to dwell on possible trouble ahead, or even to allude to it; so he dropped the subject.

"And beyond the Wild Wood again?" he asked: "Where it's all blue and dim, and one sees what may be hills or perhaps they mayn't, and something like the smoke of towns, or is it only cloud-drift?"[28]

"Beyond the Wild Wood comes the Wide World," said the

25. *The bank is so crowded nowadays that many people are moving away.* By 1908 the railroads had expanded to all rural points in Britain, easing travel for many different people. Grahame was distressed that creeping industrialization was destroying the agrarian life that he felt was integral to British identity. As people flocked to urban centers for work and suburbs sprang up all along the Thames River valley, people like Grahame, oppressed by urban life, fled to what used to be rural points, imposing themselves on the landscape.

According to Humphrey Carpenter, rivers played an important part in the collective psyche of late Victorians:

> By the middle of the nineteenth century, Britain's rivers in general and the Thames in particular had been tamed by a system of locks and weirs, and the decline of the old commercial barge traffic (taken away first by canals and then by railways) left them open, as they had never been before, as a pleasure ground for anyone who cared to pick up a pair of oars. (*Secret Gardens* [Boston: Houghton Mifflin, 1985], 155)

Grahame's weekend rowing adventures were often crowded with novice boaters. Jerome K. Jerome describes the weekend crowds along the river:

> On a fine Sunday it presents this appearance nearly all day long, while, up the stream, and down the stream, lie, waiting their turn, outside the gates, long lines of still more boats; and boats are drawing near and passing away, so that the sunny river . . . is dotted and decked with yellow, and blue, and orange, and white, and red, and pink . . . it is one of the gayest sights I know of near this dull old London town. (*Three Men in a Boat; To Say Nothing of the Dog* [Bristol: J. W. Arrowsmith, 1889], 95)

Rat. "And that's something that doesn't matter, either to you or me. I've never been there, and I'm never going, nor you either, if you've got any sense at all.[29] Don't ever refer to it again, please. Now then! Here's our backwater at last, where we're going to lunch."

Leaving the main stream, they now passed into what seemed at first sight like a little land-locked lake. Green turf sloped down to either edge, brown snaky tree-roots gleamed below the surface of the quiet water, while ahead of them the silvery shoulder and foamy tumble of a weir,[30] arm-in-arm with a restless dripping mill-wheel, that held up in its turn a grey-gabled mill-house,[31] filled the air with a soothing murmur of sound, dull and smothery, yet with little clear voices speaking up cheerfully out of it at intervals. It was so very beautiful that the Mole could only hold up both forepaws and gasp, "O my! O my! O my!"

The Rat brought the boat alongside the bank, made her fast, helped the still awkward Mole safely ashore, and swung out the luncheon-basket. The Mole begged as a favour to be allowed to unpack it all by himself; and the Rat was very pleased to indulge him, and to sprawl at full length on the grass and rest, while his excited friend shook out the table-cloth and spread it, took out all the mysterious packets one by one and arranged their contents in due order, still gasping, "O my! O my!" at each fresh revelation. When all was ready, the Rat said, "Now, pitch in, old fellow!" and the Mole was indeed very glad to obey, for he had started his spring-cleaning at a very early hour that morning, as people *will* do, and had not paused for bite or sup; and he had been through a very great deal since that distant time which now seemed so many days ago.

"What are you looking at?" said the Rat presently, when the edge of their hunger was somewhat dulled, and the Mole's eyes were able to wander off the table-cloth a little.

"I am looking," said the Mole, "at a streak of bubbles that I see travelling along the surface of the water. That is a thing that strikes me as funny."

26. *"The squirrels are all right. And the rabbits—some of 'em, but rabbits are a mixed lot."* We have met the rabbits before. They aren't as completely stupid as the author proposes, because they have been savvy enough to impose a toll on their road. Mole, of course, has the luxury of being contemptuous because he is a step above them in the social hierarchy.

27. *"but they break out sometimes, there's no denying it, and then—well, you can't really trust them, and that's the fact."* Rat is condescending. The *"them"* he's referring to is the underclass, which many Victorians of Rat's rank considered on the verge of anarchic revolution.

28. *"and something like the smoke of towns, or is it only cloud-drift?"* The "smoke of towns" is the industrial smog rising off the horizon.

29. *"I'm never going, nor you either, if you've got any sense at all."* Unlike Mr. Toad, Rat knows the risks of interacting with people. Rat also reveals his social rank by sternly putting Mole in his place, and rejecting the human world. Curiously, humans are all in the underclass in *The Wind in the Willows.*

30. *weir.* A barrier or dam in a stream to restrain water and regulate its flow.

Built across the river, weirs were common along the Thames and could be used

A weir, lock, and lockkeeper's house at Pangbourne, the last town where the Grahames lived.

"Bubbles? Oho!" said the Rat, and chirruped cheerily in an inviting sort of way.

A broad glistening muzzle showed itself above the edge of the bank, and the Otter hauled himself out and shook the water from his coat.

"Greedy beggars!" he observed, making for the provender.[32] "Why didn't you invite me, Ratty?"

"This was an impromptu affair," explained the Rat. "By the way—my friend Mr. Mole."

"Proud, I'm sure," said the Otter, and the two animals were friends forthwith.[33]

"Such a rumpus everywhere!" continued the Otter. "All the world seems out on the river to-day. I came up this backwater to try and get a moment's peace, and then stumble upon you fellows![34]—At least—I beg pardon—I don't exactly mean that, you know."

There was a rustle behind them, proceeding from a hedge wherein last year's leaves still clung thick, and a stripy head, with high shoulders behind it, peered forth on them.[35]

"Come on, old Badger!" shouted the Rat.

The Badger trotted forward a pace or two; then grunted, "H'm! Company," and turned his back and disappeared from view.

"That's *just* the sort of fellow he is!" observed the disappointed Rat. "Simply hates Society! Now we shan't see any more of him to-day. Well, tell us, *who's* out on the river?"

"Toad's out, for one," replied the Otter.[36] "In his brand-new wager-boat;[37] new togs, new everything!"

The two animals looked at each other and laughed.

"Once, it was nothing but sailing," said the Rat. "Then he tired of that and took to punting.[38] Nothing would please him but to punt all day and every day, and a nice mess he made of it. Last year it was house-boating, and we all had to go and stay with him in his house-boat, and pretend we liked it. He was going to spend the rest of his life in a house-boat. It's all

to raise the water level for driving a mill. Grahame was probably fond of them because they impeded barge and steamer traffic, and took people in small boats off the main course of the river. The meditative lull of the weir, close to where they will have their picnic, echoes the silence before Mole and Rat land on Pan Island in chapter VII, "The Piper at the Gates of Dawn."

31. *a restless dripping mill-wheel, that held up in its turn a grey-gabled mill-house.* A mill is a simple, ancient, and ecological machine—it uses no petrol, nor does it pollute the stream or air with mechanical exhaust or chemical runoff. It is an emblem of the bucolic agrarian lifestyle that Kenneth Grahame wished to hold on to.

32. *"Greedy beggars," he observed, making for the provender.* Rat has packed a feast suitable for humans, yet Otter refers to it as

A seventeenth-century sawmill upriver from Fowey, Cornwall, in Golant. The five sons of Austin Purves thought this was the mill described in chapter I. Though the present mill dates from 1729, the site has a history stretching back to the eleventh century. According to the current owners, the mill stopped turning sometime in the early 1900s and the disused wheel was buried in the river along with a tractor by American soldiers during World War II. Today the structure is used as the Sawmills recording studio. The other possible inspiration for the mill mentioned in the text is the watermill at Mapledurham House, which still produces high-quality stone-ground flour to this day. *Photo courtesy of Nigel McMorris, The Kenneth Grahame Society.*

provender—which the *OED* defines as feed: dry food for domestic animals.

33. *"Proud, I'm sure," said the Otter, and the two animals were friends forthwith.* Peter Hunt writes in depth about the social strata within *The Wind in the Willows:* "Otter—whose easy familiarity with all classes may well mark him in Grahame's scheme of things as being closest to nobility. . . . [Mole and Otter's] friendship, therefore, has to be asserted rather than described" ("Dialogue and Dialectic: Language and Class in *The Wind in the Willows,*" *Children's Literature* 16 [1988]: 167).

34. *"I came up this backwater to try and get a moment's peace, and then stumble upon you fellows!"* Otter's habitat has been invaded by outsiders. Though he's trying to avoid the crowds, and seems abrupt toward his fellow riverbankers, he is glad to have found them.

35. *a stripy head, with high shoulders behind it, peered forth on them.* A plantigrade quadruped, scientifically known as a *Meles vulgaris*, the badger is a sturdy burrowing animal about the same size as a raccoon. There are eight different species of badgers, and they are found in Europe, Asia, and in the western prairies of the United States and Canada. Badgers, however, are more part of the collective psyche in the United Kingdom than they are in the United States, due to such books as *The Wind in the Willows*, *The Tale of Mr. Tod* (1912), by Beatrix Potter, and *The Chronicles of Narnia* (1950s), by C. S. Lewis.

Lewis, some forty years after the publication of *The Wind in the Willows*, wrote of Grahame's Mr. Badger: "Consider Mr. Badger—that extraordinary amalgam of high rank, coarse manners, gruffness, shyness, and goodness. The child who has once met Mr. Badger has ever afterwards in its bones a knowledge of humanity and of English social history which it could not get in any other way" ("On Three Ways of Writing for Children," in *Only Connect: Readings on Children's Literature*, ed. S. Egoff et al. [Toronto: Oxford University Press, 1980], 212).

36. *"Toad's out, for one," replied the Otter.* Grahame has introduced all the major players in the book. Badger appears and disappears, yet the reader has met him. Though Toad never joins the picnic, he's pointed out in the distance.

37. *"wager-boat."* A light boat used in racing contests between single scullers.

38. *"took to punting."* A punt is a long, flat-bottomed boat with square fore and aft that is propelled by long poles that push off the river bottom. Punting is common in Oxford and Cambridge. It takes concentration and steady balance to push a punt along in the water, qualities Toad doesn't possess.

"Cookham Lock on a Bank Holiday c. 1885" (Green, *Beyond the Wild Wood*, 63).

Illustration by E. W. Haslehust of a punter with college barges and Folly Bridge.

the same, whatever he takes up; he gets tired of it, and starts on something fresh."[39]

"Such a good fellow, too," remarked the Otter reflectively: "But no stability—especially in a boat!"

From where they sat they could get a glimpse of the main stream across the island that separated them; and just then a wager-boat flashed into view, the rower—a short, stout figure—splashing badly and rolling a good deal, but working his hardest. The Rat stood up and hailed him, but Toad—for it was he—shook his head and settled sternly to his work.

Illustration by E. H. Shepard of Mr. Toad in a scull.

39. *"It's all the same, whatever he takes up; he gets tired of it, and starts on something fresh."* Rat's anecdotes about Toad immediately reveal that Toad is wealthy because he can afford to indulge his whims in the latest fads and then move on, and has the time and leisure to play with his expensive toys.

"He'll be out of the boat in a minute if he rolls like that,"[40] said the Rat, sitting down again.

"Of course he will," chuckled the Otter. "Did I ever tell you that good story about Toad and the lock-keeper?[41] It happened this way. Toad. . . ."

An errant May-fly[42] swerved unsteadily athwart the current in the intoxicated fashion affected by young bloods of May-flies seeing life. A swirl of water and a "cloop!" and the May-fly was visible no more.

Neither was the Otter.

The Mole looked down. The voice was still in his ears, but the turf whereon he had sprawled was clearly vacant. Not an Otter to be seen, as far as the distant horizon.

But again there was a streak of bubbles on the surface of the river.

The Rat hummed a tune, and the Mole recollected that animal-etiquette forbade any sort of comment on the sudden disappearance of one's friends at any moment,[43] for any reason or no reason whatever.

"Well, well," said the Rat, "I suppose we ought to be moving. I wonder which of us had better pack the luncheon-basket?" He did not speak as if he was frightfully eager for the treat.

"O, please let me," said the Mole. So, of course, the Rat let him.

Packing the basket was not quite such pleasant work as unpacking the basket. It never is. But the Mole was bent on enjoying everything, and although just when he had got the basket packed and strapped up tightly he saw a plate staring up at him from the grass, and when the job had been done again the Rat pointed out a fork which anybody ought to have seen, and last of all, behold! the mustard pot, which he had been sitting on without knowing it—still, somehow, the thing got finished at last, without much loss of temper.

The afternoon sun was getting low as the Rat sculled gently

40. *"He'll be out of that boat in a minute if he rolls like that."* Even though Toad never tips over in Grahame's text—he's described only as "splashing badly and rolling a great deal"—Shepard has him capsizing.

41. *"Did I ever tell you that good story about Toad and the lock-keeper?"* On July 10, 1923, young Thomas Woodman wrote to Kenneth Grahame to inquire what exactly Otter's story was about Toad and the lock-keeper. Elspeth answered the letter and Kenneth signed it: "I am afraid I must not tell you, the fact is, they both lost their tempers, and said things they much regretted afterwards. They are now friends again, so we have all agreed to let the matter drop."

Otter, however, is intimating that Toad once had a crush on the lockkeeper's daughter, which mimics the adventure that Toad will later have with the jailer's daughter. In "The Eternal Whither," a story published in his 1893 collection *Pagan Papers,* Grahame writes, "What happiness in quiet moments to tend the lock-keeper's flower beds—perhaps make love to his daughter" (91). A lock, like a weir, is part of a canal system. A lock is an enclosure within a canal with gates at either end used to raise or lower boats from one section of the river to the next.

Another work of English children's literature involving a lock and a weir is E. Nesbit's classic *The Woodbegoods* (1901),

Godstow Lock.

homewards in a dreamy mood, murmuring poetry-things over to himself, and not paying much attention to Mole. But the Mole was very full of lunch, and self-satisfaction, and pride, and already quite at home in a boat (so he thought) and was getting a bit restless besides: and presently he said, "Ratty! Please, *I* want to row, now!"

The Rat shook his head with a smile. "Not yet, my young friend," he said—'wait till you've had a few lessons.[44] It's not so easy as it looks."

The Mole was quiet for a minute or two. But he began to feel more and more jealous of Rat, sculling so strongly and so easily along, and his pride began to whisper that he could do it every bit as well. He jumped up and seized the sculls, so suddenly, that the Rat, who was gazing out over the water and saying more poetry-things to himself, was taken by surprise and fell backwards off his seat with his legs in the air for the second time, while the triumphant Mole took his place and grabbed the sculls with entire confidence.

"Stop it, you *silly* ass!" cried the Rat, from the bottom of the boat. "You can't do it! You'll have us over!"

The Mole flung his sculls back with a flourish,[45] and made a great dig at the water. He missed the surface altogether, his legs flew up above his head, and he found himself lying on the top of the prostrate Rat. Greatly alarmed, he made a grab at the side of the boat, and the next moment—Sploosh!

Over went the boat, and he found himself struggling in the river.

O my, how cold the water was, and O, how *very* wet it felt. How it sang in his ears as he went down, down, down! How bright and welcome the sun looked as he rose to the surface coughing and spluttering! How black was his despair when he felt himself sinking again! Then a firm paw gripped him by the back of his neck. It was the Rat, and he was evidently laughing—the Mole could *feel* him laughing, right down his arm and through his paw, and so into his—the Mole's—neck.

which preceded *The Wind in the Willows* by seven years. In a chapter titled "The Waterworks," the Woodbegood Bastable children open all the sluices and accidentally flood their summer home downstream. Edith Nesbit was hired by *Pall Mall* magazine to create stories about children similar to those in Grahame's 1895 *The Golden Age* and *Dream Days*. By the time Grahame got around to writing *The Wind in the Willows,* he was familiar with Nesbit's stories and her penchant for writing about children playing in the river.

42. *An errant May-fly.* A fly that lives only a couple of days once it reaches maturity. Mayflies are distinguished by a long forked tail made of hair or whisks. Their long larval stages are spent underwater, where they are easy prey for fish and small animals. (See note 20 in this chapter.) The inclusion of the mayfly suggests that *The Wind in the Willows* opens in the month of May.

43. *animal-etiquette forbade any sort of comment on the sudden disappearance of one's friends at any moment.* Because Otter is of the nobility, he is not obliged to wait around for Rat and Mole. He can come and go at will without the decorum of saying hello or goodbye.

44. *"Not yet, my young friend," he said—"wait till you've had a few lessons."* Mole has no rowing skills, and anyone who does not row is an outsider to the riverbanker's life of leisure. By the privilege of experience, Rat rows and remains in control.

45. *The Mole flung his sculls back with a flourish.* A scull is also an oar less than ten feet long, used at the stern of a boat to propel it forward.

The Rat got hold of a scull and shoved it under the Mole's arm; then he did the same by the other side of him and, swimming behind, propelled the helpless animal to shore, hauled him out, and set him down on the bank, a squashy, pulpy lump of misery.

When the Rat had rubbed him down a bit, and wrung some of the wet out of him, he said, "Now, then, old fellow! Trot up and down the towing-path as hard as you can,[46] till you're warm and dry again, while I dive for the luncheon-basket."

So the dismal Mole, wet without and ashamed within, trotted about till he was fairly dry, while the Rat plunged into the water again, recovered the boat, righted her and made her fast, fetched his floating property to shore by degrees, and finally dived successfully for the luncheon-basket and struggled to land with it.

When all was ready for a start once more, the Mole, limp and dejected, took his seat in the stern of the boat; and as they set off, he said in a low voice, broken with emotion, "Ratty, my generous friend! I am very sorry indeed for my foolish and ungrateful conduct. My heart quite fails me when I think how I might have lost that beautiful luncheon-basket. Indeed, I have been a complete ass, and I know it. Will you overlook it this once and forgive me, and let things go on as before?"

"That's all right, bless you!" responded the Rat cheerily. "What's a little wet to a Water Rat? I'm more in the water than out of it most days. Don't you think any more about it; and, look here! I really think you had better come and stop with me for a little time.[47] It's very plain and rough, you know—not like Toad's house at all—but you haven't seen that yet; still, I can make you comfortable. And I'll teach you to row, and to swim, and you'll soon be as handy on the water as any of us."[48]

The Mole was so touched by his kind manner of speaking that he could find no voice to answer him; and he had to brush away a tear or two with the back of his paw. But the Rat kindly

46. *"Now, then, old fellow! Trot up and down the towing-path as hard as you can."* Towpaths were built or worn all along canals and riverbanks in England and were more prevalent in Grahame's day than they are now. Because weirs and locks blocked nautical traffic, and because engines were less common in the early 1900s, a horse would be hitched to a boat making its way upstream, and then it would be towed against the current to its destination. Old towpaths are commonly used as riverside footpaths today.

47. *"I really think you had better come and stop with me for a little time."* Figure of speech. Rat means he'd like Mole to stay at Rat's river house for a few days.

48. *"I can make you comfortable. And I'll teach you to row, and to swim, and you'll soon be as handy on the water as any of us."* This passage reads like an homage to Grahame's boat enthusiast friend F. J. Furnivall, who mentored Grahame as a young man in London.

Photo of a towpath today with barge.

looked in another direction, and presently the Mole's spirits revived again, and he was even able to give some straight back-talk to a couple of moorhens who were sniggering to each other about his bedraggled appearance.[49]

When they got home, the Rat made a bright fire in the parlour, and planted the Mole in an arm-chair in front of it, having fetched down a dressing-gown and slippers for him, and told him river stories till supper-time.[50] Very thrilling stories they were, too, to an earth-dwelling animal like Mole. Stories about weirs, and sudden floods, and leaping pike, and steamers that flung hard bottles[51]—at least bottles were certainly flung, and *from* steamers, so presumably *by* them; and about herons, and how particular they were whom they spoke to; and about adventures down drains, and night-fishings with Otter, or excursions far a-field with Badger.[52] Supper was a most cheerful meal; but very shortly afterwards a terribly sleepy Mole had to be escorted upstairs by his considerate host, to the best bedroom, where he soon laid his head on his pillow in great peace and contentment, knowing that his new-found friend the River was lapping the sill of his window.[53]

This day was only the first of many similar ones for the emancipated Mole, each of them longer and full of interest as the ripening summer moved onward. He learnt to swim and to row, and entered into the joy of running water;[54] and with his ear to the reed-stems he caught, at intervals, something of what the wind went whispering so constantly among them.[55]

Chapter I tailpiece illustration by Nancy Barnhart, 1922. Much of the charm in Barnhart's illustrated edition comes in the small black-and-white tailpieces that she adds on the last page of each chapter (except for chapter II). Like her illustrated title page, the pen-and-ink drawings only appear in the Methuen edition.

49. *he was even able to give some straight back-talk to a couple of moorhens who were sniggering to each other about his bedraggled appearance.* Moorhens, or *Gallinula chloropus*, are a species of aquatic bird from the rail family. They are structurally related to cranes but smaller in size. Typically inhabiting the waters of Fowey, they have red beaks and very long toes for running on the soft mud of swamps. When inland rivers freeze in winter, moorhens usually move to tidal rivers. The *OED* defines the moorhen as "the female of the red grouse." Compared to Mole, they are elegant. They also are in their native environment of the riverbank, which is superior to Mole's humble Mole End.

A hen is also defined as "a fussy, middle-aged woman." Grahame's use of a hen to make Mole feel out of place suggests that he himself felt at odds with women who gravitated to the boating and yacht clubs he frequented. In a letter to A. Quiller-Couch on June 11, 1903, Grahame asks if he can secure temporary membership to the Fowey Yacht Club for a friend. "A friend of mine . . . is going to Fowey tomorrow (with his wife, whom I do *not* know)" (Trinity College Archive, DD36). Grahame words the letter carefully, adopting a tone similar to that used by Mole with the Water Rat. The emphasis on not knowing his friend's wife suggests that she, like Elspeth Grahame, is an extraneous figure when it comes to boats. The Royal Fowey Yacht Club did not admit women until after World War II. Lady visitors were relegated to the terrace. To the riverbankers, Mole included, the female character is to be tolerated, at best. Real contentment on the river involves homosocial company.

50. *told him river stories till supper-time.* Rat tells Mole stories just as the river told stories to Mole when he stumbled upon it earlier in the chapter. The telling of stories

is integral to the development of the work. Grahame composed *The Wind in the Willows* out of letters sent to his son, managing to craft each of the twelve chapters at a length perfect for reading before bedtime.

51. *steamers that flung hard bottles.* "Steamers" is a reference to the tourist steamboats that traveled along the waterways. Grahame is making an ecological statement by drawing attention to human beings who carelessly throw their empty bottles and garbage overboard as they cruise on the river.

52. *excursions far a-field with Badger.* Grahame was known for taking walking trips through the Berkshire Downs with male companions. He once led a twenty-mile walk from the small river town of Streatley to the Pagan chalk formation of the White Horse of Uffington cut into the hillside. From there, he and his companions walked along the ancient tracks to Wayland's Smithy, the prehistoric gravesite that is often compared to Stonehenge. These trips inspired such early essays as "Loafing" and "The Romance of the Road."

Graham Robertson describes Kenneth Grahame at this time:

> He was living in London where he looked all *wrong*—that is to say, as wrong as so magnificent a man could look anywhere. As he strode along the pavements one felt to him as towards a huge St. Bernard or Newfoundland dog, a longing to take him away into the open country where he could be let off the lead and allowed to range at will. He appeared happy enough and made the best of everything, as do the dogs, but he was too big for London and it hardly seemed kind of fate to keep him there. (Green, *Kenneth Grahame: A Biography*, 115)

As with all five of the major players in *The Wind in the Willows*, much of Grahame's personality surfaces in the actions and character of Mr. Badger. Badger

Photo of chalk roads, Berkshire.

embodies Kenneth Grahame's ideal life as the master of an ancient, rural estate.

53. *but very shortly afterwards a terribly sleepy Mole had to be escorted upstairs by his considerate host, to the best bedroom, where he soon laid his head on his pillow . . . knowing that his new-found friend the River was lapping the sill of his window.* Notice how comfortably Mole has moved into Rat's house. If this were a novel for adults, Mole and Rat would perhaps consummate their relationship amorously. Instead, as Peter Hunt points out, Grahame focuses on food: "Supper was a most cheerful meal;" Mole then falls into a stupor and has to be tucked into bed. The chapter ends with Mole having left his home behind for a new home, company, and adventure.

54. *He learnt to swim and to row, and entered into the joy of running water.* Variant, e. 247 and d. 524: He learnt to swim, and to row, and above all to respect and appreciate the excellent qualities of his brown and whiskered friend the Water Rat, and entered into the joy of running water.

55. *and with his ear to the reed-stems he caught, at intervals, something of what the wind went whispering so constantly among them.* The original title for the book was *The Wind in the Reeds*, but it was too close to W. B Yeats's 1899 poetry collection, *The Wind Among the Reeds.* Graham Robertson warned Grahame that the title was too close a match. Nevertheless, Methuen advertised the book as *The Wind Among the Reeds* up until the week before the book went to press.

When Algernon Methuen realized the titles were similar, he changed Grahame's to *The Wind in the Willows* at the last moment but retained the cover illustration of Pan, Mole, and Rat among the reeds. A Scribner's 1908 fall fiction advertisement also announced the book as *The Wind in the Reeds.*

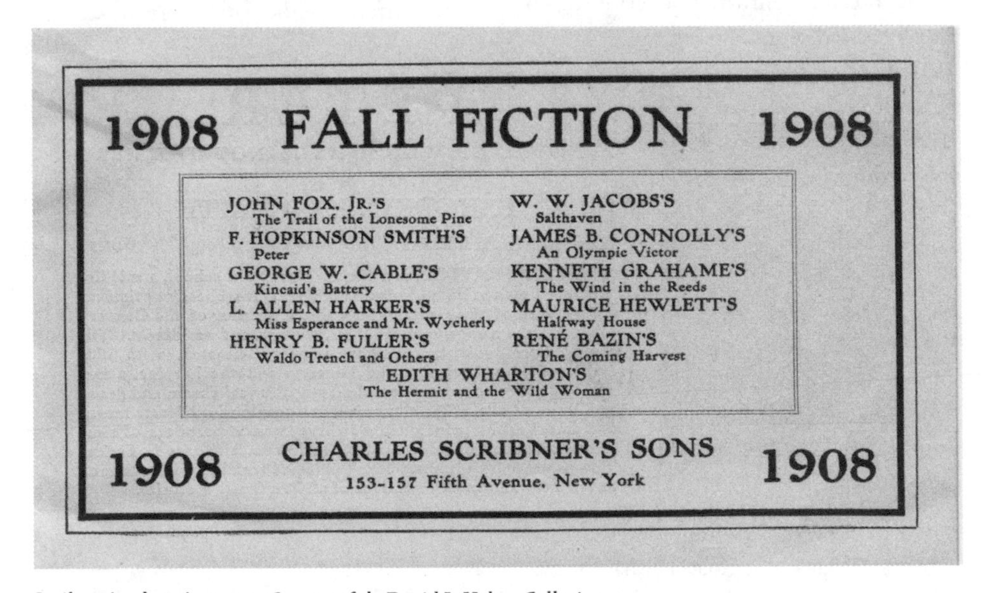

Scribner's advertisement. *Courtesy of the David J. Holmes Collection.*

II

The Open Road

"RATTY," said the Mole suddenly, one bright summer morning, "if you please, I want to ask you a favour."

The Rat was sitting on the river bank, singing a little song.[1] He had just composed it himself, so he was very taken up with it, and would not pay proper attention to Mole or anything else. Since early morning he had been swimming in the river, in company with his friends the ducks.[2] And when the ducks stood on their heads suddenly, as ducks will, he would dive down and tickle their necks, just under where their chins would be if ducks had chins, till they were forced to come to the surface again in a hurry, spluttering and angry and shaking their feathers at him, for it is impossible to say quite *all* you feel when your head is under water. At last they implored him to go away and attend to his own affairs and leave them to mind theirs. So the Rat went away, and sat on the river bank in the sun, and made up a song about them,[3] which he called

"DUCKS" DITTY."[4]

All along the backwater,
Through the rushes tall,

1. *The Rat was sitting on the river bank, singing a little song.* Rat is a bard, and *The Wind in the Willows* with its twelve chapters is meant to be a miniature epic. In antiquity the bard's place within the tribe was to compose and recite heroic verse. The Grecian bard told his epic, thus working from an oral tradition. Rat, on the other hand, is a Romantic bard. Like the romantics of the late eighteenth century, Rat writes down his poetry and songs.

The first reference to Rat's bardlike qualities is in chapter I, page 25: While rowing, Rat is distracted because he is "murmuring poetry-things over to himself."

2. *Since early morning he had been swimming in the river, in company with his friends the ducks.* One of Grahame's inspirations for Rat and the beginning of chapter II might have come from Oscar Wilde. "The Devoted Friend" (1888) tells of a water rat that makes the acquaintance of some ducks:

> One morning the old Water-rat put his head out of his hole. He had bright beady eyes and stiff grey whiskers, and

his tail was like a long bit of black india-rubber. The little ducks were swimming about in the pond looking just like a lot of yellow canaries, and their mother, who was pure white with real red legs, was trying to teach them how to stand on their heads in the water.

"You will never be in the best society unless you can stand on your heads," she kept saying to them; and every now and then she showed them how it was done. But the little ducks paid no attention to her. They were so young that they did not know what an advantage it is to be in society at all. (Wilde, *The Happy Prince* [London: David Nutt, 1888], 59)

See also Steig, "At the Back of *The Wind in the Willows*."

3. *So the Rat went away, and sat on the river bank in the sun, and made up a song about them.* Rat is at leisure to tease the ducks. The ducks, like the rabbits and the more menacing stoats and weasels of the Wild Wood, are outsiders. If Grahame in fact did use Wilde's tale as a source, then he is further tweaking the decorous behavior Wilde was satirizing.

It is interesting to note that unlike Wilde's mother duck, Grahame renders his ducks as sexless. Though the value of male company remains the unspoken maxim in Grahame's text, Grahame's Rat is similar to Wilde's overtly homosocial Water-rat: "'Ah! I know nothing about the feelings of parents,' said the Water-rat; 'I am not a family man. In fact I have never been married, and I never intend to be. Love is all very well in its way, but friendship is higher' " (Wilde, *The Happy Prince*, 61).

Peter Green aptly describes Grahame's idea of a perfect world: "where nobody who matters is married, or needs to work, and where the *summum bonum* is loyalty, with creature comforts a close second" (Green, *Kenneth Grahame: A Biography*, 281).

4. *"Ducks' Ditty."* The poem has proven immensely popular and was often anthologized. After Kenneth Grahame's death, Elspeth was paid a small fortune each time it was printed. According to Curtis Brown's royalty statements, in May 1939 Elspeth received an advance against royalties from the publishing house Longmans Green for "Ducks' Ditty," used in an English reader for children in Indian schools in the United States. In March of 1941 she was paid again for the poem to be included in the *Junior Book of Lively Verse.* The poem was also printed in 1942 in *A Book of Nonsense Poems* by the Edwards Brothers.

"Ducks' Ditty" remains popular to this day. In the center of Pangbourne, there is a small cafe called "Ducks Ditty," a tribute to the local author.

Ducks are a-dabbling,
Up tails all![5]

Ducks' tails, drakes' tails,
Yellow feet a-quiver,
Yellow bills all out of sight
Busy in the river!

Slushy green undergrowth
Where the roach swim—
Here we keep our larder,
Cool and full and dim.

Everyone for what he likes!
We *like to be*
Heads down, tails up,
Dabbling free!

High in the blue above
Swifts whirl and call[6]—
We *are down a-dabbling*
Up tails all!

"I don't know that I think so *very* much of that little song, Rat," observed the Mole cautiously. He was no poet himself and didn't care who knew it; and he had a candid nature.[7]

"Nor don't the ducks neither,"[8] replied the Rat cheerfully. "They say, '*Why* can't fellows be allowed to do what they like *when* they like and *as* they like, instead of other fellows sitting on banks and watching them all the time and making remarks and poetry and things about them? What *nonsense* it all is!' That's what the ducks say."

"So it is, so it is," said the Mole, with great heartiness.

"No, it isn't!" cried the Rat indignantly.

"Well then, it isn't, it isn't," replied the Mole soothingly. "But what I wanted to ask you was, won't you take me to call

5. *Up tails all!* Though Grahame took pains to repress sexuality in *The Wind in the Willows*, according to Michael Steig, the term "Uptails all" has long been used as a slang expression for sexual intercourse. The sixth edition of the *Dictionary of Slang and Unconventional English* includes a definition of "Up tails all" as "To coit, an expression in common usage from 1640 to 1750." It is also the title of a poem by Robert Herrick published in 1648.

Herrick was one of Grahame's favorite poets, and Grahame was probably familiar with Herrick's explicitly sexual poem. Though Grahame didn't include the sexual "Up Tails All" in the *Cambridge Book of Poetry for Children* that he edited in 1914, he included five other poems by Herrick.

Up Tails All

Begin with a kisse,
Go on too with this:
And thus, thus, thus let us smother
Our lips for awhile,
But let's not beguile
Our hope of one for the other.

This play, be assur'd,
Long enough has endur'd
Since more and more is exacted;
For love he doth call
For his Uptailes all;
And that's the part to be acted.

The first written record of the song "Up Tales All" dates to Ben Jonson's *Every man in His Humour* (1598). Other definitions include an old game of cards (dating to the 1600s) and a description of revelers and jovial fellows.

6. *Swifts whirl and call.* Swifts are plain-looking birds related to hummingbirds yet resembling swallows.

7. *He was no poet himself and didn't care who knew it; and he had a candid nature.* Before

on Mr. Toad?[9] I've heard so much about him, and I do so want to make his acquaintance."

"Why, certainly," said the good-natured Rat, jumping to his feet and dismissing poetry from his mind for the day. "Get the boat out, and we'll paddle up there at once.[10] It's never the wrong time to call on Toad. Early or late he's always the same fellow. Always good-tempered, always glad to see you, always sorry when you go!"

"He must be a very nice animal," observed the Mole, as he got into the boat and took the sculls,[11] while the Rat settled himself comfortably in the stern.[12]

Grahame's time, poetry was traditionally reserved for the well-born. Mole is candid because poetry is not part of his everyday world. He will gradually be won over by its power.

8. *"Nor don't the ducks neither."* In Grahame's time, the upper-middle class often affected indifference to grammar. Though it sounds uneducated, Rat's triple negative is actually indicative of his true class standing. See Badger on "learn 'em," chapter XI, "Like Summer Tempests Came His Tears" (page 280), and note 24 in that chapter.

Shepard's illustration of Toad Hall from the water.

9. *"But what I wanted to ask you was, won't you take me to call on Mr. Toad?"* Here again we see that Mole depends on Rat for social introductions.

10. *"Get the boat out, and we'll paddle up there at once."* In another subtle assertion of his higher class status, Rat orders Mole around as though he were a servant.

11. *observed the Mole, as he got into the boat and took the sculls.* The subject of E. H. Shepard's illustrations is addressed in a letter to Kenneth Grahame from Margaret Stewart Somerville dated December 17, 1931.

> [The illustrations] are quite all right for grown ups. But I am giving my *grandchildren* the book. . . . I read on page 29 "The Mole . . . took the sculls, while the Rat settled himself comfortably in the stern"! I turn over the leaf & what has Ernest Shepard done? He has transposed our, by now, friends, in the boat, *Rat* has the sculls, the Mole is settled comfortably in the stern.
>
> Oh woe is me!
>
> Since my earliest childhood I have wondered why artists do not read the books they illustrate. Mr. Shepard this inaccuracy proves he has missed Rat's beautiful gesture on page 24 "I'll teach you to row" and the success of his lessons.
>
> I repeat, what am I to say to my grandchildren. (Bodleian, MS. Eng. misc. d. 531, p. 186)

Grahame and Shepard had a congenial rapport, and Grahame appears to have approved of Shepard's illustrations before they went to press. Nevertheless, a letter was returned in Elspeth's loose handwriting but signed by Kenneth Grahame. Given the handwriting, it seems likely that Elspeth penned the opening sentence. The tone of the rest of the letter is witty, very much in Grahame's voice. It is possible that Grahame wrote the letter and Elspeth hand-copied it after he died.

> 20th Dec. 1931
>
> Dear Lady,
>
> Yes—it is exasperating. These artists are very tiresome fellows—and they all do it!
>
> I hardly know what to suggest that you should tell the children. You might perhaps say that the animals had evidently "changed over" for just a minute while in full view of the windows of Toad Hall, in case Toad, looking out, should say afterwards to Rat, "Who's your crab catching friend?" for poor Mole couldn't row *very* well yet. But I admit it sounds lame. Let us hope that they may not notice it (But they will!)
>
> Yours very truly,
> Kenneth Grahame
> (Bodleian, MS. Eng. Misc. d. 531, p. 188)

12. *while the Rat settled himself comfortably in the stern.* Mole has now learned to row skillfully enough for Rat to relax. Like packing and repacking the luncheon basket in chapter I, Rat once again sets Mole up to serve him.

"He is indeed the best of animals," replied Rat. "So simple, so good-natured, and so affectionate. Perhaps he's not very clever—we can't all be geniuses; and it may be that he is both boastful and conceited. But he has got some great qualities, has Toady."

Rounding a bend in the river, they came in sight of a handsome, dignified old house of mellowed red brick,[13] with well-kept lawns reaching down to the water's edge.

"There's Toad Hall," said the Rat; "and that creek on the left, where the notice-board says, 'Private. No landing allowed,' leads to his boat-house, where we'll leave the boat. The stables are over there to the right. That's the banqueting-hall you're looking at now—very old, that is. Toad is rather rich, you know, and this is really one of the nicest houses in these parts, though we never admit as much to Toad."[14]

They glided up the creek, and the Mole shipped his sculls as they passed into the shadow of a large boat-house.[15] Here they saw many handsome boats, slung from the crossbeams or hauled up on a slip,[16] but none in the water; and the place had an unused and a deserted air.

The Rat looked around him. "I understand," said he. "Boating is played out. He's tired of it, and done with it. I wonder what new fad he has taken up now?[17] Come along and let's look him up. We shall hear all about it quite soon enough."

They disembarked, and strolled across the gay flower-decked lawns in search of Toad, whom they presently happened upon resting in a wicker garden-chair, with a pre-occupied expression of face, and a large map spread out on his knees.

"Hooray!" he cried, jumping up on seeing them, "this is splendid!"[18] He shook the paws of both of them warmly, never waiting for an introduction to the Mole. "How *kind* of you!" he went on, dancing round them. "I was just going to send a boat down the river for you, Ratty, with strict orders that you were to be fetched up here at once,[19] whatever you were doing.

13. *Rounding a bend in the river, they came in sight of a handsome, dignified old house of mellowed red brick.* Red clay surrounds many of the towns along the Thames, including Cookham Dean, where the Grahames' lived when Kenneth wrote *The Wind in the Willows*. Consequently, many of the houses are made of red brick.

Toad Hall is an amalgamation of different houses that Grahame admired. It contains elements from Harleyford Manor, the ancient Mapledurham House, and Cliveden, a mansion that was within sight of Grahame's childhood home in Cookham Dean.

14. *"Toad is rather rich, you know, and this is really one of the nicest houses in these parts, though we never admit as much to Toad."* Grahame never properly explains where Toad has gotten his money. Humphrey Carpenter has said the following about Toad: "It is clear that Toad Hall has been in his family for more than one generation; yet the narrative constantly gives the impression that he is a *parvenu* whose family has bought its way into the squirearchy rather than inherited its position" (*Secret Gardens*, 164).

Like Oscar Wilde, whose trial, imprisonment, and death deeply disturbed Grahame, Toad is an aesthete. Toad's home, gardens, and belongings all have to be magnificent works. In 1906 Grahame returned to Cookham Dean to live. Peter

Photo of Mapledurham House (Green, *Beyond the Wild Wood*, 142).

Recent photo of Mapledurham House from the churchyard.

Photo of Cliveden. *Courtesy of Nigel McMorris, The Kenneth Grahame Society.*

Green speculates that from outside of his house, Grahame could see Reading Prison several miles in the distance. Wilde had been incarcerated there in the mid-1890s and published his famed "Ballad of Reading Gaol" in 1898. In many ways Grahame pays homage to Wilde through Toad. See Chapter VIII, note 1.

15. *They glided up the creek, and the Mole shipped his sculls as they passed into the shadow of a large boat-house.* Shipped: To bring the sculls aboard in preparation for docking. Variant, e. 248: They glided up the creek {and the Mole shipped his sculls as they} passed into the shadow of a large boat-house.

16. *slung from the cross-beams or hauled up on a slip.* A boat slip is a sloping ramp extending down into the water that serves as an exit or entry for boats onto the waterways.

17. *"I wonder what new fad he has taken up now?"* Grahame is preparing the reader for the entrance of the madcap Toad.

18. *"Hooray!" he cried, jumping up on seeing them, "this is splendid!"* Toad is the opposite of Mr. Badger in personality. He craves constant attention, while Badger would rather be alone.

19. *"I was just going to send a boat down the river for you, Ratty, with strict orders that you were to be fetched up here at once."* There are no servants in sight, yet someone had to tend Toad's house and the "well-kept lawns," and someone, probably a servant,

I want you badly—both of you. Now what will you take? Come inside and have something![20] You don't know how lucky it is, your turning up just now!"

"Let's sit quiet a bit, Toady!" said the Rat, throwing himself into an easy chair, while the Mole took another by the side of him and made some civil remark about Toad's "delightful residence."

"Finest house on the whole river," cried Toad boisterously. "Or anywhere else, for that matter,"[21] he could not help adding.

Here the Rat nudged the Mole. Unfortunately the Toad saw him do it,[22] and turned very red. There was a moment's painful silence. Then Toad burst out laughing. "All right, Ratty," he said. "It's only my way, you know. And it's not such a very bad house, is it? You know you rather like it yourself. Now, look here. Let's be sensible. You are the very animals I wanted. You've got to help me. It's most important!"

"It's about your rowing, I suppose,"[23] said the Rat, with an innocent air. "You're getting on fairly well, though you splash a good bit still. With a great deal of patience,[24] and any quantity of coaching, you may———"

"O, pooh! boating!" interrupted the Toad, in great disgust. "Silly boyish amusement. I've given that up *long* ago. Sheer waste of time, that's what it is. It makes me downright sorry to see you fellows, who ought to know better, spending all your energies in that aimless manner.[25] No, I've discovered the real thing, the only genuine occupation for a lifetime. I propose to devote the remainder of mine to it, and can only regret the wasted years that lie behind me, squandered in trivialities. Come with me, dear Ratty, and your amiable friend also, if he will be so very good, just as far as the stable-yard, and you shall see what you shall see!"

He led the way to the stable-yard accordingly, the Rat following with a most mistrustful expression; and there, drawn out of the coach-house into the open, they saw a gipsy cara-

would have to take out a boat to fetch Mole and Rat.

20. *"Come inside and have something!"* Shades of *The Wind in the Willows* run through both of A. A. Milne's *Pooh* books. Pooh Bear's most common refrain is the desire for "a little something" to eat.

21. *"Finest house on the whole river," cried Toad boisterously. "Or anywhere else, for that matter."* Grahame reveled in antiquities, and as he grew older he sought out antique houses. In 1910 the Grahames sold their house in Cookham Dean and moved to a mouse-infested farmhouse built in the Tudor period. The house was outside the village of Blewbury, not far from the city of Didcot. Called Bohams, the house was situated on the edge of the Berkshire Downs. All Grahame had to do was walk out his door to soon find himself on the Ridgeway, the ancient chalk track that he was fond of walking with his mates. In a letter to Constance Smedley he describes the place:

> I wish I could show you this antic [*sic*] corner of Berkshire in King Alfred's country, probably much as it was a thousand years ago. A little way off there's a farmer whose family has been here a thousand years. They are real saxons. They live in a lovely old farmhouse with a ghost in it. Indeed all the houses are old. They do not build the horrible red houses that spring up round Cookham. (Chalmers, *Kenneth Grahame*, 195)

By 1910, when Alastair Grahame was often away at boarding school, Kenneth Grahame decided it was time to retreat from the influx of newcomers who came to Cookham Dean. Grahame was disturbed by people whose lives were devoted to the acquisition of material wealth. He longed for a simpler home life, governed by the pace of an agrarian clock rather than by the

Photo of Kenneth Grahame in Blewbury, circa 1910, probably taken by Austin Purves. *Photo: Rich Grant. Courtesy of the David J. Holmes Collection.*

schedules of commuter trains that screeched through town at all hours of the day. The village of Blewbury, with its quaint and ancient houses, to this day maintains the feel of an old farming community.

Photo by Grahame's friend, Austin Purves, of the downs beyond the quiet streets of Blewbury. *Courtesy of the David J. Holmes Collection.*

22. *Here the Rat nudged the Mole. Unfortunately the Toad saw him do it.* Grahame worked out some of his frustrations by writing caricatures of his wealthy contemporaries. According to Peter Green, some of Toad's color was supplied by Horatio Bottomley, the "hearty, flamboyant, gabby vulgarian" (*Kenneth Grahame: A Biography*, 242). By 1906, when Grahame and his son were sharing their ongoing bedtime stories, Bottomley was a self-promoting journalist who was always in the spotlight. He also was a politician, financier, racehorse owner, and entrepreneur. Bottomley had a flat in London, but as his fortune grew he expanded a small cottage in East Sussex until it became a rambling mansion able to accommodate twenty to thirty guests for weekend parties. Called The Dicker, Bottomley added to the house and estate by gradually buying surrounding land and creating ornamental lakes, gardens, and tennis courts.

Photo of Horatio Bottomley (Green, *Beyond the Wild Wood*, 144).

Eight gardeners tended the grounds, and there was a large household staff to look after Bottomley, his wife, and their daughter. Bottomley was despised by the gentry and most of his fellow MPs for his unsavory business transactions. Though he twice declared bankruptcy, he always lived pretentiously and beyond his means (Alan Hyman, *The Rise and the Fall of Horatio Bottomley: The Biography of a Swindler* [London: Cassell and Co., Ltd., 1972], 281).

23. *"It's about your rowing, I suppose{?}"* In Grahame's holograph manuscript, e. 248, there is a question mark that is omitted from the typed manuscript, d. 524, and, later, the published text. The question mark gives the dialogue a comic conversational inflection. The lack of the question mark makes the sentence a flat statement. It's quite possible that the typist omitted it.

24. *"With a great deal of patience."* Patience is something Toad lacks completely. Many scholars have suggested that one of Toad's other models is Grahame's tantrum-throwing son, Alastair.

25. *"It makes me downright sorry to see you fellows, who ought to know better, spending all your energies in that aimless manner."* It is ironic that Toad chides Mole and Rat, because all of Toad's pursuits are consistently aimless.

van,[26] shining with newness, painted a canary-yellow picked out with green, and red wheels.[27]

"There you are!" cried the Toad, straddling and expanding himself. "There's real life for you, embodied in that little cart. The open road, the dusty highway, the heath, the common, the hedgerows, the rolling downs! Camps, villages, towns, cities![28] Here to-day, up and off to somewhere else to-morrow! Travel, change, interest, excitement! The whole world before you, and a horizon that's always changing! And mind! this is the very finest cart of its sort that was ever built, without any exception. Come inside and look at the arrangements. Planned 'em all myself, I did!"

The Mole was tremendously interested and excited, and followed him eagerly up the steps and into the interior of the caravan. The Rat only snorted and thrust his hands deep into his pockets,[29] remaining where he was.

It was indeed very compact and comfortable. Little sleeping bunks—a little table that folded up against the wall—a cooking-stove, lockers, bookshelves, a bird-cage with a bird in it;[30] and pots, pans, jugs and kettles of every size and variety.[31]

"All complete!" said the Toad triumphantly, pulling open a locker. "You see—biscuits, potted lobster, sardines—everything you can possibly want. Soda-water here—baccy[32] there—letter-paper, bacon, jam, cards and dominoes—you'll find," he continued, as they descended the steps again, "you'll find that nothing whatever has been forgotten, when we make our start this afternoon."

"I beg your pardon," said the Rat slowly, as he chewed a straw, "but did I overhear you say something about '*we*,' and '*start*,' and '*this afternoon*?'"

"Now, you dear good old Ratty," said Toad, imploringly, "don't begin talking in that stiff and sniffy sort of way, because you know you've *got* to come.[33] I can't possibly manage without you, so please consider it settled, and don't argue—it's the

26. *they saw a gipsy caravan.* Romani scholar Ian Hancock writes in depth about the spelling of the word Gypsy:

> The word *Gipsy/Gypsy* derives from the word "Egyptian," which was written in various ways during the sixteenth and seventeenth centuries: *Egipcian, Egypcian, 'gipcian, 'gypcian.* It is from the spellings which had lost the initial capital *E* that the word "gypsy" comes. . . . This is especially significant in English, which writes proper nouns with capital initial letters, and writing "Gypsy" as "gypsy" has only reinforced the common idea that we are a people defined by behavior rather than by ethnicity.
>
> Spelling "Gipsy" with an "i" is rare these days. The very first organization devoted to the study of our people, the Gypsy Lore Society, which was created in 1888, chose the spelling with "y," and this has become the most common. (*We Are The Romani People* [Hertfordshire: University of Hertfordshire Press, 2002], xxi)

27. *shining with newness, painted a canary-yellow picked out with green, and red wheels.* Alastair received a Gypsy caravan for his fifth birthday in May of 1905 and was captivated by it. He sold brushes and baskets from it to his parents and whoever passed by (Green, *Kenneth Grahame: A Biography*, 236).

Another early source for the caravan and Toad's change in lifestyle in chapter II is Grahame's fictional character Fothergill, in the story "A Bohemian in Exile." Fothergill was based on a fellow clerk in the Bank of London who gave up the city for a life of adventure in a Gypsy cart. While happily tramping around the Berkshire Downs for three years the fictional Fothergill inherits his father's estate from his aunt. He moves in, turns the horse out to pasture, and installs his cart in the stables. Though he's endowed with a fortune, he finds idleness confining. Fothergill chooses to resume his nomadic existence and takes to the road pushing samples, brewing beer, and telling fortunes, all occupations associated with Gypsies in traveling carts.

Grahame describes Fothergill's cart and departure:

> Fothergill bought a medium sized "developed" [cart] and also a donkey to fit; he had it painted white, picked out with green—the barrow, not the donkey—and when his arrangements were complete, stabled the whole for the night in Bloomsbury. The following morning, before the early red had faded from the sky, the exodus took place. . . . Fothergill turned down Oxford Street, sitting on the shaft. . . . So he passed out of our lives by way of the Bayswater Road . . . [his cart was] no fashionable gipsy cart, [it was a sort of house-boat on wheels. (*Pagan Papers* [London and New York: John Lane/The Bodley Head, 1898], 142)

The caravan and the incident with the Gypsy, which later appears in chapter X, "The Further Adventures of Toad," were meant to parody the Victorian works of George Borrow: *Lavengro* (1851), *The Bible in Spain* (1851), and *The Romany Rye* (1857). The books were part of the nostalgic country movement and were enormously popular with people who lived and worked in the industrial cities.

28. *"The open road, the dusty highway, the heath, the common, the hedgerows, the rolling downs! Camps, villages, towns, cities!"* Toad has a bipolar personality. His talk about the open road, though seemingly light and promising, takes on a manic quality.

29. *The Rat only snorted and thrust his hands deep into his pockets.* At this moment the Rat has hands instead of paws. He has become more human than ratlike.

30. *Little sleeping-bunks—a little table that folded up against the wall—a cooking-stove, lockers, bookshelves, a bird-cage with a bird in it.* The canary-yellow cart is symbolic of both the freedom of the open road and the confines of home. Though Rat will feel a tremendous wanderlust later in chapter IX, "Wayfarers All," Toad's cart is confining for Rat.

The caged bird is a Dickensian motif used most famously in *David Copperfield*. There will be two more caged birds in *The Wind in the Willows*: In chapter V, "Dulce Domum," Mole and Rat observe a caged bird in the window of human beings: "close against the white blind . . . clearly silhouetted, every wire, perch, and appurtenance distinct and recognizable." In chapter VIII, "Toad's Adventures," the jailer's daughter has a canary "whose cage hung on a nail . . . to the great annoyance of prisoners who relished an afternoon nap." In all three scenes Grahame has chosen a common domestic pet as the emblem of imprisoned wildlife. The bird remains characterless until the cart is run off the road, leaving the bird "sobbing pitifully and calling to be let out." (See chapter V, note 7, and chapter VIII, note 6.)

31. *and pots, pans, jugs and kettles of every size and variety.* It is unlikely that Toad's cart could be equipped with "kettles of every size and variety," because they would take up too much space. The pots and pans are an example both of Toad's excesses and of Grahame's exaggeration.

32. *baccy.* Slang; an abbreviation for tobacco.

33. *"you know you've* got *to come."* Notice how Grahame's italics here and in the next

one thing I can't stand. You surely don't mean to stick to your dull fusty old river all your life, and just live in a hole in a bank, and *boat?* I want to show you the world! I'm going to make an *animal* of you, my boy!"

"I don't care," said the Rat, doggedly. "I'm not coming, and that's flat. And I *am* going to stick to my old river, *and* live in a hole, *and* boat, as I've always done. And what's more, Mole's going to stick me and do as I do, aren't you, Mole?"

"Of course I am," said the Mole, loyally. "I'll always stick to you, Rat, and what you say is to be—has got to be. All the same, it sounds as if it might have been—well, rather fun, you know!" he added, wistfully. Poor Mole! The Life Adventurous was so new a thing to him, and so thrilling; and this fresh aspect of it was so tempting; and he had fallen in love at first sight with the canary-coloured cart and all its little fitments.

The Rat saw what was passing in his mind, and wavered. He hated disappointing people,[34] and he was fond of the Mole, and would do almost anything to oblige him. Toad was watching both of them closely.

"Come along in, and have some lunch," he said, diplomatically, "and we'll talk it over. We needn't decide anything in a hurry.[35] Of course, *I* don't really care. I only want to give pleasure to you fellows. 'Live for others!' That's my motto in life."[36]

During luncheon—which was excellent,[37] of course, as everything at Toad Hall always was—the Toad simply let himself go. Disregarding the Rat, he proceeded to play upon the inexperienced Mole as on a harp. Naturally a voluble[38] animal, and always mastered by his imagination, he painted the prospects of the trip and the joys of the open life and the roadside in such glowing colours that the Mole could hardly sit in his chair for excitement. Somehow, it soon seemed taken for granted by all three of them that the trip was a settled thing; and the Rat, though still unconvinced in his mind, allowed his good-nature to over-ride his personal objections.

two sentences emphasize Toad's choice of words. The phrase "you've *got* to come" implies that Toad will not take no for an answer. The emphatic way Toad says "live in a hole . . . and *boat?*" insults Rat's sensibilities. Finally, the word *animal* replaces the word *man* in the cliche, "I'm going to make a *man* out of you."

34. *He hated disappointing people.* Again, the riverbankers are called "people" when previously they were called "animals." See chapter I, note 25.

35. *"Come along in, and have some lunch," he said diplomatically, "and we'll talk it over. We needn't decide anything in a hurry."* Toad is seducing Mole and Rat. Once he has them inside, behaves graciously, and feeds them, he knows he'll have them.

36. *" 'Live for others!' That's my motto in life."* As we have seen, Grahame modeled Toad after an amalgam of people—Alastair Grahame, Oscar Wilde, Horatio Bottomley, and possibly Grahame's own father, who abandoned Kenneth and his siblings after their mother died. Cunningham Grahame, like Mr. Toad, was too bombastic and self-involved to provide for his children without their mother. Biographer Alison Prince writes about Cunningham Grahame:

> On both his mother's and father's side, Cunningham Grahame could trace his descent back through the Stuarts to Robert the Bruce, and he inherited an aristocratic confidence, which, coupled with a low boredom threshold, made him impatient with the mundane details of everyday life. Ostentation ruled him. He was a *bon viveur*, a poet, a spender of money; a popular man with a taste for good claret which brought him more friends than his unenthusiastically pursued legal career. (*Kenneth Grahame: An Innocent in the Wild Wood*, 3)

He could not bear to disappoint his two friends, who were already deep in schemes and anticipations, planning out each day's separate occupation for several weeks ahead.

When they were quite ready, the now triumphant Toad led his companions to the paddock and set them to capture the old grey horse,[39] who, without having been consulted, and to his own extreme annoyance, had been told off by Toad for the dustiest job in this dusty expedition. He frankly preferred the paddock, and took a deal of catching. Meantime Toad packed the lockers still tighter with necessaries, and hung nosebags, nets of onions, bundles of hay, and baskets from the bottom of the cart. At last the horse was caught and harnessed, and they set off, all talking at once, each animal either trudging by the side of the cart or sitting on the shaft,[40] as the humour took him. It was a golden afternoon. The smell of the dust they kicked up was rich and satisfying;[41] out of thick orchards on either side the road, birds called and whistled to them cheerily; good-natured wayfarers, passing them, gave them "Good-day," or stopped to say nice things about their beautiful cart; and rabbits, sitting at their front doors in the hedgerows, held up their fore-paws, and said, "O my! O my! O my!"[42]

Late in the evening, tired and happy and miles from home,[43] they drew up on a remote common[44] far from habitations, turned the horse loose to graze, and ate their simple supper sitting on the grass by the side of the cart. Toad talked big about all he was going to do in the days to come, while stars grew fuller and larger all around them, and a yellow moon, appearing suddenly and silently from nowhere in particular, came to keep them company and listen to their talk. At last they turned in to their little bunks in the cart; and Toad, kicking out his legs, sleepily said, "Well, good night, you fellows! This is the real life for a gentleman! Talk about your old river!"

"I *don't* talk about my river," replied the patient Rat. "You *know* I don't, Toad. But I *think* about it," he added pathetically, in a lower tone: "I think about it—all the time!"[45]

Like Grahame's father, Toad couldn't possibly "Live for others" because he is a self-centered spendthrift.

37. *During luncheon—which was excellent.* This is the second major feast in *The Wind in the Willows.*

38. *voluble.* Talkative.

39. *the now triumphant Toad led his companions to the paddock and set them to capture the old grey horse.* When A. A. Milne wrote *Toad of Toad Hall,* he named the horse Alfred and gave him a pessimistic voice. Milne's Alfred is based on Grahame's disagreeable horse.

> RAT. [upon seeing the gypsy cart] So this is the latest craze! I understand. Boating is played out. He's tired of it and done with it.
>
> ALFRED. Don't blame *me.* I wasn't consulted about this at all; but if I had been, I should have said boats. Stick to Boats.

Milne's Alfred is an early version of Eeyore in the Pooh books. Eeyore also has the distinction of being described as "the old grey donkey."

> Eeyore, the old grey Donkey, stood by the side of the stream, and looked at himself in the water.
>
> "Pathetic," he said. "That's what it is. Pathetic." (*Winnie-the-Pooh*, chapter 6)

Mole, Rat, and Toad catching the horse also raises the issue of size—an issue that, as mentioned earlier, delayed production of *Toad of Toad Hall* until 1929. Is the old gray horse Mole-sized, or are Mole, Rat, and Toad horse-sized?

Grahame's reference to the "old grey horse" also points out that horses are soon to become obsolete with the rise of cars in rural England.

Barnhart's cart, 1922. One of four pen-and-ink drawings in Nancy Barnhart's edition. Barnhart avoids the problem of the size of the horse in relation to the cart and riverbankers by not including it.

40. *each animal either trudging by the side of the cart or sitting on the shaft.* The shaft refers to either of two long pieces of wood between which a horse is hitched to a vehicle.

41. *It was a golden afternoon. The smell of the dust they kicked up was rich and satisfying.* Rackham worked out the issue of size with his 1940 illustration of the Gypsy cart. The humanly dressed Mole—with cap, shoes, overcoat, and loose scarf—is on friendly terms with the horse that ran away earlier. The horse appears to tip his head in affection toward the Mole. There is no sense that the horse could crush any of them with a misstep. The riverbankers are approximately two-thirds the height of the Gypsy cart, making them a perfect fit in their world. The well-dressed Toad bringing up the rear seems taller than the cartwheel. Whenever Rackham added objects such as chairs, vegetables, doorways, sculls, and interiors, he always drew them in a size associated with use for humans.

42. *and rabbits, sitting at their front doors in the hedgerows, held up their fore-paws, and said, "O my! O my! O my!"* Mole chants the same exclamation in chapter I when he unpacks the picnic basket. The rabbits are from the working class. They live right on the street and are watching the riverbankers pass from their doorsteps; the rabbits do not live in private locations like Mole End, Rat's River Bank, Toad's Toad Hall, or Badger's underground retreat in the Wild Wood.

43. *tired and happy and miles from home.* The chalk Ridgeway of the Berkshire Downs is the setting for "The Open Road." In a letter, Sidney Ward, one of Grahame's co-workers at the Bank of England, reminisced about the companionship on the walking tours they took through the region:

A photo of Austin Purves and Kenneth Grahame walking in Blewbury, circa 1910. *Courtesy of the David J. Holmes Collection.*

> A friend had lent him [Kenneth Grahame] a fourteenth-century cottage in the main street [of Streatley], and we had a grand twenty-mile walk along the Ridgeway, the subject of [Grahame's] "Romance of the Road." If we either of us said clever things that day they are forgotten, but we came home happy and tired, bought some chops and fetched a huge jug of beer from the pub. We cooked our dinner over the open wood fire, and how good those chops were! (Chalmers, *Kenneth Grahame*, 111)

44. *they drew up on a remote common.* A common is a public open area owned by the people of a municipality. The word common is derived from commonwealth, or commonweal, a fourteenth-century definition of resources to be used for the com-

Rackham's Gypsy cart.

The Mole reached out from under his blanket, felt for the Rat's paw in the darkness, and gave it a squeeze. "I'll do whatever you like, Ratty," he whispered. "Shall we run away to-morrow morning, quite early—*very* early—and go back to our dear old hole on the river?"

"No, no, we'll see it out," whispered back the Rat. "Thanks awfully, but I ought to stick by Toad till this trip is ended. It wouldn't be safe for him to be left to himself. It won't take very long. His fads never do. Good night!"

The end was indeed nearer than even the Rat suspected.

After so much open air and excitement the Toad slept very soundly, and no amount of shaking could rouse him out of bed next morning. So the Mole and Rat turned to, quietly and manfully, and while the Rat saw to the horse, and lit a fire, and cleaned last night's cups and platters, and got things ready for breakfast, the Mole trudged off to the nearest village, a long way off, for milk and eggs and various necessaries the Toad had, of course, forgotten to provide.[46] The hard work had all been done, and the two animals were resting, thoroughly exhausted, by the time Toad appeared on the scene, fresh and gay, remarking what a pleasant easy life it was they were all leading now, after the cares and worries and fatigues of housekeeping at home.

They had a pleasant ramble that day over grassy downs and along narrow by-lanes, and camped as before, on a common, only this time the two guests took care that Toad should do his fair share of work. In consequence, when the time came for starting next morning, Toad was by no means so rapturous about the simplicity of the primitive life, and indeed attempted to resume his place in his bunk, whence he was hauled by force. Their way lay, as before, across country by narrow lanes, and it was not till the afternoon that they came out on the high-road, their first high-road;[47] and there disaster, fleet and unforeseen, sprang out on them—disaster momentous indeed to their expedition, but simply overwhelming in its effect on the after-career of Toad.

mon good of the people. As in the scene of the picnic in chapter I, the riverbankers have found a place to stop that is open to the public, yet off the beaten path.

45. *"I* don't *talk about my river," replied the patient Rat. "You* know *I don't, Toad. But I* think *about it," he added pathetically, in a lower tone: "I think about it—all the time!"* Kenneth Grahame once wrote to Elspeth: "You like people. They interest you. But I am interested in places." Because Grahame went to live at St. Edward's, a boarding school in Oxford, and spent holidays staying in the homes of different aunts and uncles, he did not have a place of his own that he called home until he was well into adulthood. In his 1959 biography of Grahame, Peter Green observes:

> The result of this [lack of ties to any one place] was a psychological characteristic that recurs throughout [Grahame's] work: a strong but unanalyzed homing-instinct towards an ideal home that had never in fact existed. This instinct was a counterbalance to Grahame's equally strong wanderlust. (Green, *Kenneth Grahame: A Biography*, 86)

Rat longs for home and for his river now that he is landlocked. Yet there is no one waiting for Rat at home—it is the return to place that he wants. He will, however, rough it out on the open road for the sake of seeing Toad through his craze.

46. *the Mole trudged off to the nearest village, a long way off, for milk and eggs and various necessaries the Toad had, of course, forgotten to provide.* Immediately, the reader is confronted by more questions about the ambivalence of size. Who lives in the village Mole trudges off to—human beings, or other small animals? Are the eggs Mole-sized or is Mole human-sized? Finally, how did Mole pay for the eggs and milk?

They were strolling along the high-road easily, the Mole by the horse's head, talking to him, since the horse had complained that he was being frightfully left out of it, and nobody considered him in the least;[48] the Toad and the Water Rat walking behind the cart talking together—at least Toad was talking, and Rat was saying at intervals, 'Yes, precisely; and what did *you* say to *him?*'—and thinking all the time of something very different, when far behind them they heard a faint warning hum, like the drone of a distant bee. Glancing back, they saw a small cloud of dust, with a dark centre of energy, advancing on them at incredible speed, while from out the dust a faint "Poop-poop!" wailed like an uneasy animal in pain.[49] Hardly regarding it, they turned to resume their conversation, when in an instant (as it seemed) the peaceful scene was changed, and with a blast of wind and a whirl of sound that made them jump for the nearest ditch,[50] It was on them! The "Poop-poop" rang with a brazen shout in their ears,[51] they had a moment's glimpse of an interior of glittering plate-glass[52] and rich morocco,[53] and the magnificent motor-car, immense, breath-snatching, passionate, with its pilot tense and hugging his wheel, possessed all earth and air[54] for the fraction of a second, flung an enveloping cloud of dust that blinded and enwrapped them utterly, and then dwindled to a speck in the far distance, changed back into a droning bee once more.[55]

The old grey horse, dreaming, as he plodded along, of his quiet paddock, in a new raw situation such as this simply abandoned himself to his natural emotions.[56] Rearing, plunging, backing steadily, in spite of all the Mole's efforts at his head, and all the Mole's lively language directed at his better feelings, he drove the cart backwards towards the deep ditch at the side of the road. It wavered an instant—then there was a heartrending crash—and the canary-coloured cart, their pride and their joy, lay on its side in the ditch, an irredeemable wreck.[57]

47. *it was not till the afternoon that they came out on the high-road.* Grahame does not use the word *until* in *The Wind in the Willows*; he always uses the half word.

The term *high road* came into the English language in 1709. High road means highway, or the easiest course. High roads in Grahame's day were more traveled, yet most of them were unpaved.

48. *They were strolling along the high road easily, the Mole by the horse's head, talking to him, since the horse had complained that he was being frightfully left out of it, and nobody considered him in the least.* The horse, who remains nameless in Grahame's text, becomes anthropomorphized here for the first time. The horse "complains" yet does not join the inner circle of the riverbankers. He remains an outsider whose sole purpose is to pull the cart, not partake in the enjoyment of the adventure.

49. *Glancing back, they saw a small cloud of dust, with a dark center of energy, advancing on them at incredible speed, while from out the dust a faint "Poop-poop!" wailed like an uneasy animal in pain.* In 1896, when motorcars were first making their way on the open roads of England, there was little hostility directed toward motorists because cars were so uncommon. But within one decade, things changed rapidly. In his book *The British Motor Industry, 1896–1939*, Kenneth Richardson points out:

> On 31 March 1906 there were 23,192 private cars in use in the United Kingdom. A trip from London to Bath and back became a common weekend pastime. Clouds of dust were raised from roads which had never been intended for these new vehicles, dust which covered the green hedgerows and verges with a thick grey powder. Above all there were accidents, with faults on both sides. Pedestrians often lacked the training in

judging distances which has become second nature today, while motorists, whose vehicles had no means of identification, were known to surrender to the intoxication of speed which proved so disastrous to Mr. Toad. (London: Macmillan, 1977, 22)

50. *in an instant (as it seemed) the peaceful scene was changed, and with a blast of wind and a whirl of sound that made them jump for the nearest ditch.* Peter Green observes that "The Open Road" deals with the triumph of mechanical progress over rural traditionalism. "In [chapter II] Grahame packed a whole social revolution . . . the destruction of the caravan—which Grahame associated symbolically with untrammeled country bohemianism—by the inhuman and somehow monstrous motor-car" (*Kenneth Grahame: A Biography*, 248).

The moment the car runs them off the road, the modernism of Grahame's era and of the Wide World has shattered the dreamlike arcadia of the riverbankers' world.

51. *The "Poop-poop" rang with a brazen shout in their ears.* The "poop-poop" refers to the tooting of the horn, or "hooter," as it was sometimes called. The sound is also due to the movement of the four cylinders in the engine. As gasoline and air were pushed out of the cylinders, they popped. The sound disappeared as cars of that period went faster. If the mixture of gas and air was too rich the popping became loud, even sounding like gunfire.

52. *an interior of glittering plate-glass.* Most motorcars in 1907–1908, when Grahame wrote *The Wind in the Willows*, were luxury items owned by the few. There were nine different manufacturers of cars: Albion, Argyll, Austin, Humber, Napier, Rover, Sunbeam, Vauxhall, and Wolseley. In 1906, 3,749 motorcars were manufactured in Britain. By 1913 there were 29 manufacturers, with an annual industry output of somewhere between 32,000 and 34,000 cars. The earlier cars were open to the air, and most likely stored in barns (James Foreman-Peck, Sue Bowden, and Alan McKinlay, *The British Motor Industry* ([Manchester: Manchester University Press], 1995). Grahame's text suggests that the first car the riverbankers encounter has a windshield and windows that close. Of all the early illustrators, only Ernest Shepard added a drawing of the car.

53. *rich morocco.* Leather made from goatskins tanned with sumac. Originally produced in Morocco, it is used particularly for bookbinding and upholstery, according to the *OED*.

54. *and the magnificent motor-car, immense, breath-snatching, passionate, with its pilot tense and hugging his wheel, possessed all earth and air.* Grahame's contemporary Rudyard Kipling was a motoring enthusiast who started driving in 1897. Kipling referred to the motorcar as the "petrol-piddling monster." In 1904, he wrote to A. B. Filson Young, one of the first motoring journalists, about his early driving days, when taking a car out involved "agonies, shames, delays, rages, chills, parboilings, road-walkings, water-drawings, burns and starvations" (*The Kipling Journal*, 1927, 30). Kipling later wrote, "Any fool can invent anything, as any fool can wait to buy the invention when it is thoroughly perfected" (ibid., 32).

55. *changed back into a droning bee once more.* Variant, d. 524: becoming a distant droning bee once more.

56. *The old grey horse, dreaming, as he plodded along, of his quiet paddock, in a new raw*

situation such as this simply abandoned himself to his natural emotions. The Light Locomotives on Highways Act, passed on November 14, 1896, lifted the ban on motorcars on roadways, imposing a new speed limit of 12 mph. Cars had been banned in England because motor engines scared horses. Animals unaccustomed to the noise of machinery easily overturned their loads when they were spooked.

Before motorcars, steam-traction engines were used for agricultural purposes. The Locomotive Act of 1865 set a speed limit of 4 mph and demanded that a man waving a red flag walk ahead of the vehicle at all times. But near the turn of the century nothing could stop the rise of the horseless carriage because, unlike a train forced to stay on its track, a car could penetrate anywhere in the countryside. By 1910, the top cruising speed of a car such as a Courier Speedster Model was 35 mph (Richardson, *The British Motor Industry, 1896–1939*, 12).

57. *then there was a heartrending crash—and the canary-coloured cart, their pride and their joy, lay on its side in the ditch, an irredeemable wreck.* The public gradually embraced the car and all its hazards more readily. In a cartoon that appeared in *Punch* in 1904, one house party guest asks another cheerfully, "What luck? Killed anything?" to

Drawing by Alastair Grahame of a collision of horse and car. undated edition of *The Merry Thought* (1908). *Courtesy of the Harry Ransom Humanities Research Center, The University of Texas at Austin.*

which the other reveler answers bitterly: "No. Have you?" The rise of the motorcar was very much on the mind of Alastair Grahame, who drew this picture of a similar collision in 1908.

58. *"You scoundrels, you highwaymen, you—you—road-hogs!"* "Road-hogs!" was originally "stockbrokers!" in Grahame's holograph manuscript, e. 248. "Stockbrokers" was later scored out in black ink and "road-hogs" was written in the margin. It seems that Grahame associated the rise of the automobile with the carelessness of the nouveaux riche.

59. *steam-launches.* a steam-powered boat. The steam engine was invented in 1751, and the "steamer" came into existence by 1814. Steam engines were also used by trains throughout the United Kingdom in the Victorian/Edwardian era.

60. *Toad sat straight down in the middle of the dusty road, his legs stretched out before him.* One of the most remarkable illustrations ever published in any edition of *The Wind in the Willows* is Bransom's 1913 version of Rat leading the horse. The image depicts a moment after the cart crash; Rat has collected the birdcage from the wrecked and abandoned cart. Bransom's horse is huge, unlike those of later illustrators, who made the riverbankers large enough to ride horses and interact with human beings. The artist cropped the horse's head with the top of the illustration. As a result, the horse overflows the page and looks ominous compared to tiny Mole and Rat, who lead it on its reins.

Fourteen years later, in 1927, Payne drew a stunned Mr. Toad sitting on a tree trunk at the side of the road as he falls under the spell of the passing motorcar. Payne took liberties with Grahame's text: The tree trunk does not exist—nor is Toad sitting "down in the middle of the dusty

The Rat danced up and down in the road, simply transported with passion. "You villains!" he shouted, shaking both fists, "You scoundrels, you highwaymen, you—you—road-hogs![58]—I'll have the law of you! I'll report you! I'll take you through all the Courts!" His home-sickness had quite slipped away from him, and for the moment he was the skipper of the canary-coloured vessel driven on a shoal by the reckless jockeying of rival mariners, and he was trying to recollect all the fine and biting things he used to say to masters of steam-launches[59] when their wash, as they drove too near the bank, used to flood his parlour-carpet at home.

Toad sat straight down in the middle of the dusty road, his legs stretched out before him,[60] and stared fixedly in the direction of the disappearing motor-car. He breathed short, his face wore a placid satisfied expression, and at intervals he faintly murmured "Poop-poop!"[61]

The Mole was busy trying to quiet the horse, which he succeeded in doing after a time. Then he went to look at the cart, on its side in the ditch. It was indeed a sorry sight. Panels and windows smashed, axles hopelessly bent, one wheel off, sardine-tins scattered over the wide world, and the bird in the bird-cage sobbing pitifully and calling to be let out.

The Rat came to help him, but their united efforts were not sufficient to right the cart. "Hi! Toad!" they cried. "Come and bear a hand, can't you!"

The Toad never answered a word, or budged from his seat in the road; so they went to see what was the matter with him. They found him in a sort of a trance, a happy smile on his face, his eyes still fixed on the dusty wake of their destroyer. At intervals he was still heard to murmur "Poop-poop!"

The Rat shook him by the shoulder. "Are you coming to help us, Toad?" he demanded sternly.

"Glorious, stirring sight!" murmured Toad, never offering to move. "The poetry of motion! The *real* way to travel! The *only* way to travel! Here to-day—in next week to-morrow!

Bransom's horse, 1913. Bransom's animals stay close to their true size in scale to other animals and human beings. Though they walk upright, the animals retain hunched shapes. Bransom's riverbankers remain unclothed, unlike those of later illustrators, who went to elaborate lengths to dress the riverbankers.

road." Payne's Toad is distinguished by his foppish dress, whereas Bransom's fallen Toad is a creature from nature: ready to topple forward and hop off.

Just four years after Payne anthropomorphized Toad, Shepard drew him as a fat, middle-aged man, looking every bit the part of the Horatio Bottomley type—the super-mogul financier with an insatiable appetite for the latest gizmos.

61. *He breathed short, his face wore a placid satisfied expression, and at intervals he faintly murmured "Poop-poop!"* Toad has fallen under a spell; the magic incantation is the sound of the motorcar.

62. *"Villages skipped, towns and cities jumped—always somebody else's horizon! O bliss! O poop-poop! O my! O my!"* Toad's exclamations are like an apostrophe in Romantic period literature. The apostrophe usually addresses an abstract—"bliss"—or element of nature, as in Byron's "Roll on, thou deep and dark blue ocean, roll!" (*The Complete Works of Lord Byron: With Memoir and the Original* [London and New York: Frederick Warne and Co., 1891], clxxix, 209).

Payne's cart crash, 1927.

Villages skipped, towns and cities jumped—always somebody else's horizon! O bliss! O poop-poop! O my! O my!"[62]

"O *stop* being an ass, Toad!" cried the Mole despairingly.

"And to think I never *knew!*" went on the Toad in a dreamy monotone. "All those wasted years that lie behind me, I never knew, never even *dreamt!* But *now*—but now that I know, now that I fully realise! O what a flowery track lies spread before me, henceforth! What dust-clouds shall spring up behind me as I speed on my reckless way! What carts I shall fling carelessly into the ditch in the wake of my magnificent onset! Horrid little carts—common carts—canary-coloured carts!"

"What are we to do with him?" asked the Mole of the Water Rat.

"Nothing at all," replied the Rat firmly. "Because there is really nothing to be done. You see, I know him from of old. He is now possessed. He has got a new craze, and it always takes him that way, in its first stage.[63] He'll continue like that for days now, like an animal walking in a happy dream, quite useless for all practical purposes. Never mind him. Let's go and see what there is to be done about the cart."

A careful inspection showed them that, even if they succeeded in righting it by themselves, the cart would travel no longer. The axles were in a hopeless state, and the missing wheel was shattered into pieces.

The Rat knotted the horse's reins over his back and took him by the head, carrying the bird cage and its hysterical occupant in the other hand. "Come on!" he said grimly to the Mole. "It's five or six miles to the nearest town, and we shall just have to walk it. The sooner we make a start the better."

"But what about Toad?" asked the Mole anxiously, as they set off together. "We can't leave him here, sitting in the middle of the road by himself, in the distracted state he's in! It's not safe. Supposing another Thing were to come along?"[64]

"O, *bother* Toad," said the Rat savagely; "I've done with him!"[65]

They had not proceeded very far on their way, however, when there was a pattering of feet behind them, and Toad caught them up and thrust a paw inside the elbow of each of them;[66] still breathing short and staring into vacancy.

"Now, look here, Toad!" said the Rat sharply: "as soon as we get to the town, you'll have to go straight to the police-station, and see if they know anything about that motor-car and who

63. *"He is now possessed. He has got a new craze, and it always takes him that way, in its first stage."* Roger C. Schlobin posits that Grahame would have been familiar with Robert Louis Stevenson's *Strange Case of Dr. Jekyll and Mr. Hyde* (1886), which sold over 40,000 copies in Britain in the first six months after it was first published and was "read by those who never read fiction . . . and made the subject of leading articles in religious newspapers." According to Schlobin, Toad has a Dr. Jekyll/Mr. Hyde personality, and cars are the etherlike potion that turns Toad into the dangerous Mr. Hyde ("Danger and Compulsion in *The Wind in the Willows:* Or, Toad and Hyde Together at Last," *Journal of the Fantastic in the Arts* 8, no. 1 (1997): 34–41).

64. *"Supposing another Thing were to come along?"* Like many in rural England around 1900, Mole has never seen a car and doesn't know what to call it yet. He calls the mysterious car a "Thing," with a capital T. Grahame is also spoofing the monstrosities of Gothic literature. The mysterious and terrifying monster made by Dr. Frankenstein has been replaced by a motorcar.

65. *"O,* bother *Toad," said the Rat savagely; "I've done with him!"* "Bother" is an exclamation repeated four times in *The Wind in the Willows.* A. A. Milne—who was greatly influenced by Grahame—has Pooh repeat "Oh bother!" or "Bother!" at comic intervals throughout *Winnie-the-Pooh.*

66. *Toad caught them up and thrust a paw inside the elbow of each of them.* Variant, e. 248: Toad caught them up and thrust a paw inside ~~each of their~~ the elbow of each of them.

it belongs to, and lodge a complaint against it.[67] And then you'll have to go to a blacksmith's or a wheelwright's[68] and arrange for the cart to be fetched and mended and put to rights. It'll take time, but it's not quite a hopeless smash. Meanwhile, the Mole and I will go to an inn and find comfortable rooms where we can stay till the cart's ready, and till your nerves have recovered their shock."

"Police-station! Complaint!" murmured Toad dreamily. "Me *complain* of that beautiful, that heavenly vision that has been vouchsafed[69] me! *Mend* the *cart!* I've done with carts for ever. I never want to see the cart, or to hear of it, again. O, Ratty! You can't think how obliged I am to you for consenting to come on this trip! I wouldn't have gone without you, and then I might never have seen that—that swan, that sunbeam, that thunderbolt![70] I might never have heard that entrancing sound, or smelt that bewitching smell! I owe it all to you, my best of friends!"

The Rat turned from him in despair. "You see what it is?" he said to the Mole, addressing him across Toad's head: "He's quite hopeless. I give it up—when we get to the town we'll go to the railway station, and with luck we may pick up a train there that'll get us back to riverbank[71] to-night. And if ever you catch me going a-pleasuring with this provoking animal again!"—He snorted, and during the rest of that weary trudge addressed his remarks exclusively to Mole.

On reaching the town they went straight to the station and deposited Toad in the second-class waiting-room, giving a porter twopence to keep a strict eye on him. They then left the horse at an inn stable,[72] and gave what directions they could about the cart and its contents. Eventually, a slow train having landed them at a station not very far from Toad Hall, they escorted the spell-bound, sleep-walking Toad to his door, put him inside it, and instructed his housekeeper[73] to feed him, undress him, and put him to bed. Then they got out their boat from the boat-house, sculled down the river home, and at

67. *"you'll have to go straight to the police-station, and see if they know anything about that motor-car and who it belongs to, and lodge a complaint against it."* Motorcars, at this time, did not require a license for either the car or the driver.

68. *"blacksmith's or a wheelwright's."* Blacksmith: a smith who works in iron or black metal, as distinguished from a whitesmith, who works in tin or white metal (*OED*). Wheelwright: a maker of wheels and wheeled vehicles (*OED*).

69. *vouchsafed.* To grant or furnish often in a gracious or condescending manner; to give by way of reply; to grant as a privilege or special favor.

70. *"that swan, that sunbeam, that thunderbolt!"* These are three aspects of Zeus, king of the Olympian gods in Greek mythology. As a swan, he seduced Leda, who gave birth to Helen and Polydeuces. As a sunbeam he seduced Danae, who gave birth to Perseus. Zeus's primary identifier in antiquity was the thunderbolt. His jealous wife, Hera, convinced one of his lovers, Semele, to ask that he grant her a wish. Semele asked that he reveal his true nature to her—which of course turned out to be a thunderbolt—and she died. Zeus rescued their child, Dionysos, from her womb and sewed him into his thigh.

—J. J.

Sunbeam is also the name of a bicycle manufacturer that went into the motorcar business. Located in Wolverhampton, England, they made cars from 1899 until 1935.

Their first car, the Sunbeam-Mabley, looked like a Victorian sofa on wheels. It traveled sideways, sat up to four people, and was powered by a single-cylinder engine. Between 1902 and 1905 12-horsepower Sunbeams were manufactured based

a very late hour sat down to supper in their own cosy riverside parlour, to the Rat's great joy and contentment.

The following evening the Mole, who had risen late and taken things very easy all day, was sitting on the bank fishing,[74] when the Rat, who had been looking up his friends and gossiping, came strolling along to find him. "Heard the news?" he said. "There's nothing else being talked about, all along the river bank. Toad went up to Town by an early train this morning. And he has ordered a large and very expensive motor-car."

on the design of the French Berliet car. Between 1904 and 1907, six-cylinder engines put in a brief appearance. For more information, see http://www.localhistory.scit.wlv.ac.uk/Museum/Transport/Cars/Sunbeam.htm.

71. *riverbank.* Riverbank is an actual train stop in Grahame's text.

72. *They then left the horse at an inn stable.* This is the last that we will ever hear of the horse. We have no idea if or how the horse is returned to Toad Hall.

73. *housekeeper.* The porter and the housekeeper are two nameless servants who appear in *The Wind in the Willows*.

74. *was sitting on the bank fishing.* Besides rowing and boating, Mole has also learned how to fish. After the great adventure of the open road, from gypsy carts to motorcars, chapter II comes to a close where it began—on the river bank.

In MS. Eng. Misc. d. 524: The typescript draft was composed in different installments. Once Kenneth Grahame was confident of having written opening chapters that ran fluidly from the first to the second, he went back and scored out the typed ~~(To Be Continued)~~ at the end of the chapter with a black pen. While the first two chapters were typed in green ink, "The Wild Wood" is typed in black ink on a finer quality of paper.

III

The Wild Wood

The Mole had long wanted to make the acquaintance of the Badger. He seemed, by all accounts, to be such an important personage and, though rarely visible, to make his unseen influence felt by everybody about the place. But whenever the Mole mentioned his wish to the Water Rat he always found himself put off. "It's all right," the Rat would say. "Badger'll turn up some day or other—he's always turning up—and then I'll introduce you. The best of fellows! But you must not only take him *as* you find him, but *when* you find him."

"Couldn't you ask him here—dinner or something?" said the Mole.

"He wouldn't come," replied the Rat simply. "Badger hates Society, and invitations, and dinner, and all that sort of thing."[1]

"Well, then, supposing we go and call on *him?"* suggested the Mole.

"O, I'm sure he wouldn't like that at *all*," said the Rat, quite alarmed. "He's so very shy, he'd be sure to be offended. I've never even ventured to call on him at his own home myself, though I know him so well. Besides, we can't. It's quite out of the question, because he lives in the very middle of the Wild Wood."[2]

AN OUTLINE FOR CHAPTERS III AND IV

An undated letter from Naomi Stott to Kenneth Grahame (British Library, MS 50855, subfolder "Motor trip Easter 1909") contains what appears to be a thin outline for the third and fourth chapters of *The Wind in the Willows*. Stott's letter describes a scene told to her by Alastair Grahame. It's possible that the summary was included in *The Merry Thought* in 1908. Like so many contributions to Alastair's magazine, the pages are undated. Stott's letter reads as follows:

> The mole & the water rat go to Badger Hall in the wild wood. On their way it comes on to storm & rain, & they get lost.
>
> The mole falls over something hard that hurts him & finds that it is a door ~~step~~ scraper[. T]hen they find a door, & Mr. water rat's house keeper says "What do you mean? You must go round to the front door." She grumbles, but at last lets them in at the back door, & Mr. Badger gives them clothes & supper, &

they all have a good time, & the next day they go off

If you could tell me any leading questions I might casually be able to extract some more. Mouse has just given me the small amount I have written down.

N. S.

Grahame adds extra details to the plot: The distracted Rat composes poetry; the bored Mole leaves to visit Badger and gets lost. Mole is terrified by the rough characters of the ghettoized Wild Wood. Otter the adventurer turns up at the end of the fourth chapter to lead them back to the safety of the riverbank. Naomi Stott adds to the chapter by giving Mr. Rat a housekeeper, an extraneous detail Grahame purposely omits.

1. *"He wouldn't come," replied the Rat simply. "Badger hates Society, and invitations, and dinner, and all that sort of thing."* During the 1890s Grahame was a best-selling author. John Lane, Grahame's editor and publisher at Bodley Head, often asked Grahame out to dinner and luncheons. According to their correspondence, Grahame more often declined Lane's invitations than accepted (Bodleian, MS. don. e. 27).

Even when he was a contributor to the quarterly the *Yellow Book* (1894–1897), Grahame disliked social occasions. There are numerous witty letters from Grahame to Evelyn Sharp, a fellow *Yellow Book* contributor, turning down her repeated invitations to tea, the theater, a watercolor exhibition, and lectures (Bodleian, MS. Eng. Lett. d. 276). Sharp wrote the following letter (April 16, 1933) to Elspeth after Kenneth Grahame's death:

> He was, perhaps, shy among strangers, always looked away hastily if he caught you looking at him, simply hated being lionized but liked to talk about his work if he knew you were sympathetic and not likely to gush about it. . . . He never spoke much, only when he had something to say; he never said anything unkind about anybody, or to anybody, except through the inability to say something sincere. (Quoted from Peter Green, *Kenneth Grahame: A Biography*, 152)

Green describes Badger as Kenneth Grahame's most distinctly autobiographical character:

> But as in Mole's case, the greater part of Badger is autobiographical. It was Grahame . . . who felt awkward and out of place in "society"; and it was certainly Grahame who turned "rather low and despondent when he's wanting victuals." Slip-shod but well-equipped, indifferent to fashions but careful of comfort, Badger represents Grahame's own conception of himself as the rural *ours philanthropique.* (Ibid., 281)

2. *"It's quite out of the question, because he lives in the very middle of the Wild Wood."* Not only does Rat convey that Mr. Badger is emotionally remote, Badger has the distinction of living in the heart of what has become a dangerous district. Mr. Badger, unlike the other riverbankers, is fearless and has no intention of leaving his ancestral home.

"Well, supposing he does," said the Mole. "You told me the Wild Wood was all right, you know."

"O, I know, I know, so it is," replied the Rat evasively. "But I think we won't go there just now. Not *just* yet. It's a long way, and he wouldn't be at home at this time of year anyhow, and he'll be coming along some day, if you'll wait quietly."

The Mole had to be content with this. But the Badger never came along, and every day brought its amusements, and it was not till summer was long over, and cold and frost and miry

Nancy Barnhart, 1922. "He sometimes scribbled poetry."

ways kept them much indoors, and the swollen river raced past outside their windows with a speed that mocked at boating of any sort or kind, that he found his thoughts dwelling again with much persistence on the solitary grey Badger,[3] who lived his own life by himself, in his hole in the middle of the Wild Wood.

In the winter time the Rat slept a great deal, retiring early and rising late. During his short day he sometimes scribbled poetry[4] or did other small domestic jobs about the house; and, of course, there were always animals dropping in for a chat,[5] and consequently there was a good deal of story-telling and comparing notes on the past summer and all its doings.

Such a rich chapter it had been, when one came to look back on it all! With illustrations so numerous and so very highly coloured! The pageant of the river bank had marched steadily along, unfolding itself in scene-pictures that succeeded each other in stately procession. Purple loosestrife arrived early, shaking luxuriant tangled locks along the edge of the mirror whence its own face laughed back at it.[6] Willow-herb, tender and wistful, like a pink sunset cloud, was not slow to follow. Comfrey, the purple hand-in-hand with the white, crept forth to take its place in the line; and at last one morning the diffident and delaying dog-rose stepped delicately on the stage, and one knew, as if string-music had announced it in stately chords that strayed into a gavotte,[7] that June at last was here. One member of the company was still awaited; the shepherd-boy for the nymphs to woo, the knight for whom the ladies waited at the window,[8] the prince that was to kiss the sleeping summer back to life and love.[9] But when meadow-sweet, debonair and odorous in amber jerkin,[10] moved graciously to his place in the group, then the play was ready to begin.[11]

And what a play it had been! Drowsy animals, snug in their holes while wind and rain were battering at their doors,[12] recalled still keen mornings, an hour before sunrise, when the white mist, as yet undispersed, clung closely along the surface

3. *solitary grey Badger.* Is Mr. Badger gray or striped? In the first chapter he is described as follows: "a stripy head, with high shoulders behind it, peered forth on them."

4. *he sometimes scribbled poetry.* We've already seen that Bransom prefers to put Rat in a true riverbank rat hole. Nancy Barnhart, the second illustrator of *The Wind in the Willows*, gives Rat a more human surrounding. Her Rat seems affected; he lives in a human house, is fully dressed, and is shown writing with a quill. Rat also has long, humanlike fingers with great, creepy claws. Barnhart's illustration shows no trace of the snug "animal hole" of Grahame's text. Instead, her Rat has books and a pen-and-ink set on a side table. Much attention is given to extraneous details—the striped wallpaper, the floral armchair, the family portrait, and Rat's clothing—and all of it seems static, as if she is trying too hard to make Rat into a bard.

Ernest Shepard, on the other hand, accomplishes a great deal more with his tiny pen-and-ink drawing. The drawing appears after Mole has gone to the Wild Wood. About an eighth the size of Barnhart's full-page, full-color illustration, Shepard's tiny drawing seems curiously alive. The smoking fire evokes a sense of warmth on a dark afternoon. The handless clock sits on the mantelpiece; both the fire and clock give a sense that sound should accompany the drawing, that the crackling of burning wood and the ticking of the clock would lull the reader into a state similar to Rat's.

5. *there were always animals dropping in for a chat.* Grahame was probably less than certain of the direction of the third chapter. In the first holograph manuscript, his punctuation differs greatly from the text that was eventually published. Unlike the

first two chapters, which were set down on paper with very few errors, the beginning of "The Wild Wood" has many insertions, along with entire blocks of text hatched out. Variant, in e. 248: The following second half of the paragraph at hand is hatched out:

> But the Mole was left a good deal to himself and one afternoon, when the Rat, in his arm chair before the fire, was alternately dozing & trying over rhymes that wouldn't fit, he formed the resolution to go out by himself & explore the Wild Wood & perhaps strike up an acquaintance with Mr. Badger.

Grahame's text resumes with the new paragraph: "Such a rich chapter it had been . . ."

6. *Purple loosestrife arrived early, shaking luxuriant tangled locks along the edge of the mirror whence its own face laughed back at it.* Purple loosestrife is a flowering weed that grows along riverbanks and sedges. Called *Lythrum salicaria* (family Lythraceæ), it is tall and spiked.

7. *gavotte.* "Dance of the gavots; a name given in Provence to the natives of the Alps; a kind of dance resembling a minuet, but requiring a more lively movement; music to accompany this dance . . . in common time, moderately quick, and consisting of two parts, each of which is repeated, frequently forming one of the movements of the suite" (*OED*).

8. *One member of the company was still awaited; the shepherd-boy for the nymphs to woo, the knight for whom the ladies waited at the window.* Grahame conflates three historical visions of romance in one figure. The first is the shepherd boy from the poems of Theocritus, a Greek bucolic poet who lived in the third century BC. The second is the knight of medieval romances and chivalry. The third is the prince from the Briar Rose / Sleeping Beauty fairy tale, famously depicted in a series of four paintings in 1890 by Pre-Raphaelite painter Edward Burne-Jones.

—J. J.

9. *the prince that was to kiss the sleeping summer back to life and love.* Grahame mixes up his motifs. He puts the word *summer* where one would expect the word *princess* or *beauty*. Both the shepherd boy and the knight remain untouched by female characters.

Geraldine Poss writes:

> Laurence Lerner describes the two ways in which Arcadias can traditionally accommodate sex. The first is to offer fulfillment of desire; the second is to eliminate desire altogether. But if, in the latter case, the characters must make a conscious effort to conquer or deny desire that they actually feel, then they are experiencing the rigors of asceticism. ("An Epic in Arcadia: The Pastoral World of *The Wind in the Willows*," *Children's Literature* 4 [1975]: 80–90)

Rather than dwell on the possibilities of heterosexual symbolism, Grahame moves on to the aesthetics of perfect Nature. The focus on Nature helps prevent women from penetrating the male landscape.

10. *But when meadow-sweet, debonair and odorous in amber jerkin.* A jerkin is a close-fitting jacket, often made of leather, that was worn by men in the sixteenth and seventeenth centuries. The masculine metaphor adds to Grahame's instinct that Mother Nature is actually a Father Nature.

11. *the play was ready to begin.* The reference to the pageantry—the play—of the riverbank preceding the drama of Mole's adventure in this chapter is possibly a Shakespearean allusion: "This wide and uni-

of the water; then the shock of the early plunge,[13] the scamper along the bank, and the radiant transformation of earth, air, and water, when suddenly the sun was with them again, and grey was gold and colour was born and sprang out of the earth once more. They recalled the languorous siesta of hot mid-day, deep in green undergrowth, the sun striking through in tiny golden shafts and spots; the boating and bathing of the afternoon, the rambles along dusty lanes and through yellow cornfields; and the long, cool evening at last, when so many threads were gathered up, so many friendships rounded, and so many adventures planned for the morrow. There was plenty to talk about on those short winter days when the animals found themselves round the fire; still, the Mole had a good deal of spare time on his hands, and so one afternoon, when the Rat in his arm-chair before the blaze was alternately dozing and trying over rhymes that wouldn't fit, he formed the resolution to go out by himself and explore the Wild Wood, and perhaps strike up an acquaintance with Mr. Badger.

It was a cold still afternoon with a hard steely sky overhead, when he slipped out of the warm parlour into the open air. The country lay bare and entirely leafless around him, and he thought that he had never seen so far and so intimately into the insides of things as on that winter day when Nature was deep in her annual slumber and seemed to have kicked the clothes off.[14] Copses, dells, quarries and all hidden places, which had been mysterious mines for exploration in leafy summer, now exposed themselves and their secrets pathetically, and seemed to ask him to overlook their shabby poverty for a while, till they could riot in rich masquerade as before, and trick and entice him with the old deceptions. It was pitiful in a way, and yet cheering—even exhilarating. He was glad that he liked the country undecorated, hard, and stripped of its finery.[15] He had got down to the bare bones of it, and

versal theatre / Presents more woeful pageants than the scene / Wherein we play in" (*As You Like It,* act 2, scene 7, line 139).

12. *Drowsy animals, snug in their holes while the wind and rain were battering at their doors.* Here we see a curious combination of the natural world crossed with a doll's house: The holes have doors.

13. *then the shock of the early plunge.* Swimming, or bathing, in the river is another one of Grahame's recurring themes: Rat has already rescued the luncheon basket and Mole from the river in the previous chapter—and Otter swims into and out of the picnic scene.

14. *he thought that he had never seen so far and so intimately into the insides of things as on that winter day when Nature was deep in her annual slumber and seemed to have kicked the clothes off.* So long as Nature remains asleep, Grahame classifies the gender as female. The moment there is a suggestion of activity—namely, the kicking off of clothes—he neutralizes Nature's gender.

15. *He was glad that he liked the country undecorated, hard, and stripped of its finery.* Rackham's chapter heading for the fourth chapter, "Mr. Badger," might fit better at this point in the text. The drawing is particularly subtle and effective: In a simple winter scene, Mole's tiny footprints lead into the wood.

Arthur Rackham, 1940. Heading illustration for chapter IV.

they were fine and strong and simple. He did not want the warm clover and the play of seeding grasses; the screens of quickset,[16] the billowy drapery of beech and elm seemed best away; and with great cheerfulness of spirit he pushed on towards the Wild Wood, which lay before him low and threatening, like a black reef in some still southern sea.

There was nothing to alarm him at first entry. Twigs crackled under his feet, logs tripped him, funguses on stumps resembled caricatures,[17] and startled him for the moment by their likeness to something familiar and far away; but that was all fun, and exciting. It led him on, and he penetrated to where the light was less, and trees crouched nearer and nearer, and holes made ugly mouths at him on either side.

Everything was very still now. The dusk advanced on him steadily, rapidly, gathering in behind and before; and the light seemed to be draining away like flood-water.

Then the faces began.

It was over his shoulder, and indistinctly, that he first thought he saw a face; a little evil wedge-shaped face, looking out at him from a hole. When he turned and confronted it, the thing had vanished.

He quickened his pace, telling himself cheerfully not to begin imagining things, or there would be simply no end to it. He passed another hole, and another, and another; and then—yes!—no!—yes! certainly a little narrow face, with hard eyes, had flashed up for an instant from a hole, and was gone. He hesitated—braced himself up for an effort and strode on. Then suddenly, and as if it had been so all the time, every hole, far and near, and there were hundreds of them, seemed to possess its face, coming and going rapidly,[18] all fixing on him glances of malice and hatred:[19] all hard-eyed and evil and sharp.

If he could only get away from the holes in the banks, he thought, there would be no more faces.[20] He swung off the path and plunged into the untrodden places of the wood.[21]

Then the whistling began.

16. *quickset.* Live slips or cuttings of plants, set in the ground to grow; especially those of whitethorn or other shrubs of which hedges are made (*OED*).

17. *funguses on stumps resembled caricatures.* Variant, e. 248 and d. 524: Funguses grew on stumps like caricatures.

18. *Then suddenly, and as if it had been so all the time, every hole, far and near, and there were hundreds of them, seemed to possess its face, coming and going rapidly,* Mole has strayed into a dangerous proletarian mob. Scholars have argued that the weasels and stoats of the Wild Wood symbolize the laborers of the Edwardian Era who were becoming a social force. The most popular contemporary literary analogy would be the underworld of Sherlock Holmes's London as depicted by Sir Arthur Conan Doyle. Doyle had already published some forty of the Holmes tales by the time Grahame wrote *The Wind in the Willows*.

But if we go back to the previous literary generation, the Wild Wood can also be read as an homage to the criminal havens that flourished in the time of Charles Dickens. Describing what Dickens calls the "miserable reality" of the urban poor, *Oliver Twist* (1837–1838) launched a movement to abolish the Poor Laws that incarcerated the impoverished.

Long before Dickens, Henry Fielding offered this description of the lodging houses in St. Giles:

"[Poor people of both sexes can find] lodgings there for Twopence a Night: That the Price of a double Bed being no more than Threepence . . . these Houses, all properly accommodated with miserable Beds from the Cellar to the Garret" (*An Enquiry into the Causes of the Late Increase of Robbers and Related Writings*, ed. Malvin R. Zirker [Middletown, CT: Wesleyan University Press, 1988], 143).

Crammed into a small neighborhood,

the St. Giles's Rookery lay between Great Russell Street, St. Giles High Street, and Charlotte Street (later Bloomsbury Street). A stranger like Mole could easily get lost in the maze of narrow lanes and passages that comprised the slum. The worst parts of the rookery were demolished in 1847, when New Oxford Street was driven through the area.

Grahame would have been familiar with the contemporary Holmes mysteries, as well as the underworld integral to *Oliver Twist*. Having witnessed the Pall Mall riots of 1885, and having been attacked by an anarchist at the Bank in 1903, Grahame had firsthand experience with violent political unrest (see preface, page xxviii).

19. *all fixing on him glances of malice and hatred.* Variant, e. 248 and d. 524: all eyeing him with malice and hatred.

20. *If he could only get away from the holes in the banks, he thought, there would be no more faces.* Holes can either be benign or threatening. Mole's discovery of Rat's hole in chapter 1 is benevolent: "As he gazed, something bright and small seemed to twinkle down in the heart of it—vanished—then twinkled once more like a tiny star." It's important to note that Rat's hole sits by itself as a single dwelling, while the hundreds of occupied holes in the Wild Wood are crammed with inhabitants that dart in and out of sight.

21. *He swung off the path and plunged into the untrodden places of the wood.* By straying from the path, Mole runs into an even darker place where his imagination does as much harm to him as the Wild Wooders, if not more. The deepest recesses of the Wild Wood resemble the dilapidated street Tom-all-Alone's in *Bleak House* (1852). Also based on the St. Giles neighborhood in London, Tom-all-Alone's is a dangerous warren for the uninitiated. Dickens's child character Jo resembles the innocent Mole.

Very faint and shrill it was, and far behind him, when first he heard it; but somehow it made him hurry forward. Then, still very faint and shrill, it sounded far ahead of him, and made him hesitate and want to go back. As he halted in indecision it broke out on either side, and seemed to be caught up and passed on throughout the whole length of the wood to its farthest limit. They were up and alert and ready, evidently, whoever they were! And he—he was alone, and unarmed, and far from any help; and the night was closing in.

Then the pattering began.

He thought it was only falling leaves at first, so slight and delicate was the sound of it. Then as it grew it took a regular rhythm, and he knew it for nothing else but the pat-pat-pat of little feet still a very long way off. Was it in front or behind? It seemed to be first one, and then the other, then both. It grew and it multiplied, till from every quarter as he listened anxiously, leaning this way and that, it seemed to be closing in on him. As he stood still to hearken, a rabbit came running hard towards him through the trees. He waited, expecting it to slacken pace, or to swerve from him into a different course. Instead, the animal almost brushed him as it dashed past, his face set and hard, his eyes staring. "Get out of this, you fool, get out!" the Mole heard him mutter as he swung round a stump and disappeared down a friendly burrow.

The pattering increased till it sounded like sudden hail on the dry leaf-carpet spread around him. The whole wood seemed running now, running hard, hunting, chasing, closing in round something or—somebody? In panic, he began to run[22] too, aimlessly, he knew not whither. He ran up against things, he fell over things and into things, he darted under things and dodged round things.[23] At last he took refuge in the deep dark hollow of an old beech tree, which offered shelter, concealment—perhaps even safety, but who could tell? Anyhow, he was too tired to run any further, and could only snuggle down into the dry leaves which had drifted into the

22. *In panic, he began to run.* In the first illustrated edition, Paul Bransom paints a version of the panicked Mole running through the wood pursued by bare branches that seem to snatch at him. In the holes and between the trees, there are outlines of heads with pointed ears; multiple sets of eyes scan his every move. Mole looks to be a cross between a human being and an animal—he runs upright, yet he has threatening claws on his hands that seem to slice the air as he moves. Mole wears nothing else but flat-bottomed boots—an incongruous detail, except that in Grahame's text Rat will soon notice that Mole's new galoshes and cap are missing.

In Shepard's much later edition, Mole is drawn wandering through the woods. He seems mildly calmer in Shepard's incarnation. Though snow pelts at his back, he's wearing an overcoat that seems to hold the weather out. Under the roots of the giant tree that towers over him are tiny, barely perceptible sets of eyes. The beauty of the Shepard edition is that the artist puts opposites together—the cold, inclement weather of Mole alone in the woods is juxtaposed with the cozy warmth of Rat's parlor on the next page.

23. *he darted under things and dodged round things.* Peter Green posits that the setting for the Wild Wood is the Quarry Wood at Cookham Dean. In *Three Men in a Boat; To Say Nothing of the Dog,* Jerome K. Jerome describes the light and dark of the Quarry Wood:

> Dear old Quarry Wood! with your narrow, climbing paths, and little winding glades. . . . How haunted are your shadowy vistas with the ghosts of laughing faces! how from your whispering leaves there softly fall the voices of long ago! (Bristol: J. W. Arrowsmith, 1889, 203)

Paul Bransom's Mole, 1913. "In panic, he began to run."

hollow and hope he was safe for a time. And as he lay there panting and trembling, and listened to the whistlings and the patterings outside, he knew it at last, in all its fullness, that dread thing which other little dwellers in field and hedgerow had encountered here, and known as their darkest moment—that thing which the Rat had vainly tried to shield him from—the Terror of the Wild Wood!

Meantime the Rat, warm and comfortable, dozed by his fireside. His paper of half-finished verses slipped from his knee, his head fell back, his mouth opened, and he wandered by the verdant banks of dream-rivers. Then a coal slipped, the fire crackled and sent up a spurt of flame, and he woke with a start. Remembering what he had been engaged upon, he reached down to the floor for his verses, pored over them for a minute, and then looked round for the Mole to ask him if he knew a good rhyme for something or other.

But the Mole was not there.

He listened for a time. The house seemed very quiet.

Then he called "Moly!" several times, and, receiving no answer, got up and went out into the hall.[24]

The Mole's cap was missing from its accustomed peg. His goloshes, which always lay by the umbrella-stand, were also gone.

The Rat left the house, and carefully examined the muddy surface of the ground outside, hoping to find the Mole's tracks. There they were, sure enough. The goloshes were new, just bought for the winter, and the pimples on their soles were fresh and sharp.[25] He could see the imprints of them in the mud, running along straight and purposeful, leading direct to the Wild Wood.

The Rat looked very grave, and stood in deep thought for a minute or two. Then he re-entered the house, strapped a belt round his waist,[26] shoved a brace of pistols into it, took up a stout cudgel that stood in a corner of the hall, and set off for the Wild Wood at a smart pace.

It was already getting towards dusk when he reached the first fringe of trees and plunged without hesitation into the wood, looking anxiously on either side for any sign of his friend. Here and there wicked little faces popped out of holes, but vanished immediately at sight of the valorous animal, his pistols, and the great ugly cudgel in his grasp; and the whistling and pattering, which he had heard quite plainly on his first entry, died away and ceased, and all was very still. He made his way manfully through the length of the wood, to its

24. *receiving no answer, got up and went out into the hall.* Rat's hole now takes on the appearance of a human house with its hall, umbrella stand, missing goloshes and cap.

25. *The goloshes were new, just bought for the winter, and the pimples on their soles were fresh and sharp.* Rat uses Holmes's deductive reasoning to look for Mole. The "pimples" on Mole's boots are probably one of the more famous details in Grahame's text. At this point, Rat takes on the persona of Sherlock Holmes.

26. *Then he re-entered the house, strapped a belt round his waist.* Though Grahame never mentions the famous literary detective, he successfully imitates him. Payne, Shepard, and Rackham have taken the roles a bit further by dressing the Rat in winter clothes that Sherlock Holmes would have worn. Wyndham Payne indulged his preoccupation with costumes for men and made an illustration of Rat

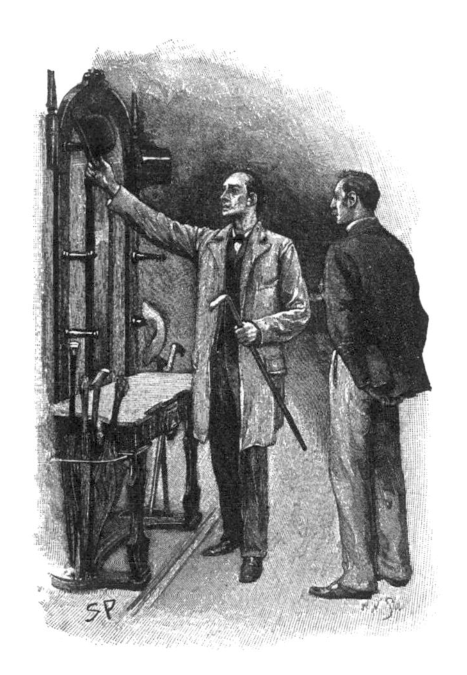

Sidney Paget's "The Crooked Man," 1893. Made for the *Strand* magazine, the quote line used is: "I'll fill a vacant peg, then."

Wyndham Payne, 1927. Rat as Holmes: "The Rat strapped a belt round his waist." The publisher adds the words "The Rat" to the caption, though they do not appear in Grahame's text.

getting dressed in front of his mirrored hat stand. The illustration looks very much like an 1893 Sidney Paget illustration for Arthur Conan Doyle's eighth episode of *The Memoirs of Sherlock Holmes,* titled "The Crooked Man."

Shepard's illustrations of Rat, four years later, are more endearing and disarming because Rat is drawn wearing clothes too snug. Of the seven small drawings about the size of a small medallion, four are of Rat dressed as Sherlock Holmes.

furthest edge; then, forsaking all paths, he set himself to traverse it, laboriously working over the whole ground, and all the time calling out cheerfully, "Moly, Moly, Moly! Where are you? It's me—it's old Rat!"

He had patiently hunted through the wood for an hour or more, when at last to his joy he heard a little answering cry. Guiding himself by the sound, he made his way through the gathering darkness to the foot of an old beech tree, with a hole in it, and from out of the hole came a feeble voice, saying "Ratty! Is that really you?"

The Rat crept into the hollow, and there he found the Mole, exhausted and still trembling. "O Rat!" he cried, "I've been so frightened, you can't think!"

"O, I quite understand," said the Rat soothingly. "You shouldn't really have gone and done it, Mole. I did my best to keep you from it. We river-bankers, we hardly ever come here by ourselves. If we have to come, we come in couples, at least; then we're generally all right. Besides, there are a hundred things one has to know, which we understand all about and you don't, as yet. I mean passwords, and signs, and sayings which have power and effect, and plants you carry in your pocket, and verses you repeat, and dodges and tricks you practise;[27] all simple enough when you know them, but they've got to be known if you're small, or you'll find yourself in trouble. Of course if you were Badger or Otter, it would be quite another matter."[28]

"Surely the brave Mr. Toad wouldn't mind coming here by himself, would he?" inquired the Mole.

"Old Toad?" said the Rat, laughing heartily. "He wouldn't show his face here alone, not for a whole hatful of golden guineas, Toad wouldn't."[29]

The Mole was greatly cheered by the sound of the Rat's careless laughter, as well as by the sight of his stick and his gleaming pistols, and he stopped shivering and began to feel bolder and more himself again.

"Now then," said the Rat presently, "we really must pull ourselves together and make a start for home while there's still a little light left. It will never do to spend the night here, you understand. Too cold, for one thing."

"Dear Ratty," said the poor Mole, "I'm dreadfully sorry, but I'm simply dead beat and that's a solid fact. You *must* let me rest here a while longer, and get my strength back, if I'm to get home at all."

27. *"there are a hundred things one has to know, which we understand all about and you don't, as yet. I mean passwords, and signs, and sayings which have power and effect, and plants you carry in your pocket, and verses you repeat, and dodges and tricks you practise."* This passage suggests that Rat is well versed in pagan spells. Alison Prince likens the pagan spells to the unspoken codes a man like Grahame had to follow to navigate a career in the city:

> As a city man, Grahame . . . was well aware that what is said may mean something quite different to those "in the know." At his level in the bank, he would undoubtedly have encountered Freemasonry, with its rituals and secrecy, but even on a normal day-to-day basis, the offering and accepting of cigarettes and drinks were the equivalent of "the plants you carry in your pocket," and the "dodges and tricks" of the City constituted the basis of normal commercial life, as they still do. (*Kenneth Grahame: An Innocent in the Wild Wood*, 230)

28. *"Of course if you were Badger or Otter, it would be quite another matter."* Badger and Otter can drift socially. See note 2, this chapter, about Badger living comfortably in the dangerous Wild Wood.

29. *"Old Toad?" said the Rat, laughing heartily. "He wouldn't show his face here alone, not for a whole hatful of golden guineas, Toad wouldn't."* A golden guinea is an English gold coin that was used from 1663 until 1813. Valued at 20 shillings, the Royal Mint was authorized to coin gold pieces in 1663 to be used by the Company of Royal Adventurers of England, who were trading with Africa. (According to the *OED*, 21 shillings equals £1.05.) The coins are distinguished by the figure of a little elephant, and were made from gold that came from Guinea. They received the name

"O, all right," said the good-natured Rat, "rest away. It's pretty nearly pitch dark now, anyhow; and there ought to be a bit of a moon later."

So the Mole got well into the dry leaves and stretched himself out, and presently dropped off into sleep, though of a broken and troubled sort; while the Rat covered himself up, too, as best he might, for warmth, and lay patiently waiting, with a pistol in his paw.

When at last the Mole woke up, much refreshed and in his usual spirits, the Rat said, "Now then! I'll just take a look outside and see if everything's quiet, and then we really must be off."

He went to the entrance of their retreat and put his head out. Then the Mole heard him saying quietly to himself, "Hullo! hullo! here—*is*—a—go!"[30]

"What's up, Ratty?" asked the Mole.

"*Snow* is up," replied the Rat briefly; "or rather, *down*. It's snowing hard."

The Mole came and crouched beside him, and, looking out, saw the wood that had been so dreadful to him in quite a changed aspect. Holes, hollows, pools, pitfalls, and other black menaces to the wayfarer were vanishing fast, and a gleaming carpet of faery was springing up everywhere, that looked too delicate to be trodden upon by rough feet. A fine powder filled the air and caressed the cheek[31] with a tingle in its touch, and the black boles of the trees showed up in a light that seemed to come from below.

"Well, well, it can't be helped," said the Rat, after pondering. "We must make a start, and take our chance, I suppose. The worst of it is, I don't exactly know where we are. And now this snow makes everything look so very different."

It did indeed. The Mole would not have known that it was the same wood. However, they set out bravely, and took the line that seemed most promising, holding on to each other and pretending with invincible cheerfulness that they recog-

guinea almost immediately because they were intended to be used in trade with Guinea. The name was extended to later coins of the same intrinsic value. The sovereign, with the same value of 20 shillings, was first issued in 1817 (*OED*).

In 1908, the value of the golden guinea would have increased significantly. A hatful would have been a great fortune.

30. *"Hullo! hullo! here—is—a—go!"* A mess or awkward state of affairs; a term used to mean encountering something astonishing. The snow falling and covering the ground is going to make it difficult for Mole and Rat to return to the riverbank.

31. *A fine powder filled the air and caressed the cheek.* Again we see an ambivalence of species: Is the human narrator's cheek caressed, or have Mole and Rat lost their fur and become human?

nized an old friend in every fresh tree that grimly and silently greeted them, or saw openings, gaps, or paths with a familiar turn in them, in the monotony of white space and black tree-trunks that refused to vary.

An hour or two later—they had lost all count of time—they pulled up, dispirited, weary, and hopelessly at sea, and sat down on a fallen tree-trunk to recover their breath and consider what was to be done. They were aching with fatigue and bruised with tumbles; they had fallen into several holes and got wet through; the snow was getting so deep that they could hardly drag their little legs through it, and the trees were thicker and more like each other than ever. There seemed to be no end to this wood, and no beginning, and no difference in it, and, worst of all, no way out.

"We can't sit here very long," said the Rat. "We shall have to make another push for it, and do something or other. The cold is too awful for anything, and the snow will soon be too deep for us to wade through." He peered about him and considered. "Look here," he went on, "this is what occurs to me. There's a sort of dell down here in front of us, where the ground seems all hilly and humpy and hummocky.[32] We'll make our way down into that, and try and find some sort of shelter, a cave or hole with a dry floor to it, out of the snow and the wind, and there we'll have a good rest before we try again, for we're both of us pretty dead beat. Besides, the snow may leave off, or something may turn up."

So once more they got on their feet, and struggled down into the dell, where they hunted about for a cave or some corner that was dry and a protection from the keen wind and the whirling snow. They were investigating one of the hummocky bits the Rat had spoken of, when suddenly the Mole tripped up and fell forward on his face with a squeal.

"O my leg!" he cried. "O my poor shin!" and he sat up on the snow and nursed his leg in both his front paws.

"Poor old Mole!" said the Rat kindly. "You don't seem to be

32. *"There's a sort of dell down here in front of us, where the ground seems all hilly and humpy and hummocky."* Kenneth Grahame was fascinated by the ancient history of rural England, and particularly the wars between the Romans and the Danes. Though Peter Green posits that the setting for the Wild Wood is the Quarry Wood at Cookham Dean, Kenneth Grahame's use of the word *hummocky* is evidence that the Wild Wood might be set in a more rural part of Berkshire.

> The Berkshire landscape, although generally level, was diversified here and there by hummocks which had been heaped up by the Danes—heaven knows how many centuries ago—and were known in that locality as barrows. One day we were sitting on the summit of a Danish barrow, to take the wind and talk without the disturbance of a roof. (*First Whisper of "The Wind in the Willows,"* 30)

Arthur Rackham, 1940. Rat and Mole as Holmes and Watson. "Rat pondered awhile, and examined the humps and slopes that surrounded them."

having much luck to-day, do you? Let's have a look at the leg. Yes," he went on, going down on his knees to look, "you've cut your shin, sure enough. Wait till I get at my handkerchief, and I'll tie it up for you."

"I must have tripped over a hidden branch or a stump," said the Mole miserably. "O, my! O, my!"

"It's a very clean cut," said the Rat, examining it again attentively. "That was never done by a branch or a stump. Looks as if it was made by a sharp edge of something in metal. Funny!" He pondered awhile, and examined the humps and slopes that surrounded them.[33]

"Well, never mind what done it," said the Mole, forgetting his grammar in his pain. "It hurts just the same, whatever done it."[34]

But the Rat, after carefully tying up the leg with his handkerchief, had left him and was busy scraping in the snow. He scratched and shovelled and explored, all four legs working busily,[35] while the Mole waited impatiently, remarking at intervals, "O, *come* on, Rat!"

Suddenly the Rat cried "Hooray!" and then "Hooray-oo-ray-oo-ray-oo-ray!" and fell to executing a feeble jig in the snow.

"What *have* you found, Ratty?" asked the Mole, still nursing his leg.

"Come and see!" said the delighted Rat, as he jigged on.

The Mole hobbled up to the spot and had a good look.

"Well," he said at last, slowly, "I *see* it right enough. Seen the same sort of thing before, lots of times. Familiar object, I call it. A door-scraper! Well, what of it? Why dance jigs around a door-scraper?"

"But don't you see what it *means*, you—you dull-witted animal?" cried the Rat impatiently.

"Of course I see what it means," replied the Mole. "It simply means that some *very* careless and forgetful person has left his door-scraper lying about in the middle of the Wild Wood,

33. *"Looks as if it was made by a sharp edge of something in metal. Funny!" He pondered awhile, and examined the humps and slopes that surrounded them.* Shepard added a full-color plate to the 100th edition of 1953, of Mole and Rat finding Mr. Badger's door. The illustration is warm and inviting, with a separate image of Mr. Badger arising from bed below them. Readers can see that Badger is waking up before he makes it to the door at the beginning of chapter IV. Instead of carrying a cudgel like Payne's Rat, Shepard's Rat carries a sensible cane. Rackham's treatment of the same scene is more disturbing. There are no reassuring images that the Badger is nearby, only gigantic bare trees, and the "humps and slopes" of snow.

Peter Hunt makes the following correlation between this episode in the Wild Wood and the Sherlock Holmes stories:

> Although intended for, and primarily read by adults, [Sherlock Holmes] ha[s] been appreciated by children and adolescents. . . . Whatever their content in terms of dealing with horror or murder, almost all of the stories are of the first of our narrative types: there is a resolution, which is reinforced by the very powerful symbols of the omnipotent, almost godlike Holmes and the comfortable lodgings of Baker Street, which contrast with the threatening, fog-filled London. Whatever adult problems are "out there," we, standing beside the childlike Dr. Watson, can be confident and comfortable in the knowledge that we can return home unharmed. (*The Wind in the Willows, A Fragmented Arcadia*, 29)

34. *"Well, never mind what done it," said the Mole, forgetting his grammar in his pain. "It hurts just the same, whatever done it."* Mole in his pain reverts to the imperfect grammar of his class. It is unlikely that Rat would ever say "what done it."

just where it's *sure* to trip *everybody* up. Very thoughtless of him, I call it. When I get home I shall go and complain about it to—to somebody or other, see if I don't!"

"O, dear! O, dear!" cried the Rat, in despair at his obtuseness. "Here, stop arguing and come and scrape!" And he set to work again and made the snow fly in all directions around him.

After some further toil his efforts were rewarded, and a very shabby door-mat lay exposed to view.

"There, what did I tell you?" exclaimed the Rat in great triumph.

"Absolutely nothing whatever," replied the Mole, with perfect truthfulness. "Well now," he went on, "you seem to have found another piece of domestic litter, done for and thrown away, and I suppose you're perfectly happy. Better go ahead and dance your jig round that if you've got to, and get it over, and then perhaps we can go on and not waste any more time over rubbish-heaps. Can we *eat* a door-mat? Or sleep under a door-mat? Or sit on a door-mat and sledge home over the snow on it, you exasperating rodent?"

"Do—you—mean—to—say," cried the excited Rat, "that this door-mat doesn't *tell* you anything?"

"Really, Rat," said the Mole, quite pettishly, "I think we'd had enough of this folly. Who ever heard of a door-mat *telling* anyone anything? They simply don't do it. They are not that sort at all. Door-mats know their place."

"Now look here, you—you thick-headed beast," replied the Rat, really angry, "this must stop. Not another word, but scrape—scrape and scratch and dig and hunt round, especially on the sides of the hummocks,[36] if you want to sleep dry and warm to-night, for it's our last chance!"

The Rat attacked a snow-bank beside them with ardour, probing with his cudgel everywhere and then digging with fury; and the Mole scraped busily too, more to oblige the Rat

35. *all four legs working busily.* Rat becomes a quadruped once again.

36. *"scrape and scratch and dig and hunt round, especially on the sides of the hummocks."* The scraping is reminiscent of the Mole's ascent on the first page: "So he scraped and scratched and scrabbled and scrooged and then he scrooged again and scrabbled and scratched and scraped."

than for any other reason, for his opinion was that his friend was getting light-headed.

Some ten minutes' hard work, and the point of the Rat's cudgel struck something that sounded hollow. He worked till he could get a paw through and feel; then called the Mole to come and help him. Hard at it went the two animals, till at last the result of their labours stood full in view of the astonished and hitherto incredulous Mole.

In the side of what had seemed to be a snow-bank stood a solid-looking little door, painted a dark green. An iron bell-pull hung by the side, and below it, on a small brass plate, neatly engraved in square capital letters, they could read by the aid of moonlight

MR. BADGER.[37]

The Mole fell backwards on the snow from sheer surprise and delight. "Rat!" he cried in penitence, "you're a wonder! A real wonder, that's what you are. I see it all now! You argued it out, step by step, in that wise head of yours, from the very moment that I fell and cut my shin, and you looked at the cut, and at once your majestic mind said to itself, 'Door-scraper!' And then you turned to and found the very door-scraper that done it! Did you stop there? No. Some people would have been quite satisfied; but not you. Your intellect went on working. 'Let me only just find a door-mat,' says you to yourself, 'and my theory is proved!' And of course you found your door-mat. You're so clever, I believe you could find anything you liked. 'Now,' says you, 'that door exists, as plain as if I saw it. There's nothing else remains to be done but to find it!' Well, I've read about that sort of thing in books, but I've never come across it before in real life. You ought to go where you'll be properly appreciated. You're simply wasted here, among us fellows. If I only had your head, Ratty———"

"But as you haven't," interrupted the Rat, rather unkindly, "I suppose you're going to sit on the snow all night and *talk?*[38]

37. *MR. BADGER.* In Grahame's holograph manuscript, he simply writes MR BADGER in the middle of the page. Over the years, various publishers have added punctuation or text boxes.

38. *"But as you haven't," interrupted the Rat, rather unkindly, "I suppose you're going to sit on the snow all night and* talk?" Three years after the publication of Peter Green's *Kenneth Grahame: A Biography*, an article appeared in the *Sherlock Holmes Journal* pointing out that Green had completely missed the Holmes sequence:

> Mole is certainly more impressed by his friend's powers than Watson ever was by Holmes's. One feels that the Rat could have been a little kinder to Mole in view of his fulsome praise, but like Holmes he cannot understand why others fail to reason as he does. "I can see nothing," said Watson on one occasion. "On the contrary, Watson," retorted Holmes, "you see everything. You fail, however, to reason from what you see." Rat's "But don't you see what it *means*" and Mole's rejoinder cataloguing the simple fact of the existence of the door-scraper echo Holmes's and Watson's dialogue. Mole is a Watson figure just as Rat is a Holmes figure. "You know my methods, Watson, apply them," we can hear Holmes say, and it is application of Rat's Holmes's-methods that Mole does after the door has been uncovered. The ratiocinative process credited to Rat in Mole's exposition could have come from no other source but Holmes. (David Skene-Melvin, *Sherlock Holmes Journal* [Winter 1962]: 16–17)

Thanks go to Leslie S. Klinger for bringing this article to my attention.

Get up at once and hang on to that bell-pull you see there, and ring hard, as hard as you can, while I hammer!"

While the Rat attacked the door with his stick, the Mole sprang up at the bell-pull, clutched it and swung there, both feet well off the ground, and from quite a long way off they could faintly hear a deep-toned bell respond.

Nancy Barnhart, 1922. Chapter tailpiece for Methuen edition of Mole on a rope.

Note: Chapter IV, "Mr. Badger," is not included in the typed manuscript in the Bodleian, MS. Eng. misc. d. 524. Yet on page 75 at the top there is a note: "To Follow Mr. Badger." The text then starts with chapter V, "Dulce Domum."

IV

Mr. Badger

They waited patiently for what seemed a very long time, stamping in the snow to keep their feet warm. At last they heard the sound of slow shuffling footsteps approaching the door from the inside.[1] It seemed, as the Mole remarked to the Rat, like some one walking in carpet slippers that were too large for him and down at heel; which was intelligent of Mole, because that was exactly what it was.

There was the noise of a bolt shot back, and the door opened a few inches, enough to show a long snout and a pair of sleepy blinking eyes.[2]

"Now, the *very* next time this happens," said a gruff and suspicious voice, "I shall be exceedingly angry. Who is it *this* time, disturbing people on such a night?[3] Speak up!"

"Oh, Badger," cried the Rat, "let us in, please. It's me, Rat, and my friend Mole, and we've lost our way in the snow."

"What, Ratty, my dear little man!" exclaimed the Badger, in quite a different voice.[4] "Come along in, both of you, at once. Why, you must be perished. Well I never! Lost in the snow! And in the Wild Wood, too, and at this time of night! But come in with you."

The two animals tumbled over each other in their eagerness

1. *At last they heard the sound of slow shuffling footsteps approaching the door from the inside.* Variant, e. 248: At last they heard the sound of slow shuffling {footsteps} ~~sounded~~ approaching the door from the inside.

2. *There was the noise of a bolt shot back, and the door opened a few inches, enough to show a long snout and a pair of sleepy blinking eyes.* So far, Badger's is the only house with a lock. He probably keeps the door bolted out of self-preservation. Because he's in the heart of the Wild Wood, he needs protection while he hibernates in winter. Badger is also tentative about opening the door, peeking to see who it is before he gives anyone a chance to enter.

Elspeth Grahame noted that the inhabitants of the high ground in Cookham Dean were mostly Gypsy in origin, and "a lawless brood" (*First Whisper of "The Wind in the Willows,"* 7). If the setting for Badger's house is indeed in the Quarry Wood, Grahame was probably wary of his nomadic neighbors.

3. *"Now, the very next time this happens," said a gruff and suspicious voice, "I shall be exceedingly angry. Who is it* this *time, disturbing people on such a night?"* Badger's tone suggests that he is ready to fight. However, illustrators have not always picked up on Grahame's cue. Wyndham Payne's illustration of Mr. Badger is more decorative than Shepard's and has a more suburban quality. The leaded glass window above the door would have made the door vulnerable to the invading weasels and stoats of the Wild Wood. Contrary to Grahame's text, Mr. Badger has left his door wide open on a blustery night. The house appears to be well lit from within, as if Payne gave Badger's house electricity.

Shepard stayed closer to Grahame's text by drawing a door that cannot be noticed. The mirrorless hat stand reminds us that the gruff Badger does not care about outward appearances. On the far left we see Mole and Rat shivering in the cold, as snow blows down upon them. Shepard had a talent for rendering inclement weather, having also illustrated the blustery day from *Winnie-the-Pooh.*

4. *"What, Ratty, my dear little man!" exclaimed the Badger, in quite a different voice.* Once Badger realizes that his friends are at the door, his manner changes. His tone becomes paternalistic. Both Peter Green and Peter Hunt have written about the influence of the late-nineteenth-century novelist Richard Jeffries on Grahame's settings and characters. According to their scholarship, Mr. Badger bears a close resemblance to two characters in Jeffries's *Amaryllis at the Fair:* The title character's father and her ninety-year-old grandfather, Mr. Iden Sr. Like Mr. Badger, Mr. Iden Jr. is constantly digging in the earth. Though the cuffs of his coat are worn through and there are holes under each arm, and though he plants his own potatoes, Jeffries lets us know that Mr. Iden is not as rustic as he appears:

> "Ah, yes," said Iden, putting his left hand to his chin, a habit of his when thinking, and suddenly quite altering his pronunciation from that of the country folk and labourers amongst whom he dwelt to the correct accent of education. . . .
>
> [Amaryllis] marveled how he could be so rough sometimes, and why he talked to labourers, and wore a ragged coat—he who was so full of wisdom in his other moods, and spoke, and thought and indeed acted as a perfect gentleman. (*Amaryllis at the Fair* [London: Duckworth and Co., 1908], 7)

5. *had probably been on his way to bed when their summons sounded.* Unlike hedgehogs, badgers do not hibernate. They put on weight in the fall months to see them through the lean winter months when earthworms and grubs—typical badger fodder—are less available. They sleep deeply and longer during the winter, and when there is inclement weather they will stay underground for days at a time.

6. *He looked kindly down on them and patted both their heads. "This is not the sort of night for small animals to be out," he said paternally. "I'm afraid you've been up to some of your pranks again, Ratty."* In keeping with the homosocial theme, there are no mother figures to answer to in *The Wind in the Willows*: only the paternalistic mentor. So far we have seen: the river as paternal to Mole, Rat to Mole, Mole and Rat to Toad, and now Badger to Rat and Mole. Mr. Badger's authority must be obeyed.

Peter Hunt writes:

> Badger represents . . . a paternalistic society: he is the old squirearchy whose power lies, literally and metaphorically, beneath the wood, and at the same time he is the uncle/grandfather figure, capable of putting Rat in his place . . . and continually treating the others as children. ("Dialogue and Dialectic," 166)

Wyndham Payne, 1927. Mr. Badger: "Who is it *this* time, disturbing people on such a night?"

to get inside, and heard the door shut behind them with great joy and relief.

The Badger, who wore a long dressing-gown, and whose slippers were indeed very down at heel, carried a flat candlestick in his paw and had probably been on his way to bed when their summons sounded.[5] He looked kindly down on them and patted both their heads. "This is not the sort of night for small animals to be out," he said paternally. "I'm afraid you've been up to some of your pranks again, Ratty.[6] But come along;

come into the kitchen. There's a first-rate fire there, and supper and everything."[7]

He shuffled on in front of them, carrying the light, and they followed him, nudging each other in an anticipating sort of way, down a long, gloomy, and, to tell the truth, decidedly shabby passage, into a sort of a central hall, out of which they could dimly see other long tunnel-like passages branching,[8] passages mysterious and without apparent end. But there were doors in the hall as well—stout oaken comfortable-looking doors. One of these the Badger flung open, and at once they found themselves in all the glow and warmth of a large fire-lit kitchen.[9]

The floor was well-worn red brick, and on the wide hearth burnt a fire of logs,[10] between two attractive chimney-corners tucked away in the wall, well out of any suspicion of draught. A couple of high-backed settles, facing each other on either side of the fire,[11] gave further sitting accommodations for the sociably disposed. In the middle of the room stood a long table of plain boards placed on trestles, with benches down each side.[12] At one end of it, where an arm-chair stood pushed back, were spread the remains of the Badger's plain but ample supper. Rows of spotless plates winked from the shelves of the dresser at the far end of the room, and from the rafters overhead hung hams, bundles of dried herbs, nets of onions, and baskets of eggs. It seemed a place where heroes could fitly feast after victory,[13] where weary harvesters could line up in scores along the table and keep their Harvest Home with mirth and song,[14] or where two or three friends of simple tastes could sit about as they pleased and eat and smoke and talk in comfort and contentment.[15] The ruddy brick floor smiled up at the smoky ceiling; the oaken settles, shiny with long wear, exchanged cheerful glances with each other; plates on the dresser grinned at pots on the shelf, and the merry firelight flickered and played over everything without distinction.

The kindly Badger thrust them down on a settle to toast

7. *"But come along, come into the kitchen. There's a first-rate fire there, and supper and everything."* Mole and Rat are rewarded for their ordeal with food, good company, and safety from the Wild Wood and Wide World beyond. The kitchen and the dishes prepared there are stabilizing factors in *The Wind in the Willows*.

8. *down a long, gloomy, and, to tell the truth, decidedly shabby passage, into a sort of a central hall, out of which they could dimly see other long tunnel-like passages branching.* Badger's house is more like a subterranean city. A whole sequel to *The Wind in the Willows* might have been written in order to untangle its mysterious and ancient history. Instead, the hint of what the place might be adds texture to the book and the authoritative, as well as paternal, role of Mr. Badger.

Mole and Rat follow him toward the warmth of the hearth that is central to Badger's house, just as Badger's house is central to the Wild Wood.

9. *But there were doors in the hall as well—stout oaken comfortable-looking doors. One of these the Badger flung open, and at once they found themselves in all the glow and warmth of a large fire-lit kitchen.* Humphrey Carpenter comments at length on the significance of Badger's kitchen in *Secret Gardens*:

> The kitchen . . . is as universal a symbol as the River. . . . Its appeal is multiple. To Grahame's generation it must also have had William Morris-like hints of an earlier, pre-industrial, and therefore ideal society where distinctions of class seemed unimportant when food was being dealt out, and men of all ranks sat together in the lord's hall or by the yeoman farmer's hearthside. And, more sharply for Edwardian readers than for those of the present day, there is a suggestion too of a return to childhood. Many of Grahame's generation spent

> much of their early life being cared for by domestic servants, and so as small children lingered in the kitchen, watching pots and the joints of meat cooking on the great ranges or spits. (162)

As in *The Wind in the Willows*, kitchen scenes appear in other important works of children's literature of the Victorian and Edwardian eras: Charles Kingsley's *The Water Babies* (1863), George McDonald's *The Princess and Curdie* (1877), Lewis Carroll's *Alice's Adventures in Wonderland* (1865), and Beatrix Potter's *Tailor of Gloucester* (1903) and *Mrs. Tiggy Winkle* (1905).

10. *The floor was well-worn red brick, and on the wide hearth burnt a fire of logs.* As Peter Hunt writes, "There is no . . . ambiguity . . . in Badger's kitchen. Here we come to the apotheosis of Grahame's idyll, in perhaps the most quoted part of *The Wind in the Willows*" ("*The Wind in the Willows*: A Fragmented Arcadia" [New York: Twayne Publishers, 1994], 95).

11. *A couple of high-backed settles, facing each other on either side of the fire.* A settle is a wooden bench with arms, a high solid back, and an enclosed foundation that can be used as a chest. The high back cut down on drafts; a settle placed near the fire would hold the heat. Commonly found in English pubs.

12. *In the middle of the room stood a long table of plain boards placed on trestles, with benches down each side.* The table in Badger's kitchen also resembles the tables in the dining halls of Oxford and Cambridge, where men met to take formal meals. A contemporary example of this kind of dining can be found in any of the dining hall scenes in the *Harry Potter* series.

13. *It seemed a place where heroes could fitly feast after victory.* Carpenter also comments that Badger's kitchen "hints at the mead halls of such poems as *Beowulf.* Grahame says that 'heroes could fitly feast' in it, a phrase whose alliteration faintly recalls Anglo-Saxon verse" (162).

The Badger's kitchen, like the hall in *Beowulf*, is a place of gathering, feasting, and celebration before and after battles and competitions.

> The time had come for the son of Healfdene to enter the hall, because the king himself wished to take part in the banquet. They say that the Danes never carried themselves better, or mustered in greater force in the presence of their sovereign. Men of note took seats on the benches and regaled themselves with the abundance set before them. Hrothgar and his valiant nephew Hrothulf toasted one another with bumpers of mead in the banqueting hall. Heorot was filled with friends. (*Beowulf*, trans. David Wright [New York: Penguin, 1951], 50)

14. *where weary harvesters could line up in scores along the table and keep their Harvest Home with mirth and song.* The term Harvest Home is defined as: "The fact, occasion, or time of bringing home the last of the harvest; the close of harvesting. . . . A shout or song of rejoicing on that occasion. . . . The festival or merry-making to celebrate the successful homing of the corn, called in Scotland 'The Kirn' " (*OED*). Robert Herrick, one of Grahame's favorite poets, in his 1648 poem "The Hock-Cart, or Harvest Home," writes of the traditionally rural, English holiday: "Crowned with the eares of corne, now come, / And, to the pipe, sing harvest home."

15. *where two or three friends of simple tastes could sit about as they pleased and eat and smoke and talk in comfort and contentment.* Nancy Barnhart's illustration of Mr. Badger's fireplace is wonderfully dark. Badger sits before the fire with his paw

Nancy Barnhart, 1922. The interior of Badger's house with caption: "Where two or three friends of simple tastes could sit about as they pleased."

themselves at the fire, and bade them remove their wet coats and boots. Then he fetched them dressing-gowns and slippers, and himself bathed the Mole's shin with warm water and mended the cut with sticking-plaster[16] till the whole thing was just as good as new, if not better. In the embracing light and warmth, warm and dry at last, with weary legs propped up in front of them, and a suggestive clink of plates being arranged on the table behind, it seemed to the storm-driven animals, now in safe anchorage, that the cold and trackless

raised as if telling a story. Badger, Mole, and Rat are bundled up in thick, long-sleeved clothing, evoking ideas of a cold winter night. Barnhart veers from the text, however: there is only one settle and Rat is seated on it, while Mole seems to be sitting on a cushion on the floor.

The editors of both the Methuen and Scribner Barnhart editions abridged Grahame's text in the captions so that readers would not immediately notice that Mole, Rat and Badger were engaging in the adult act of smoking.

Charles Dickens famously included a scene in *Oliver Twist* in which the children are smoking. George Cruikshank emphasized the smoking by including an illustration of the scene. For Dickens, having children "smoking long clay pipes, and drinking spirits, with the air of middle-aged men" in the company of a condoning adult (Fagin) comments on the fact that all is not right in the society of the 1840s.

The delightfulness of Badger's hearth and kitchen—a place of respite reached after the long ordeal—is also autobiographical. As we already know, Grahame loved to take walking tours with his male friends in remote parts of Berkshire, seeking out pre-Saxon dwellings to rent during his excursions. In Grahame's text, Badger's house is so old that no one knows when it was built. It is much like the idiosyncratic buildings Grahame preferred, with their accretion of additions since pre-Roman times.

Barnhart's illustration is dark at the top, leaving the space ambivalent. For all we know, a secret tunnel might be above the mantel. The shadows add depth and mystery to the setting—they give a sense that the subterranean house is an amalgam of pagan, Roman, medieval, and Victorian architecture.

16. *mended the cut with sticking-plaster.* Sticking plaster is the equivalent of an

early Band-Aid and was used by Grahame's generation.

It was "a material for covering and closing superficial wounds, consisting of linen, silk, or any other fabric, spread with an adhesive substance" (*OED*).

17. *where he had been busy laying a repast.* Not often used now, the word repast simply means a meal.

18. *it was that regrettable sort of conversation that results from talking with your mouth full. The Badger did not mind that sort of thing at all, nor did he take any notice of elbows on the table, or everybody speaking at once. As he did not go into Society himself, he had got an idea that these things belonged to the things that didn't really matter.* Manners are usually governed by the enforcers of etiquette, namely women. Badger's bachelor hall with its lax manners is an agreeable environment for Mole and Rat.

19. *(We know of course that he was wrong, and took too narrow a view; because they do matter very much, though it would take too long to explain why.)* This is an aside that Grahame directs at Alastair and other young readers. It is one of the few times that Grahame is didactic.

20. *and he never said, "I told you so," or, "Just what I always said," or remarked that they ought to have done so-and-so, or ought not to have done something else.* Variant, e. 248: and he never said I told you so or just what I always said, or {remarked} ~~told them~~ that they ought.

21. *When supper was really finished at last, and each animal felt that his skin was now as tight as was decently safe, and that by this time he didn't care a hang for anybody or anything.* Unlike Barnhart's illustrations, Shepard's third-of-a-page drawing needs no caption. Mole and Rat face each other,

Wild Wood just left outside was miles and miles away, and all that they had suffered in it a half-forgotten dream.

When at last they were thoroughly toasted, the Badger summoned them to the table, where he had been busy laying a repast.[17] They had felt pretty hungry before, but when they actually saw at last the supper that was spread for them, really it seemed only a question of what they should attack first where all was so attractive, and whether the other things would obligingly wait for them till they had time to give them attention. Conversation was impossible for a long time; and when it was slowly resumed, it was that regrettable sort of conversation that results from talking with your mouth full. The Badger did not mind that sort of thing at all, nor did he take any notice of elbows on the table, or everybody speaking at once. As he did not go into Society himself, he had got an idea that these things belonged to the things that didn't really matter.[18] (We know of course that he was wrong, and took too narrow a view; because they do matter very much, though it would take too long to explain why.)[19] He sat in his arm-chair at the head of the table, and nodded gravely at intervals as the animals told their story; and he did not seem surprised or shocked at anything, and he never said, "I told you so," or, "Just what I always said," or remarked that they ought to have done so-and-so, or ought not to have done something else.[20] The Mole began to feel very friendly towards him.

When supper was really finished at last, and each animal felt that his skin was now as tight as was decently safe, and that by this time he didn't care a hang for anybody or anything,[21] they gathered round the glowing embers of the great wood fire, and thought how jolly it was to be sitting up *so* late, and *so* independent, and *so* full; and after they had chatted for a time about things in general, the Badger said heartily, "Now then! tell us the news from your part of the world. How's old Toad going on?"

"Oh, from bad to worse," said the Rat gravely, while the

Ernest Shepard illustration, 1931.

Mole, cocked up on a settle and basking in the firelight, his heels higher than his head, tried to look properly mournful. "Another smash-up only last week, and a bad one. You see, he will insist on driving himself, and he's hopelessly incapable. If he'd only employ a decent, steady, well-trained animal, pay him good wages, and leave everything to him, he'd get on all right. But no; he's convinced he's a heaven-born driver, and nobody can teach him anything; and all the rest follows."[22]

"How many has he had?" inquired the Badger gloomily.

"Smashes, or machines?" asked the Rat. "Oh, well, after all, it's the same thing—with Toad. This is the seventh. As for the others—you know that coach-house of his? Well, it's piled up—literally piled up to the roof—with fragments of motor-cars, none of them bigger than your hat![23] That accounts for the other six—so far as they can be accounted for."

"He's been in hospital three times," put in the Mole; "and as for the fines he's had to pay,[24] it's simply awful to think of."

"Yes, and that's part of the trouble," continued the Rat.

their posture suggesting that they are overfed and content. Though the illustration is in black and white, there is a sense of glowing around the table, as if there is a fire—but there is no fire, only a white halo around the back of Mr. Badger's chair.

22. *"But no; he's convinced he's a heaven-born driver, and nobody can teach him anything; and all the rest follows."* Though there were plenty of automobile clubs that one could join, or publications that dealt specifically with the care of motor cars, there were no driver's education courses advertised or mentioned in the *Michelin Guide to the British Isles* of 1911. More commonly, those who didn't know how to drive hired male servants—someone to drive and care for the car in the same manner that a footman would have cared for horse and carriage. Male servants were required to obtain a license and renew it at the end of every January.

23. *"you know that coach-house of his? Well, it's piled up—literally piled up to the roof—with fragments of motor-cars, none of them bigger than your hat!"*

> For the adult reader . . . the motor car parodies the song of sirens, which enchanted Ulysses. The Homeric hero took the precaution of plugging his crew's ears with wax, so that he could listen to the song without . . . crashing his boat (Od. 12.175–177). Toad, however, seems as enamored of the crash as he is of the ride. Consequently, just as the sirens' island was festooned with the bones of mariners, so Toad's carriage-house accumulates a mountain of motor-car fragments. (Mary deForest, "*The Wind in the Willows*: A Tale for Two Readers," *Classical and Modern Literature* 10, no. 1 [1989]: 83)

See chapter II, note 32.

24. *"as for the fines he's had to pay."* According to the 1911 edition of the *Michelin Guide to the British Isles,* the fine for breaking the 20 mph speed was £10 for the first offence, £20 for the second, "and in respect of any subsequent offence, to a fine not exceeding £50." The guide adds: "but a person shall not be convicted under this provision for exceeding the limit of speed of twenty miles merely on the opinion of one witness as to the rate of speed."

In a section titled "Offences" in "The Law on Motoring" the *Michelin Guide* states, "In the case of a second or subsequent conviction of an offense . . . a term of three months' imprisonment can be imposed."

The Motor Car Act of 1903–1904 introduced traffic laws, driver's licenses, braking requirements, and registration numbers that could be affixed or painted directly on the car. Red brake lights in the rear of the car were introduced in the same act. However, anyone was allowed to gain a license so long as he or she could fill out a form and pay the fee at the local post office. For the first time, the Motor Car Act made dangerous driving an indictable offence.

In the case of Mr. Toad, he would have been required by law to register each and

— 507 — CIRCULATION

SPEED, PROHIBITION, AND CAUTION SIGNS.

The following are the signs employed on highways :—

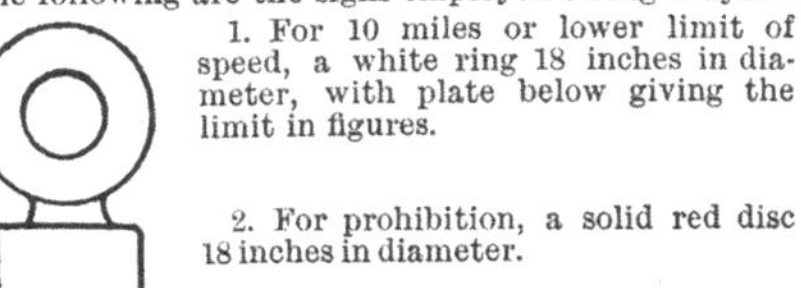

1. For 10 miles or lower limit of speed, a white ring 18 inches in diameter, with plate below giving the limit in figures.

2. For prohibition, a solid red disc 18 inches in diameter.

3. For caution (dangerous corners, cross roads, or precipitous places), a hollow red, equilateral triangle, 18-inch sides.

4. All other notices under the Act to be on diamond-shaped boards.

The above signs are placed on the near side of the road facing the driver, with their lower edges not less than 8 feet from the ground, and about 50 yards from the spot to which they apply.

CIRCULATION.

SPEED LIMITS.

No motor car may be driven at a speed exceeding twenty miles per hour, and, where an order of the Local Government Board has been obtained, at a greater speed than that stated on conspicuous notice boards or plates.

If any person acts in contravention of this provision he shall be liable, on summary conviction in respect of the first offence, to a fine not exceeding £10, and in respect of the second offence to a fine not exceeding £20, and in respect of any subsequent offence, to a fine not exceeding £50, but a person shall not be convicted under this provision for exceeding the limit of speed of twenty miles merely on the opinion of one witness as to the rate of speed.

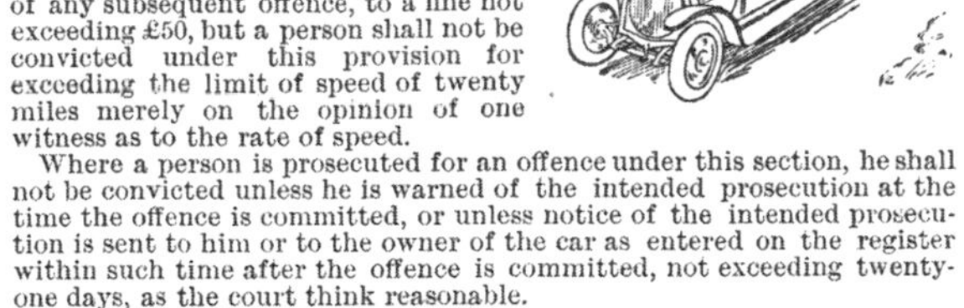

Where a person is prosecuted for an offence under this section, he shall not be convicted unless he is warned of the intended prosecution at the time the offence is committed, or unless notice of the intended prosecution is sent to him or to the owner of the car as entered on the register within such time after the offence is committed, not exceeding twenty-one days, as the court think reasonable.

RULES OF THE ROAD.

(1) On meeting a vehicle approaching from the opposite direction, keep to the left.

(2) On overtaking a vehicle proceeding in the same direction, pass on the right or off side.

(3) Tramcars may be met or overtaken on whichever side of the road is the more safe.

(4) Pass a led horse on the side on which it is led.

(5) Whenever necessary, warning of approach must be given by sounding a horn, bell, or other instrument.

(6) On the request of any police-constable in uniform, or of any person having charge of a horse, or if any such constable or person shall put up

Road signs published in the 1911 *Michelin Guide to the British Isles* (507): "1. For 10 miles or lower limit of speed a white ring 18 inches in diameter, with a plate below giving the limit in figures."

"Toad's rich, we all know; but he's not a millionaire.[25] And he's a hopelessly bad driver, and quite regardless of law and order. Killed or ruined—it's got to be one of the two things, sooner or later. Badger! we're his friends—oughtn't we to do something?"

The Badger went through a bit of hard thinking. "Now look here!" he said at last, rather severely; "of course you know I can't do anything *now?"*

His two friends assented, quite understanding his point. No animal, according to the rules of animal-etiquette, is ever expected to do anything strenuous, or heroic, or even moderately active during the off-season of winter. All are sleepy—some actually asleep. All are weather-bound, more or less; and all are resting from arduous days and nights, during which every muscle in them has been severely tested, and every energy kept at full stretch.

"Very well then!" continued the Badger. "*But*, when once the year has really turned, and the nights are shorter, and halfway through them one rouses and feels fidgety and wanting to be up and doing by sunrise, if not before—*you* know!———"

Both animals nodded gravely. *They* knew!

"Well, *then*," went on the Badger, "we—that is, you and me and our friend the Mole here—we'll take Toad seriously in hand. We'll stand no nonsense whatever. We'll bring him back to reason, by force if need be. We'll *make* him be a sensible Toad. We'll—you're asleep, Rat!"

"Not me!" said the Rat, waking up with a jerk.

"He's been asleep two or three times since supper," said the Mole, laughing.[26] He himself was feeling quite wakeful and even lively, though he didn't know why. The reason was, of course, that he being naturally an underground animal by birth and breeding, the situation of Badger's house exactly suited him and made him feel at home; while the Rat, who slept every night in a bedroom the windows of which opened on a breezy river, naturally felt the atmosphere still and oppressive.

every one of his motorcars with the authorities. If he registered his cars in Reading, Berkshire, his license plate or registration mark would have begun with the code of the district—BL—, the code for motorcars registered in Reading, Berkshire; or, if Toad registered his motorcars in the town of Oxford, in Oxfordshire, his registration would have begun with "BW—" (*Michelin Guide to the British Isles*, 1911, 498–502).

25. *"Yes, and that's part of the trouble," continued the Rat. "Toad's rich, we all know, but he's not a millionaire."* Toad has inherited his money from his father, who, most likely, was an industrialist. Though he is endowed with a fortune, it is quickly dissipating due to his compulsions and excesses. Peter Hunt says, "Toad represents rebel, Nouveau riche, fantasist, and 'personification of the spoiled infant' ("Language and Class," 166).

26. *"We'll* make *him be a sensible Toad. We'll—you're asleep, Rat!"*

"Not me!" said the Rat, waking up with a jerk.

"He's been asleep two or three times since supper," said the Mole, laughing. This exchange is reminiscent of a passage in chapter 7, "A Mad Tea Party," of *Alice's Adventures in Wonderland*: "The Dormouse had closed its eyes by this time, and was going off into a doze; but, on being pinched by the Hatter, it woke up with a little shriek, and went on."

Variant, e. 248: "He's been asleep ~~off & on~~ {two or three times} since supper," said the Mole, laughing.

"Well, it's time we were all in bed," said the Badger, getting up and fetching flat candlesticks. "Come along, you two, and I'll show you your quarters. And take your time tomorrow morning—breakfast at any hour you please!"

He conducted the two animals to a long room that seemed half bedchamber and half loft. The Badger's winter stores,[27] which indeed were visible everywhere, took up half the room—piles of apples, turnips, and potatoes, baskets full of nuts, and jars of honey; but the two little white beds on the remainder of the floor looked soft and inviting,[28] and the linen on them, though coarse, was clean and smelt beautifully of lavender;[29] and the Mole and the Water Rat, shaking off their garments in some thirty seconds, tumbled in between the sheets in great joy and contentment.

In accordance with the kindly Badger's injunctions, the two tired animals came down to breakfast very late next morning,[30] and found a bright fire burning in the kitchen, and two young hedgehogs sitting on a bench at the table, eating oatmeal porridge out of wooden bowls. The hedgehogs dropped their spoons, rose to their feet, and ducked their heads respectfully as the two entered.[31]

"There, sit down, sit down," said the Rat pleasantly, "and go on with your porridge. Where have you youngsters come from? Lost your way in the snow, I suppose?"

"Yes, please, sir," said the elder of the two hedgehogs respectfully. "Me and little Billy here, we was trying to find our way to school—mother *would* have us go, was the weather ever so—and of course we lost ourselves, sir, and Billy he got frightened and took and cried, being young and faint-hearted.[32] And at last we happened up against Mr. Badger's back door, and made so bold as to knock, sir, for Mr. Badger he's a kind-hearted gentleman, as everyone knows———"[33]

"I understand," said the Rat, cutting himself some rashers from a side of bacon, while the Mole dropped some eggs into a

27. *The Badger's winter stores.* Rackham's illustration of this subject lacks the mystery and depth that Barnhart achieves. Badger's house, as we know, is underground, and Rackham's rendering of its interior is well lit. The house is also wooden and square, as if recently built by a carpenter—missing the point that the house is actually ancient, and full of annexes and tunnels. The corners in Badger's home are always more intriguing when left dark so that the reader can't make out what's in the shadows. One of the few places Rackham remains ambivalent about size is in his rendering of the vegetables. Is the lower left corner full of watermelon-sized cucumbers or giant leeks?

28. *but the two little white beds on the remainder of the floor looked soft and inviting.* Once again, the Barnhart edition abbreviates the caption: "but the two little white beds on the remainder of the floor looked soft and inviting" has been changed to: "The two little white beds looked soft and inviting." Despite the changes, this is one of Barnhart's more successful drawings—one Shepard echoed at the end of the first chapter, when Mole goes up the stairs at Rat's house. Barnhart's bedchamber looks like an underground den. The space above and beyond the inviting beds is dark and seems to be rounded—as if dug out by a burrowing animal. The stores are mysterious, yet Mole—who is leading the reader into the illustration with his candle—makes the scene inviting. The Mole, like Badger, is most comfortable when underground. He is completely safe from the storm above in the Wild Wood.

29. *and the linen on them, though coarse, was clean and smelt beautifully of lavender.* Dried or fresh, both the stems and flowers of lavender will retain their scent indefinitely. Stored with linen or clothes that are not to be used for awhile, lavender is a common

Arthur Rackham, 1940. "The Badger's winter stores, which indeed were visible everywhere, took up half the room." Peter Hunt has pointed out that in a world where food is substituted for sex, this moment is sexually charged. Badger has left his guests to sleep in a room loaded with food.

remedy to preserve fabrics from moths. The plant *Lavendula vera* is a native of southern Europe and north Africa. Though tricky to grow in colder climates, lavender is prolific and common in southern England. Lavender can be used in sachets, carried in pockets, or folded up with laundry. Before the twentieth century, the word "lavender" was often used as the word "launder," in literature, for the plant was used for cleaning and washing (*OED*).

With the great stores of Badger's house, the anticipated respite, and the lavender, Grahame might have been making an allusion to John Keats's poem "The Eve of St. Agnes," which is based on *Romeo and Juliet*:

> *And still she slept an azure-lidded sleep,*
> *In blanched linen, smooth, and*
> *lavendered,*
> *While he from forth the closet brought a*
> *heap*
> *Of candied apple, quince, and plum, and*
> *gourd,*
> *With jellies soother than the creamy curd,*
> *And lucent syrups, tinct with cinnamon;*
> *Manna and dates, in argosy transferred*
> *From Fez; and spiced dainties, everyone*
> *From silken Samarcand to cedared*
> *Lebanon.*
> (Stanza 30, lines 262–70)

30. *In accordance with the kindly Badger's injunctions, the two tired animals came down to breakfast very late next morning.* In his holograph manuscript, e. 248, Grahame leaves a space between the beginning of this paragraph and the last.

In the section titled "Food and Kitchens" in *The Wind in the Willows: A Fragmented Arcadia*, Peter Hunt notes:

> It does not take a great deal of analysis to see that all these meals mark—celebrate—the end of an adventure, a wholesome, comforting, and satisfying resolution. Where the adventure has been particularly trying [such as being lost in the Wild Wood during a snowstorm] there is a *second* meal, to make the resolution even stronger, as with the porridge, bacon, fried ham, and eggs for breakfast at Badger's house. (93)

31. *The hedgehogs dropped their spoons, rose to their feet, and ducked their heads respectfully as the two entered.* "Hedgehog: named for its preference for hedgerows and from its pig-like snout, a hedgehog can roll itself into a ball with its spines bristling in all directions" (*OED*). Hedgehogs are used as croquet balls in *Alice's Adventures in Wonderland.* Another contemporary literary hedgehog is Beatrix Potter's *The Tale of Miss Tiggy-Winkle* (1905).

32. *"Yes, please, sir," said the elder of the two hedgehogs respectfully. "Me and little Billy here, we was trying to find our way to school—mother* would *have us go, was the weather ever so—and of course we lost ourselves, sir, and Billy he got frightened and took and cried, being young and faint-hearted."* Peter Hunt posits that the hedgehogs are the children of the poor (Hunt, "Language and Class," 163). Therefore, they jump to their feet and assume servile behavior when Mole and Rat enter. Hunt also points out that interactions between the classes are linguistically marked, such as in this passage.

In early Victorian England, many children, especially the poor, never went to school. Subsequently, much of the population remained illiterate. Wealthy families usually employed a nanny and a governess until the male children were old enough to attend Eton or Rugby. Daughters were kept at home and taught piano, singing, and sewing. In 1870, however, Parliament passed the Forster's Education Act, requiring that all children ages five through twelve attend school. However, since tuition was required by many of these schools, not all children were able to attend. Instead, many worked as laborers to help support their families. Often smaller children attended a dame school—a common term for a small private school that taught young children to read and write when they were too young to work. Usually run by an elderly woman, dame schools were not regulated and often did little more than fill the role of babysitter. Not until 1891, when the schools' pence fee was abolished, were all children throughout Britain required and able to attend. Schools accommodated as many as seventy to eighty children in a class.

On another note, Grahame emphasizes that it was the mother who sent the hedgehogs out into the storm, not the father.

33. *"And at last we happened up against Mr. Badger's back door, and made so bold as to knock, sir, for Mr. Badger he's a kind-hearted gentleman, as everyone knows———" Though quite reserved like Mr. Badger, Kenneth Grahame attracted children and animals. In First Whisper of "The Wind in the Willows," Elspeth Grahame describes her husband's interactions with the children who lived in his town:*

> Two small brothers always spoke of him as the "Sugar Man," and on their mother asking them, Why?—as she never knew he gave them any sweets—replied: "Because he is the very sweetest man we ever knew!" and if he were out, when they came to visit us, they would shed tears. (33–34)

Nancy Barnhart, 1922. "The two little white beds looked soft and inviting."

saucepan. "And what's the weather like outside? You needn't 'sir' me quite so much," he added.

"O, terrible bad, sir, terrible deep the snow is," said the hedgehog. "No getting out for the likes of you gentlemen to-day."

"Where's Mr. Badger?" inquired the Mole, as he warmed the coffee-pot before the fire.

"The master's gone into his study, sir," replied the hedgehog, "and he said as how he was going to be particular busy this morning, and on no account was he to be disturbed."

This explanation, of course, was thoroughly understood by

Wyndham Payne, 1927. "The hedgehogs ducked their heads respectfully."

every one present. The fact is, as already set forth, when you live a life of intense activity for six months in the year, and of comparative or actual somnolence for the other six, during the latter period you cannot be continually pleading sleepiness when there are people about or things to be done. The excuse gets monotonous. The animals well knew that Badger, having eaten a hearty breakfast, had retired to his study and settled himself in an arm-chair with his legs up on another and a red cotton handkerchief over his face, and was being "busy" in the usual way at this time of the year.[34]

34. *The animals well knew that Badger, having eaten a hearty breakfast, had retired to his study and settled himself in an arm-chair with his legs up on another and a red cotton handkerchief over his face, and was being "busy" in the usual way at this time of the year.* This small scene of Badger taking his catnap bears a strong resemblance to a scene in Richard Jeffries's *Amaryllis at the Fair*. After the midday meal, and a workday that starts at 4:00 AM, Mr. Iden always naps in front of the fire.

Paul Bransom, 1913. Otter: "Through the Wild Wood and the Snow." Bransom captures the Otter's playful nature: Otters like to play in the snow as much as in the water.

The front-door bell clanged loudly, and the Rat, who was very greasy with buttered toast, sent Billy, the smaller hedgehog, to see who it might be. There was a sound of much stamping in the hall, and presently Billy returned in front of the Otter, who threw himself on the Rat with an embrace and a shout of affectionate greeting.

"Get off!" spluttered the Rat, with his mouth full.

"Thought I should find you here all right," said the Otter cheerfully. "They were all in a great state of alarm along River Bank when I arrived this morning. Rat never been home all night—nor Mole either—something dreadful must have happened, they said; and the snow had covered up all your tracks, of course. But I knew that when people were in any fix they mostly went to Badger, or else Badger got to know of it somehow, so I came straight off here, through the Wild Wood and the snow![35] My! it was fine, coming through the snow as the red sun was rising and showing against the black tree-trunks! As you went along in the stillness, every now and then masses of snow slid off the branches suddenly with a flop! making you jump and run for cover. Snow-castles and snow-caverns had sprung up out of nowhere in the night—and snow bridges, terraces, ramparts—I could have stayed and played with them for hours.[36] Here and there great branches had been torn away by the sheer weight of the snow, and robins perched and hopped on them in their perky conceited way, just as if they had done it themselves. A ragged string of wild geese passed overhead, high on the grey sky, and a few rooks whirled over the trees,[37] inspected, and flapped off homewards with a disgusted expression; but I met no sensible being to ask the news of. About halfway across I came on a rabbit sitting on a stump, cleaning his silly face with his paws. He was a pretty scared animal when I crept up behind him and placed a heavy forepaw on his shoulder. I had to cuff his head once or twice to get any sense out of it at all.[38] At last I managed to extract from him that Mole had been seen in the Wild Wood last night by one of them. It was the talk of the burrows, he said, how Mole, Mr. Rat's particular friend, was in a bad fix; how he had lost his way, and 'They' were up and out hunting, and were chivvying him round and round.[39] 'Then why didn't any of you *do* something?' I asked. 'You mayn't be blest with brains, but there are hundreds and hundreds of you, big, stout fellows, as fat as butter, and your burrows running in all directions,[40] and

35. *through the Wild Wood and the snow!* Chapter IV is a favorite with illustrators because there is so much going on. Loss and recovery of home, inclement weather, scenes of comfort, and plenty of entrances and exits. Shortly after the lost hedgehogs come to stay, Otter, a sleuth very much like Holmes's brother, Mycroft, arrives. Bransom's illustration of the Otter heading into the Wild Wood in search of Mole and Rat shows a natural otter. He is not at all anthropomorphized, and could pass as one of the dreaded weasels if he needed to.

At the end of the chapter, Shepard's illustration of Mole, Rat, and Otter shows a fully dressed Mole and Rat walking upright as if on human legs, and the sleek Mr. Otter crawling animal-like, with only a scarf tied around his neck. On the cover of Shepard's 1953 edition, all the riverbankers are fully dressed as sporting English gentlemen, while Otter swimming up to the boat remains in the nude.

36. *ramparts—I could have stayed and played with them for hours.* A rampart is a broad embankment raised as a fortification and usually surrounded by a parapet.

37. *a few rooks whirled over the trees.* Rooks are black, raucous-voiced, gregarious birds about the size and color of the related American crow (*OED*).

38. *I had to cuff his head once or twice to get any sense out of it at all.* Variant, e. 248: I had to cuff his head once or twice to get any sense out of ~~him~~ it at all.

Once again, Grahame shows the rabbits as a prolific and stupid species in the social order. The rabbit in question had to be cuffed in order to communicate. He's also expendable, remaining an "it" in Grahame's final text, rather than a "him."

you could have taken him in and made him safe and comfortable, or tried to, at all events.' 'What, *us?*' he merely said: '*do* something? us rabbits?' So I cuffed him again and left him. There was nothing else to be done. At any rate, I had learnt something; and if I had had the luck to meet any of 'Them' I'd have learnt something more—or *they* would."

"Weren't you at all—er—nervous?" asked the Mole, some of yesterday's terror coming back to him at the mention of the Wild Wood.

"Nervous?" The Otter showed a gleaming set of strong white teeth as he laughed. "I'd give 'em nerves if any of them tried anything on with me.[41] Here, Mole, fry me some slices of ham, like the good little chap you are. I'm frightfully hungry, and I've got any amount to say to Ratty here. Haven't seen him for an age."

So the good-natured Mole, having cut some slices of ham, set the hedgehogs to fry it, and returned to his own breakfast, while the Otter and the Rat, their heads together, eagerly talked river-shop,[42] which is long shop and talk that is endless, running on like the babbling river itself.

A plate of fried ham had just been cleared and sent back for more, when the Badger entered, yawning and rubbing his eyes, and greeted them all in his quiet, simple way, with kind enquiries for every one. "It must be getting on for luncheon time," he remarked to the Otter. "Better stop and have it with us. You must be hungry, this cold morning."

"Rather!" replied the Otter, winking at the Mole. "The sight of these greedy young hedgehogs stuffing themselves with fried ham makes me feel positively famished."

The hedgehogs, who were just beginning to feel hungry again after their porridge, and after working so hard at their frying, looked timidly up at Mr. Badger, but were too shy to say anything.[43]

"Here, you two youngsters be off home to your mother," said the Badger kindly. "I'll send some one with you to show

39. *"'They' were up and out hunting, and were chivvying him round and round."* To chivvy is to tease or annoy with consistent petty attacks.

40. *"You mayn't be blest with brains, but there are hundreds and hundreds of you, big, stout fellows, as fat as butter, and your burrows running in all directions."* A. A. Milne repeats the motif of the inbred rabbit's prolific family in *Winnie-the-Pooh*: " 'Hush!' said Eeyore in a terrible voice to all Rabbit's friends-and-relations, and 'Hush!' they said hastily to each other all down the line, until it got to the last one of all" (110).

41. *"Nervous?" The Otter showed a gleaming set of strong white teeth as he laughed. "I'd give 'em nerves if any of them tried anything on with me."* Variant, e. 248: "Nervous?" The Otter showed a gleaming set of strong white teeth as he laughed. "I'd give 'em nerves if any {~~one~~ of them} tried anything on me."

Peter Hunt writes about the friendship between Mole and Otter:

> Little critical attention has been given to Otter, but in his few appearances his role is clearly established. He turns up in the Wild Wood, unafraid of anyone and "knowing all the paths"; he appears obliquely in "The Piper at the Gates of Dawn" as a worried parent, and has a walk-on part at Toad's final party, where it is difficult not to see him in an immaculate dinner jacket. Although [Fred] Inglis [*The Promise of Happiness: Value and Meaning in Children's Fiction* (Cambridge: Cambridge University Press, 1981), 199] thinks that the four main characters "translate readily" into the suave clubland heroes of the superior thriller-writers of the day, John Buchan and "Sapper," as well as those of P. G. Wodehouse—a view that the character Otter certainly might well be seen

as substantiating—it seems as though Grahame saw him not as middle class but as genuinely upper class. Were the passing hedgehogs to call him "my Lord" one would not be surprised. (*The Wind in the Willows : A Fragmented Arcadia*, 57)

42. *So the good-natured Mole, having cut some slices of ham, set the hedgehogs to fry it, and returned to his own breakfast, while the Otter and the Rat, their heads together, eagerly talked river-shop.* Like Mole and Badger being burrowing animals, Rat and Otter are natural companions because they have the river habitat in common. Hunt continues his observations about Otter:

> So the question turns to how Grahame describes the "friendship" between Mole and Otter; the answer can only be evasively. . . . Grahame uses language as a mask as much as a means of communication. . . . Otter is friendly, but his greeting has a certain dismissive air about it. . . . Mole, of course, *does* know his place (which is at least slightly above that of the hedgehogs). . . . The Mole is . . . accepted into this desirable society, but only on limited terms, initially at least. (Ibid., 58)

43. *The hedgehogs, who were just beginning to feel hungry again after their porridge, and after working so hard at their frying, looked timidly up at Mr. Badger but were too shy to say anything.* In the May 1908 edition of *The Merry Thought*, in her column "Nature Notes," Naomi Stott makes the following observation about a visiting hedgehog:

> One drenching afternoon a hedgehog was seen out the nursery front door at Mayfield, + he was persuaded to spend the afternoon indoors. A large open box made a good run for him, + in it he found a feast of minced beef, + brown bread + he soon unrolled, + began to smack his lips, as he tucked in + ate all he could as fast as he could. After tea he was given his freedom, + walked off across the lawn into the bushes, + we have not seen him since.

you the way. You won't want any dinner to-day, I'll be bound."

He gave them sixpence apiece and a pat on the head, and they went off with much respectful swinging of caps and touching of forelocks.[44]

Presently they all sat down to luncheon together.[45] The Mole found himself placed next to Mr. Badger, and, as the other two were still deep in river-gossip from which nothing could divert them, he took the opportunity to tell Badger how comfortable and home-like it all felt to him. "Once well underground," he said, "you know exactly where you are. Nothing can happen to you, and nothing can get at you. You're entirely your own master, and you don't have to consult anybody or mind what they say. Things go on all the same overhead, and you let 'em, and don't bother about 'em. When you want to, up you go, and there the things are, waiting for you."

The Badger simply beamed on him. "That's exactly what I say," he replied. "There's no security, or peace and tranquillity, except underground. And then, if your ideas get larger and you want to expand—why, a dig and a scrape, and there you are! If you feel your house is a bit too big, you stop up a hole or two, and there you are again![46] No builders, no tradesmen, no remarks passed on you by fellows looking over your wall, and, above all, no *weather*. Look at Rat, now. A couple of feet of flood water, and he's got to move into hired lodgings; uncomfortable, inconveniently situated, and horribly expensive. Take Toad. I say nothing against Toad Hall; quite the best house in these parts, *as* a house. But supposing a fire breaks out—where's Toad? Supposing tiles are blown off, or walls sink or crack, or windows get broken—where's Toad? Supposing the rooms are draughty—I *hate* a draught myself—where's Toad? No, up and out of doors is good enough to roam about and get one's living in; but underground to come back to at last—that's my idea of *home*!"

The Mole assented heartily; and the Badger in consequence

44. *touching of forelocks.* The hedgehogs are from the peasant class. Traditionally, peasants did not wear hats, and to show respect to the landed gentry, they pulled forelocks instead of tipping hats.

45. *Presently they all sat down to luncheon together.* This is the third feast for Mole and Rat in chapter IV. Remember, they arrived the night before, had dinner, and then ate breakfast when they awoke.

46. *"If you feel your house is a bit too big, you stop up a hole or two, and there you are again!"* Peter Green writes that Mr. Badger's elaborate house was possibly based on the tunnels and subterranean rooms built by the Fifth Duke of Portland, because the details of something called the Druce Case were often in the papers during 1907. William John Cavendish Bentinck-Scott, the Fifth Duke of Portland (1800–1879), who lived at the family seat of Welbeck Abbey in Nottinghamshire, spent a considerable part of his life constructing strategies to prevent people from seeing him. He stopped using the ornate abbey (most recently used by the Ministry of Defense [1943–2005] to train the British Army) and decided quite literally to go underground. Nicknamed "the Gentle Mole," the Fifth Duke of Portland hired hundreds of local men to dig some fifteen miles of interconnected tunnels.

Among the many large subterranean rooms, there were several libraries, a billiard room large enough to hold a dozen full-sized tables, and a roller-skating rink that doubled as a ballroom, with capacity for two thousand dancers. The space, with its arched ceiling and glass bull's-eye windows, measured 55 by 22 yards, making it the largest floor in England at the time that was unobstructed by support beams. The subterranean estate also included a gigantic stable and riding school with a glass top that was designed for the exercise

got very friendly with him. "When lunch is over," he said, "I'll take you all round this little place of mine. I can see you'll appreciate it. You understand what domestic architecture ought to be, you do."

After luncheon, accordingly, when the other two had settled themselves into the chimney-corner and had started a heated argument on the subject of *eels*, the Badger lighted a lantern and bade the Mole follow him. Crossing the hall, they passed down one of the principal tunnels, and the wavering light of the lantern gave glimpses on either side of rooms both large and small, some mere cupboards, others nearly as broad and imposing as Toad's dining-hall. A narrow passage at right angles led them into another corridor, and here the same thing was repeated. The Mole was staggered at the size, the extent, the ramifications of it all; at the length of the dim passages, the solid vaultings of the crammed store-chambers, the masonry everywhere, the pillars, the arches, the pavements. "How on earth, Badger," he said at last, "did you ever find time and strength to do all this? It's astonishing!"

"It *would* be astonishing indeed," said the Badger simply, "if I *had* done it. But as a matter of fact I did none of it—only cleaned out the passages and chambers, as far as I had need of them. There's lots more of it, all round about. I see you don't understand, and I must explain it to you. Well, very long ago,[47] on the spot where the Wild Wood waves now, before ever it had planted itself and grown up to what it now is, there was a city—a city of people, you know. Here, where we are standing, they lived, and walked, and talked, and slept, and carried on their business. Here they stabled their horses and feasted, from here they rode out to fight or drove out to trade. They were a powerful people, and rich, and great builders. They built to last, for they thought their city would last for ever."

"But what has become of them all?" asked the Mole.

"Who can tell?" said the Badger. "People come—they stay for a while, they flourish, they build—and they go.[48] It is their

of horses. The extensive tunnels were lit with gas jets placed at intervals, and it was possible for people to walk three abreast in many of the passages. One tunnel was built to come above ground near the train station of Warsop, and was wide enough to accommodate a horse-drawn carriage. The Fifth Duke of Portland had it built in order to escape being detected by the local population whenever he came from or went to London—an idea that is very much in keeping with Badger's many tunnels that lead beyond the edge of the Wild Wood.

In 1907, G. H. Druce brought Welbeck Abbey and the eccentricities of the Fifth Duke of Portland into the limelight when he laid an outrageous claim on the estate. The story is as follows:

A dealer of secondhand furniture by the name of Thomas Charles Druce died at the age of seventy-one in 1864, and was interred in the family vault at Highgate Cemetery. In 1896, Anna Maria Druce, the widow of Druce's son Walter, insisted that she was a duchess and that her father-in-law's funeral had been staged; that the coffin was full of lead weights instead of a corpse. She claimed that Thomas Charles Druce had never existed but was a persona created by the Fifth Duke of Portland. According to newspaper accounts, Anna Maria claimed that the Duke invented an alter ego of Thomas Druce in order to experience the ordinary life of a tradesman. She also claimed that a tunnel had been dug from the house in Cavendish Square to Druce's furniture shop so that he could swap personas en route from one place to the other. After Anna Maria Druce's death, her son G. H. Druce continued the allegations, making a claim on the duke's estate and Welbeck Abbey in 1907. In order to settle the case the presiding judge ordered the grave exhumed. When the coffin was opened it indeed contained a body. Mrs. Druce, it seems, had fabricated the story.

Arthur Rackham, 1940. Tour of Badger's House.
"Crossing the hall, they passed down one of the principal tunnels."

The dukedom lapsed when Victor Frederick William Cavendish-Bentinck, the Ninth Duke of Portland, died in 1990 without leaving an heir (sources: Green, *Kenneth Grahame: A Biography,* 282; R. H. Gretton, *A Modern History of the English People, 1880–1922*, 2nd ed. [London: Longmans Green, 1930], 733; Charles Archard, *The Portland Peerage Romance* [London: Greening & Co., Ltd, 1907]). Further reading: Mick Jackson, *The Underground Man* (New York: Morrow, 1997).

47. *"I see you don't understand, and I must explain it to you. Well, very long ago . . ."* One of Kenneth Grahame's favorite authors was Thomas Hughes, who is best known for Tom Brown's School Days, the first of a series of novels intended to show young gentlemen what it would be like to attend boarding school and university. One of Hughes's other books that Grahame read and reread is *The Scouring of the White Horse; or, The Long Vacation Ramble of a London Clerk* (Cambridge: Macmillan & Co., 1859). Grahame refers to it in a letter to Austin Purves when inviting him to visit Berkshire in December 1913.

Set in rural Berkshire and Oxfordshire, the book chronicles a visit from a London clerk "in black velvet," no doubt, who has come to the festival held on White Horse Hill on September 17 and 18, 1857.

Much in the style of *The Rime of the Ancient Mariner* as well as chapter IX of *The Wind in the Willows,* "Wayfarers All," *The Scouring of the White Horse* has a scene where an elderly man catches the attention of a young London clerk. The man tells the clerk the history of the battles and people around the White Horse. Like Mr. Badger's house, White Horse Hill near Uffington is layered with the evidence of previous civilizations.

> "I can't make up my mind about this castle," he went on, without noticing me: "On two sides it looks like a regular Roman castrum, and Roman remains are found scattered about; but then the other sides are clearly not Roman. The best antiquaries who have noticed it call it Danish. On the whole, I think it must have been occupied in succession by the lords of the country for the time being; and each successive occupier has left his mark more or less plainly." (*The Scouring of the White Horse*, 58–69)

48. *People come—they stay for a while, they flourish, they build—and they go."* Badger is the one static character in *The Wind in the Willows*. Like his digs in the Wild Wood that have always been there, he undergoes no personal transformation, while those around him change; nor does he travel far beyond his home, which stays the same.

way. But we remain. There were badgers here, I've been told, long before that same city ever came to be. And now there are badgers here again. We are an enduring lot, and we may move out for a time, but we wait, and are patient, and back we come. And so it will ever be."

"Well, and when they went at last, those people?" said the Mole.

"When they went," continued the Badger, "the strong winds and persistent rains took the matter in hand, patiently, ceaselessly, year after year. Perhaps we badgers too, in our small way, helped a little—who knows? It was all down, down, down, gradually—ruin and levelling and disappearance. Then it was all up, up, up, gradually, as seeds grew to saplings, and saplings to forest trees, and bramble and fern came creeping in to help. Leaf-mould rose and obliterated, streams in their winter freshets brought sand and soil to clog and to cover, and in course of time our home was ready for us again, and we moved in. Up above us, on the surface, the same thing happened. Animals arrived, liked the look of the place, took up their quarters, settled down, spread, and flourished. They didn't bother themselves about the past—they never do; they're too busy.[49] The place was a bit humpy and hillocky,[50] naturally, and full of holes; but that was rather an advantage. And they don't bother about the future, either—the future when perhaps the people will move in again—for a time—as may very well be. The Wild Wood is pretty well populated by now; with all the usual lot, good, bad, and indifferent—I name no names. It takes all sorts to make a world. But I fancy you know something about them yourself by this time."

"I do indeed," said the Mole, with a slight shiver.

"Well, well," said the Badger, patting him on the shoulder, "it was your first experience of them, you see. They're not so bad really; and we must all live and let live. But I'll pass the word around to-morrow, and I think you'll have no further

49. *They didn't bother themselves about the past—they never do; they're too busy.* Grahame is making a reference to the working poor—those, such as the rabbits, who prolifically reproduce and are so busy with family life there is little room for contemplation, let alone lessons of history. The blighted woods—representing any depressed urban area—made the riverbankers of Grahame's class anxious. Those who neither knew history nor cared about the future were doomed to encroach on land made sacred by history. Grahame, like Hughes and Jeffries, was anxious about the disappearance of Roman and pagan roads and landmarks.

50. *The place was a bit humpy and hillocky.* A little hill, or a small mound or heap of earth or stones; a hump, bump, protuberance, or prominence on any surface (*OED*).

trouble. Any friend of *mine* walks where he likes in this country, or I'll know the reason why!"[51]

When they got back to the kitchen again, they found the Rat walking up and down, very restless. The underground atmosphere was oppressing him and getting on his nerves, and he seemed really to be afraid that the river would run away if he wasn't there to look after it. So he had his overcoat on, and his pistols thrust into his belt again. "Come along, Mole," he said anxiously, as soon as he caught sight of them. "We must get off while it's daylight. Don't want to spend another night in the Wild Wood again."

"It'll be all right, my fine fellow," said the Otter. "I'm coming along with you, and I know every path blindfold;[52] and if there's a head that needs to be punched, you can confidently rely upon me to punch it."

"You really needn't fret, Ratty," added the Badger placidly. "My passages run further than you think, and I've bolt-holes to the edge of the wood in several directions,[53] though I don't care for everybody to know about them. When you really have to go, you shall leave by one of my short cuts. Meantime, make yourself easy, and sit down again."

The Rat was nevertheless still anxious to be off and attend to his river, so the Badger, taking up his lantern again, led the way along a damp and airless tunnel that wound and dipped, part vaulted, part hewn through solid rock, for a weary distance that seemed to be miles. At last daylight began to show itself confusedly through tangled growth overhanging the mouth of the passage; and the Badger, bidding them a hasty good-bye, pushed them hurriedly through the opening, made everything look as natural as possible again, with creepers, brushwood, and dead leaves, and retreated.[54]

They found themselves standing on the very edge of the Wild Wood. Rocks and brambles and tree-roots behind them, confusedly heaped and tangled; in front, a great space of quiet fields, hemmed by lines of hedges black on the snow, and, far

51. *"Any friend of* mine *walks where he likes in this country, or I'll know the reason why!"* Badger plays the role of country squire to those who live in the Wild Wood. Those who get out of line will have to answer to him—an encounter that would prove most unpleasant.

52. *"It'll be all right, my fine fellow," said the Otter. "I'm coming along with you, and I know every path blindfold."* If Otter is from the aristocracy, it is also possible that he is a gentleman adventurer, such as Sir Richard Burton, who traveled extensively through the 1890s, and was multilingual. Otter might also be an allusion to T. E. Lawrence, another Oxford man. Like the well-educated traveler, Otter is a useful guide because he has had plenty of experience adapting himself to different customs and cultures.

53. *"My passages run further than you think, and I've bolt-holes to the edge of the wood in several directions."* Bolt-hole has two definitions that fit with Grahame's text: 1) Any unknown hole by which a person makes his way in or out of the house; and 2) the hole from which the rabbit makes its escape (*OED*). Badger has many different hidden exits and entrances to his house. According to Leslie S. Klinger, Sherlock Holmes has at least five refuges in different parts of London where he is able to stop and assume a disguise. Badger's secret bolt-holes have a similar purpose. Though Mr. Badger governs the Wild Wood, he is able to avoid other inhabitants by having the run of the entire underground—a tactic of evasion that Holmes is able to employ when he needs to.

54. *and the Badger, bidding them a hasty good-bye, pushed them hurriedly through the opening, made everything look as natural as possible again, with creepers, brushwood, and dead leaves, and retreated.* Mr. Badger similarly appears and disappears in the first chapter when he comes upon the river-

ahead, a glint of the familiar old river, while the wintry sun hung red and low on the horizon. The Otter, as knowing all the paths, took charge of the party, and they trailed out on a bee-line for a distant stile.[55] Pausing there a moment and looking back, they saw the whole mass of the Wild Wood, dense, menacing, compact, grimly set in vast white surroundings; simultaneously they turned and made swiftly for home, for firelight and the familiar things it played on, for the voice, sounding cheerily outside their window, of the river that they knew and trusted in all its moods, that never made them afraid with any amazement.

As he hurried along, eagerly anticipating the moment when he would be at home again among the things he knew and liked, the Mole saw clearly that he was an animal of tilled field and hedge-row, linked to the ploughed furrow, the frequented pasture, the lane of evening lingerings, the cultivated garden-plot. For others the asperities, the stubborn endurance, or the clash of actual conflict, that went with Nature in the rough; he must be wise, must keep to the pleasant places in which his lines were laid and which held adventure enough, in their way, to last for a lifetime.

Nancy Barnhart, 1922. Methuen edition, tailpiece of hedgehogs.

bankers' picnic. While Grahame pays attention to lush foliage, surrounding Mole and Rat in Nature, Badger plays an opposite role by usually camouflaging himself with dead foliage.

55. *and they trailed out on a bee-line for a distant stile.* A stile is an arrangement of steps, or rungs, built to allow passage over or through a fence, one person at a time, while forming a barrier to the passage of sheep or cattle.

56. *As he hurried along, eagerly anticipating the moment when he would be at home again among the things he knew and liked, the Mole saw clearly that he was an animal of tilled field and hedge-row.* Though Mole has made a riverside home with Rat, his visit with Badger reaffirms that he is a native of underground. The tilled field and hedgerow is a reference to land that is carefully plowed and cultivated to raise crops. It is also a metaphor for the cultivation of the mind, as well as growing friendships between Mole and the other riverbankers. His sudden realization that living on the river with Rat estranges him to his true nature catalyzes the longing that will bring him back to the abandoned Mole End in chapter V.

Hedgerow: A row of bushes forming a hedge, with the trees growing in it; a line of hedge (*OED*). Hedgerows are common in England and are used to divide property and fields. According to Andrew Martins's *Collins Rambler's Guide to the Chilterns & Ridgeway* (London: HarperCollins, 2001), a hedgerow can be dated by how many species of plants are growing within it. Two species in a hedgerow, normally hawthorn and blackthorn, date the hedge to the nineteenth century. A new species invades a hedge at the rate of approximately one every century. Add a half-dozen species such as hazel, maple, ash, elm, quickset, and dogwood and the hedge may date from the thirteenth or fourteenth century.

V

Dulce Domum[1]

The sheep ran huddling together against the hurdles, blowing out thin nostrils and stamping with delicate forefeet, their heads thrown back and a light steam rising from the crowded sheep-pen into the frosty air, as the two animals hastened by in high spirits, with much chatter and laughter. They were returning across country[2] after a long day's outing with Otter, hunting and exploring on the wide uplands where certain streams tributary to their own River[3] had their first small beginnings; and the shades of the short winter day were closing in on them, and they had still some distance to go. Plodding at random across the plough, they had heard the sheep and had made for them; and now, leading from the sheep-pen, they found a beaten track that made walking a lighter business, and responded, moreover, to that small inquiring something which all animals carry inside them, saying unmistakably, "Yes, quite right; *this* leads home!"

"It looks as if we were coming to a village," said the Mole somewhat dubiously, slackening his pace, as the track, that had in time become a path and then had developed into a lane, now handed them over to the charge of a well-metalled road.[4] The animals did not hold with villages, and their own high-

1. *Dulce Domum.* Dulce: pleasant, charming, sweet; dulcis: a sweet drink. Domum: house, building, home, household.

"Dulce Domum" literally translates to "Home Sweet Home"; Grahame probably used Latin to avoid both a cliché and the sentimental notion of what it means to return home after a long adventure. The title, seldom used today, was prominent in two other nineteenth-century works: chapter 41 of Sir Walter Scott's *Waverly* is called "Dulce Domum" and poet T. W. H. Crosland (1865–1924) wrote a poem based on Dulce Domum, which contains the following lines:

This house is full of strange memories,
Wondrously strange, God-wot—
Dim wraiths of woes and ghosts of
tragedies,
But they disturb her not . . .

Painters approached the subject as well. The Pre-Raphaelite John Atkinson Grimshaw (1836–1893) considered his painting *Dulce Domum*, completed in 1885, to be one of his best. He wrote on the back of it: "mostly painted under great difficulties."

The Royal Academy in London compared Grimshaw's work with Crosland's poem. "If *Dulce Domum* is remarkable for its detail it is also remarkable for the balance which Grimshaw struck between describing a scene and evoking its emotional content." Likewise, Grahame goes to great lengths to render Mole's home both strange and familiar, a potent combination that makes the brief return on Christmas emotionally resonant.

The Royal Academy noted of the poem: "Crosland imagined this young woman—the subject of the painting—to be unperturbed to the point of blankness, but this seems like a misreading of the painting. The young woman listens to the music played on the piano behind her and we are invited to imagine her reveries, moods and daydreams as they shift and change with the music." Grahame's Mole, like many of the English of his era, tries to keep his emotions in check. But the sweetness of memory pulls him home—to come in out of the cold.

"Dulce Domum" is also the holiday song of Winchester College. The song is said to have been composed (in Latin) by a boy at St. Mary's College, Winchester, who was sitting through a detention for misconduct during Whitsun, or White Sunday, celebrated in late May, on the seventh Sunday after Easter. Supposedly he was tied to a pillar as part of his punishment. On the evening before the start of the Whitsun holidays, "the master, scholars, and choristers of the above college walk in procession round the 'pillar,' chanting the six stanzas of the song." In the March 1796 number of the *Gentleman's Magazine,* a translation, signed "J. R.," was given:

Domum, domum, dulce domum!
Dulce, dulce dulce domum!
Dulce domum resonemus.
Home, home, joyous home!
Joyous, joyous, joyous home!
Hurrah for joyous home!

—J. J.

Grahame occasionally used Latin titles for chapters and stories. "Non Libri Sed Liberi" and "Deus Terminus" appeared in *Punch* and later in Grahame's collection *Pagan Papers*. "Exit Tyrannus" and "Lusisti Satis" appeared in *The Golden Age* (1895), and "Dies Irae" and "Mutabile Semper" appeared in *Dream Days*.

2. *They were returning across country.* Chapter V opens with Mole and Rat on yet another great walk. According to Peter Green, the habit of walking "collected a surprising number of literary devotees, ranging from Hazlitt to Sir Leslie Stephen" (*Kenneth Grahame: A Biography,* 118). In his early story "The Romance of the Rail" Grahame writes about the significance of walking while trains and automobiles were transforming remote places into easy destinations: "annihilate time and space as you may, a man's stride remains the true standard of distance; an eternal and unalterable scale."

Though Paul Bransom contributed no illustrations for Chapter V in the 1913 illustrated edition, Wyndham Payne made three full-page drawings for the 1927 edition.

Payne often captures the unspoken homosocial/homosexual element in *The Wind in the Willows* by the dress of the characters. Mole and Rat are particularly dapper as they tramp arm in arm through the countryside. But notice that Mole is now wearing the jacket Rat wore in the previous chapter. According to Payne's illustration, Mole has gained a wardrobe by living with the Rat. By the fifth chapter, they have gone on five adventures and have become a couple. Adding to the text, Payne interprets Mole and Rat as companions who like to accessorize. They both sport different-patterned ascots, hats, riding pants, shoes with spats, and varying canes.

Payne's Mole and Rat, 1927. "They were returning across country."

ways, thickly frequented as they were, took an independent course, regardless of church, post office, or public-house.[5]

"Oh, never mind!" said the Rat. "At this season of the year they're all safe indoors by this time, sitting round the fire; men, women, and children, dogs and cats and all. We shall slip through all right, without any bother or unpleasantness, and we can have a look at them through their windows if you like, and see what they're doing."

The rapid nightfall of mid-December had quite beset the little village as they approached it on soft feet over a first thin

3. *hunting and exploring on the wide uplands where certain streams tributary to their own River.* The uplands are the rural districts or parts of the country outside of towns; an area or stretch of high ground (*OED*). Most likely, Mole and Rat have been walking on the Berkshire Downs, perhaps the Ridgeway—the higher one wanders, the more remote the area becomes. Thomas Hardy, famous for his descriptions of country life, often uses the word *upland* when describing rural England: "Their present speed on the upland being by no means slow" (*Tess of the d'Urbervilles*, 1891); "It was as old-fashioned as it was small, and it rested in the lap of an undulating upland adjoining the North Wessex downs" (*Jude the Obscure*,1895).

4. *slackening his pace, as the track, that had in time become a path and then had developed into a lane, now handed them over to the charge of a well-metalled road.* The track Grahame is referring to might be the Ridgeway:

> This road which we are upon is . . . one of the oldest roads in England. How far it once extended, or who made it, no man knows; but you may trace it away there along the ridge of the downs as far as you can see, and in fact there are still some sixty miles of it left. But they won't be left long, I fear. . . . miles of it have been ploughed up within my memory. God meant these downs, Sir, for sheep walks, and so our fathers left them. (Hughes, *The Scouring of the White Horse*, 62–63)

Well-metalled road: Because the wheels of carts were made of iron, roads were often paved with metal in order to support the weight of traffic. Mole and Rat are now on a paved road. The term can also be a reference to railways (*OED*).

5. *The animals did not hold with villages, and their own highways, thickly frequented as they were, took an independent course, regardless of church, post office, or public-house.* A

fall of powdery snow. Little was visible but squares of a dusky orange-red on either side of the street, where the firelight or lamplight of each cottage overflowed through the casements into the dark world without. Most of the low latticed windows were innocent of blinds, and to the lookers-in from outside, the inmates, gathered round the tea-table, absorbed in handiwork, or talking with laughter and gesture, had each that happy grace which is the last thing the skilled actor shall capture—the natural grace which goes with perfect unconsciousness of observation.[6] Moving at will from one theatre to another, the two spectators, so far from home themselves, had something of wistfulness in their eyes as they watched a cat being stroked, a sleepy child picked up and huddled off to bed, or a tired man stretch and knock out his pipe on the end of a smouldering log.

But it was from one little window, with its blind drawn down, a mere blank transparency on the night, that the sense of home and the little curtained world within walls—the larger stressful world of outside Nature shut out and forgotten—most pulsated. Close against the white blind hung a bird-cage, clearly silhouetted, every wire, perch, and appurtenance distinct and recognisable, even to yesterday's dull-edged lump of sugar.[7] On the middle perch the fluffy occupant, head tucked well into feathers, seemed so near to them as to be easily stroked, had they tried; even the delicate tips of his plumped-out plumage pencilled plainly on the illuminated screen. As they looked, the sleepy little fellow stirred uneasily, woke, shook himself, and raised his head. They could see the gape of his tiny beak as he yawned in a bored sort of way, looked round, and then settled his head into his back again, while the ruffled feathers gradually subsided into perfect stillness. Then a gust of bitter wind took them in the back of the neck, a small sting of frozen sleet on the skin woke them as from a dream,[8] and they knew their toes to be cold and their legs tired, and their own home distant a weary way.

public house is an inn usually licensed for the supply of ale, wines, and spirits. It also provides food, lodging, and refreshment for travelers or members of the general public. Today public houses are known as pubs. The most famous pub for Kenneth Grahame is The Red Lion (see chapter VI, note 31). Dozens of pubs called The Red Lion exist today throughout England.

6. *Most of the low latticed windows were innocent of blinds, and to the lookers-in from outside, the inmates, gathered round the tea-table, absorbed in handiwork, or talking with laughter and gesture, had each that happy grace which is the last thing the skilled actor shall capture—the natural grace which goes with perfect unconsciousness of observation.* There are echoes in this scene of Charles Dickens's *A Christmas Carol*:

> A light shone from the window of a hut, and swiftly they advanced towards it. Passing through the wall of mud and stone, they found a cheerful company assembled round a glowing fire. An old, old man and woman, with their children and their children's children, and another generation beyond that, all decked out gaily in their holiday attire. The old man, in a voice that seldom rose above the howling of the wind upon the barren waste, was singing them a Christmas song. (London: Chapman & Hall, 1843, 98)

In addition to Dickens, it is likely that Grahame would also have been familiar with Robert Louis Stevenson's *An Inland Voyage* (London: C. Kegan Paul & Co., 1874). An account of boating inland from Antwerp to Brussels—through industrial towns as well as villages—Stevenson's text contains vivid descriptions of the dangers of navigating a river full of steamers, barges, and other river traffic. Every evening as it grows dark, Stevenson and company pass through the different villages, looking for accommodation and provisions. The weather is often inclement, and the reader senses that the travelers are outsiders—strangers in a foreign land, much like Rat and Mole in this unknown village. "At last, a second gateway admitted us to the town itself. Lighted windows looked gladsome, whiffs of comfortable cookery came abroad upon the air" (79).

> Meantime the heaven wept upon our heads; and the windows grew brighter as the night increased in darkness. We trudged in and out of La Fere streets; we saw shops, and private houses where people were copiously dining; we saw stables where carters' nags had plenty of fodder and clean straw. (81)

Peter Green thanks David Daiches for pointing out that Stevenson was fond of peering through windows to observe human domesticity (Green, *Kenneth Grahame: A Biography*, 286).

7. *Close against the white blind hung a birdcage, clearly silhouetted, every wire, perch, and appurtenance distinct and recognizable, even to yesterday's dull-edged lump of sugar.* Of all the early illustrators, only E. H. Shepard draws the window scenes in the village. The birdcage in the window is a Dickensian motif that occurs three times in the text of *The Wind in the Willows*—the Gypsy cart of chapter II, the window in the village of chapter V, and in the jail, belonging to the jailer's daughter, in chapter VIII. (See chapter II, note 30, and chapter VIII, note 6.)

Shepard's Mole and Rat reflect Grahame's idea that they are watching a form of theater. However, rather than looking at the stage in a theater, Shepard draws the scene as if Mole and Rat are at the cinema—an art form then coming into its own in both the United States and England in 1931 when Shepard was at work. Beginning in 1930, American films in particular went from being silent black-and-white productions to having sound and full color. According to Ian Wojcik-Andrews's *Children's Films: History, Ideology, Pedagogy, Theory*, in the United States, between 1930 and 1945, 80 million people—over half the population—went to the movies every week. Though Grahame remained wary of technology until his death, his "illuminated screen" predicts an art form destined to become common. Shepard certainly picks up on this notion. It's as though Grahame had an inkling that the Victorian audiences entertained by books, and the immediacy of theater, will someday be replaced by a new generation that completely embraces the cinema.

8. *Then a gust of bitter wind took them in the back of the neck, a small sting of frozen sleet on the skin woke them as from a dream.* Grahame gives Mole and Rat skin instead of fur at this instant. For a moment they are fully human rather than animal.

E. H. Shepard's "illuminated screen" of a window scene in the village. Shepard has left the space above Mole and Rat's noses blank so that the white space effectively looks like steam. The illustrator also is successful in capturing the human-to-riverbanker size ratio. The door to the human cottage is huge, with the handle half the height of Mole or Rat at the top of the drawing.

Once beyond the village, where the cottages ceased abruptly, on either side of the road they could smell through the darkness the friendly fields again; and they braced themselves for the last long stretch, the home stretch, the stretch that we know is bound to end, some time, in the rattle of the door-latch, the sudden firelight, and the sight of familiar things greeting us as long-absent travellers from far oversea. They plodded along steadily and silently, each of them thinking his own thoughts. The Mole's ran a good deal on supper, as it was pitch-dark, and it was all a strange country for him as far as he knew, and he was following obediently in the wake of the Rat, leaving the guidance entirely to him. As for the Rat, he was walking a little way ahead, as his habit was, his shoulders humped, his eyes fixed on the straight grey road in front of him; so he did not notice poor Mole when suddenly the summons reached him, and took him like an electric shock.

We others, who have long lost the more subtle of the physical senses, have not even proper terms to express an animal's inter-communications with his surroundings, living or otherwise, and have only the word "smell," for instance, to include the whole range of delicate thrills which murmur in the nose of the animal night and day, summoning, warning, inciting, repelling. It was one of these mysterious fairy calls from out the void that suddenly reached Mole in the darkness, making him tingle through and through with its very familiar appeal,[9] even while yet he could not clearly remember what it was. He stopped dead in his tracks, his nose searching hither and thither in its efforts to recapture the fine filament, the telegraphic current,[10] that had so strongly moved him. A moment, and he had caught it again; and with it this time came recollection in fullest flood.

Home! That was what they meant, those caressing appeals, those soft touches wafted through the air, those invisible little hands pulling and tugging, all one way! Why, it must be quite close by him at that moment, his old home that he had hurriedly forsaken and never sought again, that day when he first found the river! And now it was sending out its scouts and its messengers to capture him and bring him in. Since his escape on that bright morning he had hardly given it a thought, so absorbed had he been in his new life, in all its pleasures, its surprises, its fresh and captivating experiences. Now, with a rush of old memories, how clearly it stood up before him, in the darkness! Shabby indeed, and small and poorly furnished, and yet his, the home he had made for himself,[11] the home he had been so happy to get back to after his day's work. And the home had been happy with him, too, evidently, and was missing him, and wanted him back, and was telling him so,

9. *It was one of these mysterious fairy calls from out the void that suddenly reached Mole in the darkness, making him tingle through and through with its very familiar appeal.* Kenneth Grahame's generation was fascinated not only with neo-paganism but with spiritualism and séances and evidence of the unseen. In 1908, while Grahame was writing *The Wind in the Willows*, his friend Graham Robertson was also busy writing a child's play, *Pinkie and the Fairies*. The play opened on December 19, 1908, at His Majesty's Theatre in London. (It was dedicated to "A Woman of Five," Marion "Binky" Melville, the daughter of his neighbor, painter Arthur Melville, to whom he dedicated many of his works.) Like the childlike Mole, only the children in Robertson's play are capable of detecting the unseen influence, or spell, of the fairies. In Mole's case, the fairy call is the spell of home.

Robertson discussed the role of fairies in his and Grahame's relationship:

> Another tie was our mutual interest in Fairyland, upon the manners and customs of which country we could both speak with authority; and we could discuss the points of view, proclivities and antecedents of its inhabitants with all the passionate earnestness displayed by really sensible people when speaking of Latest Quotations, Lunch Scores or Cup Finals.
>
> For us the Folk of Fairy Tale were genuine historical characters and we always tried to enter sympathetically into their feelings. (Chalmers, *Kenneth Grahame,* 98)

10. *his nose searching hither and thither in its efforts to recapture the fine filament, the telegraphic current.* Though he was a technophobe, Grahame never hesitated to use technological metaphors. However, by the time Grahame was born, the telegraph was

through his nose,[12] sorrowfully, reproachfully, but with no bitterness or anger; only with plaintive reminder that it was there, and wanted him.

The call was clear, the summons was plain. He must obey it instantly, and go. "Ratty!" he called, full of joyful excitement, "hold on! Come back! I want you, quick!"

"Oh, *come* along, Mole, do!" replied the Rat cheerfully, still plodding along.

"*Please* stop, Ratty!" pleaded the poor Mole, in anguish of heart. "You don't understand! It's my home, my old home! I've just come across the smell of it, and it's close by here, really quite close. And I *must* go to it, I must, I must! Oh, come back, Ratty! Please, please come back!"

The Rat was by this time very far ahead, too far to hear clearly what the Mole was calling, too far to catch the sharp note of painful appeal in his voice. And he was much taken up with the weather, for he too could smell something—something suspiciously like approaching snow.

"Mole, we mustn't stop now, really!" he called back. "We'll come for it to-morrow, whatever it is you've found. But I daren't stop now—it's late, and the snow's coming on again, and I'm not sure of the way! And I want your nose, Mole, so come on quick,[13] there's a good fellow!" And the Rat pressed forward on his way without waiting for an answer.

Poor Mole stood alone in the road, his heart torn asunder, and a big sob gathering, gathering, somewhere low down inside him, to leap up to the surface presently, he knew, in passionate escape. But even under such a test as this his loyalty to his friend stood firm. Never for a moment did he dream of abandoning him. Meanwhile, the wafts from his old home pleaded, whispered, conjured, and finally claimed him imperiously. He dared not tarry longer within their magic circle. With a wrench that tore his very heartstrings he set his face down the road and followed submissively in the track of the Rat, while faint, thin little smells, still dogging his retreating

already an antiquated invention. According to the *OED*, the original apparatus was invented by Claude Chappe (1763–1805) in France in 1792 for transmitting messages across distances. It consisted of an upright post with movable arms. Signals were made in a prearranged code with the arms. In 1805, Lord Horatio Nelson famously telegraphed to his fleet, "England expects every man will do his duty" before the battle of Trafalgar, where Napoleon's fleet was defeated with a loss of twenty-two Spanish and French ships.

11. *Now, with a rush of old memories, how clearly it stood up before him, in the darkness! Shabby indeed, and small and poorly furnished, and yet his, the home he had made for himself,* Grahame intends Mole to be the poorest of the riverbankers; Mole depends on Rat for shelter, clothing, food, and introductions to riverbanker society. More significantly, Mole is introduced to the palatial Toad Hall and Mr. Badger's ancient burrow—each in its own way the polar opposite of the humble Mole End.

12. *And the home had been happy with him, too, evidently, and was missing him, and wanted him back, and was telling him so, through his nose.* The personification of Mole's home—along with the many other homes Grahame writes into *The Wind in the Willows*—means that each dwelling plays a silent character.

13. *"I'm not sure of the way! And I want your nose, Mole, so come on quick."* One of Mole's distinguishing talents that none of the other riverbankers possess is a keen sense of smell. Moles by nature, of course, being nearly blind, are able to find their way both under and above ground by smell.

nose, reproached him for his new friendship and his callous forgetfulness.

With an effort he caught up to the unsuspecting Rat, who began chattering cheerfully about what they would do when they got back, and how jolly a fire of logs in the parlour would be, and what a supper he meant to eat; never noticing his companion's silence and distressful state of mind. At last, however, when they had gone some considerable way further, and were passing some tree-stumps at the edge of a copse that bordered the road, he stopped and said kindly, "Look here, Mole old chap, you seem dead tired. No talk left in you, and your feet dragging like lead. We'll sit down here for a minute and rest. The snow has held off so far, and the best part of our journey is over."

The Mole subsided forlornly on a tree-stump and tried to control himself,[14] for he felt it surely coming. The sob he had fought with so long refused to be beaten. Up and up, it forced its way to the air, and then another, and another, and others thick and fast; till poor Mole at last gave up the struggle, and cried freely and helplessly and openly, now that he knew it was all over and he had lost what he could hardly be said to have found.

The Rat, astonished and dismayed at the violence of Mole's paroxysm of grief, did not dare to speak for a while. At last he said, very quietly and sympathetically, "What is it, old fellow? Whatever can be the matter? Tell us your trouble, and let me see what I can do."

Poor Mole found it difficult to get any words out between the upheavals of his chest that followed one upon another so quickly and held back speech and choked it as it came.[15] "I know it's a—shabby, dingy little place," he sobbed forth at last, brokenly: "not like—your cosy quarters—or Toad's beautiful hall—or Badger's great house—but it was my own little home—and I was fond of it—and I went away and forgot all about it—and then I smelt it suddenly—on the road, when I called and you wouldn't listen, Rat—and everything came back to me with a rush—and I *wanted* it!—O dear, O dear!—

14. *The Mole subsided forlornly on a tree-stump and tried to control himself.* In "Romantic Echoes in the Willows," Richard Gillin writes about the influences of Keats, Coleridge, and Wordsworth on Kenneth Grahame's prose. Positing that Grahame's primarily Victorian readers would be familiar with the central poems of the Romantic canon—"To Autumn," "Ode to a Nightingale," "The Rime of the Ancient Mariner," and *The Prelude*—Gillan writes, of Mole's forlorn moment and return to Mole End with Rat:

> The distinctive representation of the transcendent moment coincides with a more general difference between Grahame and his predecessors in his representation of psychic growth. . . . He returns Mole to his burrow in "Dulce Domum" to underscore the love of familiar domesticity. . . .
>
> In a characteristically Romantic identification of moonlight with the imagination, which makes the influence of Wordsworth and Coleridge most palpable, Mole sees his "old haunts" in other "raiment" and "new apparel." As soon as the moon rises, the world loses its disturbing ambiguities: "all washed clean of mystery and terror, all radiant again as by day." (Richard Gillin, "Romantic Echoes in The Willows," *Children's Literature* 16 [1988]: 171)

15. *Poor Mole found it difficult to get any words out between the upheavals of his chest that followed one upon another so quickly and held back speech and choked it as it came.* Mole's longing mirrors Odysseus's at the beginning of book 5 of *The Odyssey:*

> *Meanwhile he lives and grieves upon that island*
> *in thralldom to the nymph; he cannot stir,*
> *cannot fare homeward, for no ship is left him.*

and when you *wouldn't* turn back, Ratty—and I had to leave it, though I was smelling it all the time—I thought my heart would break.—We might have just gone and had one look at it, Ratty—only one look—it was close by—but you wouldn't turn back, Ratty, you wouldn't turn back! O dear, O dear!"

Recollection brought fresh waves of sorrow, and sobs again took full charge of him, preventing further speech.

The Rat stared straight in front of him, saying nothing, only patting Mole gently on the shoulder. After a time he muttered gloomily, "I see it all now! What a *pig* I have been! A pig—that's me! Just a pig—a plain pig!"[16]

He waited till Mole's sobs became gradually less stormy and more rhythmical; he waited till at last sniffs were frequent and sobs only intermittent. Then he rose from his seat, and, remarking carelessly, "Well, now we'd really better be getting on, old chap!" set off up the road again, over the toilsome way they had come.

"Wherever are you (hic) going to (hic), Ratty?" cried the tearful Mole, looking up in alarm.[17]

"We're going to find that home of yours, old fellow," replied the Rat pleasantly; "so you had better come along, for it will take some finding, and we shall want your nose."

"Oh, come back, Ratty, do!" cried the Mole, getting up and hurrying after him. "It's no good, I tell you! It's too late, and too dark, and the place is too far off, and the snow's coming! And—and I never meant to let you know I was feeling that way about it—it was all an accident and a mistake! And think of River Bank, and your supper!"

"Hang River Bank, and supper too!" said the Rat heartily. "I tell you, I'm going to find this place now, if I stay out all night. So cheer up, old chap, and take my arm, and we'll very soon be back there again."

Still snuffling, pleading, and reluctant, Mole suffered himself to be dragged back along the road by his imperious companion, who by a flow of cheerful talk and anecdote

(Robert Fitzgerald translation [New York: Doubleday, 1961], lines 13–15)
—J. J.

16. *"What a* pig *I have been! A pig—that's me! Just a pig—a plain pig!'* Grahame is pointing out that Rat has been self-centered, but he may also be alluding to book 10 of the *Odyssey*. Circe, a witch goddess on the island of Aeaea, feeds Odysseus's men and then turns them into pigs.

> When she had got them into her house, she set them upon benches and seats and mixed them a mess with cheese, honey, meal, and Pramnian but she drugged it with wicked poisons to make them forget their homes, and when they had drunk she turned them into pigs by a stroke of her wand, and shut them up in her pigsties.

—J. J.

17. *"Wherever are you (hic) going to (hic), Ratty?" cried the tearful Mole, looking up in alarm.* The hiccups signify the depths of Mole's angst. Peter Green comments on the tumultuous emotions of Mole:

> One of the most curious (and least commented-on) features of *The Wind in the Willows* is the frequency with which characters indulge in violent, eccentric, and near-pathological emotions or actions. This psychological ferment is in striking contrast to the rural setting and tranquillity. We would expect Mole and Rat, at least, to behave with "English self-restraint"; but not a bit of it. Mole goes into hysterical sobs at a whiff of his old home. (*Kenneth Grahame: A Biography*, 282)

endeavoured to beguile his spirits back and make the weary way seem shorter. When at last it seemed to the Rat that they must be nearing that part of the road where the Mole had been "held up," he said, "Now, no more talking. Business! Use your nose, and give your mind to it."

They moved on in silence for some little way, when suddenly the Rat was conscious, through his arm that was linked in Mole's, of a faint sort of electric thrill that was passing down that animal's body. Instantly he disengaged himself, fell back a pace, and waited, all attention.

Payne's Mole in search of a signal from home, 1927. "Mole stood a moment rigid while his uplifted nose, quivering slightly, felt the air."

The signals were coming through!

Mole stood a moment rigid, while his uplifted nose, quivering slightly, felt the air.[18]

Then a short, quick run forward—a fault—a check—a try back; and then a slow, steady, confident advance.

The Rat, much excited, kept close to his heels as the Mole, with something of the air of a sleep-walker, crossed a dry ditch, scrambled through a hedge, and nosed his way over a field open and trackless and bare in the faint starlight.

Suddenly, without giving warning, he dived; but the Rat was on the alert, and promptly followed him down the tunnel to which his unerring nose had faithfully led him.

It was close and airless, and the earthy smell was strong, and it seemed a long time to Rat ere the passage ended and he could stand erect and stretch and shake himself.[19] The Mole struck a match, and by its light the Rat saw that they were standing in an open space, neatly swept and sanded underfoot, and directly facing them was Mole's little front door, with "Mole End" painted, in Gothic lettering, over the bell-pull at the side.[20]

Mole reached down a lantern from a nail on the wall and lit it, and the Rat, looking round him, saw that they were in a sort of fore-court. A garden-seat stood on one side of the door, and on the other a roller; for the Mole, who was a tidy animal when at home, could not stand having his ground kicked up by other animals into little runs that ended in earth-heaps. On the walls hung wire baskets with ferns in them, alternating with brackets carrying plaster statuary[21]—Garibaldi,[22] and the infant Samuel,[23] and Queen Victoria, and other heroes of modern Italy.[24] Down on one side of the forecourt ran a skittle-alley, with benches along it and little wooden tables marked with rings that hinted at beer-mugs.[25] In the middle was a small round pond containing gold-fish[26] and surrounded by a cockle-shell border.[27] Out of the centre of the pond rose a fanciful erection clothed in more cockle-shells and topped by a

18. *Mole stood a moment rigid, while his uplifted nose, quivering slightly, felt the air.* Though Wyndham Payne and E. H Shepard both illustrated this moment, there is something amiss about both illustrations. Rat says to the homesick Mole, "It's too late, and too dark, and the place is too far off, and the snow's coming!" Payne included a new moon in the clear night sky; Shepard drew the snow blowing across Mole, giving the impression that the drawing belongs to chapter III, when Mole is lost in the Wild Wood. If both artists had stayed true to Grahame's text, the illustrations would only have gathering clouds.

19. *It was close and airless, and the earthy smell was strong, and it seemed a long time to Rat ere the passage ended and he could stand erect and stretch and shake himself.* This sequence of Rat following Mole resembles "Down the Rabbit Hole," a scene in the first chapter of *Alice's Adventures in Wonderland:*

> Alice started to her feet . . . and, burning with curiosity, she ran across the field after [the Rabbit], and was just in time to see it pop down a large rabbit-hole under the hedge.
>
> In another moment down went Alice after it, never once considering how in the world she was to get out again.
>
> The rabbit hole went straight on like a tunnel for some way, and then dipped suddenly down, so suddenly that Alice had not a moment to think.

20. *directly facing them was Mole's little front door, with "Mole End" painted, in Gothic lettering, over the bell-pull at the side.* Variant, e. 248: directly facing them was Mole's little front door, with "Mole End" painted {in Gothic lettering} over the bell-pull at the side.

No one knows why Grahame added the detail of Gothic lettering to Mole End. What we do know from looking at the manuscript is that the detail was written above the line as an afterthought. The nameplate is the second to appear (the first is Mr. Badger's at the end of chapter III). In England, Gothic was the name of a type commonly used for printing German and was used instead of the standard Roman or Italic letters. Always fancy and elaborate, Gothic writing around 1600 in England was also called "black letter" or "Old English" and was used to reach as wide an audience as possible. It is found in such public documents as Acts of Parliament and royal proclamations, and was the style of lettering used in the Bible and on the hornbooks—a hard tablet, often covered with horn, with letters, numbers, and the Lord's Prayer written on it. The hornbook was used to teach children to read.

We know that Grahame was a bibliophile, with an extensive personal library. It is quite possible that he was enamoured with a typeface that he saw, and transposed it into the beautifully eclectic world of Mole End. Peter Green believes that Grahame's library was disposed of after Elspeth's death in 1946. Grahame may have also let many of his books go when he sold off the contents of Bohams to go abroad after Alastair's death in 1920. In any case, the complete contents of his book collection are unknown. One record that does exist is the inventory of books that Alastair Grahame made around 1911 (see appendix 1). A catalogue also exists of the contents of the Grahames' final house, Church Cottage, in Pangbourne. Made fifteen years after Kenneth Grahame's death, it is dated Thursday, March 20, 1947, and labeled "Household Furniture & Effects." The inventory lists a "quantity of books" but gives no other details about the contents of the library.

21. *On the walls hung wire baskets with ferns in them, alternating with brackets carrying plaster statuary.* The plaster statuary would be cheap copies of originals. Mole's inexpensive and eclectic decor places him as someone who imitates the upper class, with the aspiration of joining its ranks. The emphasis on the details of Mole End also reflects one of the most popular books of the 1890s, *Diary of a Nobody* (Bristol: J. W. Arrowsmith, 1892). The *Diary* first appeared in serial form in the popular magazine *Punch*. Written by George Grossmith and illustrated by his brother, Weedon, it satirizes the pretensions and values of a clerk, Mr. Pooter, and his wife,

Weedon Grossmith's illustration of The Laurels, from *Diary of a Nobody* (1892). The row house has all the marks of the Industrial Revolution running behind it—power lines, a speeding train, and billowing smoke. The common clerk wanting to be grander than his station is exactly what Grahame had in mind when Mole returns to the confines of Mole End after the comfort of Rat's riverbank hole.

Carrie. Peter Hunt writes the following about the Pooters and Mr. Mole:

> Mole is sometimes taken as just another aspect of the upper classes, but although he may be retiring and perhaps middle-aged, he is essentially a Mr. Pooter, of the clerky, villa-dwelling type immortalized in George and Weedon Grossmith's *Diary of a Nobody* (1892) and pinned down very accurately by his taste in statuary, or even, perhaps, a senior official at the Bank of England. ("Language and Class in *The Wind in the Willows*," 166)

Using language meant to describe a manor house or a great hall, the Grossmiths lampoon Mr. Pooter's sensibilities. The new home, ennobled by the name The Laurels, is a row house in the suburbs. Grahame, who disliked new buildings and chose to live in Blewbury because "they do not build the horrible red houses that spring up round Cookham" (Chalmers, *Kenneth Grahame*, 195), referred to the new suburbs as "dormitories to the great city." Known primarily as actors and entertainers, the Grossmiths created a scathing parody that takes a stab at middle-class pretensions. The Laurels is a Mole End neatly put together with whatever many would prefer to pass over.

Grahame himself was known to enjoy statuary. When he took a joint lease and lived at 5 Kensington Crescent in London with his bachelor barrister friend Tom Greg (from 1894, until he married Elspeth in 1899), he fixed a Della Robbia—Madonna and child—plaque between the drawing room windows. He had gotten the plaque while visiting Florence. Peter Green quotes a letter from Annie Grahame, Kenneth's cousin, to Elspeth about the presence of this non-English art on the front of his house:

> [This] formed a kind of landmark enabling one to find the house at once; it also served as a shrine for the Italian organ grinders, who, Kenneth said, used to come and perform their devotions in front of it and then go down into the area and demand alms from Miss Bath [Ken and Greg's house keeper], who, however (having traveled in Italy herself), was quite equal to them and sternly refused to give them anything, whereupon they departed muttering curses and shaking their fists at her. (Green, *Kenneth Grahame: A Biography*, 154 n. 17)

22. *Garibaldi.* Giuseppe Garibaldi (1807–1882) was an Italian patriot and soldier and one of the leaders in the Risorgimento, a movement that was responsible for the unification of Italy during the ninteenth century. The Risorgimento, or "resurgence" in English, was a period marked by cultural nationalism and political activism. From 1859 to 1860 Garibaldi was instrumental in the growth of the Kingdom of Italy from Piedmont in the north to include Naples and Sicily in the south. After expelling Francis II from Naples, Garibaldi organized expeditions against Rome in 1862 and 1867 but was unsuccessful: The papal seat remained unconquered. In 1870 Garibaldi commanded a French force against Germany.

In Grahame's day, Garibaldi was a world figure. Commonly appearing in the newspapers, Garibaldi's image was reproduced on trinkets throughout Europe. In a preface to *Garibaldi and His Enemies* (New York: Signet Classics, 1965), Christopher Hibbert writes about the prevalence of Garibaldi memorabilia: "There were streets and squares named after him in a hundred different towns from Naples to Montevideo; statuettes of him, busts, medallions, china figurines were almost as common in Manchester as in Milan, in Boston as in Bologna; postcards garishly depicting his messianic features were sold in their millions. You could drink a Garibaldi wine, wear a Garibaldi blouse [as did Carrie Pooter, see note 21 in this chapter], see a Garibaldi musical, eat a Garibaldi biscuit." It would not have been difficult for Mole to find a statue of Garibaldi—and probably an inexpensive statue, at that. In fact, Garibaldi actually visited Fowey in April 1864. Arthur Quiller-Couch's future wife, Polly, was one of the lucky onlookers who got to shake his hand.

23. *and the infant Samuel.* In the Book of Samuel in the Old Testament, Samuel was born to a barren woman named Hannah. Most of her youth passed without a pregnancy despite many prayers and pleas to God. When she finally conceived and gave birth to a son, she named him Samuel, which means "he who is from God." When the infant was weaned, Hannah took him to Eli the priest in the temple of the Lord, where she dedicated him to God. Samuel later became a great prophet of Israel.

The infant Samuel became a popular image with the Victorians, who worshiped children and youth. One of the more famous and early renderings was by Sir Joshua Reynolds in 1776. Hanging in the Tate Gallery in London, the painting is of a little boy on his knees in prayer. In 1853, James Sant painted a version that became overwhelmingly popular. Sant, who became Painter-in-Ordinary to Queen Victoria in 1871, was much sought after in aristocratic circles for his sentimentally appealing portraits. His obituary in the *Times* (July 13, 1916) addresses the significance of his *Infant Samuel*: "It was a very English Samuel . . . it satisfied the British middle-class and was in perfect harmony with the Low-Church sermons they were in the habit of hearing every Sunday."

It is not surprising that Grahame, who worshiped youth and whose own son was born late in life, would include a plaster infant Samuel at Mole End.

24. *and Queen Victoria, and other heroes of modern Italy.* Grahame may have gleaned his "heroes" from a quote by Alfred, Lord Tennyson, the Victorian poet. In 1864, Garibaldi visited England and—according to an account in the *Times*—was greeted with "a perfect tumult of enthusiasm" by the crowds. Though Garibaldi could barely speak English, the correspondent for the *Times* found the uncharacteristic warmth the English showed their Italian visitor "almost impossible to describe." Garibaldi paid a visit to Tennyson on the Isle of Wight. The poet later wrote:

> I had expected to see a hero, and I was not disappointed. He is more majestic than meek, and his manners have a certain divine simplicity in them such as I have never witnessed in a native of these islands, among men at least. . . . He denied that he came with any political purpose in view, merely to thank the English for their kindness to him, and the interest they had taken in himself and all Italian matters. (Hallam Tennyson, ed., *The Works of Tennyson* [New York: Macmillan, 1916], xliv)

25. *Down one side of the fore-court ran a skittle-alley, with benches along it and little wooden tables marked with rings that hinted at beer-mugs.* Skittle is an English game played with nine pins set in a square upon a wooden frame. The pins are angled toward the player, who tries to knock them down with as few throws as possible. The skittle alley is the British equivalent of the American bowling alley.

Peter Green writes at length about the setting of Mole End. Shortly after *The Golden Age* was published in February of 1895, Grahame went to Italy:

> In the spring . . . fortified by steadily accumulating royalties, Grahame was able to gratify his annual migratory

large silvered glass ball that reflected everything all wrong and had a very pleasing effect.[28]

Mole's face beamed at the sight of all these objects so dear to him, and he hurried Rat through the door, lit a lamp in the hall, and took one glance round his old home. He saw the dust lying thick on everything, saw the cheerless, deserted look of the long-neglected house, and its narrow, meagre dimensions, its worn and shabby contents[29]—and collapsed again on a hall-chair, his nose to his paws. "O Ratty!" he cried dismally, "why ever did I do it? Why did I bring you to this poor, cold little place, on a night like this, when you might have been at River Bank by this time, toasting your toes before a blazing fire, with all your own nice things about you!"

The Rat paid no heed to his doleful self-reproaches. He was running here and there, opening doors, inspecting rooms and cupboards, and lighting lamps and candles and sticking them up everywhere. "What a capital little house this is!" he called out cheerily. "So compact! So well planned! Everything here and everything in its place! We'll make a jolly night of it. The first thing we want is a good fire; I'll see to that—I always know where to find things. So this is the parlour? Splendid! Your own idea, those little sleeping-bunks in the wall?[30] Capital! Now, I'll fetch the wood and the coals, and you get a duster, Mole—you'll find one in the drawer of the kitchen table—and try and smarten things up a bit. Bustle about, old chap!"

Encouraged by his inspiriting companion, the Mole roused himself and dusted and polished with energy and heartiness, while the Rat, running to and fro with armfuls of fuel, soon had a cheerful blaze roaring up the chimney. He hailed the Mole to come and warm himself; but Mole promptly had another fit of the blues,[31] dropping down on a couch in dark despair and burying his face in his duster. "Rat," he moaned, "how about your supper, you poor, cold, hungry, weary animal? I've nothing to give you—nothing—not a crumb!"

"What a fellow you are for giving in!" said the Rat reproach-

urge. Southward he went . . . [to] Alassio on the Italian Riviera—a place to which he was to return at least twice during the next three years, and which made a lasting impression on him.

At that time Alassio had not yet become the fashionable resort it is today. It was still a picturesque, undisturbed fishing-port, and Grahame stayed, not in a smart hotel but with a private family, in their old-fashioned Ligurian home. Idiosyncratic features such as box-bunks and bowling-alley caught his fancy so strongly that later he transferred most of them to Mole End. (*Kenneth Grahame: A Biography*, 162–63)

26. *In the middle was a small round pond containing gold-fish.* See chapter I, note 6—the 1919 letter from Professor G. T. Hill, who asks who took care of Mole End and the goldfish while Mole was away.

27. *and surrounded by a cockle-shell border.* Cockleshell: a bivalve mollusk; a shell with convex radially ribbed valves; a common edible European bivalve.

The cockleshell border is another part of Mole's inexpensive decor. The shells are easily gathered along any tidal basin of any river-to-ocean estuary in southern England.

28. *a large silvered glass ball that reflected everything all wrong and had a very pleasing effect.* Silvered glass balls, often referred to as "witch balls," were originally made at a glassworks at Nailsea, a few miles west of Bristol, England. Manufactured from 1788 to the 1870s, the spherical bottles were blown with short necks in order to carry holy water. Witch balls were then hung at each door of the house to repel witches or break their power. Later manufactured with reflective silver paint on the interior, the witch ball often reflected everything upside down, making it impossible—so the folklore says—for a witch to pass into

the house. Gradually relegated to the garden, witch balls, now called "reflecting balls," have become a symbol of good luck. The interior of the ball was silvered with a preparation composed of "two parts bismuth, one part lead, one part tin, and four parts mercury. The lead, tin, and bismuth were melted together and the mercury added when the mixture was almost cold. It was then poured into the sphere. By slowly rotating the ball, the liquid amalgam was spread in a thin film over the glass, to which it adhered" (L. G. G. Ramsey, ed., *Concise Encyclopedia of Antiques* [New York: Hawthorn Books, 1955], 90).

Kenneth Grahame liked glass objects. We know from Constance Smedley's memoir that Grahame gave her the Italian goblet she drank from at the Grahames' fateful dinner party in 1907. We also know that Grahame had an extensive collection of glass rolling pins that were also made in Nailsea. Though they seem like an arcane object today, glass rolling pins were made as salt containers during the Napoleonic Wars, when the salt tax was thirty times higher than the cost of the salt itself. No longer necessary for smuggling or holding salt, glass rolling pins eventually became a symbol of good luck and could be spotted in many kitchens in England. Finally, the catalogue to the Grahames' estate contained numerous pieces of green, red, and blue Bristol glassware, including round bottles.

29. *and its narrow meager dimensions, its worn and shabby contents.* After all the time Mole has spent with Rat, Toad, and Mr. Badger, he suddenly sees his home as it truly is—worn out in comparison and put together with remnants. On his return, Mole's house bears a striking resemblance to Mr. Pooter's in *Diary of a Nobody*. Unlike the riverbankers, the middle-aged Mr. Pooter doesn't even own The Laurels. Despite his middle age and steady employment of twenty years, Pooter still makes do with the worn interior left by previous tenants. Mole, like Mr. Pooter, has made all home improvements himself, such as the whitewashing at the beginning of the first chapter. Instead of getting new stair carpets when he discovers the old carpets aren't wide enough to meet the paint on either side of the steps, Pooter decides to repaint. A frenzy of painting is set off, with Pooter absurdly taking a brush to the interior of his bathtub and painting the coal chute and the washstand in the servant's bedroom. No other riverbanker partakes in any sort of housekeeping. (At the beginning of chapter VI, Mole and Rat are getting ready for boating season by painting, varnishing, and mending paddles. Boating is a leisure activity, however, and there is never any mention of the need to maintain Rat's house.)

30. *Your own idea, those little sleeping-bunks in the wall?* None of the early artists included illustrations of the sleeping bunks, yet they become a favorite topic in editions produced later in the century (see Inga Moore's unforgivably abridged edition of 1996 and appendix 4, for Kenneth Grahame's opinion on abridgment.

31. *Mole promptly had another fit of the blues.* Mole suffers from melancholia—a recurring theme in eighteenth-century literature that carried into the Victorian period.

The term "fit of the blues" turns up in Jerome K. Jerome's satiric "Idle Thoughts of an Idle Fellow" (New York and Boston: H. M. Caldwell Co., Publishers, 1890), which pokes fun at the cult of melancholia:

> . . . there is a good deal of satisfaction about being thoroughly miserable; but nobody likes a fit of the blues. . . . Its effect upon you is somewhat similar to what would probably be produced by a combined attack of toothache, indiges-

E. H. Shepard is the only early illustrator to contribute a detailed drawing of the courtyard at Mole End. He gets the order of the statuary wrong, however. Shepard places Queen Victoria in between the statues of Garibaldi and the praying infant Samuel, when actually she should come after the other statuary. Shepard doesn't include the heroes of modern Italy, though the small drawing of Garibaldi should suffice. In illustrations of Garibaldi and his peers, they are often shown standing in the same pose—hand on hip, or, hand thrust in the lapel of the jacket—wearing the same kind of mismatching clothing as uniform.

fully. "Why, only just now I saw a sardine-opener on the kitchen dresser, quite distinctly; and everybody knows that means there are sardines about somewhere in the neighbourhood. Rouse yourself! pull yourself together, and come with me and forage."

They went and foraged accordingly, hunting through every cupboard and turning out every drawer. The result was not so very depressing after all, though of course it might have been better; a tin of sardines—a box of captain's biscuits,[32] nearly full—and a German sausage encased in silver paper.

"There's a banquet for you!" observed the Rat, as he arranged the table. "I know some animals who would give their ears to be sitting down to supper with us to-night!"

"No bread!" groaned the Mole dolorously; "no butter, no———"

"No *pâté de foie gras*, no champagne!" continued the Rat, grinning. "And that reminds me—what's that little door at the end of the passage? Your cellar, of course! Every luxury in this house! Just you wait a minute."

He made for the cellar-door, and presently reappeared, somewhat dusty, with a bottle of beer in each paw and another under each arm,[33] "Self-indulgent beggar you seem to be, Mole," he observed. "Deny yourself nothing. This is really the jolliest little place I ever was in. Now, wherever did you pick up those prints? Make the place look so home-like, they do. No wonder you're so fond of it, Mole. Tell us all about it, and how you came to make it what it is."

Then, while the Rat busied himself fetching plates, and knives and forks, and mustard which he mixed in an egg-cup, the Mole, his bosom still heaving with the stress of his recent emotion, related—somewhat shyly at first, but with more freedom as he warmed to his subject—how this was planned, and how that was thought out, and how this was got through a windfall from an aunt,[34] and that was a wonderful find and a bargain, and this other thing was bought out of laborious savings and a certain amount of "going without."[35] His spirits

> tion, and cold in the head. You become stupid, restless, and irritable . . . clumsy, maudlin, and quarrelsome; a nuisance to yourself and everybody about you. (27)

The theme is also treated in George and Weedon Grossmith's *Diary of a Nobody*. Mr. Pooter discovers that his adult son, who lives at home, has gone out in the evening:

> I was a little annoyed to find Lupin, instead of reading last night, had gone to a common sort of entertainment, given at the Assembly Rooms. I expressed my opinion that such performances were unworthy of respectable patronage; but he replied: "Oh, it was only 'for one night only.' I had a fit of the blues come on, and thought I would go to see Polly Presswell, England's Particular Spark." (62)

32. *captain's biscuits.* According to Robert Wells's cookbook *Bread and Biscuit Baker's and Sugar-Boiler's Assistant* (London: Crosby Lockwood and Son, 1890), captain's biscuits were made from water, butter, flour, and milk and were usually manufactured instead of made by hand. The box of biscuits would resemble a box of soda crackers today. Captain's biscuits were often used on long voyages because they were hard, dry, and did not spoil. Though not the most desirable fare, the captain's biscuits in Mole's cupboard have survived his absence and are still edible.

> Captains' Biscuits
>
> 7 lbs. of fine flour
> 6 ozs. of butter
> 1 quart of water or milk
>
> Rub the butter in with the flour until it is crumbled into very small pieces, make a bay in the centre of the flour, pour in the water or milk, make it into a dough, and break it when made into dough, chaff or mould up the required

size, 4 or 5 ozs. each, pin out with a rolling pin about 5 inches in diameter, dock them and lay them with their faces together. When they are ready bake them in a moderately quick oven, of a nice brown colour. These are seldom made with hand, as the machinery in use outstrips hand-made biscuits of this class in speed and gives a better appearance and quality. (Wells, *The Bread and Biscuit Baker's and Sugar-Boiler's Assistant*)

33. *He made for the cellar-door, and presently reappeared, somewhat dusty, with a bottle of beer in each paw and another under each arm.* Arthur Rackham's illustration from Mole End bears the same caption.

34. *a windfall from an aunt.* This is one of the only occasions when Grahame refers to Mole's life and relations beyond the context of the riverbankers. Readers have no idea what the windfall is, though we know that Mole "caresses" his belongings and will take Rat—who is unaccustomed to underground living—on a tour of Mole End to revisit his things. The visit is similar to Badger's tour of his underground house in chapter IV.

The evidence that Mole has familial relations recalls Grahame's early story "Bertie's Escapade," in which a mole runs a getaway elevator lift. Though the mole is not central to the action, he mentions that there is a Mrs. Mole waiting up for him when he wants to return home. (See chapter I, note 6, for evidence of other characters in Mole's life.)

35. *and this other thing was bought out of laborious savings and a certain amount of "going without."* As in *Diary of a Nobody*, the Mr. Pooter-like Mole has worked enormously hard to contrive his eclectic furnishings. Much of his décor has been built around found objects and common sale items such as plaster of Paris statuary. Though we are shown the contents and furnishings of the other riverbankers' homes—Rat's "bijoux riverside residence," Mr. Badger's underground burrow, and Toad's Toad Hall—Mole is the only one to be overtly self-conscious about the appearance of his possessions.

Arthur Rackham, 1940. "He made for the cellar-door, and presently reappeared, somewhat dusty, with a bottle of beer in each paw and another under each arm."

Christmas card by E. H. Shepard, who drew the riverbankers as band members instead of carolers. Ernest and Norah Shepard sent this card to their friends. *Courtesy of the David J. Holmes Collection.*

finally quite restored, he must needs go and caress his possessions, and take a lamp and show off their points to his visitor and expatiate on them, quite forgetful of the supper they both so much needed; Rat, who was desperately hungry but strove to conceal it, nodding seriously, examining with a puckered brow, and saying, "wonderful," and "most remarkable," at intervals, when the chance for an observation was given him.

At last the Rat succeeded in decoying him to the table, and had just got seriously to work with the sardine-opener when sounds were heard from the fore-court without—sounds like the scuffling of small feet in the gravel and a confused murmur of tiny voices, while broken sentences reached them—"Now, all in a line—hold the lantern up a bit, Tommy—clear your throats first—no coughing after I say one, two, three.—Where's young Bill?—Here, come on, do, we're all a-waiting———"

"What's up?" inquired the Rat, pausing in his labours.

"I think it must be the field-mice," replied the Mole, with a touch of pride in his manner. "They go round carol-singing regularly at this time of the year.[36] They're quite an institution in these parts. And they never pass me over—they come to Mole End last of all; and I used to give them hot drinks, and supper too sometimes, when I could afford it.[37] It will be like old times to hear them again."

"Let's have a look at them!" cried the Rat, jumping up and running to the door.

It was a pretty sight, and a seasonable one, that met their eyes when they flung the door open.[38] In the fore-court, lit by the dim rays of a horn lantern, some eight or ten little field-mice stood in a semicircle, red worsted comforters round their throats, their fore-paws thrust deep into their pockets, their feet jigging for warmth. With bright beady eyes they glanced shyly at each other, sniggering a little, sniffing and applying coat-sleeves a good deal. As the door opened, one of the elder ones that carried the lantern was just saying, "Now then, one,

36. *"I think it must be the field-mice," replied the Mole, with a touch of pride in his manner. "They go round carol-singing regularly at this time of the year."* Carolers appear in "Bertie's Escapade," when Alastair's pet rabbits go out singing with Bertie, the Grahames' black pig. The pig had recently distinguished himself by escaping from his sty. Here the animals prepare to carol:

> "Splendid!" said Bertie. "Now, we'll go right up to the house, and sing our bewitching carols under the drawing-room windows. And presently Mr. Stone will come out, and praise us, and pat our heads, and say we're dear clever animals and ask us in. And that will mean supper in the dining room, and champagne with it, and grand times!" (Bodleian, MS. Eng. Misc. d. 282)

Among the childhood playmates who spent time with Alastair's rabbits Peter and Benjamin was Peggy ("Mitey") Sullivan. In a letter dated September 30, 1943, Elspeth Grahame names Mitey's father as the artist S. Sullivan (*First Whisper of "The Wind in the Willows,"* 6). In a photograph of Alastair and a little girl taken by Naomi Stott in 1908, "Mouse and Peggy" is written on the back. The photo, which belonged to Austin Purves, is now part of the David J. Holmes Collection.

37. *And they never pass me over—they come to Mole End last of all; and I used to give them hot drinks, and supper too sometimes, when I could afford it.* This is one of the instances when Mole admits to having less than his peers. Nevertheless, he has a generous spirit—taking on a paternal and beneficial Bob Cratchit role not unlike that of the struggling father of Tiny Tim in *A Christmas Carol*. Mole may have modest means, but he will always be as generous as his purse strings will allow.

38. *It was a pretty sight, and a seasonable one, that met their eyes when they flung the door*

open. E. H. Shepard was often called upon by various charities and fundraisers to make duplicates of his illustrations, such as this undated card for the Girl Guides Association.

Payne's carolers look like adults, complete with a maestro in tails and top hat, Barnhart's field mice look like adolescents, and Shepard's carolers look like children.

This mise-en-scène has already occurred earlier in the chapter, when Mole and Rat gaze through the villagers' windows on their way home.

39. *Miry.* Marshy or swampy ground. The streets are wet from snow or rain.

40. *Though wind may follow, and snow beside.* Because the forecourt to Mole End is at the end of a tunnel underground, it is doubtful that the field mice would bring wind, let alone snow, with them.

Illustration by E. H. Shepard, revised for the Girl Guides Association. *Courtesy of the David J. Holmes Collection.*

two, three!" and forthwith their shrill little voices uprose on the air, singing one of the old-time carols that their forefathers composed in fields that were fallow and held by frost, or when snow-bound in chimney corners, and handed down to be sung in the miry[39] street to lamp-lit windows at Yule-time.

CAROL

Villagers all, this frosty tide,
Let your doors swing open wide,
Though wind may follow, and snow beside,[40]
Yet draw us in by your fire to bide;
Joy shall be yours in the morning!

Here we stand in the cold and the sleet,
Blowing fingers and stamping feet,
Come from far away you to greet—
You by the fire and we in the street—
Bidding you joy in the morning!

For ere one half of the night was gone,
Sudden a star has led us on,
Raining bliss and benison—

Wyndham Payne's Carolers, 1927. "In the fore-court some eight or ten little field-mice stood in a semicircle." Payne's carolers have a jazz element, with a grinning bohemian on bass, and a mouse with mismatched clothes playing the trumpet.

Bliss to-morrow and more anon,
Joy for every morning!

Goodman Joseph toiled through the snow—
Saw the star o'er a stable low;
Mary she might not further go—
Welcome thatch, and litter below!
Joy was hers in the morning!

And then they heard the angels tell
"Who were the first to cry Nowell*?*
Animals all, as it befell,
In the stable where they did dwell!
Joy shall be theirs in the morning!"

41. *"And now come along in, all of you, and warm yourselves by the fire, and have something hot!"* The field mice, which Rat will encounter at the opening of chapter IX, have less means than the Rat and even the Mole. They literally sing for their supper.

The dialogue in this scene is consistently more emphatic than it is in the draft that finally went to press. In the Barnhart edition the above line is used as a caption and is abridged.

"Come along, field mice!" cried the Mole. "This is quite like old times!" Nancy Barnhart's illustration of the field mice, 1923.

The voices ceased, the singers, bashful but smiling, exchanged sidelong glances, and silence succeeded—but for a moment only. Then, from up above and far away, down the tunnel they had so lately travelled was borne to their ears in a faint musical hum the sound of distant bells ringing a joyful and clangorous peal.

"Very well sung, boys!" cried the Rat heartily. "And now come along in, all of you, and warm yourselves by the fire, and have something hot!"[41]

"Villagers all, this frosty tide." E. H. Shepard's color revision of the field mice caroling at Mole End. Shepard added color and expanded the image to fill most of the page. Though they are supposed to be underground in the forecourt of Mole End, snow falls from an open sky in the upper left-hand corner.

"Yes, come along, field-mice," cried the Mole eagerly. "This is quite like old times! Shut the door after you. Pull up that settle to the fire. Now, you just wait a minute, while we—O, Ratty!" he cried in despair, plumping down on a seat, with tears impending. "Whatever are we doing? We've nothing to give them!"

"You leave all that to me," said the masterful Rat. "Here, you with the lantern! Come over this way. I want to talk to you. Now, tell me, are there any shops open at this hour of the night?"[42]

"Why, certainly, sir," replied the field-mouse respectfully. "At this time of the year our shops keep open to all sorts of hours."

"Then look here!" said the Rat. "You go off at once, you and your lantern, and you get me———"

Here much muttered conversation ensued, and the Mole

42. *"Now, tell me, are there any shops open at this hour of the night?"*

"Why certainly, sir," replied the field-mouse respectfully. "At this time of the year our shops keep open to all sorts of hours." This exchange between Rat and the field mouse resembles the scene in *A Christmas Carol* when the transformed Scrooge awakens on Christmas morning and calls out to a boy passing in the street:

> "Do you know the poulterer's, in the next street but one, at the corner?" Scrooge inquired.
>
> "I should hope I did," replied the lad.
>
> "An intelligent boy!" said Scrooge. "A remarkable boy! Do you know whether they've sold the prize turkey that was hanging up there? Not the little prize turkey: the big one?"
>
> "What, the one as big as me?" returned the boy.

In 1898, Kenneth Grahame wrote to Mary Richardson, his sister's close friend, inviting her to an impromptu feast.

> 27th Dec 98
> 5, Kensington Crescent. W.
> My dear Miss Richardson
> . . .
>
> I've just got back from spending Christmas with Roly & Joan. R. has come back with me, to stop for a night or two, & that brings me to my point, which is that somebody has sent me one of the biggest turkeys wot, you ever saw—you can't even form a notion how big he is—& he's got to be eaten tomorrow. & if you've nothing better to do you might as a favor come round at 7.30 & help Roly & me to eat him—without any dressing up, cos there won't be anyone else! It maynt sound lively, but the turkey's going to be so very good! Do come.
>
> Yours very sincerely/
> Kenneth Grahame

only heard bits of it, such as—'Fresh, mind!—no, a pound of that will do—see you get Buggins's,[43] for I won't have any other—no, only the best—if you can't get it there, try somewhere else—yes, of course, home-made, no tinned stuff—well then, do the best you can!" Finally, there was a chink of coin passing from paw to paw, the field-mouse was provided with an ample basket for his purchases, and off he hurried, he and his lantern.

The rest of the field-mice, perched in a row on the settle, their small legs swinging, gave themselves up to enjoyment of the fire, and toasted their chilblains till they tingled;[44] while the Mole, failing to draw them into easy conversation, plunged into family history and made each of them recite the names of his numerous brothers, who were too young, it appeared, to be allowed to go out a-carolling this year, but looked forward very shortly to winning the parental consent.

The Rat, meanwhile, was busy examining the label on one of the beer-bottles. "I perceive this to be Old Burton,"[45] he remarked approvingly. "*Sensible* Mole! The very thing! Now we shall be able to mull some ale![46] Get the things ready, Mole, while I draw the corks."

It did not take long to prepare the brew and thrust the tin heater well into the red heart of the fire; and soon every field-mouse was sipping and coughing and choking (for a little mulled ale goes a long way)[47] and wiping his eyes and laughing and forgetting he had ever been cold in all his life.

"They act plays too, these fellows,"[48] the Mole explained to the Rat. "Make them up all by themselves, and act them afterwards. And very well they do it, too! They gave us a capital one last year, about a field-mouse who was captured at sea by a Barbary corsair,[49] and made to row in a galley; and when he escaped and got home again, his lady-love had gone into a convent. Here, *you!* You were in it, I remember. Get up and recite a bit."

The field-mouse addressed got up on his legs, giggled shyly, looked round the room, and remained absolutely tongue-tied.

43. *"see you get Buggins's."* Very little has been written about Grahame's use of the word Buggins's. It is possible that Grahame is joking that the only food available in the local shops will be mediocre. Buggins's, as in "Buggins's turn," refers to the principle of giving jobs to people in a rotation rather than according to merit. Since the riverbankers are taking turns, going home to home, Rat settles for substandard fare at Mole End. Because Rat is a snob when it comes to food—and the nearby shops cater to the common field mice—the use of the term "Buggin's" possibly implies that Rat feels there will be nothing extraordinary. Peter Green writes: "As for Buggins's, my immediate feeling is that KG simply used it as a generic label for shopkeepers-in-general, an all-purpose name that would be recognized as such. The common phrase Buggins' turn would seem to confirm this" (Peter Green, e-mail to the author, October 2004).

According to Peter Hunt, author of *The Wind in the Willows: A Fragmented Arcadia*:

> I think you could put "Buggins's turn" in as an ingenious possibility—although *Brewer's Dictionary of Phrase and Fable* seems to suggest that it's a fairly modern term. . . . I've always assumed that it was merely Rat's food-snobbery, and that Buggins was a made-up name for a high-class product (as in Cooper's marmalade or Hamley's toys, or Harrods' . . .) It also, I think, has a period air, connoting "funny" and possibly "trade"—as in the Grossmiths' Mr. Pooter. "Juggins" was common slang for a fool, at the time. The food-snobbery ("no tinned stuff") seems to me to be of a piece with the whole nostalgic, looking-back-to-rural-arcadia atmosphere. Tins, like cars, are a sign of the times. Home made now . . . connotes, well . . . home. (Peter Hunt, e-mail to the author, October 2004)

44. *and toasted their chilblains till they tingled.* A chilblain is a small, red, swelling lesion on the skin. Often inflammatory, they can dry out and crack, exposing the skin to infection. They most commonly appear on the hands or feet and are exacerbated by damp living conditions. Chilblains become increasingly itchy and painful, often causing a burning sensation in the feet, and usually occur where the skin has been exposed to the elements. More often than not, chilblains develop whenever chilled extremities are warmed too rapidly, such as when the mice are invited to warm their feet before the fire. Chilblains were more common in England and Europe at the beginning of the twentieth century because most dwellings and buildings did not have central heating.

Illustrator Arthur Rackham comments on the field mice and their chilblains in a letter he wrote to several children on October 26, 1909. Though he didn't illustrate *The Wind in the Willows* until the end of his career, in 1939, it is obvious that he was very much a fan early on:

> My dear Betty, Joan & Gilbert
>
> Very many thanks for your kind letter I was most pleased that you thought of me when you were reading the 'Wind in the Willows
>
> Curiously enough I very nearly did illustrate it. The publishers asked me to, but at the time it would have had to be done, I was too busy illustrating the Midsummer Night Dream.
>
> But its a splendid book, isn't it! The little field mice singing carols are among the jollier things in it. I especially like when they toasted their chilblains till they tingled—(but perhaps you've never had chilblains? Well, *don't*!). (Derek Hudson, *Arthur Rackham*, 144)

45. *"I perceive this to be Old Burton."* Old Burton Ale was traditionally brewed in Burton-on-Trent, a town in Staffordshire, northeast of Birmingham, situated on the River Trent and the Trent & Mersey Canal. Founded in 1002, the town's tradition of brewing began with the Benedictine monks of Burton Abbey in the eleventh century. What made the beers of Burton famous was the quality of the local water used in the brewing. Drawn from deep wells in the Trent Valley that are full of gypsum deposits, the water is naturally high in calcium sulfate—particularly favorable for brewing—which gives the beer its distinctive flavor. Beer high in sulfate makes the drinker more gaseous—perhaps Grahame's choice of Old Burton's was intended to poke fun at the condition.

The earliest-known reference to Burton Ale was in 1295; it was available in London by 1630, and commercial production began in the mid-eighteenth century. There have been over 200 breweries in Burton since Benjamin Printon became the town's first common brewer in 1708.

Beer production in Burton-on-Trent reached its zenith late in the industrial age, when dozens of breweries were in operation and an intricate network of railways ran through the town in order to facilitate the distribution of ale throughout Britain.

A. E. Housman refers to Burton-on-Trent in poem 62 of *A Shropshire Lad* (1896), a well-known work in England at the time. Though Housman and Grahame were contemporaries, they didn't meet until 1913. The exchange between Mole and Rat in chapter V bears a resemblance to Housman's poem 62:

> *"Terence, this is stupid stuff:*
> *You eat your victuals fast enough;*
> *There can't be much amiss, 'tis clear,*
> *To see the rate you drink your beer.*
> *But oh, good Lord, the verse you make,*
> *It gives a chap the belly-ache. . . ."*

Why, if 'tis dancing you would be,
There's brisker pipes than poetry.
Say, for what were hop-yards meant,
Or why was Burton built on Trent?
Oh many a peer of England brews
Livelier liquor than the muse,
And malt does more than Milton can
To justify God's ways to man.
Ale, man, ale's the stuff to drink
For fellows whom it hurts to think:
Look into the pewter pot
To see the world as the world's not.

Unfortunately, in the 1990s, numerous long-standing brewers in Burton-on-Trent merged with larger conglomerates. Brewer Ind Coope, the latest maker of Burton Ale, was bought by Carlsberg Tetley, who have gradually been phasing out the product. The Burton Bridge Brewery—a micro-brewery—continues to brew its own real ales, but none that bear the distinctive title of "Burton Ale."

According to *Beer: The Story of the Pint*, by Martyn Cornell (London: Headline, 2003, 206), the Young's Brewery—located in Wandsworth, southwest of London—brewed their own version of Burton Ale. In 1971 Young's changed the name to Winter Warmer Ale. Though it lacks the sulfuric punch that made Burton Ale famous, the seasonal cask ale has a hearty 5 percent alcohol content.

Another contemporary variation of the old Burton Ale is Samuel Smith's Winter Welcome Ale. Brewed in Yorkshire's oldest brewery, in Tadcaster, the strong old ale has even more kick, with a 6 percent alcohol content.

46. *Now we shall be able to mull some ale!* Mulling goes back to medieval times and involves heating the ale—in the case at Mole End, over an open fire. Sugar and spices are added to sweeten it, making it more palatable to the young field mice—sometimes causing them to drink too much. Occasionally, mulled ale is thickened with beaten egg yolk. Alcohol would also aggravate the chilblains. Mulled Old Burton's would have been common fare in 1908, and most households would have had spices on hand. Below is a simple recipe for mulled ale:

Mulled Ale

Mix: 2 pints of ale
1 tablespoon of sugar
pinch of ground cloves
pinch of ground nutmeg
bigger pinch of ground ginger
Bring the mix almost to a boil, then add:

8 ounces of rum or brandy.
Taste to see if it needs more sugar or flavoring.
If it tastes right, add a cinnamon stick and serve in a mug.

(http://www.bbc.co.uk/northernireland/winter/foodanddrink/drinks/mulling_dads.shtml; Patrick Higgins, Maura Kate Kilgore, and Paul Hertlein, *The Homebrewer's Recipe Guide* [New York: Fireside/Simon & Schuster, 1996])

47. *a little mulled ale goes a long way.* The age of the field mice is unclear—Mole and Rat are certainly paternalistic toward them. The mice are diminutive, with their "small legs swinging" from the settle, yet they are older than "numerous brothers, who were too young . . . to be allowed to go out a-caroling . . . but looked forward . . . to winning the parental consent." Like when Mole and Rat smoke at Mr. Badger's house, Grahame again allows characters to transgress childhood rules. Though the mice are underage drinkers, they are not at great risk for mishap because they are on foot as a group and no automobiles are involved.

In "What They Talked About," in *The*

Golden Age, Grahame, who once promised his son £100 if he refrained from drinking, writes about the effects of alcohol on the uninitiated:

> "You'd better be careful, young man!" said his elder brother, regarding him severely. "D' you remember that night when the Mummers were here, and they had mulled port, and you went round and emptied all the glasses after they had gone away?"
>
> "Ow! I did feel funny that night," chuckled Harold. "Thought the house was comin' down, it jumped about so; and Martha had to carry me up to bed, 'cos the stairs was goin' all waggity!"

48. *"They act plays too, these fellows."* The tradition of mummers' plays rose in popularity in England during the eighteenth century. Visiting groups wearing masks, or dressed in disguise, call on private houses and perform in exchange for food and drink during major holidays—Christmas in particular. The plays usually include scenes borrowed from other works. Kenneth Grahame wrote about the tradition in "Snowbound," from *The Golden Age*:

> Twelfth-night had come and gone, and life next morning seemed a trifle flat and purposeless. But yester-eve and the mummers were here! They had come striding into the old kitchen, powdering the red brick floor with snow from their barbaric bedizenments; and stamping, and crossing, and declaiming, till all was whirl and riot and shout.

G. K. Chesterton wrote about Christmas traditions and about the origins of the mummers:

> The night before Christmas Eve I heard a burst of musical voices so close that they might as well have been inside the house instead of just outside; so I asked them inside, hoping that they might then seem farther away. Then I realised that they were the Christmas Mummers, who come every year in country parts to enact the rather rigid fragments of the old Christmas play of St. George, the Turkish Knight, and the Very Venal Doctor. (G. K. Chesterton, *A Miscellany of Men* [New York: Dodd, Mead and Company, 1912], p. 202)

49. *They gave us a capital one last year, about a field-mouse who was captured at sea by a Barbary corsair.* Barbary corsairs were typically North African pirates or privateers who came from the Barbary Coast of North Africa—Algiers, Morocco, Tripoli, or Tunis. During the Crusades (1095–1295), pirates plundered mercantile ships as well as ships carrying Christian Crusaders and pilgrims, selling many into slavery. The story of the field mouse forced to row in a galley would have been a common story at the time.

The mummers' play quite possibly could be based on the story of the Turkish Admiral of the Ottoman Navy, Turgut Reis (1485–1565), who in 1538 was called to fight against Andrea Doria, a Genoan who drove the French out of Corsica. After Doria's defeat and return to Italy, Turgut Reis reigned at sea, conquering the Kingdom of Naples and the Sicilian coasts and capturing around seven thousand men and turning them into slaves.

In 1540, his fortune changed when he was himself captured by Andrea Doria on the island of Corsica and taken to Genoa. He was held prisoner and forced to row in a galley by the admiral's nephew, Gianettino Doria. Often referred to as The Drawn Sword of Islam, Turgut Reis was imprisoned as a criminal for four years before he was ransomed by Kheyr-ud-Din from Lomellini Doria of Genoa and allowed to return home.

The term Barbary comes from the nickname Barbarossa ("red beard"), given to sixteenth-century Greek-born pirate brothers Aruj and Kheyr-ud-Din for the color of their facial hair. The brothers founded the Barbary Corsairs. A corsair is a French seaman or privateer who sailed mostly in the south Mediterranean Sea.

50. *They were all busily engaged on him like watermen applying the Royal Humane Society's regulations to a case of long submersion.* The Royal Humane Society was founded in 1774 by two London doctors, William Hawes (1736–1808) and Thomas Cogan (1736–1818), to save people by resuscitation from drowning. Then a controversial and new medical technique, resuscitation was rewarded by medals, certificates, and eventually money for those who risked their lives to save another. In the winter, the society had icemen present in London's parks in case anyone fell through the ice. The society is still active today and gives awards for bravery approximately ten times a year.

The field mouse obviously suffers from shyness and stage fright.

His comrades cheered him on, Mole coaxed and encouraged him, and the Rat went so far as to take him by the shoulders and shake him; but nothing could overcome his stage-fright. They were all busily engaged on him like watermen applying the Royal Humane Society's regulations to a case of long submersion,[50] when the latch clicked, the door opened, and the field-mouse with the lantern reappeared, staggering under the weight of his basket.

There was no more talk of play-acting once the very real and solid contents of the basket had been tumbled out on the table. Under the generalship of Rat, everybody was set to do something or to fetch something. In a very few minutes supper was ready, and Mole, as he took the head of the table in a sort of a dream, saw a lately barren board set thick with savoury comforts; saw his little friends' faces brighten and beam as they fell to without delay; and then let himself loose—for he was famished indeed—on the provender so magically provided, thinking what a happy home-coming this had turned out, after all. As they ate, they talked of old times, and the field-mice gave him the local gossip up to date, and answered as well as they could the hundred questions he had to ask them. The Rat said little or nothing, only taking care that each guest had what he wanted, and plenty of it, and that Mole had no trouble or anxiety about anything.

They clattered off at last, very grateful and showering wishes of the season, with their jacket pockets stuffed with remembrances for the small brothers and sisters at home. When the door had closed on the last of them and the chink of the lanterns had died away, Mole and Rat kicked the fire up, drew their chairs in, brewed themselves a last nightcap of mulled ale, and discussed the events of the long day. At last the Rat, with a tremendous yawn, said, "Mole, old chap, I'm ready to drop. Sleepy is simply not the word. That your own bunk over on that side? Very well, then, I'll take this. What a ripping little house this is! Everything so handy!"

He clambered into his bunk and rolled himself well up in the blankets, and slumber gathered him forthwith, as a swathe of barley is folded into the arms of the reaping machine.[51]

The weary Mole also was glad to turn in without delay, and soon had his head on his pillow, in great joy and contentment. But ere he closed his eyes he let them wander round his old room, mellow in the glow of the firelight that played or rested on familiar and friendly things which had long been unconsciously a part of him, and now smilingly received him back, without rancour. He was now in just the frame of mind that the tactful Rat had quietly worked to bring about in him. He saw clearly how plain and simple—how narrow, even—it all was; but clearly, too, how much it all meant to him, and the special value of some such anchorage in one's existence. He did not at all want to abandon the new life and its splendid spaces, to turn his back on sun and air and all they offered him and creep home and stay there; the upper world was all too strong, it called to him still, even down there, and he knew he must return to the larger stage. But it was good to think he had this to come back to, this place which was all his own,[52] these things which were so glad to see him again and could always be counted upon for the same simple welcome.

Nancy Barnhart, 1922. Chapter tailpiece for Methuen edition of Mole with his "head on his pillow."

51. *He clambered into his bunk and rolled himself well up in the blankets, and slumber gathered him forthwith, as a swathe of barley is folded into the arms of the reaping machine.* Another technological metaphor.

52. *the upper world was all too strong, it called to him still, even down there, and he knew he must return to the larger stage. But it was good to think he had this to come back to, this place which was all his own.* In a sense, Mole has come out of his burrow to join a more desirable society. Nevertheless, he discovers how far he has come by returning to his humble origins. Peter Hunt succinctly sums it up: "This . . . is the secret narrative of the *Wind in the Willows*, whose origins are uncertain, which speaks to the elements in both the adult and the child—the circle of home and experience: of finding new paths and reconciling them with old places" (*The Wind in the Willows: A Fragmented Arcadia*, 40).

VI

Mr. Toad[1]

Chapter VI is the first of the chapters that developed out of the letters sent by Kenneth Grahame to Alastair in 1907. In all, five chapters—VI, VIII, X, XI, and XII—began in the letters. Nearly all of these letters describe Toad and his exploits. In the first letter, dated May 10, Grahame addresses Alastair as "My Dearest Mouse." In the fifth letter, dated July 17, 1907, Grahame changes his greeting to "My Dear Robinson." Apparently, Grahame made this change at Alastair's request, even though Robinson was the name of the man who shot at Kenneth Grahame at the Bank in 1903. In return, Alastair began to sign his letters "Thine bad boy."

The morbid nicknames may reflect a deeper tension. During the *Wind in the Willows* correspondence, which lasted from May until September of 1907, Alastair had repeatedly requested a visit from his parents. Responding to his father from Littlehampton, Alastair writes, "You must come down for the weekend to pick a nice beef bone with me." In his next letter he writes, "I can't pick a bone by post" and in the next: "Could you come down hear [*sic*] for the weekend please do!" and again "What

It was a bright morning in the early part of summer; the river had resumed its wonted banks and its accustomed pace, and a hot sun seemed to be pulling everything green and bushy and spiky up out of the earth towards him, as if by strings. The Mole and the Water Rat had been up since dawn, very busy on matters connected with boats and the opening of the boating season; painting and varnishing, mending paddles, repairing cushions, hunting for missing boat-hooks, and so on; and were finishing breakfast in their little parlour and eagerly discussing their plans for the day, when a heavy knock sounded at the door.

"Bother!" said the Rat, all over egg.[2] "See who it is, Mole, like a good chap, since you've finished."

The Mole went to attend the summons, and the Rat heard him utter a cry of surprise. Then he flung the parlour door open, and announced with much importance, "Mr. Badger!"

This was a wonderful thing, indeed, that the Badger should pay a formal call on them, or indeed on anybody. He generally had to be caught, if you wanted him badly, as he slipped quietly along a hedgerow of an early morning or a late evening, or else hunted up in his own house in the middle of the Wood,[3] which was a serious undertaking.

do you mean by not coming down for the weekend to pick a bone with me?" Perhaps he asked his father to call him by the name of Kenneth's would-be assassin in a lonely and hurt—albeit vindictive—attempt to express his frustration at his parents' absence.

Alison Prince writes:

> There is something macabre about the fact that the man who had tried to shoot Kenneth at the Bank [in 1903] had been called Robinson. The name must have been mentioned in the house at the time and, even if Mouse had picked it up in all innocence, his insistence on adopting it for his own use is slightly horrifying. (*Kenneth Grahame: An Innocent in the Wild*, 222)

It is clear from both sets of letters—Kenneth's depictions of Toad's exploits and Alastair's responses—that the longer Kenneth and Elspeth ignored seven-year-old Alastair's requests for a visit, the angrier the boy became. Over the course of the summer, Kenneth Grahame's letters become less personal. He skips the usual greetings and news, and dwells entirely on Toad's antics. Each of Kenneth Grahame's biographers has speculated on the dynamic revealed in these letters. Alison Prince writes:

> Chalmers, writing in 1933, depicted Alastair Grahame as an outstandingly talented boy, sensitive, brilliant, witty and unusual. Green, twenty-six years later, rejected this picture as a fabrication of wish-fulfillment on Elspeth's part, and claimed that Mouse was under intolerable pressure from his ambitious parents, and that, far from being brilliant, he was an academic dullard, unable to spare any energy from the struggle of trying to overcome the handicap of his near-blindness.
>
> Neither picture rings quite true. Mouse was undoubtedly cosseted, indulged and admired from his earliest babyhood, and he certainly developed all the unlovable characteristics of the spoiled child; but if he sensed a conditionality underlying the parental rapture, it was not connected at that time with a demand for academic excellence. . . . Like the bemused and scandalized, yet still protective animals of the river bank who tried to save Toad from his own worse excesses, they did their uncomprehending best for Alastair. (Ibid., 265)

1. *VI, Mr. Toad.* In Grahame's holograph manuscript, e. 248, chapter VI first appeared as chapter IV. The IV, has been crossed out in pencil, meaning that Kenneth Grahame added "Mr. Badger" and "Dulce Domum" between chapter III ("The Wild Wood") and "Mr. Toad," which was originally chapter IV.

2. *"Bother!" said the Rat, all over egg.* Rat has egg all over his face, an embarrassing state to be in when visited by Mr. Badger.

3. *He generally had to be caught, if you wanted him badly, as he slipped quietly along a hedgerow of an early morning or a late evening, or else hunted up in his own house in the middle of the Wood.* Badger does not want to be caught off guard. Meeting others is simply too disruptive. Mr. Badger's gruffness mirrors the quiet eccentricities of the Fifth Duke of Portland (see chapter IV, note 46). Despite his antisocial nature, Badger cares a great deal about others—enough to pay a social call when he'd be more apt to go inside for a mid-morning nap.

Shepard's heading illustration for chapter VI.

The Badger strode heavily into the room, and stood looking at the two animals with an expression full of seriousness. The Rat let his egg-spoon fall on the table-cloth, and sat open-mouthed.

"The hour has come!" said the Badger at last with great solemnity.

"What hour?" asked the Rat uneasily, glancing at the clock on the mantelpiece.

"*Whose* hour, you should rather say," replied the Badger. "Why, Toad's hour! The hour of Toad! I said I would take him in hand as soon as the winter was well over, and I'm going to take him in hand to-day!"[4]

"Toad's hour, of course!" cried the Mole delightedly. "Hooray! I remember now! *We'll* teach him to be a sensible Toad!"

"This very morning," continued the Badger, taking an armchair, "as I learnt last night from a trustworthy source, another

4. *"I said I would take him in hand as soon as the winter was well over, and I'm going to take him in hand to-day!"* The term "take him in hand" has double meaning. The principal is the parental role. Toad's father made arrangements for Mr. Badger to guide Toad to adulthood. "Take him in hand" also has a corporal connotation. If a younger person can't behave with decorum, an adult might physically restrain or punish him or her—which is exactly what will happen to Toad. It seems Badger is stopping by for the support of Mole and Rat. In chapter 2 of Dickens's *Great Expectations* (1861), the term is altered to "brought up by hand." Though "by hand" originally means that the child was suckled on a bottle rather than on breast milk, the term means that young Pip is routinely beaten into submission by his sister, twenty years his senior. Though Badger has stepped into the role of mentor

new and exceptionally powerful motor-car will arrive at Toad Hall on approval or return. At this very moment, perhaps, Toad is busy arraying himself in those singularly hideous habiliments so dear to him,[5] which transform him from a (comparatively) good-looking Toad into an Object which throws any decent-minded animal that comes across it into a violent fit.[6] We must be up and doing, ere it is too late. You two animals will accompany me instantly to Toad Hall, and the work of rescue shall be accomplished."

"Right you are!" cried the Rat, starting up. "We'll rescue the poor unhappy animal! We'll convert him![7] He'll be the most converted Toad that ever was before we've done with him!"

They set off up the road on their mission of mercy, Badger leading the way. Animals when in company walk in a proper and sensible manner, in single file,[8] instead of sprawling all across the road and being of no use or support to each other in case of sudden trouble or danger.

They reached the carriage-drive of Toad Hall to find, as the Badger had anticipated, a shiny new motor-car, of great size, painted a bright red (Toad's favourite colour), standing in front of the house.[9] As they neared the door it was flung open, and Mr. Toad, arrayed in goggles, cap, gaiters, and enormous overcoat, came swaggering down the steps, drawing on his gauntleted gloves.[10]

"Hullo! come on, you fellows!" he cried cheerfully on catching sight of them. "You're just in time to come with me for a jolly—to come for a jolly—for a—er—jolly———"

His hearty accents faltered and fell away as he noticed the stern unbending look on the countenances of his silent friends, and his invitation remained unfinished.

The Badger strode up the steps. "Take him inside," he said sternly to his companions. Then, as Toad was hustled through the door, struggling and protesting, he turned to the *chauffeur* in charge of the new motor-car.

and father, no matter what kind of force is employed, his intervention is destined to backfire. Toad in his own boastful nature will later say that he is going to take Rat in hand. See note 3 in this chapter.

5. *At this very moment, perhaps, Toad is busy arraying himself in those singularly hideous habiliments so dear to him.* Habiliments are the apparel, vestments, or garments appropriate to any office or occasion. They can also mean the accessories of war that one wears over ordinary clothing.

When Toad goes driving, he dresses like a knight at a jousting tournament. The ritual of dressing prepares him for the search of other motorists who will be willing to run head on at him. In essence, Toad wants to play the game of chicken.

Grahame uses the archaic language, choosing the word habiliments to evoke the Romantic heroes of the Arthurian era. In *Le Morte d'Arthur* (1470–1485) Malory uses a version of the word: "Alle maner of **abylement** that pretendith to the werre." (book 1, chapter 18), while in Raoul Lefèvre's *L'histoire de Jason* (*History of Jason*, trans. William Caxton), there is reference to the accessories of a knight: "Hauyng the forme and **habylement** of a knight." Incidentally, the *History of Jason* was the first book printed on English soil, by William Caxton in 1477.

6. *which transform him from a (comparatively) good-looking Toad into an Object which throws any decent-minded animal that comes across it into a violent fit.* Notice that Grahame capitalizes the word Object. When dealing with the technological unknown, Grahame takes on the Gothic style of random capitalization. In Grahame's world, the madness brought on by motorcars transforms Toad and other drivers from respectable humans (or Toads) into abstract Objects. Drawing on the tone of previous Gothic works where technology and science repre-

sent a frightful and unknown future, Grahame presents the car as if it were the potion mixed by Dr. Jekyll and Mr. Hyde.

7. *"Right you are!" cried the Rat, starting up. "We'll rescue the poor unhappy animal! We'll convert him!"* The riverbankers take on a rather religious fervor in their belief that Toad's reformation can occur overnight. Mr. Badger's ominous tone is comic because none of the riverbankers consider the fact that Toad's destructive habits have taken a lifetime to develop.

8. *Animals when in company walk in a proper and sensible manner, in single file.* Mr. Badger will lead the riverbankers into battle in the same manner when they go to recapture Toad Hall in the final chapter (see chapter XII, note 3). Arthur Rackham's silhouette illustration best exemplifies the single-file lineup of the riverbankers.

9. *a shiny new motor-car, of great size, painted a bright red (Toad's favourite colour), standing in front of the house.* Only nine models of automobile—Albion, Argyll, Austin, Humber, Napier, Rover, Sunbeam, Vauxhall, and Wolseley—were manufactured in the UK in the years 1907–08, when Grahame wrote *The Wind in the Willows* (see chapter II, note 52).

According to Jan Needle's 1981 sequel, *Wild Wood*, Mr. Toad was partial to a 1907 car called the Armstrong Hardcastle Special Eight (D. Scott-Moncrieff, *Veteran and Edwardian Motor Cars* [London: B. T. Batsford, Ltd., 1955], 67–96).

10. *drawing on his gauntleted gloves.* A gauntlet is a glove, usually of leather, that is covered with plates of steel, and was often worn as part of medieval armor. The glove later evolved to cover the hand and the arm and was used for riding, driving, fencing or wicket-keeping in cricket. Toad is every part a knight as he makes his entrance. Gauntleted gloves were a traditional part of a knight's costume.

This specific line appears in chapter 38 of *Dorothy Vernon of Haddon Hall* (1902), by Charles Major. A popular novel in Grahame's day, it was published on both sides of the Atlantic. Major was a lawyer, born and raised in Indianapolis, Indiana, who wrote melodramas set during the Elizabethan period. The book so captivated readers of the era that it was made into a motion picture starring Mary Pickford in 1924.

The gauntleted glove also appears in Sir Walter Scott's "The Lady of the Lake" (1810): "Such blow no other hand could deal, / Though gauntleted in glove of steel."

Graham Robertson was the only early illustrator to draw Mr. Toad in his complete motoring garb. Robertson's pen-and-ink drawing, which appears on the spine of the first edition, was the very first illustration of Mr. Toad, and differs in style from Robertson's cover illustration and frontispiece.

Silhouette illustration by Arthur Rackham

Shepard's Toad in motoring garb.

"I'm afraid you won't be wanted to-day," he said.[11] "Mr. Toad has changed his mind. He will not require the car. Please understand that this is final. You needn't wait." Then he followed the others inside and shut the door.

"Now then!" he said to the Toad, when the four of them stood together in the Hall, "first of all, take those ridiculous things off!"

"Shan't!"[12] replied Toad, with great spirit. "What is the meaning of this gross outrage? I demand an instant explanation."

"Take them off him, then, you two," ordered the Badger briefly.

They had to lay Toad out on the floor, kicking and calling all sorts of names, before they could get to work properly. Then the Rat sat on him, and the Mole got his motor-clothes off him bit by bit, and they stood him up on his legs again. A good deal of his blustering spirit seemed to have evaporated with the removal of his fine panoply.[13] Now that he was merely Toad, and no longer the Terror of the Highway,[14] he giggled

Shepard's illustration of Toad was published in the 1930s and recycled onto the cover in 1953.

11. *he turned to the chauffeur in charge of the new motor-car.*

"I'm afraid you won't be wanted today," he said. The servants in *The Wind in the Willows* have walk-on parts at best. The chauffeur is dismissed before he can even open his mouth. In "Language and Class in *The Wind in the Willows*," Peter Hunt points out that in Jan Needle's *Wild Wood,* the chauffeur is disastrously affected when Mr. Badger dismisses him:

> "If Toad didn't have no right to sack you, what right could they [the river-bankers] possibly have? Sheer vicious arrogance is what! What do they care? What do they care about your job? About your Ma and your sisters and brothers?" (62)

Illustrators have followed Grahame's cue and kept the servants off stage by not including the chauffeur.

12. *"Shan't!"* Rarely used today, *shan't* also recalls the tantrum thrown by young Michael in chapter 2 of J. M. Barrie's *Peter Pan*:

> "I won't go to bed," he had shouted, like one who still believed that he had the last word on the subject, "I won't, I won't. Nana, it isn't six o'clock yet. Oh dear, oh dear, I *shan't* love you any more, Nana. I tell you I won't be bathed, I won't, I won't!"

13. *panoply.* A complete suit of armor from ancient or medieval times that is ornate, colorful, and worn as a trophy.

14. *Terror of the Highway.* Around the time Grahame wrote *The Wind in the Wil-*

lows, automotive mystery novels such as G. Sidney Paternoster's *The Motor Pirate* (1904) surged in popularity. Though published by L. C. Page in Boston, *The Motor Pirate* is set in rural Berkshire, England. Dressed in much the same garb that Mr. Toad later wears—leathers from head to foot and goggles—the Motor Pirate races through Berkshire terrorizing the countryside and towns, robbing other motorists, and shooting at them from his astonishingly fast, boat-shaped car. The car is distinguished by the fact that it can reach speeds upwards of 50 mph. Paternoster's books mark the first appearances of road rage and carjacking in fiction.

The Motor Pirate was followed, in 1906, by *The Cruise of the Conqueror, Being the Further Adventures of the Motor Pilot* (Boston: L. C. Page). *The Lady of the Blue Motor* (New York: Grosset & Dunlap, 1907) is a romance mystery of a young man in pursuit of a beautiful young woman who races away in a blue motorcar. (This is reminiscent of the young Constance Smedley arriving in Cookham Dean via automobile.) *The Master Criminal* (New York: Cupples & Leon, 1907) was republished with the title: *The Hand of the Spoiler* (1908) in London by Hodder & Stoughton. In 1916 the book was made into a silent film and retitled *In the Hands of the Spoiler.*

Though Grahame never mentioned

Cover illustrations for *The Motor Pirate* (1904) and *The Lady of the Blue Motor* (1907).

feebly and looked from one to the other appealingly, seeming quite to understand the situation.

"You knew it must come to this, sooner or later, Toad," the Badger explained severely. "You've disregarded all the warnings we've given you, you've gone on squandering the money your father left you,[15] and you're getting us animals a bad name in the district by your furious driving and your smashes and your rows with the police.[16] Independence is all very well, but we animals never allow our friends to make fools of themselves beyond a certain limit; and that limit you've reached. Now, you're a good fellow in many respects, and I don't want to be too hard on you. I'll make one more effort to bring you to reason. You will come with me into the smoking-room,[17] and there you will hear some facts about yourself; and we'll see whether you come out of that room the same Toad that you went in."

He took Toad firmly by the arm, led him into the smoking-room, and closed the door behind them.

"*That's* no good!" said the Rat contemptuously. "*Talking* to Toad'll never cure him. He'll *say* anything."

They made themselves comfortable in armchairs and waited patiently. Through the closed door they could just hear the long continuous drone of the Badger's voice, rising and falling in waves of oratory; and presently they noticed that the sermon began to be punctuated at intervals by long-drawn sobs, evidently proceeding from the bosom of Toad,[18]

Spine of Methuen first edition. Graham Robertson's Toad in motoring garb, 1908.

Barnhart. Badger's intervention, 1922.

who was a soft-hearted and affectionate fellow, very easily converted—for the time being—to any point of view.

After some three-quarters of an hour the door opened, and the Badger reappeared, solemnly leading by the paw a very limp and dejected Toad. His skin hung baggily about him, his legs wobbled, and his cheeks were furrowed by the tears so plentifully called forth by the Badger's moving discourse.

"Sit down there, Toad," said the Badger kindly, pointing to

these books, it is possible that he was familiar with them because he regularly read manuscripts for John Lane when these books were being edited. Whether Grahame read or knew them in manuscript form, the public obsession with faster and better cars and the taste for automotive mysteries were on the rise several years before Grahame wrote about the antics of Toad (see chapter X, note 1).

15. *"you've gone on squandering the money your father left you."* Humphrey Carpenter (Secret Gardens) speculates that Toad's father earned his fortune in "the cotton trade or something less decorous" (164). At any rate, Toad's father is an industrialist, not part of the old squirearchy that has inherited land and title. (A squirearchy is a collective body of squires, landed proprietors, or country gentry; the class to which squires belong, regarded especially in respect of its political or social influence.)

16. *"and your rows with the police."* A violent, noisy disturbance, commotion or quarrel. A word typically used in the United Kingdom and not the United States, it rhymes with browse.

17. *"You will come with me into the smoking-room."* Large old houses and halls often had smoking rooms, specifically used for after-dinner smoking. These rooms also typically functioned as places where the men would retreat from the company of women.

18. *by long-drawn sobs, evidently proceeding from the bosom of Toad.* Barnhart includes this black-and-white illustration of Mr. Badger haranguing Toad about his spendthrift ways and irresponsibility. While Badger is a stand-in for Toad's missing father, Grahame never discloses what hap-

pened to the senior Mr. Toad. This theme of the separation of children from their parents appears again in chapter VII, "The Piper at the Gates of Dawn." Perhaps this element stemmed from Kenneth Grahame's own separation from his mother at the age of four. Likewise, in the correspondence between Alastair and his father, when Alastair needs him the most, Grahame remains distant.

Badger's intervention is not easy to illustrate, and consequently, no one but Barnhart attempted it. Part of the difficulty is that, in Grahame's text, the action is seen from the point of view of Mole and Rat, who can see only the closed door—not Mr. Badger or Toad *behind* the door.

a chair. "My friends," he went on, "I am pleased to inform you that Toad has at last seen the error of his ways. He is truly sorry for his misguided conduct in the past, and he has undertaken to give up motor-cars entirely and for ever. I have his solemn promise to that effect."

"That is very good news," said the Mole gravely.

"Very good news indeed," observed the Rat dubiously, "if only—*if* only———"

He was looking very hard at Toad as he said this, and could not help thinking he perceived something vaguely resembling a twinkle in that animal's still sorrowful eye.

"There's only one thing more to be done," continued the gratified Badger. "Toad, I want you solemnly to repeat, before your friends here, what you fully admitted to me in the smoking-room just now. First, you are sorry for what you've done, and you see the folly of it all?"

There was a long, long pause. Toad looked desperately this way and that, while the other animals waited in grave silence. At last he spoke.

"No!" he said, a little sullenly, but stoutly; "I'm *not* sorry. And it wasn't folly at all! It was simply glorious!"

"What?" cried the Badger, greatly scandalised. "You backsliding animal, didn't you tell me just now, in there———"

"Oh, yes, yes, in *there*," said Toad impatiently. "I'd have said anything in *there*. You're so eloquent, dear Badger, and so moving, and so convincing, and put all your points so frightfully well—you can do what you like with me in *there*, and you know it. But I've been searching my mind since, and going over things in it, and I find that I'm not a bit sorry or repentant really, so it's no earthly good saying I am; now, is it?"

"Then you don't promise," said the Badger, "never to touch a motor-car again?"

"Certainly not!" replied Toad emphatically. "On the contrary, I faithfully promise that the very first motor-car I see, poop-poop! off I go in it!"

"Told you so, didn't I?" observed the Rat to the Mole.

"Very well, then," said the Badger firmly, rising to his feet. "Since you won't yield to persuasion, we'll try what force can do. I feared it would come to this all along. You've often asked us three to come and stay with you, Toad, in this handsome house of yours; well, now we're going to. When we've converted you to a proper point of view we may quit, but not before. Take him upstairs, you two, and lock him up in his bedroom, while we arrange matters between ourselves."

"It's for your own good, Toady, you know," said the Rat kindly, as Toad, kicking and struggling, was hauled up the stairs by his two faithful friends.[19] "Think what fun we shall all have together, just as we used to, when you've quite got over this—this painful attack of yours!"

"We'll take great care of everything for you till you're well, Toad," said the Mole; "and we'll see your money isn't wasted, as it has been."

"No more of those regrettable incidents with the police, Toad," said the Rat, as they thrust him into his bedroom.

"And no more weeks in hospital, being ordered about by female nurses, Toad," added the Mole, turning the key on him.[20]

They descended the stair, Toad shouting abuse at them through the keyhole; and the three friends then met in conference on the situation.

"It's going to be a tedious business," said the Badger, sighing. "I've never seen Toad so determined. However, we will see it out. He must never be left an instant unguarded. We shall have to take it in turns to be with him, till the poison has worked itself out of his system."[21]

They arranged watches accordingly. Each animal took it in turns to sleep in Toad's room at night, and they divided the day up between them. At first Toad was undoubtedly very trying to his careful guardians. When his violent paroxysms possessed him[22] he would arrange bedroom chairs in rude resemblance of

19. *"It's for your own good, Toady, you know," said the Rat kindly, as Toad, kicking and struggling, was hauled up the stairs by his two faithful friends.* Wyndham Payne's 1927 illustration of Rat and Mole pushing Toad up the stairs was repeated by Ernest Shepard four years later. Payne's animals are young and far more physically fit than Shepard's dumpy, rather middle-aged riverbankers.

20. *"And no more weeks in hospital, being ordered about by female nurses, Toad," added the Mole, turning the key on him.* Kenneth Grahame and his books often reflect attitudes toward the roles of women in 1908. In Victorian and Edwardian England, many women were socially a level below the riverbankers. They were the servants, washerwomen, caretakers of children. Even the wives and daughters of the upper classes were kept at home to learn such things as music and sewing, while the boys were sent off to school. As a young woman, Elspeth Grahame remained in the house of her stepfather, where she managed the house but never gained the formal education that would have put her in the same intellectual rank as her husband and his peers.

During a relapse of his pneumonia in 1899, Kenneth Grahame was nursed by his sister, Helen, and his London housekeeper, Sarah Bath. At this time Elspeth Thompson worked herself into the equation, wooing Grahame all the way to Cornwall, where he went for the summer to recuperate. They were married by the end of July. Perhaps Grahame resented these dependent months, and expresses it here when Toad is kept at home and forced into recovery.

21. *"We shall have to take it in turns to be with him, till the poison has worked itself out of his system."* Though published nearly four decades later, in 1945, Evelyn Waugh's *Brideshead Revisited* seems to have been

influenced by *The Wind in the Willows.* Waugh works with a similar theme in his novel—well-to-do characters with considerable wealth dissipate themselves through alcohol—while their devoted family and friends stand by them and unsuccessfully intervene.

In *The Picturesque Prison: Evelyn Waugh and His Writing* (Montreal: McGill-Queens University Press, 1983), Jeffrey M. Heath writes about Waugh's relationships with his students before he wrote his masterpiece:

> From September 1925 to February 1927, when his headmaster sacked him for drunkenness . . . Waugh taught at Aston Clinton in Buckinghamshire, in "a school for backward peers." . . . He developed attachments to several of his pupils, whom he soon ceased to call "lunatics" and "poor mad boys." He invited them to tea in his rooms, went swimming and played tennis with them; to one of them he read *The Wind in the Willows*. (23)

The book must have remained a favorite with Waugh; another biographer makes note that Waugh read *The Wind in the Willows* to his friend Lady Diana on a train trip to Scotland in 1932 (Douglas Lane Patey, *The Life of Evelyn Waugh: A Critical Biography* [Williston, Vermont: Blackwell Publishing, 2001], 96).

22. *When his violent paroxysms possessed him.* A paroxysm is a periodic increase in the acuteness or severity of a disease; a violent temporary fit or convulsion of laughter, rage, or excitement.

23. *he would arrange bedroom chairs in rude resemblance of a motor-car and would crouch on the foremost of them, bent forward and staring fixedly ahead, making uncouth and ghastly noises, till the climax was reached, when, turning a complete somersault, he would lie prostrate amidst the ruins of the chairs, apparently com-*

Payne's stair scene, 1927.

a motor-car and would crouch on the foremost of them, bent forward and staring fixedly ahead, making uncouth and ghastly noises, till the climax was reached, when, turning a complete somersault, he would lie prostrate amidst the ruins of the chairs, apparently completely satisfied for the moment.[23] As time passed, however, these painful seizures grew gradually less frequent, and his friends strove to divert his mind into fresh channels. But his interest in other matters did not seem to revive, and he grew apparently languid and depressed.

One fine morning the Rat, whose turn it was to go on duty, went upstairs to relieve Badger, whom he found fidgeting to

Shepard's stair scene, 1931.

be off and stretch his legs in a long ramble round his wood and down his earths and burrows. "Toad's still in bed," he told the Rat, outside the door. "Can't get much out of him, except, 'O leave him alone, he wants nothing, perhaps he'll be better presently, it may pass off in time, don't be unduly anxious,' and so on. Now, you look out, Rat! When Toad's quiet and submissive, and playing at being the hero of a Sunday-school prize, then he's at his artfullest. There's sure to be something up. I know him. Well, now, I must be off."

"How are you to-day, old chap?" inquired the Rat cheerfully, as he approached Toad's bedside.

He had to wait some minutes for an answer. At last a feeble voice replied, "Thank you so much, dear Ratty! So good of you to inquire! But first tell me how you are yourself, and the excellent Mole?"

"O, *we're* all right," replied the Rat. "Mole," he added incautiously, "is going out for a run round with Badger. They'll be out till luncheon time, so you and I will spend a pleasant morning together, and I'll do my best to amuse you. Now

pletely satisfied for the moment. Freud would have made a lot of this passage. Peter Green comments at length on Toad's histrionics:

> If . . . Toad was partially intended to satirize Alastair himself, then some of his actions can be explained as mere childishness—his wailing and leg-kicking, and refusal to be comforted. . . . But this can hardly be used as an overall explanation; for the most part . . . Toad's behaviour is irresistibly suggestive of an adult manic depressive. His entire life is a series of violent excuses matched by balancing moods of black and lachrymose despair; he shows the classic symptoms of irresponsibility, faddishness, bombastic fantasizing, tearful but impermanent repentance. Even A. A. Milne spotted something of this when he came to write *Toad of Toad Hall*: Alfred the horse remarks to Rat, after one of Toad's more curious outbursts: "Psychological—that was the word he wanted. Not encyclopaedia." (*Kenneth Grahame: A Biography*, 282)

24. *"Dear, kind Rat," murmured Toad.* Variant, e. 248: "Dear kind Rat!" murmured Toad. Grahame had originally omitted the comma and added the exclamation point to this sentence, making it sound more urgent.

Shepard was the only illustrator to pick up on Grahame's parody of a Dickensian deathbed scene. In Shepard's version Toad collapses after Mr. Badger takes away his motorcar. Shepard pushed the idea a bit further with the illustration of Toad laid out like Mr. Barkis in Cruikshank's 1850 illustration—"I find Mr. Barkis going out with the tide"—in *David Copperfield.* Toad is on his deathbed, while the Rat, paw to face, watches the ghastly unfolding melodrama.

Cruikshank's "I find Mr. Barkis going out with the tide," 1850.

Shepard's Victorian deathbed scene, 1931.

jump up, there's a good fellow, and don't lie moping there on a fine morning like this!"

"Dear, kind Rat," murmured Toad,[24] "how little you realise my condition, and how very far I am from 'jumping up' now—if ever! But do not trouble about me. I hate being a burden to my friends, and I do not expect to be one much longer. Indeed, I almost hope not."

"Well, I hope not, too," said the Rat heartily. "You've been a fine bother to us all this time, and I'm glad to hear it's going to stop. And in weather like this, and the boating season just beginning! It's too bad of you, Toad! It isn't the trouble we mind, but you're making us miss such an awful lot."

"I'm afraid it *is* the trouble you mind, though," replied the

Toad languidly. "I can quite understand it. It's natural enough. You're tired of bothering about me. I mustn't ask you to do anything further. I'm a nuisance, I know."

"You are, indeed," said the Rat. "But I tell you, I'd take any trouble on earth for you, if only you'd be a sensible animal."

"If I thought that, Ratty," murmured Toad, more feebly than ever, "then I would beg you—for the last time, probably—to step round to the village as quickly as possible—even now it may be too late—and fetch the doctor. But don't you bother. It's only a trouble, and perhaps we may as well let things take their course."

"Why, what do you want a doctor for?" inquired the Rat, coming closer and examining him. He certainly lay very still and flat, and his voice was weaker and his manner much changed.

"Surely you have noticed of late———" murmured Toad. "But, no—why should you? Noticing things is only a trouble. To-morrow, indeed, you may be saying to yourself, 'O, if only I had noticed sooner! If only I had done something!' But no; it's a trouble. Never mind—forget that I asked."

"Look here, old man," said the Rat, beginning to get rather alarmed, "of course I'll fetch a doctor to you, if you really think you want him. But you can hardly be bad enough for that yet. Let's talk about something else."

"I fear, dear friend," said Toad, with a sad smile, "that 'talk' can do little in a case like this—or doctors either, for that matter; still, one must grasp at the slightest straw. And, by the way—while you are about it—I *hate* to give you additional trouble, but I happen to remember that you will pass the door—would you mind at the same time asking the lawyer to step up? It would be a convenience to me, and there are moments—perhaps I should say there is *a* moment—when one must face disagreeable tasks, at whatever cost to exhausted nature!"

"A lawyer! O, he must be really bad!" the affrighted Rat

said to himself, as he hurried from the room, not forgetting, however, to lock the door carefully behind him.

Outside, he stopped to consider. The other two were far away, and he had no one to consult.

"It's best to be on the safe side," he said, on reflection. "I've known Toad fancy himself frightfully bad before, without the slightest reason; but I've never heard him ask for a lawyer! If there's nothing really the matter, the doctor will tell him he's

Payne. Mr. Toad's escape, 1927.

an old ass, and cheer him up; and that will be something gained. I'd better humour him and go; it won't take very long." So he ran off to the village on his errand of mercy.

The Toad, who had hopped lightly out of bed as soon as he heard the key turned in the lock, watched him eagerly from the window till he disappeared down the carriage-drive. Then, laughing heartily, he dressed as quickly as possible in the smartest suit he could lay hands on at the moment, filled his pockets with cash which he took from a small drawer in the dressing-table, and next, knotting the sheets from his bed together and tying one end of the improvised rope round the central mullion of the handsome Tudor window which formed such a feature of his bedroom,[25] he scrambled out, slid lightly to the ground,[26] and, taking the opposite direction to the Rat, marched off light-heartedly, whistling a merry tune.

It was a gloomy luncheon for Rat when the Badger and the Mole at length returned, and he had to face them at table with his pitiful and unconvincing story. The Badger's caustic, not to say brutal, remarks may be imagined, and therefore passed over; but it was painful to the Rat that even the Mole, though he took his friend's side as far as possible, could not help saying, "You've been a bit of a duffer this time, Ratty![27] Toad, too, of all animals!"

"He did it awfully well," said the crestfallen Rat.

"He did *you* awfully well!" rejoined the Badger hotly. "However, talking won't mend matters. He's got clear away for the time, that's certain; and the worst of it is, he'll be so conceited with what he'll think is his cleverness that he may commit any folly. One comfort is, we're free now, and needn't waste any more of our precious time doing sentry-go.[28] But we'd better continue to sleep at Toad Hall for a while longer. Toad may be brought back at any moment—on a stretcher, or between two policemen."

So spoke the Badger, not knowing what the future held in store,[29] or how much water, and of how turbid a character, was

25. *knotting the sheets from his bed together and tying one end of the improvised rope round the central mullion of the handsome Tudor window which formed such a feature of his bedroom.* This scene is the germ of the entire book. Grahame outlined the escape in detail in his first letter to his son, dated May 10, 1907.

My Darling Mouse

This is a birth-day letter, To wish you very many happy returns of the day. I wish we could have been all together, but we shall meet again soon, & then we will have treats. I have sent you two picture books, one about Brer Rabbit, from Daddy, & one about some other animals, from Mummy and we ~~a~~ have sent you a boat painted red, with mast & sails, to sail in the round pond by the windmill—& Mummy has sent you a boathook to catch it when it comes to shore. Also Mummy has sent you some sand-toys to play in the sand with, and a card game.

Have you heard about the Toad? He was never taken prisoner by brigands at all. It was all a horrid low trick of his. He wrote that letter himself—the letter saying that a hundred pounds must be put in the hollow tree. And he got out of the window early one morning, & went off to a town called Buggleton & went to the Red Lion Hotel & there he found a party that had just motored down from London, & while they were having breakfast he went into the stable-yard & found their motor-car & went off in it without even saying Poop-poop! And now he has vanished & every one is looking for him, including the police. I fear he is a bad low animal.

Goodbye, from

Your loving Daddy.

It is significant that Kenneth Grahame gave his son a copy of *Brer Rabbit*. Long

Grahame's favorite book, *Brer Rabbit* contains fables where animals wear clothing, behave like people, and speak in the dialect of the American South. Grahame took the book on a holiday to visit his cousin Annie after its publication in the 1880s. In her letters after Kenneth died, Annie Grahame reported that Grahame often quoted from the book. The southern dialect can be a challenge to follow—not unlike the language of the love letters Grahame wrote to Elspeth while they were courting.

Mullions are any of the usually vertical bars dividing the glass panes in a window, especially in Gothic architecture. Usually these would be in stone. Eleanor Graham wrote the following on Kenneth Grahame and authority.

> Kenneth Grahame had himself suffered all the small injustices, wrongs and humiliations endured by most children of his day, but he looked back on them without anger, without self pity, and escaped sentimentality, surely, by a miracle. In his young days he had defeated authority over and over again—far too often to have respect for it. Frequently locked in his room as a punishment, he had learned to escape by the window and to time his return comfortably before the hour of release. Often sent to bed hungry, there were always devoted housemaids who crept up back stairs to console him with cold pudding. (*Kenneth Grahame* [New York: Henry Z. Walck, 1963], 32–33)

26. *he scrambled out, slid lightly to the ground.* The scene of Toad's escape might also have its roots in an early, unsigned piece by Grahame that was published in *St. James* on November 19, 1890. According to Alison Prince:

> Grahame scored an odd success with a satirical piece about Parnell, whose divorce was linked in the public mind with a farcical episode of escape through a bedroom window from the house of Mrs. O'Shea. Grahame retold this event in the form of a conversation (overheard by the cat) between a waterspout and a verandah, both of them a little battered as a result of Parnell's flight of the previous night. As the waterspout remarked reflectively, "I've had a burglar down me, and a schoolboy or two, but never the idol of a nation's hopes and aspirations . . ."
>
> The unsigned piece survives only because Sidney Ward kept it in a file of unpublished reminiscences. . . . In conversation with Kenneth himself, Ward remarked, "I say, Grahame, did you see that gorgeous conversation between a balcony and a waterspout in the *St James* last night?' "Yes," said K. G., "I wrote it!" (*Kenneth Grahame: An Innocent in the Wild Wood*, 84). Charles Stewart Parnell, Founder of the Irish Parliamentary Party and known as the uncrowned king of Ireland, met his political downfall when he fell in love with a married aristocrat, Katherine O'Shea. The two were later wed.

27. *"You've been a bit of a duffer this time, Ratty!"* A colloquialism for a person without practical ability. An incapable, inefficient, or useless individual in business; the reverse of an adept or competent person. A fool.

28. *"we're free now, and needn't waste any more of our precious time doing sentry-go."* The term refers to an armed soldier or marine posted at a specified point to keep guard and prevent the passing of unauthorized people. Individuals stand sentry to prevent surprise attacks and to keep an eye on the enemy in the field. In this case, the riverbankers have been taking turns making sure Toad stays locked up.

Shepard. Mr. Toad's escape, 1931.

29. *So spoke the Badger, not knowing what the future held in store.* In manuscript e. 248, this paragraph sits alone on the page. All early editions have the paragraph attached to the previous block of text.

to run under bridges before Toad should sit at ease again in his ancestral Hall.

Meanwhile, Toad, gay and irresponsible, was walking briskly along the high road, some miles from home. At first he had taken by-paths, and crossed many fields, and changed his course several times, in case of pursuit; but now, feeling by this time safe from recapture, and the sun smiling brightly on him, and all Nature joining in a chorus of approval to the song of self-praise that his own heart was singing to him, he almost danced along the road in his satisfaction and conceit.

"Smart piece of work that!" he remarked to himself chuckling. "Brain against brute force—and brain came out on the top—as it's bound to do. Poor old Ratty! My! won't he catch it when the Badger gets back! A worthy fellow, Ratty, with many good qualities, but very little intelligence and absolutely no education. I must take him in hand some day,[30] and see if I can make something of him."

Filled full of conceited thoughts such as these he strode

30. *"A worthy fellow, Ratty, with many good qualities, but very little intelligence and absolutely no education. I must take him in hand some day."* See note 4 in this chapter.

Shepard's Red Lion Inn, 1931.

along, his head in the air, till he reached a little town, where the sign of "The Red Lion,"[31] swinging across the road half-way down the main street, reminded him that he had not breakfasted that day, and that he was exceedingly hungry after his long walk. He marched into the Inn, ordered the best luncheon that could be provided at so short a notice, and sat down to eat it in the coffee-room.

He was about half-way through his meal when an only too familiar sound, approaching down the street, made him start and fall a-trembling all over. The poop-poop! drew nearer and nearer, the car could be heard to turn into the inn-yard and come to a stop, and Toad had to hold on to the leg of the table to conceal his over-mastering emotion.[32] Presently the party entered the coffee-room, hungry, talkative, and gay, voluble on their experiences of the morning and the merits of the chariot that had brought them along so well. Toad listened eagerly, all ears,[33] for a time; at last he could stand it no longer. He slipped out of the room quietly, paid his bill at the bar, and as soon as he got outside sauntered round quietly to the inn-yard. "There cannot be any harm," he said to himself, "in my only just *looking* at it!"

The car stood in the middle of the yard, quite unattended, the stable-helps and other hangers-on being all at their dinner.[34] Toad walked slowly round it, inspecting, criticising, musing deeply.

"I wonder," he said to himself presently, "I wonder if this sort of car *starts* easily?"[35]

Next moment, hardly knowing how it came about, he found he had hold of the handle and was turning it. As the familiar sound broke forth, the old passion seized on Toad and completely mastered him, body and soul. As if in a dream he found himself, somehow, seated in the driver's seat; as if in a dream, he pulled the lever and swung the car round the yard and out through the archway; and, as if in a

31. *"The Red Lion."* The Red Lion is a common name for inns and establishments throughout the United Kingdom. However, there is a specific Red Lion hotel in Henley-on-Thames, across the river from Cookham Dean. The hotel is 250 years older than the eighteenth-century bridge it overlooks and has provided lodging for three different kings of England since the fifteenth century.

In his first letter to Alastair, Grahame calls the generic town Buggleton, much in the way he uses the word Buggins's in chapter V (see note 43 in that chapter).

Grahame also mentions the Red Lion in *The Golden Age,* chapter 12 ("The Roman Road"):

> I tried to imagine what it would be like when I got there. . . . The rest had to be patched up from the little grey market-town where twice a year we went to have our hair cut; hence, in the result, Vespasian's amphitheatre was approached by muddy little streets, wherein the Red Lion and the Blue Boar, with Somebody's Entire along their front.

Like the illustration of Mole and Rat looking at the birdcage in the window in "Dulce Domum," Shepard manages to master the ambiguity of size with an illustration of the cigar-smoking Toad strutting into the Red Lion pub. Toad is barely a foot high, but he looks so pompous that he seems larger than he actually is.

32. *Toad had to hold on to the leg of the table to conceal his over-mastering emotion.* Odysseus straps himself to the ship's mast in order not to be seduced by sirens singing. Likewise, Toad grabs hold of the table leg until he succumbs. Mary Deforest points out: "the motor car parodies the song of sirens, which enchanted Ulysses. The Homeric hero took the precaution of plugging his

crew's ears with wax, so that he could listen to the song without . . . crashing his boat" ("The Wind in the Willows: A Tale for Two Readers," *Classical and Modern Literature* 10, no. 1 [1989]: 83). See chapter IV, note 23.

33. *all ears.* Toads do not have external ears, but they do have external eardrums behind their eyes.

34. *the stable-helps and other hangers-on being all at their dinner.* While the need for stables, stable help, and blacksmiths diminished with the rise of the automobile, there was a sudden need for auto garages and mechanics. Many of those who had worked with horses found themselves transitioning into new car-related professions.

35. *"I wonder if this sort of car* starts *easily?"* Though there is no evidence that Toad uses a key to start the car, such common cars as the Model A Ford (circa 1903–05) did require a key to turn the ignition switch. The handle that Toad turns to start the car is most likely a hand crank starter. The visitors to the inn have possibly left the key in the ignition, which was switched on before Toad turned the handle. At any rate, with the car unattended, Toad is able to turn the key, then the crank at the front of the car, which starts it.

36. *as if in a dream, he pulled the lever and swung the car round the yard and out through the archway; and, as if in a dream, all sense of right and wrong, all fear of obvious consequences, seemed temporarily suspended.* In "A Sadder and a Wiser Rat / He Rose the Morrow Morn: Echoes of the Romantics in Kenneth Grahame's *The Wind in the Willows*," Lesley Willis points out that this passage resembles lines 554–55 of part 7 of Coleridge's "Rime of the Ancient Mariner": "But swift as dreams, myself I found

dream, all sense of right and wrong, all fear of obvious consequences, seemed temporarily suspended.[36] He increased his pace, and as the car devoured the street and leapt forth on the high road through the open country, he was only conscious that he was Toad once more, Toad at his best and highest, Toad the terror, the traffic-queller, the Lord of the lone trail, before whom all must give way or be smitten into nothingness and everlasting night.[37] He chanted as he flew, and the car responded with sonorous drone; the miles were eaten up under him as he sped he knew not whither, fulfilling his instincts, living his hour, reckless of what might come to him.

"To my mind," observed the Chairman of the Bench of Magistrates cheerfully, "the *only* difficulty that presents itself in this otherwise very clear case is, how we can possibly make it sufficiently hot for the incorrigible rogue and hardened ruffian whom we see cowering in the dock before us. Let me see: he has been found guilty, on the clearest evidence, first, of stealing a valuable motor-car; secondly, of driving to the public danger; and, thirdly, of gross impertinence to the rural police. Mr. Clerk, will you tell us, please, what is the very stiffest penalty we can impose for each of these offences? Without, of course, giving the prisoner the benefit of any doubt, because there isn't any."

The Clerk scratched his nose with his pen. "Some people would consider," he observed, "that stealing the motor-car was the worst offence; and so it is. But cheeking the police undoubtedly carries the severest penalty; and so it ought. Supposing you were to say twelve months for the theft, which is mild; and three years for the furious driving, which is lenient; and fifteen years for the cheek,[38] which was pretty bad sort of cheek, judging by what we've heard from the witness-box, even if you only believe one-tenth part of what you heard, and

I never believe more myself—those figures, if added together correctly, tot[39] up to nineteen years———"

"First-rate!" said the Chairman.

"—So you had better make it a round twenty years and be on the safe side," concluded the Clerk.

"An excellent suggestion!" said the Chairman approvingly. "Prisoner! Pull yourself together and try and stand up straight.

Bransom's Toad in jail, 1913.

/ Within the Pilot's boat" (*Children's Literature Association Quarterly* 13, no. 3 [1988]: 108–11).

37. *Toad at his best and highest, Toad the terror, the traffic-queller, the Lord of the lone trail, before whom all must give way or be smitten into nothingness and everlasting night.* As much as Grahame didn't care for cars, or drivers like Toad, he would have known a great deal about them and the culture of people who loved the new and developing technology. After taking a lackluster degree at Oxford, Grahame's brother-in-law Courtauld-Thomson decided to design cars. He founded the Coupé Company and designed and sold "well-sprung" coaches that were fitted with tires invented by his stepfather, Fletcher Moulton. Courtauld-Thomson took the venture abroad by setting up the company in Alaska as well. See Prince, *Kenneth Grahame: An Innocent in the Wild Wood*, 198.

38. *"and fifteen years for the cheek."* In "An Epic in Arcadia: The Pastoral World of *The Wind in the Willows*," Geraldine Poss points out that if Toad had fulfilled his twenty-year jail sentence, it would have been an epic term, ". . . the same amount of time Odysseus spent away from home before Athene secured Zeus' permission to free him from Calypso" (*Children's Literature* 4 [1975]: 87).

39. *tot.* To add up.

It's going to be twenty years for you this time. And mind, if you appear before us again, upon any charge whatever, we shall have to deal with you very seriously!"

Then the brutal minions of the law fell upon the hapless Toad;[40] loaded him with chains, and dragged him from the Court House, shrieking, praying, protesting; across the marketplace, where the playful populace, always as severe upon detected crime as they are sympathetic and helpful when one is merely "wanted," assailed him with jeers, carrots, and popular catch-words; past hooting school children, their innocent faces lit up with the pleasure they ever derive from the sight of a gentleman in difficulties; across the hollow-sounding drawbridge, below the spiky portcullis,[41] under the frowning archway of the grim old castle, whose ancient towers soared high overhead; past guardrooms full of grinning soldiery off duty, past sentries who coughed in a horrid, sarcastic way, because that is as much as a sentry on his post dare do to show his contempt and abhorrence of crime; up time-worn winding stairs, past men-at-arms in casquet and corselet of steel,[42] darting threatening looks through their vizards;[43] across courtyards, where mastiffs strained at their leash and pawed the air to get at him;[44] past ancient warders, their halberds leant against the wall,[45] dozing over a pasty and a flagon of brown ale;[46] on and on, past the rack-chamber and the thumbscrew-room,[47] past the turning that led to the private scaffold, till they reached the door of the grimmest dungeon that lay in the heart of the innermost keep. There at last they paused, where an ancient gaoler sat fingering a bunch of mighty keys.[48]

"Oddsbodikins!"[49] said the sergeant of police, taking off his helmet and wiping his forehead. "Rouse thee, old loon,[50] and take over from us this vile Toad, a criminal of deepest guilt and matchless artfulness and resource. Watch and ward him with all thy skill; and mark thee well, greybeard, should aught

40. *Then the brutal minions of the law fell upon the hapless Toad.* A derogatory reference to police officers. Toad is now caught in the dangerous social mechanisms of the Wide World, where the riverbankers cannot protect him.

41. *portcullis.* A strong gate made up of vertical and horizontal bars of either wood or iron. Suspended by chains, and made to slide up and down in vertical grooves at either side of the gateway, the lower vertical bars were pointed, allowing the gate to close quickly on invaders. The word *portcullis* came into the English language in the 1300s. Milton uses it in *Paradise Lost* (1667), book 2, line 874: "And towards the Gate rouling her bestial train, / Forthwith the huge Portcullis high up drew."

42. *casquet and corselet of steel.* A casquet is a light and open helmet. A corselet is a garment, usually tight-fitting, covering the body as distinct from the limbs.

43. *vizards.* A mask or visor.

44. *where mastiffs strained at their leash and pawed the air to get at him.* A mastiff is a large, powerful dog with a broad head, drooping ears, and pendulous lips. They are commonly used as guard dogs and for fighting. Graham Robertson, who, as noted earlier, lived next to Grahame while he was writing *The Wind in the Willows*, had three large sheepdogs. Though diminutive in comparison to the muscular mastiff, Robertson's Portly was just as formidable when not restrained:

> One day when I was standing at our gate, a young man on a bicycle came slowly by on the up grade. Close behind him trotted Portly with an odd, rapt expression which I knew and feared. Suddenly he rose on his hind-legs, took

the tail of the rider's coat softly between his teeth—and gave a sharp tug. Off came the young man backwards, Portly vanished into the hedge, and there was nothing to account for the catastrophe. (Graham Robertson, *Time Was* [London: Hamish Hamilton, 1931], 330)

45. *their halberds leant against the wall.* A halberd is a combination of a spear and a battle axe, and was commonly used during the fifteenth and sixteenth centuries. Primarily a military weapon, it measured five to seven feet and had a sharp blade that ended in a point.

46. *dozing over a pasty and a flagon of brown ale.* A flagon is a large glass bottle often with a metal screw-on cap that holds nearly twice the quantity of an ordinary bottle. More common in southern Europe, where wine is crafted, the flagon's metal screw cap indicates that the bottle is often refilled. A pasty is a meat pie consisting of seasoned meat and vegetables enclosed in a pastry crust. It is a Cornish delicacy.

The ancient wardens have possibly fallen asleep before finishing their meal due to the quantity of alcohol consumed. Grahame had personal experience with the effects of alcohol. After the death of his mother, Kenneth Grahame's father gradually developed crippling alcoholism. Unable to hold his post as sheriff-substitute of Argyllshire, he went abroad for the last twenty years of his life and died in a cheap rooming house in Le Havre, France, in 1887, with 15 francs to his name. Kenneth Grahame went abroad for his father's funeral and to dispose of the meager remains of his father's life. This scene may well be an evocation of his father while drunk on duty in Argyllshire.

47. *past the rack-chamber and the thumbscrew-room.* The "grim old castle" is full of rooms for separate kinds of torture. The rack refers to an iron framework that prisoners were tied to. The thumbscrew is a screw used to tighten on and compress the thumb. According to Peter Green, Grahame would have been familiar with Lord Thomas Babington MacAulay's *The History of England from the Accession of James II* (1849–1861), which refers to "The using of racks and thumbscrews for the purpose of forcing prisoners to accuse themselves" (*Kenneth Grahame: A Biography*, 28).

48. *where an ancient gaoler sat fingering a bunch of mighty keys.* Though "jail" and "jailer" are the standard spellings in the twentieth century, Grahame preferred the older, more archaic spellings. Keys are an important motif in Dickens, especially books that involve imprisonment: *Oliver Twist* and *David Copperfield*.

49. *"Oddsbodikins!"* A word not entered in the *OED*.

J. K. Rowling uses this word as a password in chapter 12 of her third book, *Harry Potter and the Prisoner of Azkaban* (New York: Arthur A. Levine Books, 1999, 249). Harry Potter mutters "Oddsbodikins" to Sir Cadogan in order to enter the common room. In correspondence with this editor, an assistant in Rowling's office wrote that, regrettably, she does not recall where she heard the term.

The 1911 *Encyclopedia Britannica* gives little more than a hint about the origin of the word: "in England the old oaths by God's body and wounds became converted into 'oddsbodikins!' and 'zounds!' " (vol. 19, 943).

50. *"Rouse thee, old loon."* In this instance, a loon is a worthless person; a rogue, scamp, or idler. Toad's visit to jail brings him into contact with dangerous and indigent men who are far removed from the benevolent male figures throughout *The Wind in the Willows*.

untoward befall, thy old head shall answer for his—and a murrain on both of them!"[51]

The gaoler nodded grimly, laying his withered hand on the shoulder of the miserable Toad.[52] The rusty key creaked in the lock, the great door clanged behind them; and Toad was a helpless prisoner in the remotest dungeon of the best-guarded keep of the stoutest castle in all the length and breadth of Merry England.[53]

Nancy Barnhart, 1922. Chapter tailpiece for Methuen edition of the "best guarded keep of the stoutest castle in all the length and breadth of Merry England." In 1928, Barnhart completed the pen-and-ink illustrations for a novel called *Little Cabbages* (Garden City, NY: Doubleday, 1928). On page 21 of that work is a pen-and-ink drawing of a Norman castle that bears a similarity to the tailpiece drawing for chapter VI of *The Wind in the Willows*.

This affected speech from the sergeant of police is a parody of the gothic style. Both Humphrey Carpenter, in *Secret Gardens* (154), and Peter Hunt liken this passage to popular novelist Harrison Ainsworth's historical fiction of the 1840s.

> The great gothic novels, such as Horace *Walpole's The Castle of Otranto* (1764) and Ann Radcliffe's *The Mysteries of Udolpho* (1794) set a fashion that survived through writers like Harrison Ainsworth (who flourished in the 1840s with such novels as *Old Saint Paul's*) and had become part of the popular culture of the "penny dreadful" by the end of the century. (Hunt, *The Wind in the Willows: A Fragmented Arcadia*, 104)

51. *"and a murrain on both of them!"* The sergeant is putting a curse on both the ancient jailer and Mr. Toad. Though a murrain is a curse, it can refer to an infectious diseases spread through cattle, poultry, or livestock. A murrain can also be a blight spreading through crops.

52. *laying his withered hand on the shoulder of the miserable Toad.* The ancient jailer seems to be a parody of Coleridge's Ancient Mariner, right down to the withered or "skinny hand" taking hold of the wedding guest.

> *He holds him with his skinny hand,*
> *"There was a ship," quoth he.*
> *"Hold off! unhand me, grey-beard loon!"*
> *Eftsoons his hand dropped he.*

The ancient jailer is taking Toad in hand, about to tell his tale of caution—the Ancient Mariner's ship transposed to Mr. Toad's doomed cars.

53. *Merry England.* According to the *OED*, the term derives from "an imagined past golden age (often identified with Elizabethan times)." It has been used with

irony, such as by Robert Blatchford, who wrote a series of essays entitled *Merrie England* (1894) that explained socialism to the working classes. A journalist turned Fabian socialist, Blatchford's essays were reprinted from the weekly paper he founded, *The Clarion*—the first working-class paper since *The Northern Star* to have gained a mass circulation and pay for itself. *The Northern Star* of the mid-nineteenth century focused on social issues that struck fear into the ruling class. Grahame was probably familiar with *Merrie England*, as it had sold 750,000 copies by 1900.

VII

The Piper at the Gates of Dawn[1]

The Willow-Wren[2] was twittering his thin little song, hidden himself in the dark selvedge of the river bank.[3] Though it was past ten o'clock at night, the sky still clung to and retained some lingering skirts of light from the departed day; and the sullen heats of the torrid afternoon broke up and rolled away at the dispersing touch of the cool fingers of the short midsummer night. Mole lay stretched on the bank, still panting from the stress of the fierce day that had been cloudless from dawn to late sunset, and waited for his friend to return. He had been on the river with some companions, leaving the Water Rat free to keep an engagement of long standing with Otter; and he had come back to find the house dark and deserted, and no sign of Rat, who was doubtless keeping it up late with his old comrade. It was still too hot to think of staying indoors, so he lay on some cool dock-leaves, and thought over the past day and its doings, and how very good they all had been.

The Rat's light footfall was presently heard approaching over the parched grass. "O, the blessed coolness!" he said, and sat down, gazing thoughtfully into the river, silent and preoccupied.

1. *The Piper at the Gates of Dawn.* The Piper is Pan, a god of Greek mythology. Pan is half-human, half-goat, and the god of fields, flocks, shepherds, and woods. The son of Hermes, Pan is the most widely known of the Arcadian theriomorphic deities—a deity worshiped in the form of a beast. In Roman times he came to be seen as the god of Nature.

Pan made many literary appearances during the Victorian and Edwardian eras. In Grahame's first book, *Pagan Papers* (1884), in "The Rural Pan (An April Essay)," "the sinuous Mole" meets with "his foster-brothers the dab-chick and water-rat" (68). The entire essay is reprinted in appendix 4. Other beastly deities appear in the final essays: "The Lost Centaur" and "Orion." Pan is so prominent in the collection—along with Grahame's reverence for the nonindustrial world—that the title page for the first edition includes an illustration of a figure that may very well be Pan.

Pan appears in the short story by Saki (H. H. Munro) called "The Music on the Hill" (1911), as well as in E. M. Forster's

PAGAN PAPERS

BY KENNETH GRAHAME

LONDON: ELKIN MATHEWS AND
JOHN LANE: VIGO STREET
CHICAGO: STONE AND KIMBALL
MDCCCXCIV

Aubrey Beardsley illustration for the title page of *Pagan Papers* (1894).

early short fiction "The Story of a Panic" (1911) J. M. Barrie's children's play *Peter Pan* was first performed in 1904, and his novelization of the stage play, *Peter and Wendy*, was published in 1911. Barrie's first sketch for Peter Pan appeared in his 1902 novel *The Little White Bird*. The American poet Robert Frost included the poem "Pan With Us" in his first collection, *A Boy's Will* (1914).

Grahame's Piper might have been influenced by Robert Browning's 1842 poem "The Pied Piper of Hamelin." In 1888 Frederick Warne published a deluxe children's edition of the poem that was illustrated by Kate Greenaway. Browning's poem imagines a town inundated with rodents; the pied piper plays his flute and lures the rodents to the river to be drowned—and later all the children of Hamelin. Grahame's Piper has the power to call Mole and Rat forth for his blessing and to reunite Mole and Rat with the sleeping child otter.

On August 5, 1967, the rock band Pink Floyd released their first album. Founding singer and guitarist Syd Barrett titled the album *The Piper at the Gates of Dawn*. Apparently Barrett felt Grahame's dreamy seventh chapter properly evoked the mood of the recording. According to CD Universe, the album was

> recorded at Abbey Road Studios, [in] London, England. Pink Floyd's debut was its only recording based on the vision of Syd Barrett, an art student whose world revolved around music, mysticism, and liberal doses of hallucinogens. . . . Recorded at Abbey Road at the same time The Beatles were cutting *Sgt. Pepper's Lonely Hearts Club Band*, *Piper at the Gates of Dawn* is an avant-garde pastiche of trippy improvisation and snappy pop snippets—a blurring of musical borders that went far beyond what the Fab Four were doing a couple of rooms away. (www.cduniverse.com)

On the album *The Healing Game* (1997), Van Morrison includes a lovely track called "The Piper at the Gates of Dawn" recounting chapter VII.

"You stayed to supper, of course?" said the Mole presently.

"Simply had to," said the Rat. "They wouldn't hear of my going before. You know how kind they always are. And they made things as jolly for me as ever they could, right up to the moment I left. But I felt a brute all the time, as it was clear to me they were very unhappy, though they tried to hide it. Mole, I'm afraid they're in trouble. Little Portly is missing again;[4] and you know what a lot his father thinks of him,[5] though he never says much about it."

"What, that child?" said the Mole lightly. "Well, suppose he is; why worry about it? He's always straying off and getting lost, and turning up again; he's so adventurous. But no harm ever happens to him. Everybody hereabouts knows him and likes him, just as they do old Otter, and you may be sure some animal or other will come across him and bring him back again all right. Why, we've found him ourselves, miles from home, and quite self-possessed and cheerful!"

"Yes; but this time it's more serious," said the Rat gravely. "He's been missing for some days now, and the Otters have hunted everywhere, high and low, without finding the slightest trace. And they've asked every animal, too, for miles around, and no one knows anything about him. Otter's evidently more anxious than he'll admit. I got out of him that young Portly hasn't learnt to swim very well yet, and I can see he's thinking of the weir. There's a lot of water coming down still, considering the time of the year, and the place always had a fascination for the child. And then there are—well, traps and things—*you* know.[6] Otter's not the fellow to be nervous about any son of his before it's time.[7] And now he *is* nervous. When I left, he came out with me—said he wanted some air, and talked about stretching his legs. But I could see it wasn't that, so I drew him out and pumped him, and got it all from him at last. He was going to spend the night watching by the ford. You know the place where the old ford used to be, in bygone days before they built the bridge?"[8]

2. *Willow-Wren.* Any of various small birds resembling the common wren in appearance and habit—also called a willow warbler.

3. *hidden himself in the dark selvedge of the river bank.* A selvedge is the marginal tract, border, or edge. Oliver Goldsmith describes the term in *Natural History* (1774): "Where the stream is selvaged with sedges, or the pond edged with shrubby trees" (vol. 6, 37).

4. *"Little Portly is missing again."* Grahame named the missing baby otter after one of Graham Robertson's bobtail sheepdogs.

"My trio of Bobtail Sheepdogs accepted him [Kenneth Grahame] at once as a friend and welcomed him with effusion whenever he appeared; and on one of them, called Portly, he conferred immortality by giving his name to the lost baby otter in *The Wind in the Willows.* 'I hope you don't mind' he said to me, 'but I must call him Portly because—well, because it is his name. What else am I to call him?' " (Chalmers, *Kenneth Grahame*, 97–98). Of Portly, Robertson fondly recalled:

> the gay, the stout, the irresponsible . . . the light heart, the merry eye, the happy go lucky, devil-may-care temperament of the born Jester. . . . As a puppy, Portly was irresistible—so fat, so round, so jolly. . . . Poor Portly: he was the child of misfortune, always in scrapes, always meeting with accidents. Disasters of all kinds were perpetually overtaking him, yet never could they crush his high spirits nor sour his sunny nature. (Robertson, *Time Was*, 330)

5. *"you know what a lot his father thinks of him."* Where is Portly's mother, and why isn't she out looking for her son? In the search for Portly, there is no mention of his mother. In fact, the word "mother" is used

only six times in *The Wind in the Willows*. The word "father," however, is mentioned eleven times—almost twice as many as "mother."

6. *"And then there are—well, traps and things—*you *know."* Traps are an intruding danger from the Wide World. Though Grahame mentions the possibility that Portly might be in physical danger, he never goes further. Peter Green and Peter Hunt have written that Grahame undoubtedly knew Richard Jeffries's "unfocussed" nature novels from the 1880s. In *Wood Magic* Jeffries creates a pre-automobile natural world of beauty and stark brutality. There is an elaborate description of a weasel caught in a "gin," a contrivance or trap for catching game. The trap is released by a foot spring that opens it when stepped on. Rat and Mole are fearful that Portly is caught somewhere in this same kind of trap.

In *Nature Near London* (1883; New York: Thomas Y. Crowell and Company, 1907), Richard Jeffries describes the hunting of river otter for sport on the Thames, another unnamed peril.

> Every effort is made to exterminate the otter. No sooner does one venture down the river than traps, gins, nets, dogs, prongs, brickbats, every species of missile, all the artillery of vulgar destruction, are brought against its devoted head. Unless my memory serves me wrong, one of these creatures caught in a trap not long since was hammered to death with a shovel or a pitchfork. . . . Londoners, I think, scarcely recognise the fact that the otter is one of the last links between the wild past of ancient England and the present days of high civilization. (154)

7. *"Otter's not the fellow to be nervous about any son of his before it's time."* Grahame never intimates how many children Otter has—but if he is anything like Grahame's neighbor Graham Robertson, it is possible that he has as many children as Robertson has sheepdogs—four, at the time. Otter could also be a representation of Grahame's American friend Austin Purves who had five small boys, all of whom enjoyed boating and being on the water.

Oddly enough, while Grahame shared boating adventures with the Purves family, his own son was at Littlehampton with his governess. The continual separation of child and parents would be practically unthinkable today. Still, looking at the family history of each of the Grahames, it is easy to see why they chose to be separate. After the death of his mother and early demise of his father, Kenneth was at the mercy and will of his aunts and uncles. Elspeth Grahame's brother, Courtauld-Thomson, recalled the role of parents and servants in 1860s–1870s:

> "For twenty three and a half hours out of twenty four we were left in charge of our Scotch nurses. About six in the evening, after much washing behind ears, I was forced into a highly starched white picque suit and my hair so amply smeared with pomatum that I think it made me prematurely bald. We were then marched in full dress kit down to the drawing-room, where we found our parents. Thus it was that we saw them for the first time during the day.
>
> "After 'Children's Hour'—which was in fact about thirty minutes—the nurse tapped on the door and said 'Is my little gentleman ready?' and, parade having been dismissed, with my brother and sisters I returned to 'barracks' as it were. Except for these visits, and an occasional inspection of the nursery by our mother, we rarely saw our parents. On our holidays we were sent to the seaside with our nurse or governess." (Biogra-

phy of Courtauld-Thomson in manuscript, by Peter Green, 1950s, 3. Courtesy of the Harry Ransom Humanities Research Center, The University of Texas at Austin)

8. *"You know the place where the old ford used to be, in by-gone days before they built the bridge?"* A ford is a shallow place in a river or in a body of water, where one may cross by wading. In this case, the recent building of a bridge has caused the river currents to push up sandbars.

There are several bridges in Cookham. The most recognizable is the wrought-iron Cookham Bridge. Resting on cylindrical iron piers, the bridge was remodeled in 1867 from an earlier wooden bridge built circa 1840. The decorative iron construction is a product of the modern era and likely would have caused a ford to form in the river. The Cookham Lock Cut Bridge is only 12' 6" high at its center, the lowest bridge on the River Thames below Osney. The bridge provides a footpath from Formosa Island to Cookham Lock.

A suspension bridge, simply called the Marlow Bridge, reaches across the Thames from Cookham to Marlow and commands a spectacular view of the river, especially of the weir and lock that allow boats to navigate the river. Built by Tierney Clark in 1832, Marlow Bridge's "clean, angelic shiny white colour and aura brings forth visions of a gateway to an idyllic world that knows no hardships" (see www.the-river-thames.co.uk). Both the Shelleys and T. S. Eliot lived in Marlow.

"I know it well," said the Mole. "But why should Otter choose to watch there?"

"Well, it seems that it was there he gave Portly his first swimming-lesson," continued the Rat. "From that shallow, gravelly spit near the bank. And it was there he used to teach him fishing, and there young Portly caught his first fish, of which he was so very proud. The child loved the spot, and Otter thinks that if he came wandering back from wherever he is—if he *is* anywhere by this time, poor little chap—he might make for the ford he was so fond of; or if he came across it he'd remember it well, and stop there and play, perhaps. So Otter goes there every night and watches—on the chance, you know, just on the chance!"

They were silent for a time, both thinking of the same thing—the lonely, heart-sore animal, crouched by the ford, watching and waiting, the long night through—on the chance.

"Well, well," said the Rat presently, "I suppose we ought to be thinking about turning in." But he never offered to move.

"Rat," said the Mole, "I simply can't go and turn in, and go to sleep, and *do* nothing, even though there doesn't seem to be anything to be done. We'll get the boat out, and paddle up stream. The moon will be up in an hour or so, and then we will search as well as we can—anyhow, it will be better than going to bed and doing *nothing*."

"Just what I was thinking myself," said the Rat. "It's not the sort of night for bed anyhow; and daybreak is not so very far off, and then we may pick up some news of him from early risers as we go along."

They got the boat out, and the Rat took the sculls, paddling with caution. Out in midstream, there was a clear, narrow track that faintly reflected the sky; but wherever shadows fell on the water from bank, bush, or tree, they were as solid to all appearance as the banks themselves, and the Mole had to steer with judgment accordingly. Dark and deserted as it was,

A sketch by E. H. Shepard of Otter searching for Portly (1931). "So Otter goes there every night and watches." *Courtesy of the David J. Holmes Collection.*

the night was full of small noises, song and chatter and rustling, telling of the busy little population who were up and about, plying their trades and vocations through the night till sunshine should fall on them at last and send them off to their well-earned repose. The water's own noises, too, were more apparent than by day, its gurglings and "cloops" more unexpected and near at hand; and constantly they started at what seemed a sudden clear call from an actual articulate voice.

The line of the horizon was clear and hard against the sky, and in one particular quarter it showed black against a silvery climbing phosphorescence that grew and grew. At last, over the rim of the waiting earth the moon lifted with slow majesty till it swung clear of the horizon and rode off, free of moorings; and once more they began to see surfaces—meadows wide-spread, and quiet gardens, and the river itself from bank to bank, all softly disclosed, all washed clean of mystery and terror, all radiant again as by day, but with a difference that was tremendous. Their old haunts greeted them again in other raiment, as if they had slipped away and put on this pure new apparel and come quietly back, smiling as they shyly waited to see if they would be recognised again under it.

Fastening their boat to a willow, the friends landed in this silent, silver kingdom, and patiently explored the hedges, the hollow trees, the runnels and their little culverts, the ditches and dry water-ways.[9] Embarking again and crossing over, they worked their way up the stream in this manner, while the moon, serene and detached in a cloudless sky, did what she could, though so far off, to help them in their quest; till her hour came and she sank earthwards reluctantly,[10] and left them, and mystery once more held field and river.

Then a change began slowly to declare itself. The horizon became clearer, field and tree came more into sight, and somehow with a different look; the mystery began to drop away from them. A bird piped suddenly, and was still; and a light breeze sprang up and set the reeds and bulrushes rustling.[11]

9. *the runnels and their little culverts, the ditches and dry water-ways.* A runnel is a small stream of water; a brooklet, rivulet, rill, or trickle.

10. *till her hour came and she sank earthwards reluctantly.* Variant, e. 248: till her hour came and she ~~sank~~ dropped away earthwards reluctantly.

11. *and a light breeze sprang up and set the reeds and bulrushes rustling.* A bulrush is also known as a cattail or a reed mace. In the Bible, baby Moses is set on the water in a cradle made of bulrushes. The innocent Portly is to be protected by Pan. According to the *OED*, bulrushes in the Bible are also known as the papyrus of Egypt.

Rat, who was in the stern of the boat, while Mole sculled, sat up suddenly and listened with a passionate intentness. Mole, who with gentle strokes was just keeping the boat moving while he scanned the banks with care, looked at him with curiosity.

"It's gone!" sighed the Rat, sinking back in his seat again. "So beautiful and strange and new![12] Since it was to end so soon, I almost wish I had never heard it. For it has roused a longing in me that is pain, and nothing seems worth while but just to hear that sound once more and go on listening to it for ever. No! There it is again!" he cried, alert once more. Entranced, he was silent for a long space, spellbound.

"Now it passes on and I begin to lose it," he said presently. "O Mole! the beauty of it! The merry bubble and joy, the thin, clear, happy call of the distant piping! Such music I never dreamed of, and the call in it is stronger even than the music is sweet! Row on, Mole, row! For the music and the call must be for us."[13]

The Mole, greatly wondering, obeyed. "I hear nothing myself," he said, "but the wind playing in the reeds and rushes and osiers."[14]

The Rat never answered, if indeed he heard. Rapt, transported, trembling, he was possessed in all his senses by this new divine thing that caught up his helpless soul and swung and dandled it,[15] a powerless but happy infant in a strong sustaining grasp.

In silence Mole rowed steadily, and soon they came to a point where the river divided, a long backwater branching off to one side. With a slight movement of his head Rat, who had long dropped the rudder-lines, directed the rower to take the backwater. The creeping tide of light gained and gained, and now they could see the colour of the flowers that gemmed the water's edge.

"Clearer and nearer still," cried the Rat joyously. "Now you must surely hear it! Ah—at last—I see you do!"

12. *"So beautiful and strange and new!"* Grahame alludes to Matthew Arnold's "Dover Beach" (1867), line 32:

> *Ah, love, let us be true*
> *To one another! for the world, which seems*
> *To lie before us like a land of dreams,*
> *So various, so beautiful, so new.*

—J. J.

13. *"the call in it is stronger even than the music is sweet! Row on, Mole, row! For the music and the call must be for us."* This is perhaps an allusion to Shakespeare's *Twelfth Night*, act 1, scene 1: "If music be the food of love, play on; / Give me excess of it, that, surfeiting."

14. *"I hear nothing myself," he said, "but the wind playing in the reeds and rushes and osiers."* The original title is inherent in this sentence. Reeds was changed to willows shortly before publication by Algernon Methuen.

15. *he was possessed in all his senses by this new divine thing that caught up his helpless soul and swung and dandled it.* Dandle is an unusual word. It means to move a child lightly up and down in the arms or on the knee; to fuss over, pamper, and fondle affectionately.

Breathless and transfixed the Mole stopped rowing as the liquid run of that glad piping broke on him like a wave, caught him up, and possessed him utterly. He saw the tears on his comrade's cheeks, and bowed his head and understood.[16] For a space they hung there, brushed by the purple loose-strife that fringed the bank; then the clear imperious summons that marched hand-in-hand with the intoxicating melody imposed its will on Mole, and mechanically he bent to his oars again. And the light grew steadily stronger, but no birds sang[17] as they were wont to do at the approach of dawn; and but for the heavenly music all was marvellously still.

On either side of them, as they glided onwards, the rich meadow-grass seemed that morning of a freshness and a greenness unsurpassable. Never had they noticed the roses so vivid, the willow-herb so riotous, the meadow-sweet so odorous and pervading.[18] Then the murmur of the approaching weir began to hold the air, and they felt a consciousness that they were nearing the end, whatever it might be, that surely awaited their expedition.

A wide half-circle of foam[19] and glinting lights and shining shoulders of green water, the great weir closed the backwater from bank to bank, troubled all the quiet surface with twirling eddies and floating foam-streaks, and deadened all other sounds with its solemn and soothing rumble. In midmost of the stream, embraced in the weir's shimmering arm-spread, a small island lay anchored,[20] fringed close with willow and silver birch and alder. Reserved, shy, but full of significance, it hid whatever it might hold behind a veil, keeping it till the hour should come, and, with the hour, those who were called and chosen.

Slowly, but with no doubt or hesitation whatever, and in something of a solemn expectancy, the two animals passed through the broken, tumultuous water and moored their boat at the flowery margin of the island. In silence they landed, and pushed through the blossom and scented herbage and under-

16. *He saw the tears on his comrade's cheeks, and bowed his head and understood. Comrade* derives from the Spanish *camarada*, meaning barrack mate, which in turn derives from the Latin *camera*, for room. Besides the more popular socialist connotation, there is a long history of a homosexual subtext to this word. Walt Whitman used it to refer specifically to men who loved men ("the soul of the man I speak for rejoices in comrades"), as did A. E. Housman in his translation of Horace's ode 4.7 ("And Theseus leaves Pirithous in the chain / The love of comrades cannot take away"). In this sense, it reaches back to soldiers in the Spartan army, which consisted of pairs of lovers.

—J. J.

17. *but no birds sang.* This is a variation of the fourth and forty-eighth lines of John Keats's "La Belle Dame sans Merci":

> *O what can ail thee, knight at arms,*
> *Alone and palely loitering?*
> *The sedge has withered from the lake*
> *And no birds sing*
>
> *And this is why I sojourn here,*
> *Alone and palely loitering,*
> *Though the sedge has withered from the lake,*
> *And no birds sing.*

—J. J.

18. *Never had they noticed the roses so vivid, the willow-herb so riotous, the meadow-sweet so odorous and pervading.* Willow herb is an easy-spreading weed that grows close to water. A perennial, it has long, narrow leaves that resemble those of a willow, and purple to rose-colored flowers. Also known as purple loosestrife.

Meadowsweet, another perennial herb, is a tall plant found in damp meadows, ditches, and bogs and beside streams. It has clusters of tiny cream-colored flowers that are very fragrant. Like those of purple loosestrife, they bloom from June to

August. Meadowsweet was one of the three most sacred herbs used by ancient Celtic Druid priests (water mint and vervain are the other two), and it is mentioned in the *Knight's Tale* by Geoffrey Chaucer. Meadowsweet is described in John Gerard's *The Herball* (1597) and in Nicholas Culpepper's *The English Physitian* (1652). See the American Botanical Council's Herb-Ed-Web™.

19. *A wide half-circle of foam.* This is a weir, used as a barrier or dam to restrain water. A weir is usually built across a river or canal in order to raise the water to drive a mill wheel. Weirs are also used to retain and regulate the flow of a river.

In a letter to Peter Green dated April 10, 1957, Green's brother-in-law Len Smith speculates that Mapledurham Weir is Portly's weir. Mapledurham Lock is a perfect distance for a day's outing, which fits not only the picnic sequence in chapter I but also the overnight search upriver. Smith also speculates that Mapledurham house—a red brick mansion on the riverbank—is Toad Hall. (See chapter II, note 13.)

20. *a small island lay anchored.* Len Smith speculated that Pan Island is located at Temple Lock, one mile upriver from Marlow: "The connection between Temple and the God Pan seemed too obvious. The book description fits perfectly, the terry being Otter's ford" (letter to Peter Green, Harry Ransom Humanities Research Center, The University of Texas at Austin). The idea that an island can be "anchored" is a metaphor for how transient the appearance of Pan will be.

In "Toad Hall Revisited," Lois Kuznets writes about the significance of the circular imagery of the path that leads to Pan:

> his paradisal island emerges through images of roundness: the great weir is a "wide half-circle." . . . The island is "midmost of the stream, embraced in the weir's shimmering arm-spread" . . . it is "fringed close with willow"; on it is a lawn "set round with nature's own orchard-trees." (117)

Quoting Gaston Bachelard's *Poetics of Space*, Kuznets comments that "images of roundness tend to 'help us collect ourselves, permit us to confer an initial constitution on ourselves, and confirm our being intimately inside' " (ibid.).

growth that led up to the level ground, till they stood on a little lawn of a marvellous green, set round with Nature's own orchard-trees—crab-apple, wild cherry, and sloe.[21]

"This is the place of my song-dream, the place the music played to me," whispered the Rat, as if in a trance. "Here, in this holy place, here if anywhere, surely we shall find Him!"

Then suddenly the Mole felt a great Awe fall upon him, an awe that turned his muscles to water, bowed his head, and rooted his feet to the ground. It was no panic terror[22]—indeed he felt wonderfully at peace and happy—but it was an awe that smote and held him and, without seeing, he knew it could only mean that some august Presence[23] was very, very near. With difficulty he turned to look for his friend, and saw him at his side cowed, stricken, and trembling violently. And still there was utter silence in the populous bird-haunted branches around them; and still the light grew and grew.

Perhaps he would never have dared to raise his eyes, but that, though the piping was now hushed, the call and the summons seemed still dominant and imperious. He might not refuse, were Death himself waiting to strike him instantly, once he had looked with mortal eye on things rightly kept hidden.[24] Trembling he obeyed, and raised his humble head; and then, in that utter clearness of the imminent dawn, while Nature, flushed with fulness of incredible colour, seemed to hold her breath for the event, he looked in the very eyes of the Friend and Helper;[25] saw the backward sweep of the curved horns, gleaming in the growing daylight; saw the stern, hooked nose between the kindly eyes that were looking down on them humourously, while the bearded mouth broke into a half-smile at the corners; saw the rippling muscles on the arm that lay across the broad chest, the long supple hand still holding the pan-pipes only just fallen away from the parted lips; saw the splendid curves of the shaggy limbs disposed in majestic ease on the sward;[26] saw, last of all, nestling between his very hooves, sleeping soundly in entire peace and contentment, the little, round, podgy, childish form of

21. *set round with Nature's own orchard-trees—crab-apple, wild cherry, and sloe.* All three fruits are circular in shape and very sour—not the kind of fruit picnickers would seek out. Sloe is a small plum that grows on a blackthorn bush. Left in the wild, blackthorn grows into a dense, impenetrable thicket complete with large thorns that grow out of the branches. The two- to three-inch thorns act as a barrier to intruders—animal and human alike. The dark purple-black plums are used to make gin. Many have thought that the crown of thorns placed on the head of Christ during the Crucifixion came from the blackthorn. The blackthorn protects Pan and the island from invaders.

22. *It was no panic terror.* Though rarely used in the context of the Greek god, the word *panic* was capitalized when it entered the English language in the sixteenth century. For ancient Greeks, panic connoted being under the mercurial influence of Pan.

23. *august Presence.* A magnificent and wise presence that inspires a worshipful stately dignity. The word comes from the name of the first Roman emperor, Augustus Caesar, who lived from 63 BC to 14 AD.

24. *He might not refuse, were Death himself waiting to strike him instantly, once he had looked with mortal eye on things rightly kept hidden.* In his 1981 article "At the Back of *The Wind in the Willows*: An Experiment in Biographical and Autobiographical Interpretation," Michael Steig comments that Pan is the embodiment of mother and father in one figure:

> the animals' response combines a worship of the nurturing mother . . . with a submission to the all-powerful but benign father. Perhaps in part through an unconscious sense of this I

felt (and still feel) that Mole and Rat's experiences in the seventh chapter are intensely erotic, from the initial intoxications of melody, to the violent trembling at the sight of "things rightly kept hidden," the peak of intense experience in the combination of love, fear, and worship, followed by the gradually falling intensity of emotion (as the animals move into forgetfulness), to the physical exhaustion that leaves Mole "half dozing in the hot sun," and "the weary Rat . . . fast asleep." (*Victorian Studies* 24, no. 3 [1981]: 303–23)

25. *Friend and Helper.* In psalm 54:4, the term *helper* denotes a spiritual deity: "Behold, God is mine helper: the Lord is with them that uphold my soul."

Peter Green writes of one of Grahame's "older, more eccentric friend[s] Dr. Furnivall":

> Furnivall also provided one aspect of the appearance and *mise-en-scène* of Pan in "The Piper at the Gates of Dawn." Professor Livingston Lowes describes "an island in the Thames, where, of a Sunday afternoon, [Furnivall] used to recline against a tree, like a glorious old British river-god with white and curling beard." (*Kenneth Grahame: A Biography*, 280, quoting John Livingston Lowes, *The Road to Xanadu: A Study in the Ways of the Imagination* [Boston: Houghton Mifflin, 1927], 430)

26. *saw the splendid curves of the shaggy limbs disposed in majestic ease on the sward.* Variant, e. 248: saw the splendid curves of the shaggy ~~flanks and~~ limbs disposed in majestic ease on the sward.

Grahame crossed out the word flanks in the manuscript. Defined as "the fleshy or muscular part of the side of an animal or a man between the ribs and the hip" (*OED*), the word enhances Grahame's description of Pan as a hairy, muscular beast. A sward is a bed. By crossing out flanks, Grahame makes the setting a little bit less potent.

Grahame's Pan has a touch of the homoerotic, something that Grahame shied away from elsewhere in the manuscript. While he was very much a part of the bacchanalian, neo-pagan literary set of the 1880s and 1890s, Grahame chose what Peter Green called "the cult of innocence" rather than a self-destructive path. Nevertheless, in a reader's report to John Lane, dated January 7, 1900, Grahame gave a favorable review of a manuscript by Frederic Baron Corvo (later called *In his Own Image*). Corvo wrote homoerotic prose, his primary interest in adolescent males. He, too, was a contributer to John Lane's *Yellow Book*, having published six essays that were later republished in a collection called *Stories Toto Told Me* (London: The Bodley Head, 1898). Grahame's letter attests to his fascination with paganism and his preference for the male form and company, yet it is proof, too, of his squeamishness to see anything remotely resembling what Oscar Wilde called the "love that dare not speak its name" committed to print. In 1895, Wilde had been sentenced to two years hard labor at Reading Jail; he was released in May of 1897. With the trials of Wilde fresh in the public memory in 1900, Grahame was discreet about supporting homoerotic literature. He even wrote the word "confidential" at the top of the hotel stationery (*In His Own Image* [London: John Lane, 1901]; *Stories Toto Told Me* [London: The Bodley Head, 1898]).

> [January 7, 1900]
> Dear Lane
>
> I have read the M.S. of the Corvo book through. There is no doubt that the man plays on a pipe of his own,—individual, + true melody. Thin at times—rather often,—but never "scrannel" I know of nobody doing the same

kind of work at all. Your line has always been to discover + deal with the individual note, + I think you would be right—and consistent—in publishing this. The Strand Magaziners + war episode people won't read it, but there are lots of Italy-lovers + medievalists who will welcome it warmly.

To descend more to particulars: It is a most interesting exposition of the essential continuity of Paganism into the new religion. We all know the thing was so, till Puritanism came + killed out the Paganism—substituting Judaism—but I don't know another demonstration of the thing itself, as still to be found in the Southern Italian. . . .

One word more. There's a good deal of *boy* in it—passion of boy. Lithe limbs of boy, subtle curves of boy, tawny skin of boy + so on.

A few years ago I should have said let it alone. But all that has passed by now—+ honestly there's not a jot of uncleanness or suggestiveness, + more, its almost necessary. For this is the old Paganism, not the late Empire, + *they* knew as all artists do, how much finer an animal the male is than the female.

The title won't do. He must find a more concrete + salient one. Had I my books I might suggest something—Without them I find the task difficult. I'll return the m.s. tomorrow

Yours very truly Kenneth Grahame

(John Lane company files. Harry Ransom Humanities Research Center, University of Texas at Austin)

Nancy Barnhart's 1923 illustration with the caption "looked in the very eyes of the Friend and Helper."

the baby otter. All this he saw, for one moment breathless and intense, vivid on the morning sky; and still, as he looked, he lived; and still, as he lived, he wondered.

"Rat!" he found breath to whisper, shaking. "Are you afraid?"[27]

"Afraid?" murmured the Rat, his eyes shining with unutterable love. "Afraid! Of *Him?* O, never, never! And yet—and yet—O, Mole, I am afraid!"

Then the two animals, crouching to the earth, bowed their heads and did worship.

27. *"Rat!" he found breath to whisper, shaking. "Are you afraid?"* It appears that an error was made in the binding of the holograph manuscript pages in the Bodleian Library (e. 248). Manuscript e. 248 ends after this line. The text from chapter VII, "The Piper at the Gates of Dawn," resumes on page 17 in manuscript e. 247 with the following line: "'Afraid?' murmured the Rat, his eyes shining with unutterable love. 'Afraid! Of Him? O, never, never! And yet—and yet—O, Mole, I am afraid!'"

Graham Robertson contributed this sun worship cover illustration to Patrick Chalmers's 1933 biography *Kenneth Grahame.*

Paul Bransom's illustration captioned "The Piper at the Gates of Dawn." This illustration appears as the frontispiece in this 1913 edition.

Sudden and magnificent, the sun's broad golden disc showed itself over the horizon facing them; and the first rays, shooting across the level water-meadows, took the animals full in the eyes and dazzled them. When they were able to look once more, the Vision had vanished, and the air was full of the carol of birds that hailed the dawn.

As they stared blankly, in dumb misery deepening as they slowly realised all they had seen and all they had lost, a capricious little breeze, dancing up from the surface of the water, tossed the aspens,[28] shook the dewy roses, and blew lightly and caressingly in their faces; and with its soft touch came instant oblivion. For this is the last best gift that the kindly demi-god is careful to bestow on those to whom he has revealed himself in their helping: the gift of forgetfulness.[29] Lest the awful remembrance should remain and grow, and overshadow mirth and pleasure, and the great haunting memory should spoil all the afterlives of little animals helped out of difficulties, in order that they should be happy and lighthearted as before.

Mole rubbed his eyes and stared at Rat, who was looking about him in a puzzled sort of way. "I beg your pardon; what did you say, Rat?" he asked.

"I think I was only remarking," said Rat slowly, "that this was the right sort of place, and that here, if anywhere, we should find him. And look! Why, there he is, the little fellow!" And with a cry of delight he ran towards the slumbering Portly.

But Mole stood still a moment, held in thought. As one wakened suddenly from a beautiful dream, who struggles to recall it, and can re-capture nothing but a dim sense of the beauty of it, the beauty! Till that, too, fades away in its turn, and the dreamer bitterly accepts the hard, cold waking and all its penalties; so Mole, after struggling with his memory for a brief space, shook his head sadly and followed the Rat.

Portly woke up with a joyous squeak, and wriggled with pleasure at the sight of his father's friends, who had played with him so often in past days. In a moment, however, his face grew blank, and he fell to hunting round in a circle with pleading whine. As a child that has fallen happily asleep in its nurse's arms, and wakes to find itself alone and laid in a strange place,[30] and searches corners and cupboards, and runs from room to room, despair growing silently in its heart, even so Portly searched the island and searched, dogged and unweary-

28. *aspens.* Aspens are trees from the poplar family that have leaves that tremble in the wind.

29. *For this is the last best gift that the kindly demi-god is careful to bestow on those to whom he has revealed himself in their helping: the gift of forgetfulness.* A demigod is a deity that is half human and half god.

30. *As a child that has fallen happily asleep in its nurse's arms, and wakes to find itself alone and laid in a strange place.* See notes 23 and 24 in this chapter. This is another metaphor comparing the mortal riverbankers to helpless infants in the presence of the divine. In 1908, a nurse would have been female. This is one of few places in *The Wind in the Willows* where a woman takes on a benevolent role.

ing, till at last the black moment came for giving it up, and sitting down and crying bitterly.

The Mole ran quickly to comfort the little animal; but Rat, lingering, looked long and doubtfully at certain hoof-marks deep in the sward.

"Some—great—animal—has been here," he murmured slowly and thoughtfully; and stood musing, musing; his mind strangely stirred.

"Come along, Rat!" called the Mole. "Think of poor Otter, waiting up there by the ford!"

Portly had soon been comforted by the promise of a treat—a jaunt on the river in Mr. Rat's real boat; and the two animals conducted him to the water's side, placed him securely between them in the bottom of the boat, and paddled off down the backwater. The sun was fully up by now, and hot on them, birds sang lustily and without restraint, and flowers smiled and nodded from either bank, but somehow—so thought the animals—with less of richness and blaze of colour than they seemed to remember seeing quite recently somewhere—they wondered where.

The main river reached again, they turned the boat's head upstream, towards the point where they knew their friend was keeping his lonely vigil. As they drew near the familiar ford, the Mole took the boat in to the bank, and they lifted Portly out and set him on his legs on the tow-path, gave him his marching orders[31] and a friendly farewell pat on the back, and shoved out into mid-stream. They watched the little animal as he waddled along the path contentedly and with importance; watched him till they saw his muzzle suddenly lift and his waddle break into a clumsy amble as he quickened his pace with shrill whines and wriggles of recognition. Looking up the river, they could see Otter start up, tense and rigid, from out of the shallows where he crouched in dumb patience, and could hear his amazed and joyous bark as he bounded up through the osiers on to the path.[32] Then the Mole, with a

31. *marching orders.* An order from a superior officer for troops to depart; a dismissal.

32. *Looking up the river, they could see Otter start up, tense and rigid, from out of the shallows where he crouched in dumb patience, and could hear his amazed and joyous bark as he bounded up through the osiers on to the path.* Payne included this drawing of Portly as he is reunited with his fully dressed father but avoided an image of Pan altogether. As in Payne's illustration of Mole and Rat in the first chapter, Portly and Otter's hats have popped off their heads. Payne makes the moment comic rather than trying to relay the quasi mysticism inherent in Grahame's text.

This is the last time that Otter will be seen in *The Wind in the Willows* until the party of the final chapter, when he reappears with no mention of Portly, Mrs. Otter, or his family. He arrives as a bachelor. Badger mentions Otter in chapter XI: " 'I've found out a thing or two lately,' continued the Badger. 'I got Otter to disguise himself as a sweep and call at the back-door with brushes over his shoulder, asking for a job' " (278).

strong pull on one oar, swung the boat round and let the full stream bear them down again whither it would, their quest now happily ended.

"I feel strangely tired, Rat," said the Mole, leaning wearily over his oars as the boat drifted. "It's being up all night, you'll say, perhaps; but that's nothing. We do as much half the nights of the week, at this time of the year. No; I feel as if I had been through something very exciting and rather terrible, and it was just over; and yet nothing particular has happened."

"Or something very surprising and splendid and beautiful," murmured the Rat, leaning back and closing his eyes. "I feel

Wyndham Payne's reunion of Otter and Portly, 1927.

just as you do, Mole; simply dead tired, though not body-tired. It's lucky we've got the stream with us, to take us home.[33] Isn't it jolly to feel the sun again, soaking into one's bones! And hark to the wind playing in the reeds!"

"It's like music—far away music," said the Mole nodding drowsily.

"So I was thinking," murmured the Rat, dreamful and languid. "Dance-music—the lilting sort that runs on without a stop—but with words in it, too—it passes into words and out of them again—I catch them at intervals—then it is dance-music once more, and then nothing but the reeds' soft thin whispering."

"You hear better than I," said the Mole sadly. "I cannot catch the words."

"Let me try and give you them," said the Rat softly, his eyes still closed.[34] "Now it is turning into words again—faint but clear—*Lest the awe should dwell—And turn your frolic to fret—You shall look on my power at the helping hour—But then you shall forget!* Now the reeds take it up—*forget, forget,* they sigh, and it dies away in a rustle and a whisper. Then the voice returns—

"*Lest limbs be reddened and rent—I spring the trap that is set—As I loose the snare you may glimpse me there—For surely you shall forget!* Row nearer, Mole, nearer to the reeds! It is hard to catch, and grows each minute fainter.

"*Helper and healer, I cheer—Small waifs in the woodland wet—Strays I find in it, wounds I bind in it—Bidding them all forget!* Nearer, Mole, nearer! No, it is no good; the song has died away into reed-talk."

"But what do the words mean?" asked the wondering Mole.

"That I do not know," said the Rat simply. "I passed them on to you as they reached me. Ah! now they return again, and this time full and clear! This time, at last, it is the real, the unmistakable thing, simple—passionate—perfect———"

33. *It's lucky we've got the stream with us, to take us home.* See note 20 in this chapter concerning Len Smith's speculation that Pan's island is upstream at Temple Island. Peter Green writes at length about the river as the book's all-persuasive symbol. In "The Eternal Whither," in *Pagan Papers*, Grahame aptly calls the river "the silent liquid Highway to the West" (91).

34. *"Let me try and give you them," said the Rat softly, his eyes still closed.* Here is another example of Rat as the poet. He writes "Ducks' Ditty" in chapter II, "scribbles" poetry at the beginning of chapter III, and will be saved from despair when Mole gives him half sheets of paper and a pencil to write verse with after his visit with the sea rat.

"Well, let's have it, then," said the Mole, after he had waited patiently for a few minutes, half-dozing in the hot sun.

But no answer came. He looked, and understood the silence. With a smile of much happiness on his face, and something of a listening look still lingering there, the weary Rat was fast asleep.[35]

Tailpiece illustration by Nancy Barnhart.

35. *Rat was fast asleep.* The waking and dreaming—and the blurred line that enables Mole and Rat to have a vision of Pan—is not unlike the pagan vision in Tom Hughes's *The Scouring of the White Horse.*

Illustration from *The Scouring of the White Horse* (p. 201). The great ancient angel takes the scourers of the white horse protectively into his lap. He then fades, leaving the small men behind.

VIII

Toad's Adventures

When Toad found himself immured in a dank and noisome dungeon, and knew that all the grim darkness of a medieval fortress lay between him and the outer world of sunshine and well-metalled high roads where he had lately been so happy, disporting himself as if he had bought up every road in England, he flung himself at full length on the floor, and shed bitter tears, and abandoned himself to dark despair.[1] "This is the end of everything" (he said), "at least it is the end of the career of Toad, which is the same thing; the popular and handsome Toad, the rich and hospitable Toad, the Toad so free and careless and debonair! How can I hope to be ever set at large again" (he said), "who have been imprisoned so justly for stealing so handsome a motor-car in such an audacious manner, and for such lurid and imaginative cheek, bestowed upon such a number of fat, red-faced policemen!"[2] (Here his sobs choked him.) "Stupid animal that I was" (he said), "now I must languish in this dungeon, till people who were proud to say they knew me, have forgotten the very name of Toad! O wise old Badger!" (he said), "O clever, intelligent Rat and sensible Mole! What sound judgments, what a knowledge of men and matters you possess! O unhappy and forsaken Toad!" With lamentations such as these he passed

Grahame originally sent the Toad letters to Alastair while he and his governess, Naomi Stott, were on holiday in Littlehampton. Grahame later revised the letters at Durham Villas in London while Alastair, Elspeth, and Stott stayed in Cookham Dean (see Prince, *Kenneth Grahame: An Innocent in the Wild Wood*, 227). Humphrey Carpenter (*Secret Gardens*) likens the Toad sequences to an "eighteenth-century picaresque," with "Toad as an amiable trickster of the standard folk-tale type" (154). Picaresque refers to a style of literary fiction dealing with the adventures of rogues; the picaresque hero is a vagrant or wanderer.

Chapter VIII is comprised of the second, third, and fourth "My Dearest Mouse" letters, dated May 23, 1907, May 28, 1907, and May 31, 1907. The letters also detail small events in the Grahames' lives.

1. *he flung himself at full length on the floor, and shed bitter tears, and abandoned himself to dark despair.* Building on the idea that Mr. Toad was modeled after Oscar Wilde, Toad's lamentations and bitter tears bear a striking resemblance to the opening of Oscar Wilde's *De Profundis*—the letter

Reading Prison. According to Peter Green, "Cookham Dean was almost in sight of the gaol, scene of [Oscar] Wilde's incarceration."

his days and nights for several weeks, refusing his meals or intermediate light refreshments, though the grim and ancient gaoler,[3] knowing that Toad's pockets were well lined, frequently pointed out that many comforts, and indeed luxuries, could by arrangement be sent in—at a price—from outside.[4]

Now the gaoler had a daughter, a pleasant wench and good-hearted, who assisted her father in the lighter duties of his post.[5] She was particularly fond of animals, and, besides her canary, whose cage hung on a nail in the massive wall of the keep[6] by day, to the great annoyance of prisoners who relished an after-dinner nap, and was shrouded in an antimacassar[7] on the parlour table at night, she kept several piebald[8] mice and a restless revolving squirrel.[9] This kind-hearted girl, pitying the misery of Toad, said to her father one day, "Father! I can't bear to see that poor beast so unhappy, and getting so thin! You let me have the managing of him. You know how fond of animals I am. I'll make him eat from my hand, and sit up, and do all sorts of things."

Her father replied that she could do what she liked with him. He was tired of Toad, and his sulks and his airs and his

Wilde addressed to his lover, Bosie, while he was incarcerated in Reading Prison: "If there be in it one single passage that brings tears to your eyes, weep as we weep in prison where the day no less than the night is set apart for tears." Wilde's poem "The Ballad of Reading Gaol" also bears testament to his grief:

And all the woe that moved him so
That he gave that bitter cry,
And the wild regrets, and the bloody sweats,
None knew so well as I:
For he who lives more lives than one
More deaths than one must die.

2. *bestowed upon such a number of fat, red-faced policemen!"* It seems Grahame dislikes overweight people as much as he dislikes women, using the adjective "fat" six times to describe minor characters. *Red-faced* (possibly angry and alcoholic) and *fat* are signifiers that the police are of a class well below Toad's. In *Class: A Guide Through the American Status System* (New York: Simon & Schuster, 1983), Paul Fussell comments that being overweight is an advertisement of

social standing. "Flaunting obesity is a prole[tarian] sign, as if the object were to offer maximum aesthetic offense to the higher classes and thus exact a form of revenge" (53). Grahame puts his minor characters in their place throughout the book:

> "You mayn't be blest with brains, but there are hundreds and hundreds of you, big, stout fellows, as fat as butter"—Otter (95).
>
> "You common, low, *fat* barge-woman!" [Toad] shouted (245).
>
> "Mole," said the Badger, in his dry, quiet way, "I perceive you have more sense in your little finger than some other animals have in the whole of their fat bodies" (282).
>
> Toad kicked terribly at this, holding himself to be an instrument of Fate, sent to punish fat women with mottled arms who couldn't tell a real gentleman when they saw one (300).

3. *ancient gaoler.* See chapter VI, note 52.

4. *knowing that Toad's pockets were well lined, frequently pointed out that many comforts, and indeed luxuries, could by arrangement be sent in—at a price—from outside.* In Victorian prisons, debtors and wealthy prisoners were allowed to pay for special privileges. Prisoners such as Mr. Toad could pay for sheets, towels, bedding, food, furniture, coal, and, of course, the privilege of wearing their own clothes and having them laundered. In Dickens's *David Copperfield*, the Micawbers move into the King's Bench (a k a Marshalsea) debtor's prison and bring all their amenities from home. For more on debtor's prisons. see Trey Philpotts. *The Dickens Companions, 9: Companion to Little Dorrit* (East Sussex: Helm Information Ltd, 2003).

5. *Now the gaoler had a daughter, a pleasant wench and good-hearted, who assisted her father in the lighter duties of his post.* A possible source of inspiration for the jailer's daughter is William Shakespeare and William Fletcher's *Two Noble Kinsmen*—a retelling of Chaucer's *Knight's Tale. Two Noble Kinsmen* includes a jailer's daughter who's gone mad with unrequited love. She helps her beloved, the imprisoned Palamon, escape to the nearby forest and helps sustain him. We know Grahame would have been familiar with Fletcher's play because he joined Furnivall's New Shakespere Society, which published an edition of the play in 1876. Grahame joined the society with his cousin Annie in June of 1877 and became secretary in 1880. He kept a detailed ledger for the society until the organization dissolved in 1891 (see Green, *Kenneth Grahame: A Biography*, 66).

6. *besides her canary, whose cage hung on a nail in the massive wall of the keep.* This is the third time a canary in a cage appears in *The Wind in the Willows*—the first in the Gypsy cart of chapter II, the second in the window of the human villagers in chapter 5 (see chapter II, note 30, and chapter V, note 7).

7. *antimacassar.* A covering typically thrown over cushions, sofas, or chairs to protect them from grease in the hair; also used as an ornament.

8. *piebald.* A mixture of colors—usually light upon dark; in this case, mice of mixed colors. Often used to describe horses.

9. *a restless revolving squirrel.* Like a squirrel revolving endlessly in an exercise wheel in a cage, a popular means of punishment in the Victorian/Edwardian eras was to send the prisoner to the treadmill—a punishment Oscar Wilde endured.

Illustration by Nancy Barnhart: "O unhappy and forsaken Toad!" Barnhart's Toad has been completely anthropomorphized—he is more like a buffoonish man who happens to resemble a toad. Unlike Bransom's natural and nude toad, Barnhart's is dressed as a dandy, complete with plaid suit, red vest, bow tie, shoes, and spats.

meanness. So that day she went on her errand of mercy, and knocked at the door of Toad's cell.

"Now, cheer up, Toad," she said, coaxingly, on entering, "and sit up and dry your eyes and be a sensible animal. And do try and eat a bit of dinner. See, I've brought you some of mine, hot from the oven!"

It was bubble-and-squeak, between two plates, and its fragrance filled the narrow cell. The penetrating smell of

10. *Cabbage.* Compared to buttered toast and all the other food feasted upon at Toad Hall, cabbage would reek. It was also known to be the fare of a commoner.

Paul Bransom painted the most flattering image of a woman ever published in *The Wind in the Willows*. His jailer's daughter is a cunning young lass with a pretty face. She stares down at the prostrate Toad, who is flipped on his back, bemoaning his fate. Unlike later illustrators, Bransom keeps his riverbankers close to their original animal size. They are also anatomically correct and don't bother with such human constraints as clothing. Bransom's Toad is probably a three-pound fellow.

Bransom. The jailer's daughter, 1913.

cabbage[10] reached the nose of Toad as he lay prostrate in his misery on the floor, and gave him the idea for a moment that perhaps life was not such a blank and desperate thing as he had imagined. But still he wailed, and kicked with his legs, and refused to be comforted. So the wise girl retired for the time, but, of course, a good deal of the smell of hot cabbage remained behind, as it will do, and Toad, between his sobs, sniffed and reflected, and gradually began to think new and inspiring thoughts: of chivalry, and poetry, and deeds still to be done; of broad meadows, and cattle browsing in them, raked by sun and wind; of kitchen-gardens, and straight herb-borders,[11] and warm snap-dragon beset by bees; and of the comforting clink of dishes set down on the table at Toad Hall, and the scrape of chair-legs on the floor as every one pulled himself close up to his work. The air of the narrow cell took a rosy tinge; be began to think of his friends, and how they would surely be able to do something; of lawyers, and how they would have enjoyed his case, and what an ass he had been not to get in a few; and lastly, he thought of his own great cleverness and resource, and all that he was capable of if he only gave his great mind to it; and the cure was almost complete.

When the girl returned, some hours later, she carried a tray, with a cup of fragrant tea steaming on it; and a plate piled up with very hot buttered toast, cut thick, very brown on both sides, with the butter running through the holes in it in great golden drops, like honey from the honeycomb. The smell of that buttered toast simply talked to Toad, and with no uncertain voice; talked of warm kitchens, of breakfasts on bright frosty mornings, of cosy parlour firesides on winter evenings, when one's ramble was over and slippered feet were propped on the fender; of the purring of contented cats, and the twitter of sleepy canaries.[12] Toad sat up on end once more, dried his eyes, sipped his tea and munched his toast, and soon began talking freely about himself, and the house he lived in, and his doings there, and how important he was, and what a lot his friends thought of him.

The gaoler's daughter saw that the topic was doing him as much good as the tea, as indeed it was, and encouraged him to go on.

"Tell me about Toad Hall," said she. "It sounds beautiful."

"Toad Hall," said the Toad proudly, "is an eligible self-contained gentleman's residence, very unique; dating in part from

11. *of kitchen-gardens, and straight herb-borders.* Cooking remains a central theme in all the homes within *The Wind in the Willows*, as it did in the Grahames' lives. In Naomi Stott's letters to Elspeth (1907–08), and in the segments of *The Merry Thought* titled "Nature Notes," Stott often refers to the gardens around Mayfield, Cookham Dean. Herb and kitchen gardens made a significant contribution to the food prepared by cooks. Even Alastair Grahame kept a garden. Stott makes the following observation in the April 1908 edition of *The Merry Thought*:

> A. G. . . . has started work as a gardener. Sweet pea seeds, + nasturtium seeds have been planted. The chief work at present is to pick stones off the bed. Any visitor who goes to look at the garden, sees just an expanse of brown earth, + a few sticks. In June there may be a different sight for him to see.

An advertisement in *The Merry Thought*:

> *Wanted*
> At Mayfield a Cook, one who wants to cook preferred. Kitchen fire is provided, but she must be willing to poke it occasionally, + put on coal

12. *the purring of contented cats, and the twitter of sleepy canaries.* There are sleepy canaries at the beginning of chapter V; see note 9 in that chapter.

the fourteenth century, but replete with every modern convenience. Up-to-date sanitation. Five minutes from church, post-office, and golf-links, Suitable for———"

"Bless the animal," said the girl, laughing, "I don't want to *take* it. Tell me something *real* about it. But first wait till I fetch you some more tea and toast."

She tripped away, and presently returned with a fresh trayful; and Toad, pitching into the toast with avidity,[13] his spirits quite restored to their usual level, told her about the boathouse, and the fish-pond, and the old walled kitchen-garden; and about the pig-styes, and the stables,[14] and the pigeon-house, and the henhouse; and about the dairy, and the wash-house, and the china-cupboards, and the linen-presses (she liked that bit especially); and about the banqueting-hall, and the fun they had there when the other animals were gathered round the table and Toad was at his best, singing songs, telling stories, carrying on generally. Then she wanted to know about his animal-friends, and was very interested in all he had to tell her about them and how they lived, and what they did to pass their time. Of course, she did not say she was fond of animals as *pets*, because she had the sense to see that Toad would be extremely offended.[15] When she said good night, having filled his water-jug and shaken up his straw for him, Toad was very much the

E. H. Shepard's jailer's daughter with toast.

13. *avidity.* Greediness.

14. *told her about the boathouse, and the fish-pond, and the old walled kitchen-garden; and about the pig-styes, and the stables.* This location indeed sounds like Mapledurham House. Like many manor houses with medieval history, Mapledurham included a carefully stocked fishpond to feed its residents.

The Grahames kept a sty at Cookham Dean and owned a great black pig named Bertie. They also had a pony called Firefly. Alastair often rode Firefly in the Mayfield paddock. The animals as well as the gardens were tended by a groundskeeper named Mr. King. Naomi Stott's letters routinely refer to him and his role as caretaker. See Michael A. Aston, ed., *Medieval Fish, Fisheries, and Fishponds in England* (Oxford: Archaeopress/British Archaeological Reports, 1988), and Christopher C. Dyer, *Everyday Life in Medieval England* (London: Hambledon & London, Ltd., 2000).

15. *Of course, she did not say she was fond of animals as* pets, *because she had the sense to see that Toad would be extremely offended.* Though *The Wind in the Willows* is layered with the assumed privileges of class, Grahame allows all the male characters to be trumped by the jailer's daughter. The daughter is one up in the social strata due to her species, not her gender.

same sanguine, self-satisfied animal that he had been of old. He sang a little song or two, of the sort he used to sing at his dinner-parties, curled himself up in the straw, and had an excellent night's rest and the pleasantest of dreams.

They had many interesting talks together, after that, as the dreary days went on; and the gaoler's daughter grew very sorry for Toad, and thought it a great shame that a poor little animal should be locked up in prison for what seemed to her a very trivial offence. Toad, of course, in his vanity, thought that her interest in him proceeded from a growing tenderness; and he could not help half-regretting that the social gulf between them was so very wide, for she was a comely lass, and evidently admired him very much.[16]

One morning the girl was very thoughtful, and answered at random, and did not seem to Toad to be paying proper attention to his witty sayings and sparkling comments.

"Toad," she said presently, "just listen, please. I have an aunt who is a washerwoman."

16. *Toad, of course, in his vanity, thought that her interest in him proceeded from a growing tenderness; and he could not help half-regretting that the social gulf between them was so very wide, for she was a comely lass, and evidently admired him very much.* Peter Hunt writes the following about the relationship between Mr. Toad and the females in *The Wind in the Willows*:

> The gaoler's daughter's interest in Toad's "animal friends" might just be equated with a working girl's interest in the aristocracy—but it reads rather more like Alice looking down on the creatures in the pool of tears: they are seen as mere whimsies . . .
>
> On the other hand, the gaoler's daughter is portrayed as kind, gentle—and the provider of the nursery delight of hot buttered toast. In one sense, this "compassionate virgin" image is also oppressive of women, but within it may lie Grahame's fundamental longing for a caring woman in an asexual relationship. (*The Wind in the Willows: A Fragmented Arcadia*, 87)

"There, there," said Toad, graciously and affably, "never mind; think no more about it. *I* have several aunts who *ought* to be washerwomen."[17]

"Do be quiet a minute, Toad," said the girl. "You talk too much, that's your chief fault, and I'm trying to think, and you hurt my head. As I said, I have an aunt who is a washerwoman; she does the washing for all the prisoners in this castle—we try to keep any paying business of that sort in the family, you understand. She takes out the washing on Monday morning, and brings it in on Friday evening. This is a Thursday. Now, this is what occurs to me: you're very rich[18]—at least you're always telling me so—and she's very poor. A few pounds wouldn't make any difference to you, and it would mean a lot to her. Now, I think if she were properly approached—squared, I believe is the word you animals use—you could come to some arrangement by which she would let you have her dress and bonnet and so on, and you could escape from the castle as the official washerwoman. You're very alike in many respects—particularly about the figure."

"We're *not*," said the Toad in a huff. "I have a very elegant figure—for what I am."[19]

"So has my aunt," replied the girl, "for what *she* is. But have it your own way. You horrid, proud, ungrateful animal, when I'm sorry for you, and trying to help you!"

Toad and the Washerwoman, by E. H. Shepard.

17. *"I have several aunts who* ought *to be washerwomen."* Grahame was known as an authority on aunts and uncles, having written of their tyranny throughout his previous works, starting with the opening of *The Golden Age*:

> Looking back to those days of old, ere the gate shut behind me, I can see now that to children with a proper equipment of parents these things would have worn a different aspect. But to those whose nearest were aunts and uncles, a special attitude of mind may be allowed. They treated us, indeed, with kindness enough as to the needs of the flesh, but after that with indifference (an indifference, as I recognise, the result of a certain stupidity), and therewith the commonplace conviction that your child is merely animal. (3)

18. *"Now, this is what occurs to me: you're very rich."* Toad's adventures as a washerwoman are very much like Falstaff's misadventures in *The Merry Wives of Windsor:* when Mistress Page assists in dressing Falstaff as the fat woman of Brentford.

> MISTRESS PAGE
> Alas the day, I know not! There is no woman's gown big enough for him otherwise he might put on a hat, a muffler and a kerchief, and so escape. (act 4, scene 2)

19. *"We're* not,*" said the Toad in a huff. "I have a very elegant figure—for what I am."* The one equalizing factor between Toad and the aunt is the fact that he is fat. Though he is usually in denial about his physique, he is startled by the truth when he meets the washerwoman. E. H. Shepard catches this moment beautifully, drawing Toad and the elderly washerwoman side by side.

Another possible model for this scene is Beatrix Potter's *The Tale of Mrs. Tiggy-Winkle* (1905). Inspired by a Scottish wash-

"Yes, yes, that's all right; thank you very much indeed," said the Toad hurriedly. "But look here! you wouldn't surely have Mr. Toad, of Toad Hall, going about the country disguised as a washerwoman!"

"Then you can stop here as a Toad," replied the girl with much spirit. "I suppose you want to go off in a coach-and-four!"

Honest Toad was always ready to admit himself in the wrong. "You are a good, kind, clever girl," he said, "and I am indeed a proud and a stupid toad. Introduce me to your worthy aunt, if you will be so kind, and I have no doubt that the excellent lady and I will be able to arrange terms satisfactory to both parties."

Next evening the girl ushered her aunt into Toad's cell, bearing his week's washing pinned up in a towel. The old lady had been prepared beforehand for the interview, and the sight of certain gold sovereigns that Toad had thoughtfully placed on the table in full view practically completed the matter and left little further to discuss. In return for his cash, Toad received a cotton print gown, an apron, a shawl, and a rusty black bonnet; the only stipulation the old lady made being that she should be gagged and bound and dumped down in a corner. By this not very convincing artifice, she explained,

erwoman named Kitty McDonald, Mrs. Tiggy-Winkle is "a comical, round little old woman, as brown as a berry and wears a multitude of petticoats." The sixth of Beatrix Potter's books, *The Tale of Mrs. Tiggy-Winkle* follows the meticulous washerwoman completing her bundles of laundry. At the end, she throws off her costume and runs up the hill, receiving neither payment nor thanks, which is when young Lucie realizes —much in the same way the bargewoman will discover that the washerwoman is just a toad—"Why! Mrs. Tiggy-Winkle was nothing but a HEDGEHOG."

Branson's jailer's daughter bears an uncanny resemblance to the illustration to Walter Crane's rendering of The Frog Prince, circa 1890.

aided by picturesque fiction which she could supply herself, she hoped to retain her situation, in spite of the suspicious appearance of things.

Toad was delighted with the suggestion. It would enable him to leave the prison in some style, and with his reputation for being a desperate and dangerous fellow untarnished; and he readily helped the gaoler's daughter to make her aunt appear as much as possible the victim of circumstances over which she had no control.

"Now it's your turn, Toad," said the girl. "Take off that coat and waistcoat of yours; you're fat enough as it is."[20]

Shaking with laughter, she proceeded to "hook-and-eye" him into the cotton print gown,[21] arranged the shawl with a professional fold, and tied the strings of the rusty bonnet under his chin.

"You're the very image of her," she giggled, "only I'm sure you never looked half so respectable in all your life before.[22] Now, good-bye, Toad, and good luck. Go straight down the way you came up; and if any one says anything to you, as they probably will, being but men, you can chaff back a bit, of course, but remember you're a widow woman, quite alone in the world, with a character to lose."

With a quaking heart, but as firm a footstep as he could command, Toad set forth cautiously on what seemed to be a most hare-brained and hazardous undertaking; but he was soon agreeably surprised to find how easy everything was made for him, and a little humbled at the thought that both his popularity, and the sex that seemed to inspire it, were really another's. The washerwoman's squat figure in its familiar cotton print seemed a passport for every barred door and grim gateway; even when he hesitated, uncertain as to the right turning to take, he found himself helped out of his difficulty by the warder at the next gate, anxious to be off to his tea, summoning him to come along sharp and not keep him waiting there all night. The chaff and the humourous sallies

20. *"Now it's your turn, Toad," said the girl. "Take off that coat and waistcoat of yours; you're fat enough as it is."* Toad is receiving a double blow to the ego. He must dress in women's clothing, and when he does, it reveals that he is fat.

21. *Shaking with laughter, she proceeded to "hook-and-eye" him into the cotton print gown.* A term for corseting an individual into a garment—usually a dress. The eye is a wire loop and the hook is made from double-flattened wire on which the hook catches.

22. *"You're the very image of her," she giggled, "only I'm sure you never looked half so respectable in all your life before."* According to Geraldine Poss's "An Epic in Arcadia: *The Wind in the Willows*," Toad's departure recalls the scene in the *Odyssey* when Athene helps to set Odysseus free.

> It would have been an epic term, had [Toad] served it, the same length of time Odysseus spent away from home before Athene secured Zeus' permission to free him from Calypso. Toad's escape is likewise arranged through the efforts of a woman . . . who, like Athene (and perhaps Nausicaa?), appeals to her father for mercy and plans on her own to let him slip out, disguising his aristocratic toad's body in the clothing of a washerwoman, as Odysseus was disguised and withered, upon his return to Ithaca, to look like an old warrior. (87)

The scene has another Homeric ancestor in the *Iliad*. Like Toad escaping prison in *The Wind in the Willows* by dressing up as a washerwoman, in the *Iliad* Achilles tries (unsuccessfully) to escape the draft for the Trojan War by dressing up as a young woman at his mother's insistence.

—*J. J.*

Shepard. Toad's escape, 1931.

to which he was subjected, and to which, of course, he had to provide prompt and effective reply, formed, indeed, his chief danger; for Toad was an animal with a strong sense of his own dignity, and the chaff was mostly (he thought) poor and clumsy, and the humour of the sallies entirely lacking. However, he kept his temper, though with great difficulty, suited his retorts to his company and his supposed character, and did his best not to overstep the limits of good taste.

It seemed hours before he crossed the last courtyard, rejected

Payne. Toad's escape, 1927.

the pressing invitations from the last guardroom, and dodged the outspread arms of the last warder, pleading with simulated passion for just one farewell embrace.[23] But at last he heard the wicket-gate in the great outer door click behind him,[24] felt the fresh air of the outer world upon his anxious brow,[25] and knew that he was free![26]

Dizzy with the easy success of his daring exploit, he walked quickly towards the lights of the town, not knowing in the least what he should do next, only quite certain of one thing, that he must remove himself as quickly as possible from the neighbourhood where the lady he was forced to represent was so well-known and so popular a character.

As he walked along, considering, his attention was caught by some red and green lights a little way off, to one side of the town, and the sound of the puffing and snorting of engines and the banging of shunted trucks fell on his ear. "Aha!" he thought, "this is a piece of luck! A railway station is the thing I want most in the whole world at this moment; and what's more, I needn't go through the town to get it, and shan't have to support this humiliating character[27] by repartees which, though thoroughly effective, do not assist one's sense of self-respect."

He made his way to the station accordingly, consulted a time-table, and found that a train, bound more or less in the direction of his home, was due to start in half-an-hour. "More luck!" said Toad, his spirits rising rapidly, and went off to the booking-office to buy his ticket.

He gave the name of the station that he knew to be nearest to the village of which Toad Hall was the principal feature, and mechanically put his fingers, in search of the necessary money, where his waiscoat pocket should have been. But here the cotton gown, which had nobly stood by him so far, and which he had basely forgotten, intervened, and frustrated his efforts. In a sort of nightmare he struggled with the strange uncanny thing that seemed to hold his hands, turn all muscu-

23. *rejected the pressing invitations from the last guardroom, and dodged the outspread arms of the last warder, pleading with simulated passion for just one farewell embrace.* Nearly all of the illustrators have attempted this scene, to varying effect. Wyndham Payne drew Toad leaving jail dressed as the washerwoman. Shepard repeated the image but showed Toad from the back. Payne added the heckling guards, but they do not give the impression that Toad is in peril and that he "dodged the outspread arms of the last warder." Payne's Toad passes nonthreatening sentinels; they are far more friendly than the men described by Grahame. Shepard dismissed the misogynist threat inherent in Grahame's text by illustrating Toad walking out of the gates of the jail with no guards. Instead, the illustration focuses on the city beyond the gate, defusing the tension of Toad escaping sexually unscathed. Shepard's Toad has also hitched up his skirt and looks ready to click his heels, making the escape seem too easy.

24. *But at last he heard the wicket-gate in the great outer door click behind him.* In Grahame's original letter to Alastair, a guard beats Toad because he mistakes him for the washerwoman who has shorted him on his laundry. Toad takes the beating so that he can escape. In revision, Grahame removed the beating but retained the guards as vile and threatening sentinels.

25. *felt the fresh air of the outer world upon his anxious brow.* This is Grahame's letter that includes the beating of Toad. Naomi Stott and Alastair were staying in Littlehampton when they received it. At the time, Kenneth Grahame would have been writing from Cornwall.

Green Bank Hotel
Falmouth
23rd May 1907

My Dearest Mouse

Thank you very much for your nice letter. It was very interesting + full of news, and I read it through several times. I hope you have got some warm weather again by this time. It is very hard to live in sight of a beach + not be able to dig, + dig + dig + dig—all day long. No doubt you have met some of the animals + have heard about Toad's Adventures since he was dragged off to prison by the bobby + the constable. At first he lay full length on the floor, and shed bitter tears, and abandoned himself to dark dispair. For he said "How can I ever hope to be set free again. I who have been imprisoned—and justly—so often, for stealing so many—so many———he could not utter the word, for his sobs choked him. Base animal that I am (he said): O unhappy + abandoned Toad (he said): I must languish in this dungeon (he said) till people have forgotten the very name of Mr. Toad. With lamentations such as these he passed his days + nights, refusing consolation, refusing food or other light refreshments: till one day the gaoler's daughter, who was a tender-hearted young woman, took pity on him + said "cheer up Toad! + try + eat a bit of dinner". But the toad lay on the floor + wailed + wouldn't eat his dinner. Then the gaoler's daughter went + fetched a cup of hot tea + some very hot buttered toast, cut thick, very brown on both sides, with the butter running through the holes in it in great golden drops like honey. When the Toad smelt the buttered toast he sat up + dried his eyes for he was exceedingly fond of buttered toast; + the gaoler's daughter comforted him + he drank his tea + had another plate of toast. Then they discussed plans for his escape from the dungeon, + the gaoler's daughter said "Tomorrow my aunt, who is the washer woman to the prison, will bring home your week's washing, + I will dress you up in her clothes + you will escape as the washer woman" So when the washer woman came with the linen, they dressed Toad up in her clothes + put a bonnet on his head, + out he marched, past the gaolers, as bold as you please. As he was passing one of them, the man said "Hullo mother washer woman, why didn't you send home my Sunday shirt last week, you lazy old pig?" + he took his stick + beat her full sore. And the toad was mad with rage, because he wanted to give him a punch in the eye, but he controlled himself + ran on through the Door, which banged behind him + he was Free. This is as far as I have heard at present.

Your affectionate
Daddy.

26. *and knew that he was free!* The events so far come from Grahame's first "Dearest Mouse" letter. The narrative moves on in his next, dated May 28, 1907. Between letters, Kenneth and Elspeth had moved to Fowey.

The Fowey Hotel
Fowey, Cornwall, 28 May 1907.

My dearest Mouse

I am very glad to hear that you have got rid of your cold, + have been able to sail your boat, in the pond. Now I daresay you will want to hear something more of the sad misadventures of Mr. Toad. Well, when he found himself outside the prison gates it was quite dark + he was in a strange land, with no ~~no~~ friends, + he was frightened, + didn't know what to do. But he could hear the puffing of steam-engines not very far off, + he saw some red + green lights through the trees, + he said to himself "That must be a railway station, + if I am to get home the first thing to do is to get in to a train that goes there! So he made his way down to the station + went into the ticket office + asked for a ticket. And the man said "Where for?" And the Toad told him. And the man said "That will cost five shillings". So the Toad felt for his pocket, to find his money, when to his horror + dismay he couldn't find any pocket! Because he had got the washer woman's dress on. Then he remembered that when he had changed clothes in such a hurry he had left all his money, + his keys, + pencil, + watches, + everything, in the pockets of his clothes he had taken off. So there he was, miles + miles from home, dressed like a washerwoman, without a penny of money. Then Mr. Toad shed bitter tears, + said to the man "Please I have lost all my money—will you be very kind + give me a ticket for nothing." But this man only laughed and said "go away old woman! We don't carry washer women for nothing on this railway!" So the Toad went away crying, and wandered down the platform by the side of the train, thinking whatever should he do, till he came to where the engine was. And the engine-driver saw he was crying, + said cheerfully, "What's the matter, Mother?" And the Toad replied "I want to get home, so badly, but I've lost all my money + I can't buy a ticket". Now the engine-driver was a kind-hearted man, + he said "Look here, ~~cc~~ washerwoman! This engine-driving is very dirty work, and I dirty so many shirts that my wife says she's tired of washing 'em. If you will wash two shirts for me, next week, I'll let you ride on the engine with me now, + so you will get home for nothing!" Then the Toad was overjoyed, and he sprang up on the engine with great delight. Of course he had never washed a shirt in his life, and couldn't if he tried, but he thought "when I get home, + get some more money, I will send the engine-driver some, to pay for his washing, + that will be just the same." Presently the engine driver blew his whistle + the train began to move out of the station; + soon they were puffing + rattling through the country, ever so fast, + the Toad was jumping up + down with sheer delight, to think that soon he would be home again.

Suddenly the engine driver began to listen + presently he said "Its very funny but I believe I hear another train following us!" The Toad began to feel nervous. Then the engine driver looked over the back of the train, for the moon was shining brightly + he could see a long way down the line, + at last he cried out "Yes! I see an engine! It is coming along very fast I believe we are being pursued!" And the Toad began to feel very nervous. Presently the engine-driver looked again, + then he cried "Yes, they are gaining on us! I can see them clearly now! It is an engine pursuing us! It is full of policemen, and they are all brandishing revolvers + calling out "Stop, Stop, Stop, Stop STOP!!!!

This is all the news I have up to the present time.

Your affectionate
Daddy

27. *"A railway station is the thing I want most in the whole world at this moment; and what's more, I needn't go through the town to get it, and shan't have to support this humiliating character."* Railway stations in the Edwardian Era were bustling places of commerce, with people constantly coming and going. It's the perfect place for Toad to lose himself in a crowd. Railways had begun to replace horse-drawn coaches, and stations became the hubs of the villages and towns they served, "a center of news, gossip, and

lar strivings to water, and laugh at him all the time; while other travellers, forming up in a line behind, waited with impatience, making suggestions of more or less value and comments of more or less stringency and point. At last—somehow—he never rightly understood how—he burst the barriers, attained the goal, arrived at where all waistcoat pockets are eternally situated, and found—not only no money, but no pocket to hold it, and no waistcoat to hold the pocket!

To his horror he recollected that he had left both coat and waistcoat behind him in his cell, and with them his pocket-book, money, keys, watch, matches, pencil-case—all that makes life worth living, all that distinguishes the many-pocketed animal,[28] the lord of creation, from the inferior one-pocketed or no-pocketed productions that hop or trip about permissively, unequipped for the real contest.

In his misery he made one desperate effort to carry the thing off, and, with a return to his fine old manner—a blend of the Squire and the College Don[29]—he said, "Look here! I find I've left my purse behind. Just give me that ticket, will you, and I'll send the money on to-morrow? I'm well-known in these parts."

The clerk stared at him and the rusty black bonnet a moment, and then laughed.[30] "I should think you were pretty well known in these parts," he said, "if you've tried this game on often. Here, stand away from the window, please, madam; you're obstructing the other passengers!"

An old gentleman who had been prodding him in the back for some moments here thrust him away, and, what was worse, addressed him as his good woman, which angered Toad more than anything that had occurred that evening.[31]

Baffled and full of despair, he wandered blindly down the platform where the train was standing, and tears trickled down each side of his nose. It was hard, he thought, to be within sight of safety and almost of home, and to be baulked by the want of a few wretched shillings and by the pettifogging[32] mistrustfulness of paid officials. Very soon his escape

advice. The home of bookstall and telegraph office" (Jeffrey Richards and John M. MacKenzie, *The Railway Station: A Social History* [Oxford: Oxford University Press, 1986], 7). Established 1792, W. H. Smith, stationers, a series of bookstore and newstand franchises located in train stations across England, became instrumental in Charles Dickens's rise as a novelist because they sold his first books as serials.

The rise of the railway also coincided with the demise of canal boats and barges. Canals were built throughout England from the 1790s to around 1840 and were an easier and more economical mode of transport for heavy cargo such as coal.

28. *many-pocketed animal.* The "many-pocketed animal" or "lord of creation," is a reference to the entitlements of males. In 1908 women were excluded from most businesses and commerce. Rare was the woman who had social power beyond the confines of marriage or a service job such as a laundress. Constance Smedley, who prompted Grahame to work his Dearest Mouse letters into *The Wind in the Willows*, was a rare exception, working as a literary scout for the American magazine *Everybody's*.

29. *a blend of the Squire and the College Don.* Both are positions of authority in English society. A squire is a country gentleman, usually a landowner. In some cases, he is the principal landowner in a village or a district.

Grahame dreamed of becoming a college don. Lewis Carroll was a don at Christ Church, Oxford, having received recognition as a mathematician and author. (Alastair Grahame became a member of Christ Church—referred to as Ch Ch—and was last seen dining within the college hall before he committed suicide on May 7, 1920.)

30. *The clerk stared at him and the rusty black bonnet a moment, and then laughed.* Regula-

would be discovered, the hunt would be up, he would be caught, reviled, loaded with chains, dragged back again to prison and bread-and-water and straw; his guards and penalities would be doubled; and O, what sarcastic remarks the girl would make! What was to be done? He was not swift of foot; his figure was unfortunately recognisable. Could he not squeeze under the seat of a carriage? He had seen this method adopted by schoolboys, when the journey-money provided by thoughtful parents had been diverted to other and better ends. As he pondered, he found himself opposite the engine, which was being oiled, wiped, and generally caressed by its affectionate driver, a burly man with an oil-can in one hand and a lump of cotton-waste in the other.

"Hullo, mother!" said the engine-driver, "what's the trouble? You don't look particularly cheerful."

"O, sir!" said Toad, crying afresh, "I am a poor unhappy washerwoman, and I've lost all my money, and can't pay for a ticket, and I *must* get home to-night somehow, and whatever I am to do I don't know. O dear, O dear!"

"That's a bad business, indeed," said the engine-driver reflectively. "Lost your money—and can't get home—and got some kids, too, waiting for you, I dare say?'

"Any amount of 'em," sobbed Toad. "And they'll be hungry—and playing with matches—and upsetting lamps, the little innocents!—and quarrelling, and going on generally. O dear, O dear!"

"Well, I'll tell you what I'll do," said the good engine-driver. "You're a washerwoman to your trade, says you. Very well, that's that. And I'm an engine-driver, as you well may see, and there's no denying it's terribly dirty work. Uses up a power of shirts, it does, till my missus is fair tired of washing of 'em. If you'll wash a few shirts for me when you get home, and send 'em along, I'll give you a ride on my engine. It's against the Company's regulations,[33] but we're not so very particular in these out-of-the-way parts."

tion 25 for Station Masters and Clerks from the London and North-Western Railway Company states the following: "The clerks at the several Stations are to deliver Tickets to all persons booking their places for conveyance by the railway, and no person is to be allowed to pass on the platform without producing his ticket" (F. B. Head, *Stokers and Pokers; Or, the London and North-Western Railway* [New York: Augustus M. Kelley, Publishers, 1969], 189).

According to Derek Hudson's *Arthur Rackham,* in the 1939 illustration the clerk behind the ticket counter is a self-portrait of Rackham (149).

31. *An old gentleman who had been prodding him in the back for some moments here thrust him away, and, what was worse, addressed him as his good woman, which angered Toad more than anything that had occurred that evening.*

Ernest Shepard embellished Grahame's text by giving the prodding gentleman an umbrella to poke at Mr. Toad. Eight years later, Arthur Rackham followed suit and also gave the gentleman an umbrella.

The "gentleman" is anything but gentle—because he is further up on the social ladder than a washerwoman, his behavior is tolerable. The greatest irony is that Toad is even further up in the social hierarchy than the old gentleman: In reality Toad would not need to bother with public transportation. Back at Toad Hall he has any number of cars at his disposal.

32. *pettifogging.* Wrangling or quibbling about small, petty points.

33. *It's against the Company's regulations.* The trading of laundry service for a free ride would have been against regulations for anyone working for the London and North-Western Railway Company. Any employee who "receive[d] any gratuity from the public [did so] on pain of dismissal" (Head, *Stokers and Pokers*, 161).

The Toad's misery turned into rapture as he eagerly scrambled up into the cab of the engine. Of course, he had never washed a shirt in his life, and couldn't if he tried and, anyhow, he wasn't going to begin; but he thought: "When I get safely home to Toad Hall, and have money again, and pockets to put it in, I will send the engine-driver enough to pay for quite a quantity of washing, and that will be the same thing, or better."

The guard waved his welcome flag, the engine-driver whistled in cheerful response, and the train moved out of the station.[34] As the speed increased, and the Toad could see on either side of him real fields, and trees, and hedges, and cows, and horses, all flying past him, and as he thought how every minute was bringing him nearer to Toad Hall, and sympathetic friends, and money to chink in his pocket, and a soft bed to sleep in, and good things to eat, and praise and admiration at the recital of his adventures and his surpassing cleverness, he began to skip up and down and shout and sing snatches of song, to the great astonishment of the engine-driver, who had come across washerwomen before, at long intervals, but never one at all like this.

They had covered many and many a mile, and Toad was already considering what he would have for supper as soon as he got home, when he noticed that the engine-driver, with a puzzled expression on his face, was leaning over the side of the engine and listening hard. Then he saw him climb on to the coals and gaze out over the top of the train; then he returned and said to Toad: "It's very strange; we're the last train running in this direction to-night, yet I could be sworn that I heard another following us!"

Toad ceased his frivolous antics at once. He became grave and depressed, and a dull pain in the lower part of his spine, communicating itself to his legs, made him want to sit down and try desperately not to think of all the possibilities.

Regulation 22 of Section V, "Regulations for Guards," is more concise: "The guard must not allow any passenger or parcel to be conveyed by the Train unless properly booked; and if he has reason to suppose that any passenger is without ticket, or is not in the proper Carriage, he must request the passenger to show the ticket" (ibid.,183).

34. *The guard waved his welcome flag, the engine-driver whistled in cheerful response, and the train moved out of the station.* Grahame does not condemn trains the way he does other modern inventions, such as the car. A railway passing through a town connects the individual with both rural England and the metropolis of London, and Grahame, of course, depended on trains to take him to and from the Bank of England. At an early age, trains—though a product of the Industrial Revolution—were Grahame's means of escape: to and from Scotland, to and from school in Oxford, and, later, as a commuter from Cookham Dean to London.

> For myself, I probably stand alone in owning to a sentimental weakness for the night-piercing whistle—judiciously remote, as some men love the skirl of the pipes. In the days when streets were less wearily familiar than now, or ever the golden cord was quite loosed that led back to relinquished fields and wider skies, I have lain awake on stifling summer nights, thinking of luckier friends by moor and stream, and listening for the whistles from certain railway stations, veritable "horns of Elf-land, faintly blowing." Then, a ghostly passenger, I have taken my seat in a phantom train, and sped up, up, through the map, rehearsing the journey bit by bit: through the furnace-lit Midlands, and on till the grey glimmer of dawn showed

By this time the moon was shining brightly, and the engine-driver, steadying himself on the coal, could command a view of the line behind them for a long distance.

Presently he called out, "I can see it clearly now! It is an engine, on our rails, coming along at a great pace! It looks as if we were being pursued!"

The miserable Toad, crouching in the coal-dust, tried hard to think of something to do with dismal want of success.

"They are gaining on us fast!" cried the engine-driver. And the engine is crowded with the queerest lot of people! Men like ancient warders,[35] waving halberds; policemen in their helmets, waving truncheons;[36] and shabbily dressed men in pot-hats, obvious and unmistakable plain-clothes detectives even at this distance, waving revolvers and walking-sticks; all waving, and all shouting the same thing—'Stop, stop, stop!' "[37]

Then Toad fell on his knees among the coals and, raising his clasped paws in supplication, cried, "Save me, only save me, dear kind Mr. Engine-driver, and I will confess everything! I am not the simple washerwoman I seem to be! I have no children waiting for me, innocent or otherwise! I am a toad—the well-known and popular Mr. Toad, a landed proprietor;[38] I have just escaped, by my great daring and cleverness, from a loathsome dungeon into which my enemies had flung me; and if those fellows on that engine recapture me, it will be chains and bread-and-water and straw and misery once more for poor, unhappy, innocent Toad!"

The engine-driver looked down upon him very sternly, and said, "Now tell the truth; what were you put in prison for?'

"It was nothing very much," said poor Toad, colouring deeply. "I only borrowed a motor-car while the owners were at lunch; they had no need of it at the time. I didn't mean to steal it, really; but people—especially magistrates—take such harsh views of thoughtless and high-spirited actions."

stone walls in place of hedges, and masses looming up on either side; till the bright sun shone upon brown leaping streams and purple heather, and the clear, sharp northern air streamed in through the windows. Return, indeed, was bitter; Endymion-like, "my first touch of the earth went nigh to kill:" but it was only to hurry northwards again on the wings of imagination, from dust and heat to the dear mountain air. (Grahame, "The Romance of the Rail," *Pagan Papers*, 13)

35. *"ancient warders."* Elderly soldiers who guard an entrance or keep watch from a tower. In this case, the company of the ancient jailer.

36. *"waving truncheons."* A short thick staff, club, or cudgel; a piece broken from a spear—in other words, an improvised weapon.

37. *"all waving, and all shouting the same thing—'Stop, stop, stop!' "* This is where the story takes up again in the letters. (See "The Letters" for the complete text.)

38. *"a landed proprietor."* Landed: One who possesses land or has an estate. Proprietor: One who owns property or has an exclusive right to use that property.

The engine-driver looked very grave and said, "I fear that you have been indeed a wicked toad, and by rights I ought to give you up to offended justice. But you are evidently in sore trouble and distress, so I will not desert you. I don't hold with motor-cars, for one thing; and I don't hold with being ordered about by policemen when I'm on my own engine, for another. And the sight of an animal in tears always makes me feel queer and soft-hearted. So cheer up, Toad! I'll do my best, and we may beat them yet!"[39]

They piled on more coals, shovelling furiously; the furnace roared, the sparks flew, the engine leapt and swung, but still their pursuers slowly gained. The engine-driver, with a sigh, wiped his brow with a handful of cotton-waste, and said, "I'm afraid it's no good, Toad. You see, they are running light, and they have the better engine. There's just one thing left for us to do, and it's your only chance, so attend very carefully to what I tell you. A short way ahead of us is a long tunnel, and on the other side of that the line passes through a thick wood.[40] Now, I will put on all the speed I can while we are running through the tunnel, but the other fellows will slow down a bit, naturally, for fear of an accident. When we are through, I will shut off steam and put on brakes as hard as I can, and the moment it's safe to do so you must jump and hide in the wood, before they get through the tunnel and see you. Then I will go full speed ahead again, and they can chase me if they like, for as long as they like, and as far as they like. Now mind and be ready to jump when I tell you!"

They piled on more coals, and the train shot into the tunnel, and the engine rushed and roared and rattled, till at last they shot out at the other end into fresh air and the peaceful moonlight, and saw the wood lying dark and helpful upon either side of the line. The driver shut off steam and put on brakes, the Toad got down on the step, and as the train slowed down to almost a walking pace he heard the driver call out, "Now, jump!"

39. *"And the sight of an animal in tears always makes me feel queer and soft-hearted. So cheer up, Toad! I'll do my best, and we may beat them yet!"* The engine driver has no accent or demarcation of his class, and he stands to gain nothing from helping Toad. Perhaps he is simply a commoner willing to help a convict—a particularly Dickensian sensibility.

What is certain is that the engine driver's convenient cooperation with Toad is a plot device: an easy means of escape. Peter Hunt writes, in "Language and Class in *The Wind in the Willows*":

> Th[e] instability of the text, with characters vacillating between parody, normal or "authentic" speech, and authorially mediated speech, allows the text to evade very potent linguistic class distinction and to evade the confrontations latent in a book which deals obliquely with so many societal issues. (160)

40. *A short way ahead of us is a long tunnel, and on the other side of that the line passes through a thick wood.* Tunnels play an important role in *The Wind in the Willows*. Mole comes up through a tunnel at Mole End on the first page of the book; Badger's house is full of tunnels that reach beyond the Wild Wood. The field mice in chapter IX tunnel in preparation for winter. And later, in chapter XII, Badger will reveal that there are similar tunnels beneath Toad Hall that come up in "the butler's pantry, next to the dining-hall."

Grahame was obsessed with tunnels and their potentially secretive nature. See chapter IV, note 53.We know that the story of the Fifth Duke of Portland's tunnels was much in the news in 1908. Alastair Grahame and Naomi Stott wrote a story together for *The Merry Thought* in April 1908 that included a tunnel that led under the river to a playground:

Toad jumped, rolled down a short embankment, picked himself up unhurt, scrambled into the wood and hid.

Peeping out, he saw his train get up speed again and disappear at a great pace. Then out of the tunnel burst the pursuing engine, roaring and whistling, her motley crew waving their various weapons and shouting, "Stop! stop! stop!" When they were past, the Toad had a hearty laugh—for the first time since he was thrown into prison.

But he soon stopped laughing when he came to consider that it was now very late and dark and cold, and he was in an unknown wood, with no money and no chance of supper, and still far from friends and home; and the dead silence of everything, after the roar and rattle of the train, was something of a shock. He dared not leave the shelter of the trees, so he struck into the wood, with the idea of leaving the railway as far as possible behind him.

After so many weeks within walls, he found the wood strange and unfriendly and inclined, he thought, to make fun

The Witch of the Old Tree

The Witch, one night, had that little wood of dark trees on Winter Hill, near the tree she sometimes visits, all decked with lights. What do you think was going to happen when the moon shone bright? There was to be a party, + all the guests met there, + by a secret underground passage were shewn the way to her playground under the river. (April 1908, Harry Ransom Humanities Resarch Center, The University of Texas at Austin)

Grahame was also well aware of the trains that passed through Cookham Dean, as one of Naomi Stott's letters attests:

At/ Mayfield, Cookham Dean, Berks
March 21st 1908
Dear Mrs: Grahame,

I received your note, + told Miss Passey about the lobster + the stout. Mouse is ready with a lot of news. We

Shepard. The fox, 1931.

of him. Night-jars,[41] sounding their mechanical rattle, made him think that the wood was full of searching warders, closing in on him. An owl, swooping noiselessly towards him, brushed his shoulder with its wing,[42] making him jump with the horrid certainty that it was a hand; then flitted off, moth-like, laughing its low ho! ho! ho! which Toad thought in very poor taste. Once he met a fox, who stopped, looked him up and down in a sarcastic sort of way,[43] and said, "Hullo, washerwoman! Half a pair of socks and a pillow-case short this week! Mind it doesn't occur again!" and swaggered off, sniggering. Toad looked about for a stone to throw at him, but could not succeed in finding one, which vexed him more than anything. At last, cold, hungry, and tired out, he sought the shelter of a hollow tree, where with branches and dead leaves he made himself as comfortable a bed as he could, and slept soundly till the morning.

Toad at the ticket counter.
Barnhart's tailpiece for chapter VIII.

had a good day out yesterday. Near Marsh's farm we went across fields to a lane that leads over a railway bridge to Cookham. We halted at the bridge to watch the 11.10 train pass under. (Harry Ransom Humanities Resarch Center, The University of Texas at Austin)

41. *Night-jars.* Nightjars are a nocturnal, insect-eating, migratory bird native to Europe and East and central Asia. They arrive in the United Kingdom in mid-May, migrating south, again, in September or October. In Europe, nightjars often nest near livestock, where insects are often plentiful. Called *Caprimulgus europaeus* (family Caprimulgidae)—which translates to "around goats"—nightjars are also known as "goatsuckers," a name derived from the mistaken belief that they suck milk from lactating goats.

Having what is called "cryptic plumage," nightjars are easily camouflaged with their surroundings. They usually raise two broods of one to two chicks in secluded patches of bare ground within low, often shrubby, vegetation. They are known for their distinctive "churring" call. In this case, their cry adds to the frightfulness of the wood.

42. *An owl, swooping noiselessly towards him, brushed his shoulder with its wing,* Arthur Rackham drew the owl and what must be a nightjar "sounding [its] mechanical rattle," but the illustration was placed as the heading for chapter VIII rather than at the end of the chapter where the encounter occurs. Likewise, Grahame's final Dearest Mouse letter for chapter VIII includes a sequence much like the passage in chapter III when Mole discovers he's being watched: "Then the faces began. It was over his shoulder, and indistinctly, that he first thought he saw a face; a little evil wedge-shaped face, looking out at him from a hole." This is possibly revised from Grahame's original letter to be used in

Rackham. Heading for chapter X, 1940.

chapters III and VIII: "And little animals peeped out of their holes + pointed at him + made fun of him" (May 31, 1907).

43. *Once he met a fox, who stopped, looked him up and down in a sarcastic sort of way.* Shepard's final drawing of the chapter is of Toad's encounter with the fox in the Wild Wood. The fox, like every other male in this chapter, makes demands of the washerwoman when they meet, revealing how difficult it is for a female to exist in the Edwardian context of Grahame's book. In chapter III Rat tells us, "[Toad] wouldn't show his face here alone [in the Wild Wood], not for a whole hatful of golden guineas." Yet here is Toad, dressed as a *femme fatale*, face to face with a drinking and smoking fox who is quite possibly volatile.

Though used for the heading illustration of chapter X, Rackham's illustration of Toad in the trunk of the tree really belongs at the end of chapter VIII. As Toad sleeps in the root of a hollow tree, the fox is shown looking in on him, his handlike paw curling over the root in a sinister manner. The fox is long gone at the beginning of chapter X.

IX

Wayfarers[1] All

The Water Rat was restless, and he did not exactly know why. To all appearance the summer's pomp was still at fullest height, and although in the tilled acres green had given way to gold, though rowans[2] were reddening, and the woods were dashed here and there with a tawny fierceness, yet light and warmth and colour were still present in undiminished measure, clean of any chilly premonitions of the passing year. But the constant chorus of the orchards and hedges had shrunk to a casual evensong from a few yet unwearied performers;[3] the robin was beginning to assert himself once more; and there was a feeling in the air of change and departure. The cuckoo, of course, had long been silent; but many another feathered friend, for months a part of the familiar landscape and its small society, was missing too, and it seemed that the ranks thinned steadily day by day. Rat, ever observant of all winged movement, saw that it was taking daily a southing tendency; and even as he lay in bed at night he thought he could make out, passing in the darkness overhead, the beat and quiver of impatient pinions,[4] obedient to the peremptory call.

Nature's Grand Hotel has its Season, like the others. As the guests one by one pack, pay, and depart, and the seats at the

1. *Wayfarers.* Road travelers, especially those who journey on foot.

Chapter IX was the last to be added to the manuscript. In a letter to Scribners dated July 11, 1908, Curtis Brown lists the chapter order. "Wayfarers All" is omitted, with Brown noting: "[Grahame] will be sending enough additional material to come probably between 6 and 7 to make up the 60,000 words."

2. *rowans.* Trees also known as mountain ash.

3. *But the constant chorus of the orchards and hedges had shrunk to a casual evensong from a few yet unwearied performers.* Evensong is the English name of a service (also called vespers) usually sung shortly before sunset.

4. *pinions.* The distal or terminal segment of a bird's wing.

table-d'hôte[5] shrink pitifully at each succeeding meal; as suites of rooms are closed, carpets taken up, and waiters sent away; those boarders who are staying on, *en pension*,[6] until the next year's full re-opening, cannot help being somewhat affected by all these flittings and farewells, this eager discussion of plans, routes, and fresh quarters, this daily shrinkage in the stream of comradeship. One gets unsettled, depressed, and inclined to be querulous. Why this craving for change? Why not stay on quietly here, like us, and be jolly? You don't know this hotel out of the season, and what fun we have among ourselves, we fellows who remain and see the whole interesting year out. All very true, no doubt, the others always reply; we quite envy you—and some other year perhaps—but just now we have engagements—and there's the bus at the door[7]—our time is up! So they depart, with a smile and a nod, and we miss them, and feel resentful. The Rat was a self-sufficing sort of animal, rooted to the land, and, whoever went, he stayed; still, he could not help noticing what was in the air, and feeling some of its influence in his bones.[8]

It was difficult to settle down to anything seriously, with all this flitting going on. Leaving the water-side, where rushes stood thick and tall in a stream that was becoming sluggish and low, he wandered country-wards, crossed a field or two of pasturage[9] already looking dusty and parched, and thrust into the great sea of wheat,[10] yellow, wavy, and murmurous, full of quiet motion and small whisperings. Here he often loved to wander,[11] through the forest of stiff strong stalks that carried their own golden sky away over his head—a sky that was always dancing, shimmering, softly talking; or swaying strongly to the passing wind and recovering itself with a toss and a merry laugh. Here, too, he had many small friends, a society complete in itself, leading full and busy lives, but always with a spare moment to gossip, and exchange news with a visitor. Today, however, though they were civil enough, the field-mice and harvest-mice seemed preoccupied.[12] Many were digging and

5. *table-d'hôte.* A common table for guests at a hotel or eating house; a public meal served there at a stated hour and at a fixed price.

6. *en pension.* The status of a boarder in lodgings.

7. *and there's the bus at the door.* Grahame shortens autobus to bus. According to the *OED*, the word autobus came into the English language in 1895. In 1914 the classical scholar and public orator of Oxford, A. D. Godley, wrote the poem "Motor Bus," which J. R. R. Tolkien illustrated in 1927.

What is it that roareth thus?
Can it be a Motor Bus?
Yes, the smell and hideous hum
Indicat Motorem Bum!
Implet in the Corn and High
Terror me Motoris Bi:
Bo Motori clamitabo
Ne Motore caedar a Bo—
Dative be or Ablative
So thou only let us live:
Whither shall thy victims flee?
Spare us, spare us, Motor Be!
Thus I sang; and still anigh
Came in hordes Motores Bi,
Et complebat omne forum
Copia Motorum Borum.
How shall wretched lives like us
Cincti Bis Motoribus?
Domine, defende nos
Contra hos Motores Bos!

8. *The Rat was a self-sufficing sort of animal, rooted to the land, and, whoever went, he stayed; still, he could not help noticing what was in the air, and feeling some of its influence in his bones.* Kenneth Grahame longed to travel unfettered by familial or professional responsibility. In a letter from 1933, Graham Robertson recalls his friendship with Kenneth and Elspeth Grahame and how Kenneth preferred travel to

the company of his wife: "Oddly enough (for he was a most attractive man) Kenneth had few friends. He simply didn't want them. He would say rather wonderingly to his wife: 'You like people. They interest you. But I am interested in *places*' " (W. Graham Robertson, *Letters from Graham Robertson, 1908–1948*, ed. Kerrison Preston [London: Hamish Hamilton, 1953], 284).

Also see Green, *Kenneth Grahame: A Biography*, 226.

9. *pasturage* Pastures of grass or other herbage on which to graze livestock.

10. *great sea of wheat.* Early editions, up to the Bransom (1913), use the word sea. Later editions—Barnhart, Payne, Shepard, and others—use the word realm.

11. *Here he often loved to wander.* Peter Hunt comments on Grahame's love of walking:

> Peter Haining [*Paths to the River Bank*] has suggested that "Wayfarers All," "the most quoted chapter in the book," was presaged by an essay that Grahame had written for *The Yellow Book* in July 1895, called "The Wanderer." [According to Haining, the essay is called "The Wayfarer." Green refers to the essay as "Long Odds".] In this, the writer walks along the sand listening to the tales of a London businessman who has had "the rare courage . . . to kick the board over and declare against further play." (*The Wind in the Willows: A Fragmented Arcadia*, 32)

See also Peter Haining, *Paths to the River Bank* (London: Souvenir Press, 1983), 97.

Rat's wanderings are a conflation of places that Kenneth Grahame liked to visit—Fowey and the pastures around the seaside town in Cornwall, Cookham, and, of course, Venice. The farmland in and around Fowey has been thought of as one of Grahame's primary sources for "Wayfarers All." In an 1899 letter, Grahame wrote, "My sister said she went along the cliffs and climbed down to a little cove and as she sat there a big rat came out and sat beside her and ate winkles!"

12. *Today, however, though they were civil enough, the field-mice and harvest-mice seemed preoccupied.* The mice in Arthur Rackham's illustration, titled after this fragment of text, are all gangly, with long feet, claws, and scraggly tails. They are made all the more grotesque by the fact that they are wearing human clothing.

tunnelling busily; others, gathered together in small groups, examined plans and drawings of small flats, stated to be desirable and compact, and situated conveniently near the Stores. Some were hauling out dusty trunks and dress-baskets,[13] others were already elbow-deep packing their belongings; while everywhere piles and bundles of wheat, oats, barley, beech-mast and nuts, lay about ready for transport.[14]

"Here's old Ratty!" they cried as soon as they saw him. "Come and bear a hand, Rat, and don't stand about idle!"

Wyndham Payne's illustration with abridged caption: EVERYWHERE PILES AND BUNDLES . . . LAY ABOUT READY FOR TRANSPORT.

13. *dress-basket.* A traveling case for a woman's dresses.

14. *while everywhere piles and bundles of wheat, oats, barley, beech-mast and nuts, lay about ready for transport.* Wyndham Payne drew a full-page cameo of the mice packing up and preparing for winter. Though the wheat above the mice seems to dwarf them, Payne added miniature furniture: a perfectly round hole that looks like it has been excavated by machinery rather than paws, and a well-formed set of stairs. Four of the adult male mice are dapperly dressed, one in a top hat and black-tailed coat, another in a black dinner jacket and bowler hat, and yet another in sporty yachting pants, plaid jacket, and sailor's hat. Three more worker mice, sleeves rolled up, are moving a piano. As noted earlier, Grahame originally did not want his characters overdressed, writing to Curtis Brown after the publication of the Bransom edition in 1913, "I was much relieved to find no bowler hats or plaid waistcoats" (Scribner Archives, Princeton University). Yet fifteen years later, Grahame was cordial to Wyndham Payne, the young illustrator who consistently interpreted the riverbankers as dandies.

In a letter to Grahame, sent care of the Garrick Club on October 26, 1927, Payne wrote: "Having had the distinction of illustrating the latest edition of one of your works . . . I am taking the liberty of asking if you will be so good as to autograph the enclosed copy for me."

Grahame responded, on January 13, 1928:

> I was much concerned, on going up to town yesterday, to find that your copy of "The Wind in the Willows" and letter had been lying so long at the Garrick. I only go to London nowadays when some actual business takes me there, + it so happens that no need has arisen for quite a long time . . .

"What sort of games are you up to?" said the Water Rat severely.[15] "You know it isn't time to be thinking of winter quarters yet, by a long way!"

"O yes, we know that," explained a field-mouse rather shamefacedly; "but it's always as well to be in good time, isn't it? We really *must* get all the furniture and baggage and stores moved out of this before those horrid machines begin clicking round the fields;[16] and then, you know, the best flats get picked up so quickly nowadays, and if you're late you have to put up with *anything*;[17] and they want such a lot of doing up, too, before they're fit to move into. Of course, we're early, we know that; but we're only just making a start."

"O, bother *starts*," said the Rat. "It's a splendid day. Come for a row, or a stroll along the hedges, or a picnic in the woods, or something."

"Well, I *think* not *to-day*, thank you," replied the field-mouse hurriedly. "Perhaps some *other* day—when we've more *time*———"

The Rat, with a snort of contempt, swung round to go, tripped over a hat-box, and fell, with undignified remarks.

"If people would be more careful," said a field-mouse rather stiffly, "and look where they're going, people wouldn't hurt themselves[18]—and forget themselves. Mind that hold-all, Rat! You'd better sit down somewhere. In an hour or two we may be more free to attend to you."

"You won't be 'free' as you call it, much this side of Christmas, I can see that," retorted the Rat grumpily, as he picked his way out of the field.

He returned somewhat despondently to his river again—his faithful, steady-going old river, which never packed up, flitted, or went into winter quarters.

In the osiers which fringed the bank he spied a swallow sitting. Presently it was joined by another, and then by a third; and the birds, fidgeting restlessly on their bough, talked together earnestly and low.

> I was greatly amused by your spirited little drawings, + expect the edition will be a great success I see it displayed in every window. (Bodleian, MS. Eng. Misc. d. 527, pp. 146, 148)

Beech mast is the fruit of the beech.

15. *"What sort of games are you up to?" said the Water Rat severely.* "In Dialogue and Dialectic: Language and Class in *The Wind in the Willows*," Peter Hunt notes that Rat sees the work of the field mice as a game.

> Thus in "Wayfarers All" when Rat comes across the field mice getting ready for winter, we see the upper class talking to the lower class, and, probably because *rural* poor were not such a threat to Grahame, it emerges as an adult addressing the children. (*Children's Literature* 16 [1988]: 163)

16. *before those horrid machines begin clicking round the fields.* At the end of chapter V (see note 51), Grahame uses the metaphor of a threshing machine when Rat falls asleep: "He clambered into his bunk and rolled himself well up into the blankets, and slumber gathered him forthwith, as a swath of barley is folded into the arms of the reaping machine."

Rackham ignored the wheat in Grahame's text, while Payne and many illustrators after Rackham (see, for example, the edition illustrated by Patrick Benson [New York: St. Martin's Press, 1995], 179) paid close attention to the detail. The full-grown wheat is the very reason the mice must move on and rent other flats. They are in a hurry to avoid the thresher. The animals are being squeezed out of their habitat by machinery that was as new to the English countryside of 1908 as the motorcar.

17. *the best flats get picked up so quickly nowadays, and if you're late you have to put up with* anything. The riverbankers all live in sep-

"What, *already*," said the Rat, strolling up to them. "What's the hurry? I call it simply ridiculous."

"O, we're not off yet, if that's what you mean," replied the first swallow. "We're only making plans and arranging things. Talking it over, you know—what route we're taking this year, and where we'll stop, and so on. That's half the fun!"

"Fun?" said the Rat; "now that's just what I don't understand. If you've *got* to leave this pleasant place, and your friends who will miss you, and your snug homes that you've just settled into, why, when the hour strikes I've no doubt you'll go bravely, and face all the trouble and discomfort and change and newness, and make believe that you're not very unhappy. But to want to talk about it, or even think about it, till you really need———"

"No, you don't understand, naturally," said the second swallow. "First, we feel it stirring within us, a sweet unrest; then back come the recollections one by one, like homing pigeons. They flutter through our dreams at night, they fly with us in our wheelings and circlings by day. We hunger to inquire of each other, to compare notes and assure ourselves that it was all really true, as one by one the scents and sounds and names of long-forgotten places come gradually back and beckon to us."

"Couldn't you stop on for just this year?" suggested the Water Rat, wistfully. "We'll all do our best to make you feel at home. You've no idea what good times we have here, while you are far away."

"I tried 'stopping on' one year," said the third swallow. "I had grown so fond of the place that when the time came I hung back and let the others go on without me. For a few weeks it was all well enough, but afterwards, O the weary length of the nights! The shivering, sunless days! The air so clammy and chill, and not an insect in an acre of it! No, it was no good; my courage broke down, and one cold, stormy night I took wing, flying well inland on account of the strong east-

arate houses, or holes. The mice, with fewer resources, lead a more nomadic existence: They take summer lodgings and move to apartments, or flats, for the winter.

Shepard also ignored the wheat, contributing a drawing of the mice crowded around an advertisement that says "Plan Flats."

18. *"If people would be more careful," said a field-mouse rather stiffly, "and look where they're going, people wouldn't hurt themselves."* The field mouse has anthropomorphized Rat into a human being.

erly gales. It was snowing hard as I beat through the passes of the great mountains, and I had a stiff fight to win through; but never shall I forget the blissful feeling of the hot sun again on my back as I sped down to the lakes that lay so blue and placid below me,[19] and the taste of my first fat insect! The past was like a bad dream; the future was all happy holiday as I moved southwards week by week, easily, lazily, lingering as long as I dared, but always heeding the call![20] No, I had had my warning; never again did I think of disobedience."

"Ah, yes, the call of the South, of the South!" twittered the other two dreamily. "Its songs its hues, its radiant air! O, do you remember———" and, forgetting the Rat, they slid into passionate reminiscence, while he listened fascinated, and his heart burned within him. In himself, too, he knew that it was vibrating at last, that chord hitherto dormant and unsuspected. The mere chatter of these southern-bound birds, their pale and secondhand reports, had yet power to awaken this wild new sensation and thrill him through and through with it; what would one moment of the real thing work in him—one passionate touch of the real southern sun, one waft of the authentic odor? With closed eyes he dared to dream a moment in full abandonment, and when he looked again the river seemed steely and chill, the green fields grey and lightless. Then his loyal heart seemed to cry out on his weaker self for its treachery.

"Why do you ever come back, then, at all?" he demanded of the swallows jealously. "What do you find to attract you in this poor drab little country?"

"And do you think," said the first swallow, "that the other call is not for us too, in its due season? The call of lush meadow-grass, wet orchards, warm, insect-haunted ponds, of browsing cattle, of haymaking, and all the farm-buildings clustering round the House of the perfect Eaves?"[21]

"Do you suppose," asked the second one,"that you are the only living thing that craves with a hungry longing to hear the cuckoo's note again?"

19. *"as I sped down to the lakes that lay so blue and placid below me."* The swallow most likely crossed over the Alps in winter before coming upon the Italian Lake District. Perhaps the most recognizable of all the lakes—especially by the Romantic poets—is Lake Como, mentioned in Wordsworth's *The Prelude,* starting on line 721:

> *And, lastly, the withdrawing moon, that set*
> *Before us, while she still was high in*
> *heaven;—*
> *These were our food; and such a summer's*
> *night*
> *Followed that pair of golden days that shed*
> *On Como's Lake, and all that round it lay,*
> *Their fairest, softest, happiest influence.*

(*Complete Poetical Works* [London: Macmillan, 1888], 316–17)

20. *"lingering as long as I dared, but always heeding the call!"* Previous biographers have speculated that Kenneth Grahame's friend Atky, the Fowey Yacht Club commodore, was the model for both the Water Rat and Sea Rat. In September of 1904, against Elspeth's wishes, Kenneth and Atky went on an adventure south into France, heading toward Spain. Green speculates that Grahame might have considered leaving Elspeth at this time. The trip was cut short when Alastair became critically ill with peritonitis (see Prince, *Kenneth Grahame: An Innocent in the Wild Wood,* 203).

21. *"House of the perfect Eaves?"* An ideal house with large enough eaves to protect visitors from bad weather. Visitors can sit outdoors but still be shaded and kept out of the rain.

"In due time," said the third, "we shall be home-sick once more for quiet water-lilies swaying on the surface of an English stream. But to-day all that seems pale and thin and very far away. Just now our blood dances to other music."

They fell a-twittering among themselves once more, and this time their intoxicating babble was of violet seas, tawny sands, and lizard-haunted walls.

Restlessly the Rat wandered off once more, climbed the slope that rose gently from the north bank of the river, and lay looking out towards the great ring of Downs that barred his vision further southwards—his simple horizon hitherto, his Mountains of the Moon,[22] his limit behind which lay nothing he had cared to see or to know. To-day, to him gazing South with a new-born need stirring in his heart, the clear sky over their long low outline seemed to pulsate with promise; to-day, the unseen was everything, the unknown the only real fact of life. On this side of the hills was now the real blank, on the other lay the crowded and coloured panorama that his inner eye was seeing so clearly. What seas lay beyond, green, leaping, and crested! What sun-bathed coasts, along which the white villas glittered against the olive woods! What quiet harbours, thronged with gallant shipping bound for purple islands of wine and spice, islands set low in languorous waters!

He rose and descended river-wards once more; then changed his mind and sought the side of the dusty lane. There, lying half-buried in the thick, cool under-hedge tangle that bordered it, he could muse on the metalled road and all the wondrous world that it led to;[23] on all the wayfarers, too, that might have trodden it, and the fortunes and adventures they had gone to seek or found unseeking—out there, beyond—beyond!

Footsteps fell on his ear, and the figure of one that walked somewhat wearily came into view; and he saw that it was a Rat, and a very dusty one. The wayfarer, as he reached him,

22. *his Mountains of the Moon* The term comes from a group of snow-capped mountains in central Africa—now identified with the Mount Ruwenzori mountain group between Uganda and Zaire—that feed into several lakes said to be the source of the Nile.

Sir Richard Francis Burton was the first European to venture to central Africa in search of the source of the Mountains of the Moon and the source of the Nile. Burton's adventure is chronicled in *The Lake Regions of Central Africa* (1860) and starts in 1855, when Burton and John Hanning Speke traveled from Zanzibar to Lake Tanganyika. They were the first Europeans to see the lake. Too sick to travel further, Burton stayed behind as Speke pressed on to find another lake, which he named Lake Victoria and which in fact is the true source of the Nile. Though Kenneth Grahame was unable to travel extensively, Alastair's nursery library was stocked with adventure books—stories Alastair mimicked for *The Merry Thought*, such as: "Sphinx Island" and "Leaves from a Pirate Diary."

The *OED* also defines Mountains of the Moon as "The type of a very remote place; further than one can imagine, the ends of the earth" and the exact distance that the birds will migrate.

A complete list of Alistair Grahame's books as he listed them in a school ledger, circa 1911—including a significant collection of adventure books—is included in appendix 1.

In 1990, TriStar distributed a film, *Mountains of the Moon*, chronicling the stormy relationship of Richard Francis Burton and John Hanning Speke as they traveled to find the source of the Nile. Written by William Harrison and directed by Robert Rafelson, the adventure/history film tells the story of the men's meeting, their friendship amid hardship, and their estrangement upon returning to England.

23. *and all the wondrous world that it led to.* This line is a takeoff on the adage "All roads lead to Rome," which dates from the days of the Roman Empire, when all roads indeed radiated out from Rome. Southern England is covered with Roman roads built after 55 BC, when Julius Caesar invaded England. Roads were built to be as straight as possible, connecting points in order to move commerce and soldiers. The most famous is Watling Street, a long, straight road still in use today that starts on the Kent coast, passes through London to Leicester and turns toward Wales. The road was built to allow the Roman army to march into England as swiftly as possible once they arrived.

After Alastair Grahame's suicide in 1920, Elspeth and Kenneth finally went South, traveling the Roman roads. They lived in Italy from February of 1922 until the spring of 1924.

24. *The wayfarer, as he reached him, saluted with a gesture of courtesy that had something foreign about it.* After Atky's death from drowning in 1911, Grahame wrote the following reminiscence to the Purveses in Philadelphia:

> I loved Atky—in perhaps a selfish way first of all, because all of his special "passions" appealed to me so—boats, Bohemianism, Burgundy—tramps & travel—books & pictures—but also, & I hope & believe chiefly—for his serene and gentle nature . . .
>
> Again & again in imagination I get into my boat at Whitehouse Steps & scull up the river by the grey old sea-wall, under the screaming gulls, past the tall Russian & Norwegian ships at their moorings & so into Mixtow Pill, & ship my oars at the little stone pier, & find Atky waiting on the steps, thin, in blue serge, with his "Elizabethan" head: & stroll up the pathway you know to the

saluted with a gesture of courtesy that had something foreign about it[24]—hesitated a moment—then with a pleasant smile turned from the track and sat down by his side in the cool herbage. He seemed tired, and the Rat let him rest unquestioned, understanding something of what was in his thoughts; knowing, too, the value all animals attach at times to mere silent companionship, when the weary muscles slacken and the mind marks time.

The wayfarer was lean and keen-featured, and somewhat bowed at the shoulders; his paws were thin and long, his eyes much wrinkled at the corners, and he wore small gold ear rings in his neatly-set well-shaped ears. His knitted jersey was of a faded blue, his breeches, patched and stained, were based on a blue foundation, and his small belongings that he carried were tied up in a blue cotton handkerchief.

When he had rested awhile the stranger sighed, snuffed the air, and looked about him.

"That was clover, that warm whiff on the breeze," he remarked; "and those are cows we hear cropping the grass behind us and blowing softly between mouthfuls. There is a sound of distant reapers, and yonder rises a blue line of cottage smoke against the woodland. The river runs somewhere close by, for I hear the call of a moorhen, and I see by your build that you're a freshwater mariner.[25] Everything seems asleep, and yet going on all the time. It is a goodly life that you lead, friend; no doubt the best in the world, if only you are strong enough to lead it!"

"Yes, it's *the* life, the only life, to live," responded the Water Rat dreamily, and without his usual whole-hearted conviction.

"I did not say exactly that," replied the stranger cautiously; "but no doubt it's the best. I've tried it, and I know. And because I've just tried it—six months of it—and know it's the best, here am I, footsore and hungry, tramping away from it, tramping southward, following the old call, back to the old life, *the* life which is mine and which will not let me go."

Rackham's meeting with the Sea Rat with abridged caption: "The wayfarer saluted with a gesture of courtesy that had something foreign about it."

"Is this, then, yet another of them?" mused the Rat. "And where have you just come from?" he asked. He hardly dared to ask where he was bound for; he seemed to know the answer only too well.

"Nice little farm," replied the wayfarer, briefly. "Upalong in that direction"—he nodded northwards. "Never mind about it. I had everything I could want—everything I had any right to expect of life, and more; and here I am! Glad to be here all the same, though, glad to be here! So many miles further on the road, so many hours nearer to my heart's desire!"

His shining eyes held fast to the horizon, and he seemed to be listening for some sound that was wanting from that inland acreage, vocal as it was with the cheerful music of pasturage and farmyard.

"You are not one of *us*," said the Water Rat, "nor yet a farmer; nor even, I should judge, of this country."

"Right," replied the stranger. "I'm a seafaring rat, I am, and the port I originally hail from is Constantinople,[26] though I'm a sort of a foreigner there too, in a manner of speaking. You will have heard of Constantinople, friend? A fair city, and an ancient and glorious one. And you may have heard, too, of Sigurd, King of Norway, and how he sailed thither with sixty ships,[27] and how he and his men rode up through streets all canopied in their honour with purple and gold; and how the Emperor and Empress came down and banqueted with him on board his ship. When Sigurd returned home, many of his Northmen remained behind and entered the Emperor's bodyguard, and my ancestor, a Norwegian born, stayed behind too,[28] with the ships that Sigurd gave the Emperor. Seafarers we have ever been, and no wonder; as for me, the city of my birth is no more my home than any pleasant port between there and the London River.[29] I know them all, and they know me. Set me down on any of their quays or foreshores, and I am home again."

"I suppose you go great voyages," said the Water Rat with

> little house above it, he talking all the time & always some French whimsicality. I had a letter from him a very few weeks ago, telling of a yachting dinner they had just had—he, apparently in the chair—& his spirits seemed as buoyant as ever. (Chalmers, *Kenneth Grahame*, 321)

The Whitehouse Steps are next to Quiller-Couch's "The Haven," and across the street and far below the Fowey Hotel.

25. *"I see by your build that you're a freshwater mariner."* Peter Hunt points out a similarity between the Water Rat and the Sea Rat versus the freshwater sailing children who meet a saltwater sailor in *Coot Club* (1934), the fifth book of Arthur Ransome's series *Swallows and Amazons*. The saltwater sailor shows the children many different sorts of nautical knots, just as the Sea Rat tells the Water Rat about all of the places he has been, and the culture of those who are well traveled. Hunt writes, "When the Sea Rat says 'I see by your build that you're a freshwater mariner' he is acknowledging a profound brotherhood" (*The Wind in the Willows: A Fragmented Arcadia*, 91).

26. *"and the port I originally hail from is Constantinople."* Previous to 1923, the city of Istanbul in Turkey was called Constantinople. The city was reconstituted from an earlier settlement (AD 330) on the site of Byzantium (a Greek colony in Thrace) by Roman Emperor Constantine I.

27. *"And you may have heard, too, of Sigurd, King of Norway, and how he sailed thither with sixty ships."* Sigurd "Jorsalfare" Magnusson I (reigned 1103–1130) was the first Scandinavian king to take part in the Crusades. He sailed for Palestine in 1107, visiting England, France, Spain, and Sicily on the way. He arrived in Palestine in 1110, where he was received by King Baldwin I of Jerusalem. Sigurd helped the

growing interest. "Months and months out of sight of land, and provisions running short,[30] and allowanced as to water, and your mind communing with the mighty ocean, and all that sort of thing?"

"By no means," said the Sea Rat frankly. "Such a life as you describe would not suit me at all. I'm in the coasting trade, and rarely out of sight of land. It's the jolly times on shore that appeal to me, as much as any seafaring. O, those southern seaports! The smell of them, the riding-lights at night, the glamour!"

"Well, perhaps you have chosen the better way," said the Water Rat, but rather doubtfully. "Tell me something of your coasting, then, if you have a mind to, and what sort of harvest an animal of spirit might hope to bring home from it to warm his latter days with gallant memories by the fireside; for my life, I confess to you, feels to me to-day somewhat narrow and circumscribed."

"My last voyage," began the Sea Rat, "that landed me eventually in this country, bound with high hopes for my inland farm, will serve as a good example of any of them, and, indeed, as an epitome of my highly-coloured life. Family troubles, as usual, began it. The domestic storm-cone was hoisted,[31] and I shipped myself on board a small trading vessel bound from Constantinople, by classic seas whose every wave throbs with a deathless memory, to the Grecian Islands and the Levant.[32] Those were golden days[33] and balmy nights! In and out of harbour all the time—old friends everywhere—sleeping in some cool temple or ruined cistern during the heat of the day[34]—feasting and song after sundown, under great stars set in a velvet sky! Thence we turned and coasted up the Adriatic, its shores swimming in an atmosphere of amber, rose, and aquamarine; we lay in wide land-locked harbours, we roamed through ancient and noble cities, until at last one morning, as the sun rose royally behind us, we rode into Venice down a path of gold. O, Venice is a fine city, wherein a rat can wander at his ease and take his pleasure![35] Or, when weary

Franks capture Sidon and left his fleet at Constantinople as a gift to Byzantine Emperor Alexius Comnenus (reigned 1081–1118). Sigurd returned to Norway by land in 1111.

28. *"and my ancestor, a Norwegian born, stayed behind too."* Variant, e. 247: and my ancestor, {a Norwegian born,} stayed behind too.

From the manuscripts, we see that Grahame added the fact that the Sea Rat's ancestor is Norwegian very late in the editorial process. According to Giles E. M. Gasper, of Wolfson College, Oxford, Grahame drew inspiration for the Sea Rat from William Morris and Eirikr Magnusson's translation of a Norse saga, the *Saga of Sigurd the Jerusalem-Farer*, rather than—as has been suggested—from *Sigurd the Volsung*, which appeared in six translated volumes published in 1891. Grahame wrote an essay about the sagas in the *National Observer* (November 5, 1892). Gasper writes that the translation of *Saga of Sigurd the Jerusalem-Farer* follows the Sea Rat's tale exactly. In chapter 3 Sigurd left Norway with "sixty ships," and when he reached Constantinople, "King Sigurd said to his men that they should ride proudly into the city, and let them look to be heeding little, whatever new things they might see, and so they did" (Gasper, "Kenneth Grahame's *The Wind in the Willows* and William Morris's Old Norse Translations," *Oxford Journals, Notes and Queries* 50 [September 2003]: 323–24).

29. *"London River."* The River Thames.

30. *"Months and months out of sight of land, and provisions running short."* Variant, e. 247:

"Months and m~~M~~onths out of sight of land, and ~~allows~~ provisions running short."

Possibly an allusion to *The Rime of the Ancient Mariner*:

Water, water, every where,
And all the boards did shrink;
Water, water, every where,
Nor any drop to drink.

31. *"The domestic storm-cone was hoisted."* A storm cone is a canvas cone hoisted to warn of high winds. Rudyard Kipling published a poem in 1932 called "The Storm Cone."

32. *"to the Grecian Islands and the Levant."* The Levant is the eastern part of the Mediterranean, with its islands and adjoining countries.

33. *"Those were golden days."* Barnhart's colorful painting titled "Those were golden days" is the most notable illustration of her edition. No other artist has duplicated the image or its colors. The scene is vibrant, the artist having mastered the craft of color separation to bring out rich tones. Barnhart's Rat is similar to Bransom's. Both versions of the Sea Rat wear an earring and patched trousers.

34. *sleeping in some cool temple or ruined cistern during the heat of the day.* A cistern is a man-made reservoir for the storage of water.

35. *"O, Venice is a fine city, wherein a rat can wander at his ease and take his pleasure!"* Payne drew the Sea Rat dressed in a navy costume, sitting in a cafe in Venice, where he is being serenaded by a male troubadour.

Peter Green writes about Grahame's time spent in Venice: "About 1890 Grahame visited Venice for the first time. . . . And one summer day barefoot and paddling . . . in the crinkled sandy shallows of the Lido, his mind full of Ulysses, Grahame encountered an expatriate Englishman who gave him the material for one of his oddest and most revealing stories" (*Kenneth Grahame: A Biography*, 128).

The elderly well-traveled man with the "mark of Cheapside" about him—a man who has been to all the markets of the world—mentors the younger, less-experienced man, transporting him with stories about traveling and his adventures abroad.

Nancy Barnhart, 1922: "Those were golden days."

of wandering, can sit at the edge of the Grand Canal at night, feasting with his friends, when the air is full of music and the sky full of stars, and the lights flash and shimmer on the polished steel prows of the swaying gondolas, packed so that you could walk across the canal on them from side to side! And then the food—do you like shellfish? Well, well, we won't linger over that now."[36]

He was silent for a time; and the Water Rat, silent too and

Wyndham Payne, 1927: "O, Venice is a fine city, wherein a rat can wander at his ease and take his pleasure!" The troubadour is a figment of Payne's imagination; he does not exist in Grahame's text.

36. *"And then the food—do you like shellfish? Well, well, we won't linger over that now."* Grahame often conflated the pleasures of Fowey with those of southern Europe when he wrote to the Purves family in Philadelphia. Wildly fond of lobsters, Grahame mentions them in several letters, always addressing one of the Purveses' servants, Jerry, who evidently cooked lobster for them.

> . . . remembrances to Jerry (I eat a ~~cold~~ lobster every Sunday for lunch & mournfully think what might have been if you were all over on this side & lobsters were cheap. (November 3, 1908; courtesy of the David J. Holmes Collection)
>
> The enclosed lobster is for Jerry, in memory of past lobsters that died nobly in a good cause. Alas! I never see a lobster now, in this inland village [Blewbury]. If I were to meet one walking on

A stairway on North Street in Fowey. "There through the dark doorways you look down flights of stone steps, overhung by great pink tufts of valerian and ending in a patch of sparkling bluewater." (See letter quoted in note 50 in this chapter.)

enthralled, floated on dream-canals and heard a phantom song pealing high between vaporous grey wave-lapped walls.

"Southwards we sailed again at last," continued the Sea Rat, "coasting down the Italian shore, till finally we made Palermo,[37] and there I quitted for a long, happy spell on shore. I never stick too long to one ship; one gets narrow-minded and prejudiced. Besides, Sicily is one of my happy hunting-grounds.[38] I know everybody there, and their ways just suit me. I spent

Paul Bransom's 1913 encounter with the Sea Rat: " 'It's a hard life, by all accounts,' murmured the Rat, sunk in deep thought."

the downs I would fall on his neck with tears of joy—& I would lead him gently home, & we would not part again—never, never. (May 15, 1911; courtesy of the David J. Holmes Collection)

Please give our kindest regards to Miss Rohn, whom I always connect with red valerian and Readymoney Cove. We also wish to be warmly remembered to Jerry, who would really weep if he knew how long it was since I saw a lobster! (February 18, 1915; courtesy of the David J. Holmes Collection)

In her considerable correspondence, Miss Stott passed on information from Kenneth Grahame to the cook, Miss Passey, about lobster.

> At / Mayfield, Cookham Dean, Berks
> March 21st 1908
> Dear Mrs: Grahame,
> I received your note, + told Miss Passey about the lobster + the stout. Mouse is ready with a lot of news. We had a good day out yesterday . . .

In regards to lobster and stout: if one, 12-ounce beer is placed in the water used to steam shellfish, it enhances the flavor greatly. (Harry Ransom Humanities Research Center, The University of Texas at Austin)

37. *Palermo.* A city in Sicily known for its sherry—also called Palermo.

38. *Sicily is one of my happy hunting-grounds.* "Happy hunting grounds" is a figure of speech attributed to Native Americans meaning the world to come—or a state of grace after death where hunting is plentiful and easy. According to the *OED*, the phrase is first found in nineteenth-century literature. It appears in the last chapter of James Fenimore Cooper's *The Last of the Mohicans* (1826) when Chin-

many jolly weeks in the island, staying with friends up country. When I grew restless again I took advantage of a ship that was trading to Sardinia and Corsica; and very glad I was to feel the fresh breeze and the sea-spray in my face once more."

"But isn't it very hot and stuffy, down in the—hold, I think you call it?" asked the Water Rat.

The seafarer looked at him with the suspicion of a wink. "I'm an old hand," he remarked with much simplicity. "The captain's cabin's good enough for me."

"It's a hard life, by all accounts," murmured the Rat, sunk in deep thought.[39]

"For the crew it is," replied the seafarer gravely, again with the ghost of a wink.

"From Corsica," he went on, "I made use of a ship that was taking wine to the mainland. We made Alassio in the evening,[40] lay to, hauled up our wine-casks, and hove them overboard, tied one to the other by a long line. Then the crew took to the boats and rowed shorewards, singing as they went, and drawing after them the long bobbing procession of casks, like a mile of porpoises. On the sands they had horses waiting, which dragged the casks up the steep street of the little town with a fine rush and clatter and scramble. When the last cask was in, we went and refreshed and rested, and sat late into the night, drinking with our friends, and next morning I took to the great olive-woods for a spell and a rest. For now I had done with islands for the time, and ports and shipping were plentiful; so I led a lazy life among the peasants, lying and watching them work, or stretched high on the hillside with the blue Mediterranean far below me. And so at length, by easy stages, and partly on foot, partly by sea, to Marseilles, and the meeting of old shipmates, and the visiting of great ocean-bound vessels, and feasting once more. Talk of shell-fish! Why, sometimes I dream of the shell-fish of Marseilles, and wake up crying!"

gachgook comments after the death of his son, "Why do my brothers mourn? why do my daughters weep? that a young man has gone to the happy hunting-grounds."

39. *"It's a hard life, by all accounts," murmured the Rat, sunk in deep thought.* The illustration is odd because both rats are of the same species, yet one looks human and the other like a rodent. Bransom also gives this illustration an excellent texture by drawing shadows underneath branches and tree trunks. The tangled vine lends a sense of mystery, suggesting that some invisible force has a hold of the Water Rat, keeping him in place as he is gradually seduced with longing by the tales of the Sea Rat's wanderlust.

40. *"We made Alassio in the evening."* See Chapter V, note 25. In Grahame's youth, Alassio was a quaint fishing village on the Italian Riviera. According to Peter Green, Grahame first visited in February 1895 after the publication of *The Golden Age* and returned at least two times before 1900.

"That reminds me," said the polite Water Rat; "you happened to mention that you were hungry, and I ought to have spoken earlier. Of course, you will stop and take your midday meal with me? My hole is close by; it is some time past noon, and you are very welcome to whatever there is."

"Now I call that kind and brotherly of you," said the Sea Rat. "I was indeed hungry when I sat down, and ever since I inadvertently happened to mention shell-fish,[41] my pangs have been extreme. But couldn't you fetch it along out here? I am none too fond of going under hatches, unless I'm obliged to; and then, while we eat, I could tell you more concerning my voyages and the pleasant life I lead—at least, it is very pleasant to me, and by your attention I judge it commends itself to you; whereas if we go indoors it is a hundred to one that I shall presently fall asleep."

"That is indeed an excellent suggestion," said the Water Rat, and hurried off home. There he got out the luncheon-basket and packed a simple meal, in which, remembering the stranger's origin and preferences, he took care to include a yard of long French bread, a sausage out of which the garlic sang, some cheese which lay down and cried, and a long-necked straw-covered flask[42] wherein lay bottled sunshine shed and garnered on far Southern slopes. Thus laden, he returned with all speed, and blushed for pleasure at the old seaman's commendations of his taste and judgment, as together they unpacked the basket and laid out the contents on the grass by the roadside.

The Sea Rat, as soon as his hunger was somewhat assuaged, continued the history of his latest voyage, conducting his simple hearer from port to port of Spain, landing him at Lisbon, Oporto,[43] and Bordeaux, introducing him to the pleasant harbours of Cornwall and Devon, and so up the Channel to that final quayside, where, landing after winds long contrary, storm-driven and weather-beaten, he had caught the first

41. *"I was indeed hungry when I sat down, and ever since I inadvertently happened to mention shell-fish."* Grahame wrote "shellfish" as both one and two words, and his publishers let the inconsistency stand, or did not notice it.

42. *a sausage out of which the garlic sang, some cheese which lay down and cried, and a long-necked straw-covered flask.* Variant, e. 247: a sausage out of which the garlic sang, {some cheese which lay down and cried,} and a long-necked straw-covered flask.

43. *Lisbon, Oporto.* Towns on the coast of Portugal. Oporto is known for its most famous wine: port.

magical hints and heraldings of another Spring, and, fired by these, had sped on a long tramp inland, hungry for the experiment of life on some quiet farmstead, very far from the weary beating of any sea.

Spell-bound and quivering with excitement, the Water Rat followed the Adventurer league by league, over stormy bays, through crowded roadsteads, across harbour bars on a racing tide, up winding rivers that hid their busy little towns round a sudden turn; and left him with a regretful sigh planted at his dull inland farm, about which he desired to hear nothing.

By this time their meal was over, and the Seafarer, refreshed and strengthened, his voice more vibrant, his eye lit with a brightness that seemed caught from some far-away sea-beacon, filled his glass with the red and glowing vintage of the South, and, leaning towards the Water Rat, compelled his gaze and held him, body and soul, while he talked.[44] Those eyes were of the changing foam-streaked grey-green of leaping Northern seas; in the glass shone a hot ruby that seemed the very heart of the South, beating for him who had courage to respond to its pulsation. The twin lights, the shifting grey and the steadfast red, mastered the Water Rat and held him bound, fascinated, powerless. The quiet world outside their rays receded far away and ceased to be. And the talk, the wonderful talk flowed on—or was it speech entirely, or did it pass at times into song—chanty of the sailors weighing the dripping anchor, sonorous hum of the shrouds in a tearing North-Easter,[45] ballad of the fisherman hauling his nets at sundown against an apricot sky,[46] chords of guitar and mandoline from gondola or caique?[47] Did it change into the cry of the wind, plaintive at first, angrily shrill as it freshened, rising to a tearing whistle, sinking to a musical trickle of air from the leech of the bellying sail? All these sounds the spell-bound listener seemed to hear, and with them the hungry complaint of the gulls and the sea-mews, the soft thunder of the breaking wave,

44. *and, leaning towards the Water Rat, compelled his gaze and held him, body and soul, while he talked.* The Sea Rat resembles Coleridge's Ancient Mariner:

> *He holds him with his glittering eye—*
> *The Wedding-Guest stood still,*
> *And listens like a three years' child:*
> *The Mariner hath his will.*

45. *sonorous hum of the shrouds in a tearing North-Easter.* A wind or great storm blowing from the northeast. Most common in the eastern United States, where it is often called a nor'easter. According to the *OED*, the term northeaster entered the English language by way of a diary kept by L. Carter in 1770.

46. *ballad of the fisherman hauling his nets at sundown against an apricot sky.* There is a fisherman's saying, loosely derived from Matthew 16:2–3: "Red sky at night, sailor's delight, red sky at morning, sailor take warning." Shakespeare used the image in *Venus and Adonis* (1593): "Like a red morn, that ever yet betokened / Wreck to the seaman, tempest to the field, / sorrow to the shepherds, woe unto the birds, gusts and foul flaws to herdmen and to herds" (quarto 1, 453–54). When the sunrise is red it means the sun is reflecting dust particles and water in the air from a storm system moving from the west. A red sky at night indicates high pressure and stable air from the west. As in Grahame's text, good weather most likely will follow.

47. *from gondola or caique?* A caique is a light boat or skiff propelled by one or more rowers.

the cry of the protesting shingle. Back into speech again it passed, and with beating heart he was following the adventures of a dozen seaports, the fights, the escapes, the rallies, the comradeships, the gallant undertakings; or he searched islands for treasure,[48] fished in still lagoons and dozed daylong on warm white sand. Of deep-sea fishings he heard tell, and mighty silver gatherings of the mile-long net; of sudden perils, noise of breakers on a moonless night, or the tall bows of the great liner taking shape overhead through the fog; of the merry home-coming, the headland rounded, the harbour lights opened out; the groups seen dimly on the quay, the cheery hail, the splash of the hawser;[49] the trudge up the steep little street towards the comforting glow of red-curtained windows.

Lastly, in his waking dream it seemed to him that the Adventurer had risen to his feet, but was still speaking, still holding him fast with his sea-grey eyes.

"And now," he was softly saying, "I take to the road again, holding on southwestwards for many a long and dusty day; till at last I reach the little grey sea town I know so well, that clings along one steep side of the harbour.[50] There through dark doorways you look down flights of stone steps, overhung by great pink tufts of valerian and ending in a patch of sparkling blue water. The little boats that lie tethered to the rings and stanchions of the old sea-wall are gaily painted as those I clambered in and out of in my own childhood; the salmon leap on the flood tide, schools of mackerel flash and play past quaysides and foreshores, and by the windows the great vessels glide, night and day, up to their moorings or forth to the open sea. There, sooner or later, the ships of all seafaring nations arrive; and there, at its destined hour, the ship of my choice will let go its anchor. I shall take my time, I shall tarry and bide, till at last the right one lies waiting for me, warped out into midstream, loaded low, her bowsprit pointing down har-

48. *he searched islands for treasure.* When Alastair was twelve, Kenneth wrote him a letter describing a treasure hunt. See "A Treasure Hunt" in "The Letters" for the complete text.

49. *the splash of the hawser.* A hawser is a large rope or small cable used to moor larger seafaring vessels. Any number of yarns, divided equally, are twisted into three heavy strands.

50. *"till at last I reach the little grey sea town I know so well, that clings along one steep side of the harbour."* This description sounds like the town of Fowey, where Grahame went for holidays. In a letter to Austin Purves (May 15, 1911), Grahame describes the town in detail.

> The town itself, the harbour, the river, greeted us with all their old charm. Bigger steamers than ever come up to the "tips", the day is loaded in by electricity, & the work goes on night & day. Fowey is prospering, & new houses have been built, out Point Neptune way, but the quays & the old town & the harbour front are the same as ever—the same mud, the same fish-heads and guts. . . . Mouse and Foy [Quiller-Couch] became good friends at once, & had many teas and walks together, & expeditions to the farm—"Priam's Cellars"—which flourishes exceedingly. One sunny day we all went over there with a large luncheon basket, & lunched in the open, off "hoggy puddin" and other good things, in a riot of daffodils and primroses, with three big foreign ships—Danes & Norwegians—moored right below us, and all the merry harbour-traffic passing busily up and down. (Chalmers, *Kenneth Grahame*, 233)

The farm Grahame mentions is a stretch of riverfront land on the east bank of the

bour. I shall slip on board,[51] by boat or along hawser; and then one morning I shall wake to the song and tramp of the sailors, the clink of the capstan,[52] and the rattle of the anchor-chain coming merrily in. We shall break out the jib and the foresail,[53] the white houses on the harbour side will glide slowly past us[54] as she gathers steering-way, and the voyage will have begun! As she forges towards the headland she will clothe herself with canvas; and then, once outside, the sounding slap of great green seas as she heels to the wind, pointing South!

"And you, you will come too, young brother; for the days pass, and never return, and the South still waits for you. Take the Adventure, heed the call, now ere the irrevocable moment passes!"[55] 'Tis but a banging of the door behind you, a blithesome[56] step forward, and you are out of the old life and into the new! Then some day, some day long hence, jog home here if you will, when the cup has been drained and the play has been played,[57] and sit down by your quiet river with a store of goodly memories for company. You can easily overtake me on the road, for you are young, and I am ageing and go softly. I will linger, and look back; and at last I will surely see you coming, eager and light-hearted, with all the South in your face!"

The voice died away and ceased as an insect's tiny trumpet dwindles swiftly into silence; and the Water Rat, paralysed and staring, saw at last but a distant speck on the white surface of the road.

Mechanically he rose and proceeded to repack the luncheon-basket, carefully and without haste. Mechanically he returned home, gathered together a few small necessaries and special treasures he was fond of, and put them in a satchel; acting with slow deliberation, moving about the room like a sleep-walker; listening ever with parted lips. He swung the satchel over his shoulder, carefully selected a stout stick for his wayfaring, and with no haste, but with no hesitation at all, he stepped across the threshold just as the Mole appeared at the door.

River Fowey that was owned and cultivated by Quiller-Couch. "Priam's Cellars," or "Primes Cellars," was an old alehouse dating to 1600. The place is accessible by boat only.

51. *"I shall slip on board."* Grahame never discusses the fact that the plague was spread by the fleas that live on rats. Various migrations of black rats, *Rattus rattus,* via merchant ships resulted in several devastating waves of plague in England. The Sea Rat, however, probably was a brown rat, *Rattus norvegicus*—the Norwegian rat, commonly called a wharf rat. Brown rats were not carriers of *Yersinia pestis,* the bacteria that, when transmitted by flea bite, causes all three kinds of plague: bubonic, pneumonic, and septicemic.

Originating in Central Asia, the bubonic plague killed an estimated 25 million people before it reached Constantinople in 1347. The disease spread to the Mediterranean on black rats who arrived on ships through ports such as Naples and Venice. By June of 1348, Paris was in the grips of the plague. With overcrowding, poor sanitation, and warm summer weather, urban areas were ripe for transmission of disease. The Black Death, as the first wave of plague was called, reached England when a sailor from Bristol came ashore on the Dorset coast in 1348. By 1349 a quarter to one-third of the population of England died in the first wave of the epidemic. The slums of London were especially hard hit. As the plague flourished, the city gates were closed. Only those with a certificate of health issued by the lord mayor were allowed to leave. It was not uncommon to see mass burials of up to a hundred people in local churchyards.

Two factors contributed to the eventual decline of plague in England: the great fire of 1666, when most of London, including the slums and other common habitats for rats, burned to the ground and had to be rebuilt, and the eventual invasion of the bigger *Rattus norvegicus*. (The Norwegian rat, or brown rat, was a natural bully to the black rat and eventually displaced the latter from its habitat.)

52. *"capstan."* A vertical wheel and axis mechanism on the deck of a ship used for weighing anchor and hoisting heavy sails. The capstan is a manual device that is cranked by a team of men who walk around the apparatus in order to wind the cable around its cylinder.

53. *"jib and the foresail."* Jib: triangular staysail stretching from the outer end of the jibboom to the foretopmast head in large ships, and from the bowsprit to the masthead in smaller craft. Foresail: the principal sail set on the foremast; in square-rigged vessels, the lowest square sail on the foremast; in fore-and-aft rigged, the triangular sail before the mast (*OED*).

54. *"the white houses on the harbour side will glide slowly past us."* Variant, e. 247: the white houses on the harbour side will ~~begin~~ glide slowly past us.

The brightly painted Whitehouse next to The Haven in Fowey is so named because it is the first house seen when sailing into Fowey Harbor.

55. *"Take the Adventure, heed the call, now ere the irrevocable moment passes!"* Horace, ode 1.11.7–8: Dum loquimur, fugerit inuida / aetas: carpe diem, quam minimum credula postero.—While we speak, envious time has / fled: seize the day, trust in the future as little as possible.

The Sea Rat is telling Rat that life is short—act now; "seize the day."

—J. J.

56. *"blithesome."* Cheerful.

57. *"when the cup has been drained and the play has been played."* "Acta est fabula," or "the play is over," was announced at Greek/Roman dramatic performances and uttered by Augustus on his deathbed. Also, William Shakespeare's Falstaff says, "Play out the play!" in *Henry IV, Part 1*, act 2, scene 4, line 484.

58. *waiting for the strange seizure to pass. Gradually the Rat sank into a troubled doze, broken by starts and confused murmurings of things strange and wild and foreign to the unenlightened Mole.* Rat is bewitched by the call of the South, much in the same manner Toad falls under the spell of motorcars.

"Why, where are you off to, Ratty?" asked the Mole in great surprise, grasping him by the arm.

"Going South, with the rest of them," murmured the Rat in a dreamy monotone, never looking at him. "Seawards first and then on shipboard, and so to the shores that are calling me!"

He pressed resolutely forward, still without haste, but with dogged fixity of purpose; but the Mole, now thoroughly alarmed, placed himself in front of him, and looking into his eyes saw that they were glazed and set and turned a streaked and shifting grey—not his friend's eyes, but the eyes of some other animal! Grappling with him strongly he dragged him inside, threw him down, and held him.

The Rat struggled desperately for a few moments, and then his strength seemed suddenly to leave him, and he lay still and exhausted, with closed eyes, trembling. Presently the Mole assisted him to rise and placed him in a chair, where he sat collapsed and shrunken into himself, his body shaken by a violent shivering, passing in time into an hysterical fit of dry sobbing. Mole made the door fast, threw the satchel into a drawer and locked it, and sat down quietly on the table by his friend, waiting for the strange seizure to pass. Gradually the Rat sank into a troubled doze, broken by starts and confused murmurings of things strange and wild and foreign to the unenlightened Mole;[58] and from that he passed into a deep slumber.

Very anxious in mind, the Mole left him for a time and busied himself with household matters; and it was getting dark when he returned to the parlour and found the Rat where he had left him, wide awake indeed, but listless, silent, and dejected. He took one hasty glance at his eyes; found them, to his great gratification, clear and dark and brown again as before; and then sat down and tried to cheer him up and help him to relate what had happened to him.

Poor Ratty did his best, by degrees, to explain things; but how could he put into cold words what had mostly been suggestion? How recall, for another's benefit, the haunting sea voices that had sung to him, how reproduce at second-hand the magic of the Seafarer's hundred reminiscences? Even to himself, now the spell was broken and the glamour gone, he found it difficult to account for what had seemed, some hours ago, the inevitable and only thing. It is not surprising, then, that he failed to convey to the Mole any clear idea of what he had been through that day.

To the Mole this much was plain: the fit, or attack, had passed away, and had left him sane again, though shaken and cast down by the reaction. But he seemed to have lost all interest for the time in the things that went to make up his daily life, as well as in all pleasant forecastings of the altered days and doings that the changing season was surely bringing.

Casually, then, and with seeming indifference, the Mole turned his talk to the harvest that was being gathered in, the towering wagons and their straining teams, the growing ricks,[59] and the large moon rising over bare acres dotted with sheaves. He talked of the reddening apples around, of the browning nuts, of jams and preserves and the distilling of cordials;[60] till by easy stages such as these he reached mid-winter, its hearty joys and its snug home life, and then he became simply lyrical.

By degrees the Rat began to sit up and to join in. His dull eye brightened, and he lost some of his listening air.

Presently the tactful Mole slipped away and returned with a pencil and a few half-sheets of paper, which he placed on the table at his friend's elbow.[61]

"It's quite a long time since you did any poetry," he remarked. "You might have a try at it this evening, instead of—well, brooding over things so much. I've an idea that you'll feel a lot better when you've got something jotted down—if it's only just the rhymes."

The Rat pushed the paper away from him wearily, but the discreet Mole took occasion to leave the room, and when he

59. *the towering wagons and their straining teams, the growing ricks.* Ricks are stacks of mown hay, corn, peas, wheat, and so forth.

60. *and the distilling of cordials.* Variant, e. 247: and the {distilling} ~~making~~ of cordials.

Cordials are a sweetened and distilled alcoholic spirit. Traditionally thought to be medicinal, cordials often begin as wine or brandy and are flavored with herbs and sugar. The *OED* describes a cordial as "medicine, food, or beverage which invigorates the heart and stimulates the circulation; a comforting or exhilarating drink."

61. *Presently the tactful Mole slipped away and returned with a pencil and a few half-sheets of paper, which he placed on the table at his friend's elbow.* Mole has come to understand that the cure for Rat's wanderlust is poetry. Mole encourages Rat to write in order to win Rat back to life on the riverbank.

peeped in again some time later, the Rat was absorbed and deaf to the world; alternately scribbling and sucking the top of his pencil. It is true that he sucked a good deal more than he scribbled; but it was joy to the Mole to know that the cure had at least begun.

Nancy Barnhart's dreamy Rat (1922).

The Further Adventures of Toad[1]

The front door of the hollow tree faced eastwards, so Toad was called at an early hour; partly by the bright sunlight streaming in on him, partly by the exceeding coldness of his toes,[2] which made him dream that he was at home in bed in his own handsome room with the Tudor window, on a cold winter's night, and his bedclothes had got up, grumbling and protesting they couldn't stand the cold any longer, and had run downstairs to the kitchen fire to warm themselves; and he had followed, on bare feet,[3] along miles and miles of icy stone-paved passages, arguing and beseeching them to be reasonable. He would probably have been aroused much earlier, had he not slept for some weeks on straw over stone flags,[4] and almost forgotten the friendly feeling of thick blankets pulled well up round the chin.

Sitting up, he rubbed his eyes first and his complaining toes next, wondered for a moment where he was, looking round for familiar stone wall and little barred window; then, with a leap of the heart, remembered everything—his escape, his flight, his pursuit; remembered, first and best thing of all, that he was free!

Free! The word and the thought alone were worth fifty blankets. He was warm from end to end as he thought of the

1. *The Further Adventures of Toad.* The chapter title could be a take on Sidney G. Paternoster's sequel to *The Cruise of the Conqueror*. Though Paternoster's books were primarily published in the United States, Grahame's publisher, John Lane, knew of them. Detailed readers' reports of Paternoster's books exist in Lane's publication files (see chapter VI, note 14); the reports may be found at the Harry Ransom Humanities Research Center, The University of Texas at Austin.

2. *by the exceeding coldness of his toes.* Adult toads have five toes on each hind foot. Some toads have a prominent tubercle near the first toe that can be mistaken for an extra toe. Each toe consists of two types of bones: one metatarsal and multiple phalanges. (Toes are counted from the outside region inwards and are usually assigned roman numerals I through V, with the first, shortest, or medial digit being digit I; digit IV is the longest.) Digits I and II have two phalanges each, digits III and V have three phalanges each, and digit IV has four phalanges (http://www.nwhc.usgs.gov/research/amph_dc/sop_toeclip.html).

jolly world outside, waiting eagerly for him to make his triumphal entrance, ready to serve him and play up to him, anxious to help him and to keep him company, as it always had been in days of old before misfortune fell upon him. He shook himself and combed the dry leaves out of his hair with his fingers;[5] and, his toilet complete, marched forth into the comfortable morning sun, cold but confident, hungry but hopeful, all nervous terrors of yesterday dispelled by rest and sleep and frank and heartening sunshine.

He had the world all to himself, that early summer morning. The dewy woodland, as he threaded it, was solitary and still: the green fields that succeeded the trees were his own to do as he liked with; the road itself, when he reached it, in that loneliness that was everywhere, seemed, like a stray dog, to be looking anxiously for company.[6] Toad, however, was looking for something that could talk, and tell him clearly which way he ought to go. It is all very well, when you have a light heart, and a clear conscience, and money in your pocket, and nobody scouring the country for you to drag you off to prison again, to follow where the road beckons and points, not caring whither. The practical Toad cared very much indeed, and he could have kicked the road for its helpless silence when every minute was of importance to him.

The reserved rustic road was presently joined by a shy little brother in the shape of a canal,[7] which took its hand and ambled along by its side in perfect confidence, but with the same tongue-tied, uncommunicative attitude towards strangers. "Bother them!" said Toad to himself. "But, anyhow, one thing's clear. They must both be coming *from* somewhere, and going *to* somewhere. You can't get over that, Toad, my boy!" So he marched on patiently by the water's edge.

Round a bend in the canal came plodding a solitary horse, stooping forward as if in anxious thought. From rope traces attached to his collar stretched a long line, taut, but dipping with his stride,[8] the further part of it dripping pearly drops.

3. *and he had followed, on bare feet.* The only time that shoes are mentioned in *The Wind in the Willows* is in chapter XI, when Mr. Badger turns up: "His shoes were covered with mud, and he was looking very rough and touzled; but then he had never been a very smart man, the Badger" (274). Toad does don his set of gaiters in chapter VI, and Mole and Rat are both wearing boots when they get lost in the Wild Wood.

4. *had he not slept for some weeks on straw over stone flags.* Variant, e. 247: had he not slept for some weeks on straw over a stone-paved floor.

A stone flag is a flat slab of fine-grained rock that may be split into flagstones; suitable to be used for paving.

5. *He shook himself and combed the dry leaves out of his hair with his fingers.* In a letter to her neighbor Mrs. Wight dated June 26, 1942, Beatrix Heelis (née Potter) replies to Mrs. Wight's regrets that Kenneth Grahame had not illustrated *The Wind in the Willows*:

> Yes—Kenneth Grahame ought to have been an artist—at least all writers for children ought to have a sufficient recognition of what things look like—did he not describe Toad as combing his hair? A mistake to fly in the face of nature—a frog may wear galoshes; but I dont hold with toads having beards and wigs! So I prefer Badger. (Leslie Linder, *A History of the Writings of Beatrix Potter* [London: Frederick Warne & Co. Ltd, 1971], 175)

Toad will also comb his hair in the final chapter, "The Return of Ulysses": "Then he dipped his hairbrush in the water-jug, parted his hair in the middle, and plastered it down very straight and sleek on each side of his face" (297). See chapter XII, note 16.

6. *seemed, like a stray dog, to be looking anxiously for company.* We know that Grahame was fond of dogs. So much so that Naomi Stott appealed to the Grahames to adopt a local Cookham farm dog that they often met when she and Alastair were out for their afternoon walks.

> At / Mayfield, Cookham Dean, Berks
> March 3rd 1908
> Dear Mrs: Grahame,
>
> Yesterday we had good outings. In the morning, we went to Pinkney's Green, + mouse enjoyed some runs with his hoop, but the roads were too muddy to be pleasant. The Park Farm dog accompanied us, + the boy + he had some good games together. Faring the midday interval, he waited about the outside of the house, + as soon as we came out at the Paddock gate to walk up to Winter Hill, he joined us. We returned by way of the wood, + the dog would carry a long stick with branches, + for him to get the narrow path, with such an impediment in his mouth was amusing to watch, + when he tried to pass one of us, it was more difficult still. If that dog were for sale, he would be a fine comrad [*sic*] for Mouse, + he seems to be such a trust worthy animal, + so full of fun. He plays alone if the boy ignores him, = pulls sticks out of the hedge for toys. (Harry Ransom Humanities Research Center, The University of Texas at Austin)

7. *The reserved rustic road was presently joined by a shy little brother in the shape of a canal.* Canals were built during the Industrial Revolution and were in the prime of their use from 1795 to 1840. Linked up with the natural waterways throughout England, canals were initially used to move coal, iron, salt, and other heavy cargo from the Midlands to the south of England. Because the canals were terrifically expensive to build, narrow boats were built to navigate them. Usually measuring only seven feet across, they were typically ten times as long as they were wide.

8. *From rope traces attached to his collar stretched a long line, taut, but dipping with his stride.* For the first fifty years of the canals, horses were the main power driving the boats, and for obvious reason: A horse can pull approximately fifty times as much weight in a boat as it can in a cart over primitively paved roads. P. A. L. Vine observes:

> In 1811 it is no surprise to read in Jane Austen's *Sense and Sensibility* that all of Mrs. Dashwood's furniture, including the linen, plate, china, and books, had been conveyed from her Sussex home to Devonshire by boat. By road the cost would have been more than doubled. (*London's Lost Route to the Sea*, 4th ed. [London: David & Charles,1986], 1)

Toad let the horse pass, and stood waiting for what the fates were sending him.

With a pleasant swirl of quiet water at its blunt bow the barge slid up alongside of him,[9] its gaily painted gunwale level with the towing-path,[10] its sole occupant a big stout woman wearing a linen sun-bonnet, one brawny arm laid along the tiller.[11]

"A nice morning, ma'am!" she remarked to Toad, as she drew up level with him.

"I dare say it is, ma'am!" responded Toad politely, as he walked along the tow-path abreast of her. "I dare it *is* a nice morning to them that's not in sore trouble, like what I am. Here's my married daughter, she sends off to me post-haste to come to her at once; so off I comes, not knowing what may be happening or going to happen, but fearing the worst, as you will understand, ma'am, if you're a mother, too. And I've left my business to look after itself—I'm in the washing and laundering line, you must know, ma'am—and I've left my young children to look after themselves, and a more mischievous and troublesome set of young imps doesn't exist, ma'am; and I've lost all my money, and lost my way, and as for what may be happening to my married daughter, why, I don't like to think of it, ma'am!"

"Where might your married daughter be living, ma'am?" asked the barge-woman.[12]

"She lives near to the river, ma'am," replied Toad. "Close to a fine house called Toad Hall, that's somewheres hereabouts in these parts. Perhaps you may have heard of it."

"Toad Hall? Why, I'm going that way myself," replied the barge-woman. "This canal joins the river some miles further on, a little above Toad Hall; and then it's an easy walk. You come along in the barge with me, and I'll give you a lift."

She steered the barge close to the bank, and Toad, with many humble and grateful acknowledgments, stepped lightly on board and sat down with great satisfaction. "Toad's luck again!" thought he. "I always come out on top!"

9. *With a pleasant swirl of quiet water at its blunt bow the barge slid up alongside of him.* Because canals were built as interconnected inland roads, the water in them was without current and often murky. The *OED* describes a barge as a "flat-bottomed freight-boat, chiefly for canal—and river-navigation, either with or without sails." A barge is usually at least twice as wide as it is long. According to www.canaljunction.com, barges are "proportionally . . . more like little ships, seaworthy enough to operate in the choppy waters of deep rivers as well as on the still waters of artificial canals."

The use of canals declined with the rise of the steam railway. Grahame does not condemn canal boats as he does other technology—probably because they were pulled by horses and didn't rely on the use of motors or petrol. Recently, there has been a revival of narrow boating through the existing canals for leisure and tourism.

10. *its gaily painted gunwale level with the towing-path.* The gunwale is the upper edge of the boat's side. In this smaller boat the gunwale is a piece of timber extending around the topside of the hull. Grahame is paying homage to an English form of transportation that was swiftly becoming obsolete. The "gaily painted gunwale" is probably a vivid folk art form called "castle and roses." Specific to English canal boats, the small painted panels

Photo of a narrow boat, Henley-on-Thames.

on the typical narrow boats are full of colorful images of horses, country houses, churches, cottages, lighthouses, and, of course, castles and roses. The most common pattern is a trim of brightly painted diamonds, making the boat stand out as it navigates the narrow canals. The culture of painted canal boats recalls two of Grahame's other loves—the Gypsy caravan and the canary cart.

11. *its sole occupant a big stout woman wearing a linen sun-bonnet, one brawny arm laid along the tiller.* Toad's other most recent contact with a person of the Wide World was the engine driver of the train, whom Grahame describes as "brawney."

It is evident from Grahame's papers that the women's suffrage movement was very much on his mind. On December 10, 1908, Elspeth Grahame wrote to the Purveses, in Philadelphia:

> Today is a great day for Mouse[.] his magazine "The Merry Thought" has its first Xmas number—and he has got a story from K. & 2 verses about a cat that wanted the suffrage (perfectly darling) [.] Mouse is great on women's suffrage & has made friends with 2 real suffragettes at Cookham. (Courtesy of the David J. Holmes Collection)

Alastair had his own take on women gaining the vote, having composed a singsong rhyme about the event that Naomi Stott wrote down and sent to Elspeth. Stott also saved the boy's pencil drawings:

Scan of poem and page from *The Merry Thought*. Mentioned by Elspeth Grahame in her letter to the Purveses written on December 10, 1908. *Courtesy of the Harry Ransom Humanities Research Center, The University of Texas at Austin.*

April 7, 1907
7.4.07

Dear Mrs: Grahame,

Today this was a song I heard—

"The Suffragettes have no votes today
So they are sulky + in dismay
Because they have not won the day."

A.G.

In May, 1908, more than a year later, *The Merry Thought* was still covering the issues of women's suffrage by including the following poem by Alastair:

Suffragette Ode.
There was a grand sight of purple, green, + white
When the gallant suffragettes Captured Parliament last night.
There was a chivying of M.P.s
That fainted on the floor
When the gallant Suffragettes rushed in + burst down the door

12. *"Where might your married daughter be living, ma'am?" asked the barge-woman.* In Grahame's original letter to Mouse, the bargewoman was male and referred to as the bargee. See letter of June 7, 1907, included in "The Letters."

Somehow, Toad is placed in a precarious position by becoming beholden to a barge-woman instead of the original bargee.

Pencil drawing by Alastair Grahame from *The Merry Thought*. Titled in Naomi Stott's hand: "Picture to encourage Votes for Women." *Courtesy of the Harry Ransom Humanities Research Center, The University of Texas at Austin.*

"So you're in the washing business, ma'am?" said the barge-woman politely, as they glided along. "And a very good business you've got too, I dare say, if I'm not making too free in saying so."

"Finest business in the whole country," said Toad airily. "All the gentry come to me—wouldn't go to any one else if they were paid, they know me so well. You see, I understand my work thoroughly, and attend to it all myself. Washing, ironing, clear-starching, making up gents' fine shirts for evening wear—everything's done under my own eye!"[13]

13. *"Washing, ironing, clear-starching, making up gents' fine shirts for evening wear—everything's done under my own eye!"* Alastair Grahame made several stories and drawings of boats, including this of "Cook's useful kitchen houseboat," for the May edition of *The Merry Thought*. The boat is very much a working vessel, in the same manner as the bargewoman's.

A *the place where the kitchen cat sits to steer.*

B *the place where cook sits*

"Here is a picture of Cook's useful kitchen houseboat." Pencil drawing by A. Grahame. *Courtesy of the Harry Ransom Humanities Research Center, The University of Texas at Austin.*

C the pastry rolling table with room for boats below.
E Machinery box
F oven
G Cupboard.
Button A of Machinery Box will make it go to the right
B to the left.
C is the reversing button, it makes your little machine go backwards, sail upside down, + spill you out. This useful instrument is to be procured for 3 d at John Barker's + Whiteley's shop.

14. ***"But you know what*** **girls** ***are, ma'am! Nasty little hussies, that's what*** **I** ***call 'em!"*** **Kenneth Grahame's attitude toward**

"But surely you don't *do* all that work yourself, ma'am?" asked the barge-woman respectfully.

"O, I have girls," said Toad lightly: "twenty girls or thereabouts, always at work. But you know what *girls* are, ma'am! Nasty little hussies, that's what *I* call 'em!"[14]

"So do I, too," said the barge-woman with great heartiness. "But I dare say you set yours to rights, the idle trollops! And are you *very* fond of washing?"

"I love it," said Toad. "I simply dote on it. Never so happy as when I've got both arms in the wash-tub. But, then, it comes so easy to me! No trouble at all! A real pleasure, I assure you, ma'am!"

"What a bit of luck, meeting you!" observed the bargewoman, thoughtfully. "A regular piece of good fortune for both of us!"

"Why, what do you mean?" asked Toad, nervously.

"Well, look at me, now," replied the barge-woman. "*I* like washing, too, just the same as you do; and for that matter, whether I like it or not I have got to do all my own, naturally, moving about as I do.[15] Now my husband, he's such a fellow for shirking his work and leaving the barge to me, that never a moment do I get for seeing to my own affairs. By rights he ought to be here now, either steering or attending to the horse, though luckily the horse has sense enough to attend to himself. Instead of which, he's gone off with the dog, to see if they can't pick up a rabbit for dinner somewhere.[16] Says he'll catch me up at the next lock. Well, that's as may be—I don't trust him, once he gets off with that dog, who's worse than he is. But meantime, how am I to get on with my washing?"

"O, never mind about the washing," said Toad, not liking the subject. "Try and fix your mind on that rabbit. A nice fat young rabbit, I'll be bound. Got any onions?"[17]

"I can't fix my mind on anything but my washing," said the barge-woman, "and I wonder you can be talking of rabbits, with such a joyful prospect before you. There's a heap of things of mine that you'll find in a corner of the cabin. If you'll just take one or two of the most necessary sort—I won't venture to describe them to a lady like you, but you'll recognize them at a glance[18]—and put them through the wash-tub as we go along, why, it'll be a pleasure to you, as you rightly say, and a real help to me. You'll find a tub handy, and soap, and a kettle on the stove, and a bucket to haul up water from the canal with. Then I shall know you're enjoying yourself, instead of sitting here idle, looking at the scenery and yawning your head off."

"Here, you let me steer!" said Toad, now thoroughly frightened, "and then you can get on with your washing your own way. I might spoil your things, or not do 'em as you like. I'm more used to gentlemen's things myself. It's my special line."

working women, and women in general, was usually negative. But such attitudes were also a sign of the times. Even Naomi Stott had a strong bias against girls and women. In a letter dated March 9, 1908, she writes about Alastair's friend Mitey Sullivan:

> Mitey has not been to see us lately, probably because I asked her not to let Neb [her dog] come indoors. She will lose a lot of happiness, if she continues to make grievances out of trifles. An only girl is apt to think too much of her self importance. Mouse is going on well + happily, + is on very good terms with Miss Passey + Rose.

Both Miss Passey and Rose, who also worked in the Grahames' kitchen, appeared often in *The Merry Thought* and in letters to Elspeth Grahame.

> *Ode to Miss Passey*
> *by A.G.*
>
> *Two lovely blue eyes'*
> *And a beautiful smile*
> *And lovers put their hands on their*
> *hearts all the while*
> *And lovers all flock to see her*
> *fine frock*
> *And all the cats don their*
> *top hats*
> *To see Miss Passey + Rose*
> (*The Merry Thought*, February 1908)

> . . . If anyone wants a sample of this cake, please apply to Miss Passey's Rose at Mayfield. (*The Merry Thought*, March 1908)

> . . . Mouse was disappointed that he could not be present. He keeps well, + is on excellent terms with the ladies in the kitchen. Miss Passey is always ready for a game with him— (Naomi Stott to Elspeth Grahame, March 23, 1908)

15. *"whether I like it or not I have got to do all my own, naturally, moving about as I do."* It

normally took two people to guide the boat through the canal—one to tend to the horse and another to guide the tiller. That the bargewoman is able to run the boat by herself is testament to how skilled she is.

Commonly, several generations of the same family lived an itinerant life on a boat, shipping from one part of the country to the next. Because boatmen traveled the canals and received no formal schooling, whole generations remained illiterate. It has even been suggested that many canal boats were originally piloted by Gypsies, much in the same way the British Romani traveled the countryside in horse-drawn caravans. In *The Canal Boatmen, 1760–1914* [Manchester: Manchester University Press, 1975], Harry Hanson explores the myth:

> Joseph Phipkin, the owner of the *Flower of Gloster* [a narrow boat], confirmed Temple Thurston's suspicions in 1911 when he confided, "You'll find all these people are dark—dark hair, dark eyes, that browny sort of skin, winter and summer. It ain't the sun." Temple Thurston seems finally to have mused himself to the conclusion that the boatmen were gypsies of Spanish origins (1).

Hanson concludes that the canal boats were run by only 10 percent Romani people, and that the myth arose after the rise of the steam engines. When families who depended on the boats to make a living could no longer afford to keep a house on shore, they consolidated their belongings and moved onto their boats to live. "It was not until railway competition brought hard times to the canals that the boatman was compelled to take his wife and family on to the boats with him" (ibid.). The lavish decoration of the canal boats began at this time as well, along with the tendency to keep the tight living quarters of the boat fastidiously clean. The dirtier the cargo—such as coal, for instance—the cleaner the boat: bleached white lace curtains and well-swabbed decks to at least present a meticulously clean appearance.

16. *"he's gone off with the dog, to see if they can't pick up a rabbit for dinner somewhere."* Like the Gypsies, boat people had a reputation for poaching game for their meals. They also maintained their horses by pilfering hay and oats from along fields near the canals.

17. *"A nice fat young rabbit, I'll be bound. Got any onions?"* See chapter I, note 8. Grahame is making a joke: Onion sauce was always served with baked rabbit.

18. *"I won't venture to describe them to a lady like you, but you'll recognise them at a glance."* She wants Toad to wash her most intimate undergarments—which quite possibly are stained.

Shepard's Toad at washbasin, 1931.

"Let you steer?" replied the barge-woman, laughing. "It takes some practice to steer a barge properly.[19] Besides, it's dull work, and I want you to be happy. No, you shall do the washing you are so fond of, and I'll stick to the steering that I understand. Don't try and deprive me of the pleasure of giving you a treat!"

Toad was fairly cornered. He looked for escape this way and that, saw that he was too far from the bank for a flying leap, and sullenly resigned himself to his fate. "If it comes to that," he thought in desperation, "I suppose any fool can *wash!*"

He fetched tub, soap, and other necessaries from the cabin, selected a few garments at random, tried to recollect what he had seen in casual glances through laundry windows, and set to.

A long half-hour passed, and every minute of it saw Toad getting crosser and crosser. Nothing that he could do to the things seemed to please them or do them good. He tried coaxing, he tried slapping, he tried punching; they smiled back at him out of the tub unconverted, happy in their original sin. Once or twice he looked nervously over his shoulder at the barge-woman, but she appeared to be gazing out in front of her, absorbed in her steering. His back ached badly, and he noticed

19. *"Let you steer?" replied the barge-woman, laughing. "It takes some practice to steer a barge properly."* In chapter I, Mole wanted to row and ended up in the river.

with dismay that his paws were beginning to get all crinkly.[20] Now Toad was very proud of his paws. He muttered under his breath words that should never pass the lips of either washer-women or Toads; and lost the soap, for the fiftieth time.

A burst of laughter made him straighten himself and look

20. *he noticed with dismay that his paws were beginning to get all crinkly.* Actually, a toad does not have paws—he has front legs and webbed feet, with toes (see note 2 in this chapter). A paw is the foot of an animal that has claws and pads, not an animal with digits.

Pen-and-ink illustration of Toad and the bargewoman by Nancy Barnhart (1924): LOST THE SOAP, FOR THE FIFTIETH TIME. The first person to illustrate the bargewoman was Barnhart, who contributed a black-and-white drawing of her with Toad at a washbasin. Shepard's tiny spot of an illustration of Toad at the washbasin, without the goading bargewoman, is more effective because the artist manages to convey Toad's utter misery. Unlike Barnhart's illustration, Shepard's drawing doesn't need a caption.

round. The barge-woman was leaning back and laughing unrestrainedly, till the tears ran down her cheeks.

"I've been watching you all the time," she gasped. "I thought you must be a humbug[21] all along, from the conceited way you talked. Pretty washerwoman you are! Never washed so much as a dish-clout[22] in your life, I'll lay!"

Toad's temper, which had been simmering viciously for some time, now fairly boiled over, and he lost all control of himself.

"You common, low, *fat* barge-woman!" he shouted; "don't you dare to talk to your betters like that! Washerwoman indeed! I would have you to know that I am a Toad, a very well-known, respected, distinguished Toad! I may be under a bit of a cloud at present, but I will *not* be laughed at by a barge-woman!"

The woman moved nearer to him and peered under his bonnet keenly and closely. "Why, so you are!" she cried. "Well, I never! A horrid, nasty, crawly Toad! And in my nice clean barge, too![23] Now that is a thing that I will *not* have."

She relinquished the tiller for a moment. One big mottled arm shot out and caught Toad by a fore-leg, while the other gripped him fast by a hind-leg. Then the world turned suddenly upside down, the barge seemed to flit lightly across the sky, the wind whistled in his ears, and Toad found himself flying through the air, revolving rapidly as he went.[24]

The water, when he eventually reached it with a loud splash, proved quite cold enough for his taste, though its chill was not sufficient to quell his proud spirit, or slake the heat of his furious temper. He rose to the surface spluttering, and when he had wiped the duck-weed out of his eyes the first thing he saw was the fat barge-woman looking back at him over the stern of the retreating barge and laughing; and he vowed, as he coughed and choked, to be even with her.

He struck out for the shore, but the cotton gown greatly impeded his efforts,[25] and when at length he touched land he

21. *"humbug."* A thing that is not really what it pretends to be; a deception or fraud.

22. *"Dish-clout."* Dishcloth.

23. *"And in my nice clean barge, too!"* In contrast to the filthy cargo that barges carried, boat people—the women in particular—became obsessed, as noted earlier, with keeping the living quarters and decks of their boats clean.

> These "dirty bargees" turned their boats into models of ostentatious cleanliness with polished brasswork and woodwork scrubbed to snowy whiteness, and their squalid little box cabins were transformed into domestic palaces of lace edged curtains and china plates. If they could not impress with quantity on their tiny floating homes they would dazzle with quality, and every surface was painted, every moulding picked out with strong colour, and every tin utensil smothered in painted roses and romantic landscapes. (http://www.canaljunction.com/narrowboat/folk_art.htm)

24. *and Toad found himself flying through the air, revolving rapidly as he went.* Payne's bargewoman stands in the very male posture of having her hands on her hips while she laughs at Toad in flight. While considerably more hideous, Payne's bargewoman is not as fat as Barnhart's. Barnhart's bargewoman's forearms are muscular, and her hips under her skirt are giant. By far the most frightening rendering is Shepard's color drawing, added in 1953. The bargewoman has muscular forearms and hunched posture, and it looks like she could eat ground glass. A scarf frames her broad face. Worst of all, Shepard drew her with a lazy eye. She looks at Toad, who is crying, yet one of her eyes drifts slightly.

25. *He struck out for the shore, but the cotton gown greatly impeded his efforts.* At the end of the chapter, Toad, hindered by the washerwoman's dress, will nearly drown—like Ophelia in *Hamlet* when she is pulled under the water by the weight of her dress and the currents in the river. See note 49 in this chapter.

26. *"Put yourself through your mangle."* A machine for squeezing water from and pressing clothing and linen after washing.

Payne's bargewoman, 1927.

found it hard to climb up the steep bank unassisted. He had to take a minute or two's rest to recover his breath; then, gathering his wet skirts well over his arms, he started to run after the barge as fast as his legs would carry him, wild with indignation, thirsting for revenge.

The barge-woman was still laughing when he drew up level with her. "Put yourself through your mangle,[26] washerwoman," she called out, "and iron your face and crimp it, and you'll pass for quite a decent-looking Toad!"

Toad never paused to reply. Solid revenge was what he

Shepard. Color revision of the bargewoman, 1953.

wanted, not cheap, windy, verbal triumphs, though he had a thing or two in his mind that he would have liked to say. He saw what he wanted ahead of him. Running swiftly on he overtook the horse, unfastened the towrope and cast off, jumped lightly on the horse's back, and urged it to a gallop by kicking it vigorously in the sides. He steered for the open country, abandoning the tow-path, and swinging his steed down a rutty lane. Once he looked back, and saw that the barge had run

Shepard. Horse theft and bargewoman, 1931.

aground on the other side of the canal, and the barge-woman was gesticulating wildly and shouting, "Stop, stop, stop!"[27] "I've heard that song before," said Toad, laughing, as he continued to spur his steed onward in its wild career.

The barge-horse was not capable of any very sustained effort, and its gallop soon subsided into a trot, and its trot into an easy walk;[28] but Toad was quite contented with this, knowing that he, at any rate, was moving, and the barge was not. He had quite recovered his temper, now that he had done something he thought really clever; and he was satisfied to jog along quietly in the sun, steering his horse along by-ways and bridle-paths, and trying to forget how very long it was since he had had a square meal, till the canal had been left very far behind him.

He had travelled some miles, his horse and he, and he was feeling drowsy in the hot sunshine, when the horse stopped, lowered his head, and began to nibble the grass; and Toad, waking up, just saved himself from falling off by an effort. He looked about him and found he was on a wide common, dot-

27. *"Stop, stop, stop!"* Shepard has two very different pen-and-ink illustrations of the bargewoman. Though both appear in every Scribner edition illustrated by Shepard, since 1953 the two depict different women. In the 1931 edition, as Toad rides off with her horse, a young and vital bargewoman shakes her fists from the next page. While she is strong and capable of physical work, she is not fat, nor is she unattractive. She is angry but not at all as frightening as Shepard's older bargewoman with her wandering eye.

28. *The barge-horse was not capable of any very sustained effort, and its gallop soon subsided into a trot, and its trot into an easy walk.* Barge-pulling horses were not used to moving quickly—they plodded along, steadily, pulling their heavy loads. They were and are to this day sturdy working horses. The text at this point in the chapter was revised from Grahame's Dearest Mouse letter of June 21, 1907. See "The Letters" for complete text.

ted with patches of gorse and bramble as far as he could see. Near him stood a dingy gipsy caravan,[29] and beside it a man was sitting on a bucket turned upside down, very busy smoking and staring into the wide world.[30] A fire of sticks was burning near by, and over the fire hung an iron pot, and out of that pot came forth bubblings and gurglings, and a vague suggestive steaminess. Also smells—warm, rich, and varied smells—that twined and twisted and wreathed themselves at last into one complete, voluptuous, perfect smell that seemed like the very soul of Nature taking form and appearing to her children, a true Goddess, a mother of solace and comfort.[31] Toad now knew well that he had not been really hungry before.

Rackham's horse and Gypsy, 1940.

29. *Near him stood a dingy gipsy caravan.* See chapter II, note 26, on the origin and spelling of Gypsy. The proper word for Gypsy is Romani, which is easily confused with Romania.

In Grahame's original letters to Alastair the Gypsy caravan is a tent. Grahame changed the tent to a caravan in holograph manuscript e. 247. The rise of the decorated caravan, much like Mr. Toad's in chapter II, occurred during the late Victorian and Edwardian periods as motor traffic became more prevalent through the English countryside. However, for Gypsies, or the Romani, the caravan was home—it was foremost a possession of utility and survival.

The Romani people are believed to have emerged from India around 1001, when the Ghaznavids advanced against Peshawar in the Panjab to defeat the Indian king, Jayapala; they continued their incursions into northern India, taking 500,000 prisoners, by their own account. The Romani are said to have ventured into Europe, gradually reaching England by the sixteenth century. On a timeline published on radoc.net at the University of Texas, Austin, the first presence of the Romani in England is reported as 1514. However, by 1530, Romanies had their property confiscated and were ordered to leave England within a fortnight.

The timeline continues, providing a record of discrimination against a landless people, lending insight into the marginalized lives of the Romani people who continue to live among the British.

Elspeth Grahame also notes that Gypsies lived in the Quarry Wood around Cookham Dean—see *First Whisper of "The Wind in the Willows"* (7).

30. *and beside it a man was sitting on a bucket turned upside down, very busy smoking and staring into the wide world.* Among the complicated class distinctions in *The Wind in the Willows*, the Gypsy is an anomaly. He is from the wide world but is also an out-

sider. Romani scholar Ian Hancock writes about the nomadism of Gypsies:

> Traveling is a part of our history. Our ancestors trekked for thousands of miles from India to Europe and out into the world, so there is certainly some truth to the stereotype of the "traveling gypsy." But a distinction must be made between traveling on a journey, with a purpose, and traveling because local laws in an area forbid one to stop and therefore leave no choice. (Hancock, *We Are the Romani People* [Hatfield: The University of Hertfordshire Press, 2002], 101)

31. *one complete, voluptuous, perfect smell that seemed like the very soul of Nature taking form and appearing to her children, a true Goddess, a mother of solace and comfort.* This is one of the few places in *The Wind in the Willows* where female imagery or the role of the nurturing mother is beneficent.

32. *Presently the gipsy took his pipe out of his mouth and remarked in a careless way, "Want to sell that there horse of yours?"* Hancock writes in depth about the stereotype of Gypsies dealing horses.

> Once reaching Europe, our ancestors soon became subject to legislation (especially in northern and western Europe) that kept them on the move. . . . Ways of making a living had to be developed which were portable and which did not require fixed, heavy equipment. In time, occupations such as horse trading, metal-smithing, fortune telling and so on became family professions and have been kept up even when forced removal is no longer everywhere a factor. Remember that there is no "genetic" disposition to travel; it is solely the result of circumstances. (Ibid.)

33. *"Try and love a donkey," suggested the gipsy. "Some people do."* Arthur Rackham

What he had felt earlier in the day had been a mere trifling qualm. This was the real thing at last, and no mistake; and it would have to be dealt with speedily, too, or there would be trouble for somebody or something. He looked the gipsy over carefully, wondering vaguely whether it would be easier to fight him or cajole him. So there he sat, and sniffed and sniffed, and looked at the gipsy; and the gipsy sat and smoked, and looked at him.

Presently the gipsy took his pipe out of his mouth and remarked in a careless way, "Want to sell that there horse of yours?"[32]

Toad was completely taken aback. He did not know that gipsies were very fond of horse-dealing, and never missed an opportunity, and he had not reflected that caravans were always on the move and took a deal of drawing. It had not occurred to him to turn the horse into cash, but the gipsy's suggestion seemed to smooth the way towards the two things he wanted so badly—ready money, and a solid breakfast.

"What?" he said, "me sell this beautiful young horse of mine? O, no; it's out of the question. Who's going to take the washing home to my customers every week? Besides, I'm too fond of him, and he simply dotes on me."

"Try and love a donkey," suggested the gipsy. "Some people do."[33]

"You don't seem to see," continued Toad, "that this fine horse of mine is a cut above you altogether. He's a blood horse,[34] he is, partly; not the part you see, of course—another part. And he's been a Prize Hackney,[35] too, in his time—that was the time before you knew him, but you can still tell it on him at a glance, if you understand anything about horses. No, it's not to be thought of for a moment. All the same, how much might you be disposed to offer me for this beautiful young horse of mine?"

The gipsy looked the horse over, and then he looked Toad over with equal care, and looked at the horse again. "Shillin' a leg," he said briefly, and turned away, continuing to smoke and try to stare the wide world out of countenance.[36]

"A shilling a leg?" cried Toad. "If you please, I must take a little time to work that out, and see just what it comes to."

He climbed down off his horse, and left it to graze, and sat down by the gipsy, and did sums on his fingers, and at last he said, "A shilling a leg? Why, that comes to exactly four shillings, and no more. O, no; I could not think of accepting four shillings for this beautiful young horse of mine."

"Well," said the gipsy, "I'll tell you what I will do. I'll make it five shillings, and that's three-and-sixpence more than the animal's worth. And that's my last word."

Then Toad sat and pondered long and deeply. For he was hungry and quite penniless, and still some way—he knew not how far—from home, and enemies might still be looking for him. To one in such a situation, five shillings may very well appear a large sum of money. On the other hand, it did not seem very much to get for a horse. But then, again, the horse hadn't cost him anything; so whatever he got was all clear profit. At last he said firmly, "Look here, gipsy! I tell you what we will do; and this is *my* last word. You shall hand me over six shillings and sixpence, cash down; and further, in addition thereto,[37] you shall give me as much breakfast as I can possibly eat, at one sitting of course, out of that iron pot of yours that keeps sending forth such delicious and exciting smells. In return, I will make over to you my spirited young horse, with all the beautiful harness and trappings that are on him, freely thrown in. if that's not good enough for you, say so, and I'll be getting on. I know a man near here who's wanted this horse of mine for years."

The gipsy grumbled frightfully, and declared if he did a few more deals of that sort he'd be ruined. But in the end he lugged a dirty canvas bag out of the depths of his trouser pocket, and counted out six shillings and sixpence into Toad's paw. Then he disappeared into the caravan for an instant, and returned

didn't draw the bargewoman, but he did make an illustration of Toad riding into the Gypsy camp on the bargewoman's horse. Rackham's Gypsy is unlike any other illustration for *The Wind in the Willows*. He diminished the size of the horse by drawing it with its head down—in the same manner as the horse pulling the Gypsy cart in chapter II.

Rackham's Sea Rat from "Wayfarers All" looks similar to his Gypsy. They are both wiry and thin, wear well-worn shoes, and have dark complexions: visual cues that they, like the women, don't fit in with the riverbankers.

34. *"He's a blood horse."* A thoroughbred or pedigree horse.

35. *"And he's been a Prize Hackney."* A horse of middle size and quality, used for ordinary riding, as distinguished from a warhorse, a hunter, or a draft horse. Toad is exaggerating—the horse is anything but young and energetic.

36. *"Shillin' a leg," he said briefly, and turned away, continuing to smoke and try to stare the wide world out of countenance.* Toad's interaction with the Gypsy parallels a scene in *The Romany Rye*, the sequel to *Lavengro*, when the protagonist is asked to sell his horse to the surgeon. Hugely popular with Victorian readers, George Borrow's *Lavengro: The Scholar, the Gypsy, the Priest* (1851) and *The Romany Rye: A Sequel to Lavengro* (1857) chronicle the author's nomadic life spent with Gypsies in England and on the continent.

Though *Lavengro* is set in the 1820s, the price for a horse is much higher than the absurdly low amount Toad parts with for the bargewoman's horse.

> "This is no time for bargaining," said I, "if you wish to have the horse for a hundred guineas, you may; if not—"

"A hundred guineas!" said the surgeon, "my good friend, you must surely be light-headed; allow me to feel your pulse," and he attempted to feel my left wrist.

"I am not light-headed," said I, "and I require no one to feel my pulse; but I should be light-headed if I were to sell my horse for less than I have demanded; but I have a curiosity to know what you would be willing to offer."

"Thirty pounds," said the surgeon, "is all I can afford to give; and that is a great deal for a country surgeon to offer for a horse."

"Thirty pounds!" said I, "why, he cost me nearly double that sum. To tell you the truth, I am afraid that you want to take advantage of my situation."

"Not in the least, friend," said the surgeon, "not in the least; I only wished to set your mind at rest about your horse; but as you think he is worth more than I can afford to offer, take him to Horncastle by all means . . . (George Burrow, *The Romany Rye* [New York: Harper & Brothers, 1857], p. 67)

37. *"You shall hand me over six shillings and sixpence, cash down; and further, in addition thereto."* This is the language of a true banker. Grahame always kept very careful personal accounts of all monies owed to him. In July 1908, he had a falling-out with his publisher John Lane after the American literary agent Curtis Brown took Grahame on as a client. The first detail Brown saw to was the prompt collection of royalties—much to the annoyance of John Lane, who was always late with payments. Royalties in arrears, Grahame wrote a long letter, dated July 26, 1908—two months before publicaton of *The Wind in the Willows*—listing the exact amounts still owed him.

Dear Lane,

I have your long letter, dated the 17th but received the 22nd, + seem to detect therein two grievances, though not very clearly or categorically expressed, so I may have misunderstood them. The first seems to be based upon my having—as I was quick to inform you—instructed an agent as to my future business arrangements. This, as I indicated to you, had become, through circumstances (actual + prospective), a necessity for me; + you must surely understand that it is a corollary of such arrangement that I act on the advice + information given me; for I have no intention of keeping a dog + doing the barking myself. But you seem to imply that there is imposed on me some sort of restraint or obligation or qualified serfdom—not upon you too, upon me only—which entirely + for all time prevents my ever doing freely what I may think best for myself. Such a position would be entirely intolerable—I would not live under it for a day, + I repudiate it absolutely. But I can hardly think you really mean to imply this: nor do I think, though some people might consider your letter an uncalled-for intrusion into my private affairs, that any such intention was in your mind. . . .

Your further letter of the 23rd (for which + for its kind expressions I am much obliged) corrects the mistake you made as to English royalties, but should have gone a little further + added " . . . and on the two American edns I only pay you 10%. I having "voluntarily lowered" your royalty—!

Upon ten editions of three books that you publish for me, the present royalties are: 20, 20, 15, 15, 15, 12½, 10, 10, 10, 10: not a very high range, nor an onerous one.

with a large iron plate and a knife, fork, and spoon. He tilted up the pot, and a glorious stream of hot rich stew gurgled into the plate. It was, indeed, the most beautiful stew in the world, being made of partridges, and pheasants, and chickens, and hares, and rabbits, and peahens, and guinea-fowls, and one or two other things.[38] Toad took the plate on his lap, almost crying, and stuffed, and stuffed, and stuffed, and kept asking for more, and the gipsy never grudged it him. He thought that he had never eaten so good a breakfast in all his life.

When Toad had taken as much stew on board as he thought he could possibly hold, he got up and said good-bye to the gipsy, and took an affectionate farewell of the horse; and the gipsy, who knew the riverside well, gave him directions which way to go, and he set forth on his travels again in the best possible spirits. He was, indeed, a very different Toad from the animal of an hour ago. The sun was shining brightly, his wet clothes were quite dry again, he had money in his pocket once more,[39] he was nearing home and friends and safety, and, most and best of all, he had had a substantial meal, hot and nourishing, and felt big, and strong, and careless, and self-confident.

As he tramped along gaily, he thought of his adventures and escapes, and how when things seemed at their worst he had always managed to find a way out; and his pride and conceit began to swell within him. "Ho, ho!" he said to himself as he marched along with his chin in the air, "what a clever Toad I am! There is surely no animal equal to me for cleverness in the whole world! My enemies shut me up in prison, encircled by sentries, watched night and day by warders; I walk out through them all, by sheer ability coupled with courage. They pursue me with engines, and policemen, and revolvers; I snap my fingers at them, and vanish, laughing, into space. I am, unfortunately, thrown into a canal by a woman fat of body and very evil-minded. What of it? I swim ashore, I seize her horse, I ride off in triumph, and I sell the horse for a whole pocketful

The above is my only address for the present.

Yours very faithfully
Kenneth Grahame
John Lane, Esq.
(John Lane Company Records, Harry Ransom Humanities Research Center, The University of Texas at Austin)

After this letter there is a gap in John Lane and Kenneth Grahame's correspondence until 1910. The agent Grahame mentions is Curtis Brown.

Grahame also lent large sums of money to his younger brother, Roland, in 1912. The brothers eventually became estranged after Roland stopped returning Kenneth's letters, which began to contain detailed requests for repayment. Though Roland defaulted on his loans in 1914, six years after *The Wind in the Willows* was published, Kenneth's relationship with his brother may have very easily been the model for Toad and Badger's ersatz father-and-son relationship.

38. *It was, indeed, the most beautiful stew in the world, being made of partridges, and pheasants, and chickens, and hares, and rabbits, and peahens, and guinea-fowls, and one or two other things.* This is an unlikely concoction, "a luck [*sic*] day indeed when all those ingredients could be found. Possible but quite unlikely" (Ian Hancock, e-mail to the author, 2006).

The text at this point in chapter X was revised from Grahame's letter of July 17, 1907, addressed to "My Dear Robinson." The change of name coincides with the quickening pace of Toad's adventures, including the mention of being pursued by police waving revolvers. (See "The Letters" for complete text.)

39. *he had money in his pocket once more.* Anomaly: previously when Toad

arrived at the train station, the dress had no pockets: "he burst the barriers, attained the goal, arrived at where all waistcoat pockets are eternally situated, and found—not only no money, but no pocket to hold it, and no waistcoat to hold the pocket!" (200)

40. *The clever men at Oxford / Know all that there is to be knowed.* Because Kenneth Grahame was denied the chance to attend Oxford, he did everything he could to enable Alastair to attend. When Alastair's time at Christ Church ended disastrously, Sir Arthur Quiller-Couch wrote a letter of condolence to Grahame, acknowledging that they had both lost beloved sons: Bevil Quiller-Couch had died of Spanish influenza in the epidemic fifteen months previously, en route to England at the close of World War I. A lackluster student who had a difficult time managing Oxford, Alastair was anything but one of the "clever men at Oxford." Grahame responded to his boating friend in a typed letter on May 15, 1920:

> Our dear boy went up to Oxford this term—three weeks ago yesterday—under conditions which made for quite special happiness. First he had got through the tiresome exam. of mods, which had been troubling him & keeping him back, & he was at last free to choose just what line of reading he might like. . . . By good luck & a friend's help we secured him rooms in a stately Queen Anne house in Long Wall Street, belonging to New Coll. & tenanted by a widow lady for whom it was too big, & who was taking in 2 or 3 men during the present congestion. The hostess really mothered the men and looked after them. But all the same they each had their separate set of two rooms, as an undergraduate should. . . . Mouse's bedroom overlooked Magdalen Grove. (Trinity College Archives DD36, Kenneth Grahame, May 15, 1920)

of money and an excellent breakfast! Ho, ho! I am The Toad, the handsome, the popular, the successful Toad!" He got so puffed up with conceit that he made up a song as he walked in praise of himself, and sang it at the top of his voice, though there was no one to hear it but him. It was perhaps the most conceited song that any animal ever composed.

The world has held great Heroes,
As history-books have showed;
But never a name to go down to fame
Compared with that of Toad!
The clever men at Oxford
Know all that there is to be knowed.[40]
But they none of them know one half as much
As intelligent Mr. Toad!
The animals sat in the Ark and cried,
Their tears in torrents flowed.
Who was it said, "There's land ahead?"
Encouraging Mr. Toad!
The army all saluted
As they marched along the road.[41]
Was it the King? Or Kitchener?[42]
No. It was Mr. Toad.
The Queen and her Ladies-in-waiting
Sat at the window and sewed.
She cried, "Look! who's that handsome *man?"*
They answered, "Mr. Toad."

There was a great deal more of the same sort, but too dreadfully conceited to be written down. These are some of the milder verses.

He sang as he walked, and he walked as he sang, and got more inflated every minute. But his pride was shortly to have a severe fall.

After some miles of country lanes he reached the high road, and as he turned into it and glanced along its white length, he

41. *The army all saluted / As they marched along the road.* Grahame is referring to the Edwardian Army, which underwent a transformation in the years leading to World War I. According to military historian Tim Travers:

> In the period 1900–1914 . . . the Army was reforming, not only in terms of Haldane's administrative reforms of 1905–12, but also in terms of its methods and attitudes; the Edwardian Army . . . was halfway between the amateur colonial army of Victorian times, and a modern professional army. Inevitably, the Edwardian Army—whilst trying to make itself more professional and "modern"—mirrored Edwardian beliefs and attitudes. It included elements which were openly anti-intellectual, rejecting "theory" and "doctrine" and preferring experience, common sense, breeding and a classical education. . . . It was class-conscious and embraced Social Darwinism—including the belief that the football-loving working classes . . . were not the same quality of man as the upper classes, and therefore neither as patriotic nor as reliable. (Travers, *The Killing Ground: the British Army, the Western Front and the Emergence of Modern War, 1900–1918* [London: Allen & Unwin, 1987], 21)

Kenneth Grahame also became involved in an organization called the London Scottish. According to David Gooderson, "As a young man Grahame had joined the Volunteers and became a drill sergeant. He paraded with his regiment . . . on Queen Victoria's Jubilee Day" (Kenneth Grahame, *My Dearest Mouse*, introduction by David Gooderson [London: Pavilion Books, 1988], 68). See also Chalmers, *Kenneth Grahame*, 40.

42. *Was it the King? Or Kitchener? / No. It was Mr. Toad.* The king would be King Edward. Kitchener is a reference to Lord Horatio Herbert Kitchener (1850–1916). At the time that Kenneth Grahame wrote *The Wind in the Willows*, Lord Kitchener was the commander in chief of the British forces situated in India.

saw approaching him a speck that turned into a dot and then into a blob, and then into something very familiar; and a double note of warning, only too well known, fell on his delighted ear.

"This is something like!" said the excited Toad. "This is real life again, this is once more the great world from which I have been missed so long! I will hail them, my brothers of the wheel, and pitch them a yarn, of the sort that has been so successful hitherto; and they will give me a lift, of course, and then I will talk to them some more; and, perhaps, with luck, it may even end in my driving up to Toad Hall in a motor-car! That will be one in the eye for Badger!"

He stepped confidently out into the road to hail the motor-car, which came along at an easy pace, slowing down as it neared the lane; when suddenly he became very pale, his heart turned to water, his knees shook and yielded under him, and he doubled up and collapsed with a sickening pain in his interior. And well he might, the unhappy animal; for the approaching car was the very one he had stolen out of the yard of the Red Lion Hotel on that fatal day when all his troubles began! And the people in it were the very same people he had sat and watched at luncheon in the coffee-room!

He sank down in a shabby, miserable heap in the road, murmuring to himself in his despair,[43] "It's all up! It's all over now! Chains and policemen again! Prison again! Dry bread and water again! O, what a fool I have been! What did I want to go strutting about the country for, singing conceited songs, and hailing people in broad day on the high road, instead of hiding till nightfall and slipping home quietly by back ways! O hapless Toad! O ill-fated animal!"

The terrible motor-car drew slowly nearer and nearer, till at last he heard it stop just short of him. Two gentlemen got out and walked round the trembling heap of crumpled misery lying in the road, and one of them said, "O dear! this is very sad! Here is a poor old thing[44]—a washerwoman apparently—who has fainted in the road! Perhaps she is overcome by the

43. *He sank down in a shabby, miserable heap in the road, murmuring to himself in his despair.* Alison Prince writes that by the age of three and a half, Alastair had devised a game of lying down in the middle of the street to stop traffic. During that period the boy was sent to Broadstairs with Mrs. Merrick, a cousin of Elspeth's. At the time there was no motorcar traffic in the seaside town due to the steeply sloped streets (*Kenneth Grahame: An Innocent in the Wild Wood*, 193).

44. *Two gentlemen got out and walked round the trembling heap of crumpled misery lying in the road, and one of them said, "O dear! this is very sad! Here is a poor old thing."* Shepard's first illustration for Chapter X shows the good Samaritans taking the ailing Toad into their motorcar. Both the illustration and Grahame's text imitate a scene in Dickens's *Our Mutual Friend* when passersby assist the elderly Betty Higden, whose only wish is not to die in the poor house. Grahame and Shepard parody the sentimental Dickensian moment. Shepard draws what looks like a sickly little old lady. Also, there are no motorcars in *Our Mutual Friend* because it is set in 1865.

heat, poor creature; or possibly she has not had any food to-day. Let us lift her into the car and take her to the nearest village, where doubtless she has friends."

They tenderly lifted Toad into the motor-car and propped him up with soft cushions, and proceeded on their way.[45]

When Toad heard them talk in so kind and sympathetic a way, and knew that he was not recognised, his courage began to revive, and he cautiously opened first one eye and then the other.

"Look!" said one of the gentlemen, "she is better already. The fresh air is doing her good. How do you feel now, ma'am?"

"Thank you kindly, Sir," said Toad in a feeble voice, "I'm feeling a great deal better!" "That's right," said the gentleman. "Now keep quite still, and, above all, don't try to talk."

"I won't," said Toad. "I was only thinking if I might sit on

E. H. Shepard's rescue of Mr. Toad dressed as the elderly washerwoman, 1931.

45. *They tenderly lifted Toad into the motor-car and propped him up with soft cushions, and proceeded on their way.* There were no seatbelts or safety features in motorcars in 1908. Seatbelts were not enforced by law in England until January 1983.

the front seat there, beside the driver, where I could get the fresh air full in my face, I should soon be all right again."

"What a very sensible woman!" said the gentleman. "Of course you shall." So they carefully helped Toad into the front seat beside the driver, and on they went again.

Toad was almost himself again by now. He sat up, looked about him, and tried to beat down the tremors, the yearnings, the old cravings that rose up and beset him and took possession of him entirely.[46]

"It is fate!" he said to himself. "Why strive? why struggle?" and he turned to the driver at his side.

"Please, Sir," he said, "I wish you would kindly let me try and drive the car for a little. I've been watching you carefully, and it looks so easy and so interesting, and I should like to be able to tell my friends that once I had driven a motor-car!"

The driver laughed at the proposal, so heartily that the gentleman inquired what the matter was. When he heard, he said, to Toad's delight, "Bravo, ma'am! I like your spirit. Let her have a try, and look after her. She won't do any harm."

Toad eagerly scrambled into the seat vacated by the driver, took the steering-wheel in his hands, listened with affected humility to the instructions given him, and set the car in motion, but very slowly and carefully at first, for he was determined to be prudent.

The gentlemen behind clapped their hands and applauded, and Toad heard them saying, "How well she does it! Fancy a washerwoman driving a car as well as that, the first time!"

Toad went a little faster; then faster still, and faster.

He heard the gentlemen call out warningly, "Be careful, washerwoman!" And this annoyed him, and he began to lose his head.

The driver tried to interfere, but he pinned him down in his seat with one elbow, and put on full speed. The rush of air in his face, the hum of the engines, and the light jump of the car beneath him intoxicated his weak brain. "Washerwoman,

46. *Toad was almost himself again by now. He sat up, looked about him, and tried to beat down the tremors, the yearnings, the old cravings that rose up and beset him and took possession of him entirely.* The motorcar has taken on the sound of the sirens—and Toad, like a sailor, can't fight his compulsion to wreck the ship for their cries.

indeed!" he shouted recklessly. "Ho! ho! I am the Toad, the motor-car snatcher, the prison-breaker, the Toad who always escapes! Sit still, and you shall know what driving really is, for you are in the hands of the famous, the skilful, the entirely fearless Toad!"

With a cry of horror the whole party rose and flung themselves on him. "Seize him!" they cried, "seize the Toad, the wicked animal who stole our motor-car! Bind him, chain him, drag him to the nearest police-station! Down with the desperate and dangerous Toad!"

Alas! they should have thought, they ought to have been more prudent, they should have remembered to stop the motor-car somehow before playing any pranks of that sort. With a half-turn of the wheel the Toad sent the car crashing through the low hedge that ran along the roadside. One mighty bound, a violent shock, and the wheels of the car were churning up the thick mud of a horse-pond.[47]

Toad found himself flying through the air with the strong upward rush and delicate curve of a swallow. He liked the motion, and was just beginning to wonder whether it would go on until he developed wings and turned into a Toad-bird, when he landed on his back with a thump, in the soft rich grass of a meadow. Sitting up, he could just see the motor-car in the pond, nearly submerged; the gentlemen and the driver, encumbered by their long coats, were floundering helplessly in the water.

He picked himself up rapidly, and set off running across country as hard as he could, scrambling through hedges, jumping ditches, pounding across fields, till he was breathless and weary, and had to settle down into an easy walk. When he had recovered his breath somewhat, and was able to think calmly, he began to giggle, and from giggling he took to laughing, and he laughed till he had to sit down under a hedge. "Ho, ho!" he cried, in ecstasies of self-admiration, "Toad again! Toad, as usual, comes out on the top! Who was it

47. *One mighty bound, a violent shock, and the wheels of the car were churning up the thick mud of a horse-pond.* In a short invitation addressed to H.R.H. (on stationery from 16 Durham Villas, Campden Hill West, the Grahames' London home), Grahame adds as a postscript: "Mouse has fallen into a pond and is frightfully pleased with himself. His anxious mother is convinced it must have been an accident!" (n.d., courtesy of the David J. Holmes Collection).

Shepard. Toad's escape, 1931.

got them to give him a lift? Who managed to get on the front seat for the sake of fresh air? Who persuaded them into letting him see if he could drive? Who landed them all in a horse-pond? Who escaped, flying gaily and unscathed through the air, leaving the narrow-minded, grudging, timid excursionists in the mud where they should rightly be? Why, Toad, of course; clever Toad, great Toad, *good* Toad!"

Then he burst into song again, and chanted with uplifted voice—

The motor-car went Poop-poop-poop,
As it raced along the road.
Who was it steered it into a pond?
Ingenious Mr. Toad!
O, how clever I am! How clever, how clever, how very clev———

A slight noise at a distance behind him made him turn his head and look. O horror! O misery! O despair!

About two fields off, a chauffeur in his leather gaiters and two large rural policemen were visible, running towards him as hard as they could go!

Poor Toad sprang to his feet and pelted away again, his heart in his mouth. "O, my!" he gasped, as he panted along, "what an *ass* I am! What a *conceited* and heedless ass! Swaggering again![48] Shouting and singing songs again! Sitting still and gassing again! O my! O my! O my!"

48. *Swaggering again!* Variant, e. 247: ~~Gassing~~ {Swaggering} again!

Grahame crossed out the word gassing but then chose to use it anyway in the next sentence. "Gassing" originated in America and is slang for impressing and exciting one's company.

Payne. Toad's escape, 1927. Contrary to the tension in E. H. Shepard's drawing, in Payne's illustration Toad is fleet of foot, and suspended over the water the moment before he falls in. The land is the domain of the dangerous Wide World, whereas the river represents the safety of the animal world. With Toad's pursuers far behind him, Payne compromises the moment, letting us see that Toad will escape.

Shepard. Rat's "Tradesmen's Entrance" (1931). Shepard's last illustration of the chapter is unlike his drawing of the Rat's river house in chapter I. In this latter drawing he adds an entrance that does not exist in the text and a sign to mark it: "Mr. Rat's Tradesmen's Entrance, no bottles." (Shepard's drawings for the *Pooh* books often included signs.) Though this back door of sorts does not exist in Grahame's text, he does make the entrance a hole, very much as in Paul Bransom's first illustration.

He glanced back, and saw to his dismay that they were gaining on him. On he ran desperately, but kept looking back, and saw that they still gained steadily. He did his best, but he was a fat animal, and his legs were short, and still they gained. He could hear them close behind him now. Ceasing to heed where he was going, he struggled on blindly and wildly, looking back over his shoulder at the now triumphant enemy, when suddenly the earth failed under his feet, he grasped at the air, and, splash! he found himself head over ears in deep water, rapid water, water that bore him along with a force he could not contend with; and he knew that in his blind panic he had run straight into the river!

He rose to the surface and tried to grasp the reeds and the rushes that grew along the water's edge close under the bank, but the stream was so strong that it tore them out of his hands. "O my!" gasped poor Toad, "if ever I steal a motor-car again! If ever I sing another conceited song"—then down he went, and came up breathless and spluttering.[49] Presently he saw that he was approaching a big dark hole in the bank, just above his head, and as the stream bore him past he reached up with a paw and caught hold of the edge and held on. Then slowly and with difficulty he drew himself up out of the water, till at last he was able to rest his elbows on the edge of the hole. There he remained for some minutes,[50] puffing and panting, for he was quite exhausted.

As he sighed and blew and stared before him into the dark hole, some bright small thing shone and twinkled in its depths, moving towards him. As it approached, a face grew up gradually around it, and it was a familiar face!

Brown and small, with whiskers.

Grave and round, with neat ears and silky hair.

It was the Water Rat!

Tailpiece by Nancy Barnhart. Rat peering out from his riverbank hole (1922).

49. *then down he went, and came up breathless and spluttering.* The dress, unfortunately, is a thing of the Wide World. Hindered by excessive clothing, Toad almost drowns. The scene recalls Queen Gertrude's Ophelia drowning speech from *Hamlet*, act 4, scene 7.

When down her weedy trophies and herself
Fell in the weeping brook. Her clothes spread wide;
And, mermaid-like, awhile they bore her up:
Which time she chanted snatches of old tunes;
As one incapable of her own distress,
Or like a creature native and indued
Unto that element: but long it could not be
Till that her garments, heavy with their drink,
Pull'd the poor wretch from her melodious lay
To muddy death.

50. *There he remained for some minutes.* Grahame references Odysseus's struggle to shore and onto the riverbank in book 5 of *The Odyssey*: "Swolen from head to foot he was, and sea water / gushed from his mouth and nostrils. There he lay, / scarce drawing breath, unstirring, deathly spent."

XI

"Like Summer Tempests Came His Tears"[1]

The Rat put out a neat little brown paw, gripped Toad firmly by the scruff of the neck, and gave a great hoist and a pull; and the water-logged Toad came up slowly but surely over the edge of the hole, till at last he stood safe and sound in the hall, streaked with mud and weed to be sure, and with the water streaming off him, but happy and high-spirited as of old, now that he found himself once more in the house of a friend, and dodgings and evasions were over, and he could lay aside a disguise that was unworthy of his position and wanted such a lot of living up to.

"O, Ratty!" he cried. "I've been through such times since I saw you last, you can't think! Such trials, such sufferings, and all so nobly borne! Then such escapes, such disguises such subterfuges, and all so cleverly planned and carried out! Been in prison—got out of it, of course! Been thrown into a canal—swam ashore! Stole a horse—sold him for a large sum of money! Humbugged everybody—made 'em all do exactly what I wanted! Oh, I *am* a smart Toad, and no mistake! What do you think my last exploit was? Just hold on till I tell you———"

"Toad," said the Water Rat, gravely and firmly, "you go off

1. *"Like Summer Tempests Came His Tears."* The chapter title is drawn from Tennyson's poem "The Princess: Home They Brought Her Warrior Dead":

> *Rose a nurse of ninety years,*
> *Set his child upon her knee—*
> *"Like summer tempest came her tears—*
> *'Sweet my child, I live for thee' "*

(*The Princess: A Medley*, 3rd ed. [London: E. Moxen, 1850])

upstairs at once, and take off that old cotton rag that looks as if it might formerly have belonged to some washerwoman, and clean yourself thoroughly, and put on some of my clothes, and try and come down looking like a gentleman if you *can;* for a more shabby, bedraggled, disreputable-looking object than you are I never set eyes on in my whole life! Now, stop swaggering and arguing, and be off! I'll have something to say to you later!"

Toad was at first inclined to stop and do some talking back at him. He had had enough of being ordered about when he was in prison, and here was the thing being begun all over again, apparently; and by a Rat, too! However, he caught sight of himself in the looking-glass over the hat-stand, with the rusty black bonnet perched rakishly over one eye, and he changed his mind and went very quickly and humbly upstairs to the Rat's dressing-room. There he had a thorough wash and brush-up, changed his clothes, and stood for a long time before the glass, contemplating himself with pride and pleasure, and thinking what utter idiots all the people must have been to have ever mistaken him for one moment for a washerwoman.

By the time he came down again luncheon was on the table, and very glad Toad was to see it, for he had been through some trying experiences and had taken much hard exercise since the excellent breakfast provided for him by the gipsy. While they ate Toad told the Rat all his adventures, dwelling chiefly on his own cleverness, and presence of mind in emergencies,[2] and cunning in tight places; and rather making out that he had been having a gay and highly-coloured experience. But the more he talked and boasted, the more grave and silent the Rat became.

When at last Toad had talked himself to a standstill, there was silence for a while; and then the Rat said, "Now, Toady, I don't want to give you pain, after all you've been through already; but, seriously, don't you see what an awful ass you've been making of yourself? On your own admission you have

2. *dwelling chiefly on his own cleverness, and presence of mind in emergencies,* There is nothing humanlike about Toad in Paul Bransom's illustration, though Toad looks like he is in a human setting. On his left is a framed work of art—obviously covered in glass because the artist drew light reflecting off the surface. Bransom's wall is two-toned: the décor differs from the exterior of Rat's hole in chapter 1. Toad looks like he's ready for a science class dissection, while Rat's interiors have morphed into a human's home.

In Shepard's illustrations, Rat and Toad are pictured with their backs to the readers drinking tea at the table.

Paul Bransom's version of the swaggering Toad, 1913.

been handcuffed, imprisoned, starved, chased, terrified out of your life, insulted, jeered at, and ignominiously flung into the water—by a woman, too! Where's the amusement in that? Where does the fun come in? And all because you must needs go and steal a motor-car. You know that you've never had anything but trouble from motor-cars from the moment you first set eyes on one. But if you *will* be mixed up with them—as you generally are, five minutes after you've started—why *steal* them? Be a cripple, if you think it's exciting; be a bankrupt, for a change, if you've set your mind on it; but why choose to be a convict? When are you going to be sensible, and think of your friends, and try and be a credit to them? Do you suppose it's any pleasure to me, for instance, to hear animals saying, as I go about, that I'm the chap that keeps company with gaol-birds?"

Now, it was a very comforting point in Toad's character that he was a thoroughly good-hearted animal, and never minded being jawed[3] by those who were his real friends. And even when most set upon a thing, he was always able to see the other side of the question. So although, while the Rat was talking so seriously, he kept saying to himself mutinously, "But it *was* fun, though! Awful fun!" and making strange suppressed noises inside him, k-i-ck-ck-ck, and poop-p-p, and other sounds resembling stifled snorts, or the opening of soda-water bottles, yet when the Rat had quite finished, he heaved a deep sigh and said, very nicely and humbly, "Quite right, Ratty! How *sound* you always are! Yes, I've been a conceited old ass, I can quite see that; but now I'm going to be a good Toad, and not do it any more. As for motor-cars, I've not been at all so keen about them since my last ducking in that river of yours. The fact is, while I was hanging on to the edge of your hole and getting my breath, I had a sudden idea—a really brilliant idea—connected with motor-boats[4]—there, there! don't take on so, old chap, and stamp, and upset things; it was only an idea, and we won't talk any more about it now. We'll have our coffee, *and* a smoke, and a quiet chat, and then I'm going to stroll quietly down to Toad Hall, and get into clothes of my own, and set things going again on the old lines. I've had enough of adventures. I shall lead a quiet, steady, respectable life, pottering about my property, and improving it, and doing a little landscape gardening at times. There will always be a bit of dinner for my friends when they come to see me; and I shall keep a pony-chaise to jog about the country in,[5] just as I

3. *and never minded being jawed.* To talk or jabber. Impudent argument or backtalk.

4. *connected with motor-boats.* In *The Cruise of the Motor-Boat Conqueror; Being the Further Adventures of the Motor Pirate* (Boston: L. C. Page & Company, 1906), Sidney Paternoster shifts his passion for the car to the motorboat, perhaps much in the way Toad would likely have shifted his focus if Grahame had written a sequel:

> Motoring on land with a 40 or 60 h.p. engine throbbing under the bonnet of the car, when, coming into the straight you see a white ribbon of road stretching for miles ahead, and giving her a full dose of petrol you sit firm while the hedges flit by like a skein of green silk, is exciting enough, but it is nothing to the sensation which grips you when you take the wheel of the motor-boat in your hand and put her full speed ahead in the face of a twenty mile breeze. . . .
>
> I started with a little 14 h.p. Brooke, and when she became insufficient for my desires I bought a 28 b.h.p. Thorneycroft, only to find that I could never get an opportunity of finding out her capabilities without interfering with the comfort of the adoring couples who drift down the river in a skiff or canoe absolutely regardless of anything in the universe but themselves. (2)

Like cars, the popularity of motorboats was on the rise. In the fourth Olympic games, held in London in 1908, Olympic motorboat racing was introduced as an event for the first and only time. Races commenced in Southampton Water, the great estuary, on August 28 and 29, only to be moved to N. W. Netley due to a downpour. N. W. Netley is further upstream in the estuary. Only gentlemen of means (like Mr. Toad) participated. The Duke of Westminster raced in the *Wolseley*

used to in the good old days, before I got restless, and wanted to *do* things."

"Stroll quietly down to Toad Hall?" cried the Rat, greatly excited. "What are you talking about? Do you mean to say you haven't *heard?*"

"Heard what?" said Toad, turning rather pale. "Go on, Ratty! Quick! Don't spare me! What haven't I heard?"

"Do you mean to tell me," shouted the Rat, thumping with his little fist upon the table, "that you've heard nothing about the Stoats and Weasels?"[6]

"What, the Wild Wooders?" cried Toad, trembling in every limb.[7] "No, not a word! What have they been doing?"

"—And how they've been and taken Toad Hall?" continued the Rat.

Toad leaned his elbows on the table, and his chin on his paws; and a large tear welled up in each of his eyes, overflowed and splashed on the table, plop! plop!

"Go on, Ratty," he murmured presently; "tell me all. The worst is over. I am an animal again. I can bear it."

"When you—got—into that—that—trouble of yours," said the Rat, slowly and impressively; "I mean, when you—disappeared from society for a time, over that misunderstanding about a—a machine, you know—"

Toad merely nodded.

"Well, it was a good deal talked about down here, naturally," continued the Rat, "not only along the river-side, but even in the Wild Wood. Animals took sides, as always happens. The River-bankers stuck up for you, and said you had been infamously treated, and there was no justice to be had in the land nowadays. But the Wild Wood animals said hard things, and served you right, and it was time this sort of thing was stopped. And they got very cocky, and went about saying you were done for this time! You would never come back again, never, never!"

Toad nodded once more, keeping silence.

Siddeley against Lord Howard de Walden, in the *Dylan*. Typically, the *Wolseley Siddeley* was a 400-horsepower wonder, with an eight-cylinder engine, that measured 39 feet, 4 inches in length. The gold medal was eventually awarded to the *Gyrinus*, piloted by Isaac Thomas Thornycroft, Bernard Boverton Redwood, and John Charles Field-Richards. The course was 40 sea miles, raced at 17¾ knots in gale-force winds. See Theodore Andrea Cook, *The Fourth Olympiad, Being the Official Report, The Olympic Games of 1908, Celebrated in London* (London: The British Olympic Association, 1909).

5. *"and I shall keep a pony-chaise to jog about the country in."* The Grahames kept a pony for Alastair at Cookham Dean. The pony's name was Firefly, and Naomi Stott often mentions him in her correspondence and in *The Merry Thought.*

6. *"Do you mean to tell me," shouted the Rat, thumping with his little fist upon the table, "that you've heard nothing about the Stoats and Weasels?"* At the time Grahame wrote *The Wind in the Willows*, the working class and working poor—the stoats and weasels of English society—were gaining power through social reform. New laws that favored the proletarian classes meant the beginning of gradual taxation. David Lloyd George, the chancellor of the exchequer in the liberal government (led by Herbert Asquith), introduced radical policies to eradicate poverty. Long an enemy of the Poor Law, which forced the indigent to toil in "workhouses" for their alms, George was determined to "lift the shadow of the workhouse from the homes of the poor." His Old Age Pension Act of 1908 guaranteed an income to people who were too old to work. The Radical People's Budget (passed in 1909) placed a direct income tax with a surcharge on higher incomes, created car and gas levies to pay for road construction, and boosted inheritance taxes by

"That's the sort of little beasts they are," the Rat went on. "But Mole and Badger, they stuck out, through thick and thin, that you would come back again soon, somehow. They didn't know exactly how, but somehow!"

Toad began to sit up in his chair again, and to smirk a little.

"They argued from history," continued the Rat. "They said that no criminal laws had ever been known to prevail against cheek and plausibility such as yours,[8] combined with the power of a long purse. So they arranged to move their things in to Toad Hall, and sleep there, and keep it aired, and have it all ready for you when you turned up. They didn't guess what was going to happen, of course; still, they had their suspicions of the Wild Wood animals.[9] Now I come to the most painful and tragic part of my story. One dark night—it was a *very* dark night, and blowing hard, too, and raining simply cats and dogs—a band of weasels, armed to the teeth, crept silently up the carriage-drive to the front entrance. Simultaneously, a body of desperate ferrets, advancing through the kitchen-garden, possessed themselves of the backyard and offices; while a company of skirmishing stoats who stuck at nothing occupied the conservatory and the billiard-room, and held the French windows opening on to the lawn.

"The Mole and the Badger were sitting by the fire in the smoking-room, telling stories and suspecting nothing, for it wasn't a night for any animals to be out in, when those bloodthirsty villains broke down the doors and rushed in upon them from every side. They made the best fight they could, but what was the good? They were unarmed, and taken by surprise, and what can two animals do against hundreds? They took and beat them severely with sticks, those two poor faithful creatures, and turned them out into the cold and the wet, with many insulting and uncalled-for remarks!"

Here the unfeeling Toad broke into a snigger, and then pulled himself together and tried to look particularly solemn.

"And the Wild Wooders have been living in Toad Hall ever

charging 20 percent on capital gains when ownership of land changed hands. Peter Green writes:

> Q[uiller-Couch], to Grahame's irritation, came out strongly in favour of [David] Lloyd George: "Q is frightfully busy over the election," he wrote to [Austin] Purves, "propagating his pernicious doctrines throughout the west country"; and to Q himself he declared . . . "I must not wish you luck in your nefarious designs on our savings, our cellars, and our garden-plots; but I do hope you'll get some fun out of it." (*Kenneth Grahame: A Biography*, 299)

7. *"What, the Wild Wooders?" cried Toad, trembling in every limb.* For Grahame, Stoats and Weasels might have been allegorical characters.

Stoat: the European ermine when it has its brown summer coat. Also defined as a treacherous, sexually aggressive man; a lecher. In E. M. Forster's *Maurice,* written around 1913 but published posthumously in 1971, Forster writes, "His feeling for Dickie required a very primitive name. . . . what a stoat he had been!"

Weasel: a carnivorous animal remarkable for its slender body and its ferociously bloodthirsty nature. They are known to rob eggs from nests and suck them dry. Both species and genus of these animals live in the Wild Wood, making the woods dangerous to all that inhabit them, because weasels behave as predators.

8. *"They said that no criminal laws had ever been known to prevail against cheek and plausibility such as yours."* Variant, e. 247: "They said that no criminal laws ~~could stand~~ {had ever been known to prevail} against cheek and plausibility such as yours.["]

9. *"they had their suspicions of the Wild Wood animals."* Peter Green writes about the

nervous mood of the English as the social classes began to drift, threatening the sensibilities of the bourgeoisie.

> [T]he whole business of the Wild Wood and Toad Hall's capture takes on an unmistakable social symbolism. The Wild Wooders, stoats, weasels, and the rest, are clearly identified in Grahame's mind with the stunted, malevolent proletariat . . . like the urban-mob-anarchist of every Edwardian upper-class nightmare [the Wild Wood animals] have no notion of how to behave. . . . Nothing could be more evocative of that nervous mood, half-contemptuous, half-terrified, which ran through the English bourgeoisie with increasing insistence from the turn of the century. (Ibid., 246)

10. *"And the Wild Wooders have been living in Toad Hall ever since," continued the Rat; "and going on simply anyhow!"* This is the final full-page illustration by Nancy Barnhart for her 1924 edition. The scene of four weasels and stoats tumbling from the windows of Toad Hall never occurs in Grahame's text; it is only alluded to in the riverbankers' conversation. The drawing appears to take place on a sunny day rather than on Grahame's "*very* dark night" when the wind is "blowing hard . . . and raining simply cats and dogs." Nevertheless, Barnhart pays tribute to Grahame's love of architectural detail. Her Toad Hall reflects his description of it in chapter VI: "the central mullion of the handsome Tudor window" (153).

Nancy Barnhart's last full-page illustration: THE WILD WOODERS HAVE BEEN LIVING IN TOAD HALL.

since," continued the Rat; "and going on simply anyhow![10] Lying in bed half the day, and breakfast at all hours, and the place in such a mess (I'm told) it's not fit to be seen! Eating your grub, and drinking your drink, and making bad jokes about you, and singing vulgar songs, about—well, about prisons and magistrates, and policemen; horrid personal songs, with no humour in them. And they're telling the tradespeople and everybody that they've come to stay for good."

"O, have they!" said Toad getting up and seizing a stick. "I'll jolly soon see about that!"

"It's no good, Toad!" called the Rat after him. "You'd better come back and sit down; you'll only get into trouble."

But the Toad was off, and there was no holding him. He marched rapidly down the road, his stick over his shoulder, fuming and muttering to himself in his anger, till he got near his front gate, when suddenly there popped up from behind the palings a long yellow ferret with a gun.

"Who comes there?" said the ferret sharply.

"Stuff and nonsense!" said Toad,[11] very angrily. "What do you mean by talking like that to me? Come out of that at once, or I'll———"

The ferret said never a word, but he brought his gun up to his shoulder. Toad prudently dropped flat in the road, and *Bang!* a bullet whistled over his head.

The startled Toad scrambled to his feet and scampered off down the road as hard as he could; and as he ran he heard the ferret laughing and other horrid thin little laughs taking it up and carrying on the sound.

He went back, very crestfallen, and told the Water Rat.

"What did I tell you?" said the Rat. "It's no good. They've got sentries posted, and they are all armed. You must just wait."

Still, Toad was not inclined to give in all at once. So he got out the boat, and set off rowing up the river to where the garden front of Toad Hall came down to the waterside.

Arriving within sight of his old home, he rested on his oars and surveyed the land cautiously. All seemed very peaceful and deserted and quiet. He could see the whole front of Toad Hall, glowing in the evening sunshine, the pigeons settling by twos and threes along the straight line of the roof; the garden, a blaze of flowers; the creek that led up to the boat-house, the little wooden bridge[12] that crossed it; all tranquil, uninhabited, apparently waiting for his return. He would try the

11. *"Stuff and nonsense!" said Toad.* A recurring figure of speech in Dickens.

12. *the little wooden bridge.* Many footbridges cross the Thames, especially in backwaters where there is less nautical traffic. Grahame's footbridge is wooden, but Shepard, the only illustrator to include a bridge, drew small iron footbridges on three occasions. In the endpaper maps, Shepard dubbed the bridge by Toad Hall "New Iron Bridge." A lacelike footbridge appears in the background of chapter I when Mole announces, "Ratty! Please, I want to row, now!" Shepard's third and final bridge appears in chapter XI.

Metal footbridge, Port Meadow, Oxford. Whether wooden or metal, the small footbridges that dot the backwaters of the rivers, such as this one near Oxford, are quintessentially English. *Photo: Seymour Snapdragon.*

boat-house first, he thought. Very warily he paddled up to the mouth of the creek, and was just passing under the bridge, when . . . *Crash!*

A great stone, dropped from above, smashed through the bottom of the boat. It filled and sank, and Toad found himself struggling in deep water. Looking up, he saw two stoats leaning over the parapet of the bridge and watching him with great glee. "It will be your head next time, Toady!" they called out to him. The indignant Toad swam to shore, while the stoats laughed and laughed, supporting each other, and laughed again, till they nearly had two fits—that is, one fit each, of course.

The Toad retraced his weary way on foot, and related his disappointing experiences to the Water Rat once more.

"Well, *what* did I tell you?" said the Rat very crossly. "And, now, look here! See what you've been and done! Lost me my boat that I was so fond of, that's what you've done! And simply ruined that nice suit of clothes that I lent you! Really, Toad, of all the trying animals—I wonder you manage to keep any friends at all!"

The Toad saw at once how wrongly and foolishly he had acted. He admitted his errors and wrong-headedness and made a full apology to Rat for losing his boat and spoiling his clothes. And he wound up by saying, with that frank self-surrender which always disarmed his friends' criticism and won them back to his side, "Ratty! I see that I have been a headstrong and a wilful Toad! Henceforth, believe me, I will be humble and submissive, and will take no action without your kind advice and full approval!"

"If that is really so," said the good-natured Rat, already appeased, "then my advice to you is, considering the lateness of the hour, to sit down and have your supper, which will be on the table in a minute,[13] and be very patient. For I am convinced that we can do nothing until we have seen the Mole and the Badger, and heard their latest news, and held conference and taken their advice in this difficult matter."

13. *"sit down and have your supper, which will be on the table in a minute."* The supper has probably been prepared by a servant, who remains purposely out of sight.

Shepard's final bridge should be wooden but it appears to be metal, with a brick base.

"Oh, ah, yes, of course, the Mole and the Badger," said Toad, lightly. "What's become of them, the dear fellows? I had forgotten all about them."

"Well may you ask!" said the Rat reproachfully. "While you were riding about the country in expensive motor-cars, and galloping proudly on blood-horses, and breakfasting on the fat of the land,[14] those two poor devoted animals have been camping out in the open, in every sort of weather, living very rough by day and lying very hard by night; watching over your house, patrolling your boundaries, keeping a constant

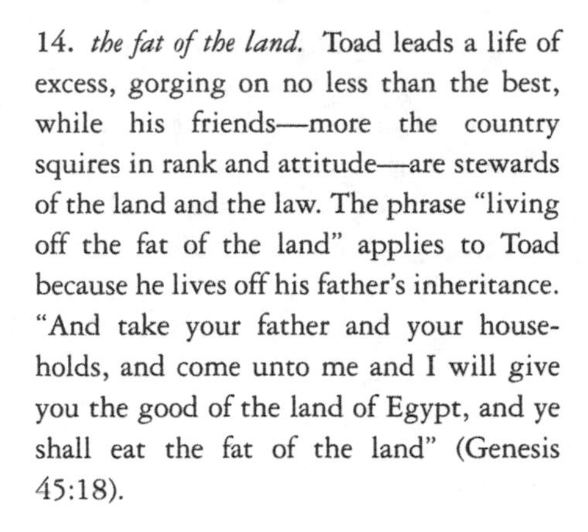

14. *the fat of the land.* Toad leads a life of excess, gorging on no less than the best, while his friends—more the country squires in rank and attitude—are stewards of the land and the law. The phrase "living off the fat of the land" applies to Toad because he lives off his father's inheritance. "And take your father and your households, and come unto me and I will give you the good of the land of Egypt, and ye shall eat the fat of the land" (Genesis 45:18).

15. *but then he had never been a very smart man, the Badger, at the best of times.* The narrative point of view shifts around in this chapter: This statement has to be from Toad's point of view, because Badger is extremely intelligent—he will be instrumental in winning back Toad Hall.

eye on the stoats and the weasels, scheming and planning and contriving how to get your property back for you. You don't deserve to have such true and loyal friends, Toad, you don't, really. Some day, when it's too late, you'll be sorry you didn't value them more while you had them!"

"I'm an ungrateful beast, I know," sobbed Toad, shedding bitter tears. "Let me go out and find them, out into the cold, dark night, and share their hardships, and try and prove by——

——Hold on a bit! Surely I heard the chink of dishes on a tray! Supper's here at last, hooray! Come on, Ratty!"

The Rat remembered that poor Toad had been on prison fare for a considerable time, and that large allowances had therefore to be made. He followed him to the table accordingly, and hospitably encouraged him in his gallant efforts to make up for past privations.

They had just finished their meal and resumed their armchairs, when there came a heavy knock at the door.

Toad was nervous, but the Rat, nodding mysteriously at him, went straight up to the door and opened it, and in walked Mr. Badger.

He had all the appearance of one who for some nights had been kept away from home and all its little comforts and conveniences. His shoes were covered with mud, and he was looking very rough and tousled; but then he had never been a very smart man, the Badger, at the best of times.[15] He came solemnly up to Toad, shook him by the paw, and said, "Welcome home, Toad! Alas! what am I saying? Home, indeed! This is a poor home-coming. Unhappy Toad!" Then he turned his back on him, sat down to the table, drew his chair up, and helped himself to a large slice of cold pie.

Toad was quite alarmed at this very serious and portentous style of greeting; but the Rat whispered to him, "Never mind; don't take any notice; and don't say anything to him just yet. He's always rather low and despondent when he's wanting his victuals. In half an hour's time he'll be quite a different animal."

So they waited in silence, and presently there came another and a lighter knock. The Rat, with a nod to Toad, went to the door and ushered in the Mole, very shabby and unwashed, with bits of hay and straw sticking in his fur.

"Hooray! Here's old Toad!" cried the Mole, his face beaming. "Fancy having you back again!" And he began to dance round him. "We never dreamt you would turn up so soon! Why, you must have managed to escape, you clever, ingenious, intelligent Toad!"

The Rat, alarmed, pulled him by the elbow; but it was too late. Toad was puffing and swelling already.

"Clever? O, no!" he said. "I'm not really clever, according to my friends. I've only broken out of the strongest prison in England,[16] that's all! And captured a railway train and escaped on it, that's all! And disguised myself and gone about the country humbugging everybody, that's all! O, no! I'm a stupid ass, I am! I'll tell you one or two of my little adventures, Mole, and you shall judge for yourself!"

"Well, well," said the Mole, moving towards the supper-table; "supposing you talk while I eat. Not a bite since breakfast! O my! O my!" And he sat down and helped himself liberally to cold beef and pickles.

Toad straddled on the hearth-rug, thrust his paw into his trouser-pocket and pulled out a handful of silver. "Look at that!" he cried, displaying it. "That's not so bad, is it, for a few minutes' work? And how do you think I done it, Mole? Horse-dealing! That's how I done it!"[17]

"Go on, Toad," said the Mole, immensely interested.

"Toad, do be quiet, please!" said the Rat. "And don't you egg him on, Mole, when you know what he is; but please tell us as soon as possible what the position is, and what's best to be done, now that Toad is back at last."

16. *"the strongest prison in England."* The strongest prison in England was probably either the Tower of London or the notorious Reading Prison, which very publicly broke the spirit of Oscar Wilde while he was incarcerated there in the 1890s.

Reading Prison, formerly Her Majesty's Prison, was built in 1844 in the heart of Reading on the site of the former country jail. The jail is typical of Victorian prison architecture, built in the shape of a crucifix. It served as a site for public executions until 1913.

Founded in 1066 by Duke William, who invaded from Normandy, the Tower of London has a bloody history of imprisonment and execution that runs into the twentieth century. Eleven prisoners were executed during World War I, and the final execution took place in World War II.

17. *"And how do you think I done it, Mole? Horse-dealing! That's how I done it!"* Toad's lapse in grammar is probably in imitation of the bargewoman from whom he stole the horse and the Gypsy to whom he sold it.

"The position's about as bad as it can be," replied the Mole grumpily; "and as for what's to be done, why, blest if I know! The Badger and I have been round and round the place, by night and by day; always the same thing. Sentries posted everywhere, guns poked out at us, stones thrown at us; always an animal on the look-out, and when they see us, my! how they do laugh! That's what annoys me most!"

"It's a very difficult situation," said the Rat, reflecting deeply. "But I think I see now, in the depths of my mind, what Toad really ought to do. I will tell you. He ought to———"

"No, he oughtn't!" shouted the Mole, with his mouth full. "Nothing of the sort! You don't understand. What he ought to do is, he ought to———"

"Well, I shan't do it, anyway!" cried Toad, getting excited. "I'm not going to be ordered about by you fellows! It's my house we're talking about, and I know exactly what to do, and I'll tell you. I'm going to———"

By this time they were all three talking at once, at the top of their voices, and the noise was simply deafening, when a thin, dry voice made itself heard, saying, "Be quiet at once, all of you!" and instantly every one was silent.

It was the Badger, who, having finished his pie, had turned round in his chair and was looking at them severely. When he saw that he had secured their attention, and that they were evidently waiting for him to address them, he turned back to the table again and reached out for the cheese. And so great was the respect commanded by the solid qualities of that admirable animal, that not another word was uttered until he had quite finished his repast and brushed the crumbs from his knees. The Toad fidgeted a good deal, but the Rat held him firmly down.

When the Badger had quite done, he got up from his seat and stood before the fireplace, reflecting deeply. At last he spoke.

"Toad!" he said severely. "You bad, troublesome little animal! Aren't you ashamed of yourself? What do you think your father, my old friend, would have said if he had been here to-night, and had known of all your goings on?"

Toad, who was on the sofa by this time, with his legs up, rolled over on his face, shaken by sobs of contrition.

"There, there!" went on the Badger, more kindly. "Never mind. Stop crying. We're going to let bygones be bygones, and try and turn over a new leaf. But what the Mole says is quite true. The stoats are on guard, at every point, and they make the best sentinels in the world. It's quite useless to think of attacking the place. They're too strong for us."

"Then it's all over," sobbed the Toad, crying into the sofa cushions. "I shall go and enlist for a soldier,[18] and never see my dear Toad Hall any more!"

"Come, cheer up, Toady!" said the Badger. "There are more ways of getting back a place than taking it by storm. I haven't said my last word yet. Now I'm going to tell you a great secret."

Toad sat up slowly and dried his eyes. Secrets had an immense attraction for him, because he never could keep one, and he enjoyed the sort of unhallowed thrill he experienced when he went and told another animal, after having faithfully promised not to.

"There—is—an—underground—passage," said the Badger, impressively, "that leads from the river-bank, quite near here, right up into the middle of Toad Hall."

"O, nonsense! Badger," said Toad, rather airily. "You've been listening to some of the yarns they spin in the public-houses about here. I know every inch of Toad Hall, inside and out. Nothing of the sort, I do assure you!"

"My young friend," said the Badger, with great severity, "your father, who was a worthy animal—a lot worthier than some others I know—was a particular friend of mine,[19] and told me a great deal he wouldn't have dreamt of telling you. He discovered that passage—he didn't make it, of course; that was done hundreds of years before he ever came to live

18. *"I shall go and enlist for a soldier."* See chapter X, note 41.

19. *"your father, who was a worthy animal—a lot worthier than some others I know—was a particular friend of mine."* Badger is Toad's surrogate father figure. As Lois Kuznets writes:

> Badger has special knowledge denied to Toad—knowledge of a secret, significantly underground passageway to Toad Hall. In his possessing it and dispensing it to Toad at the proper moment, Badger indicates most explicitly that he is the surrogate father and guardian to Toad, who has yet to come into his inheritance in any meaningful way. In addition, as an already formed character, Badger is the main reforming force in Toad's life, a super-ego who has not yet been internalized. The language of chapter six, where the three friends attempt to keep Toad under house arrest, is shot through with missionary fervor; it confirms Badger's instrumental and dedicated role long before the final crisis. ("Toad Hall Revisited," *Children's Literature* 7 [1978]: 125)

there[20]—and he repaired it and cleaned it out, because he thought it might come in useful some day, in case of trouble or danger; and he showed it to me. 'Don't let my son know about it,' he said. 'He's a good boy, but very light and volatile in character, and simply cannot hold his tongue. If he's ever in a real fix, and it would be of use to him, you may tell him about the secret passage; but not before.' "

The other animals looked hard at Toad to see how he would take it. Toad was inclined to be sulky at first; but he brightened up immediately, like the good fellow he was.

"Well, well," he said; "perhaps I am a bit of a talker. A popular fellow such as I am—my friends get round me—we chaff, we sparkle, we tell witty stories—and somehow my tongue gets wagging. I have the gift of conversation. I've been told I ought to have a *salon*,[21] whatever that may be. Never mind. Go on, Badger. How's this passage of yours going to help us?"

"I've found out a thing or two lately," continued the Badger. "I got Otter to disguise himself as a sweep and call at the back-door with brushes over his shoulder, asking for a job.[22] There's going to be a big banquet to-morrow night. It's somebody's birthday—the Chief Weasel's, I believe—and all the weasels will be gathered together in the dining-hall, eating and drinking and laughing and carrying on, suspecting nothing. No guns, no swords, no sticks, no arms of any sort whatever!"

"But the sentinels will be posted as usual," remarked the Rat.

"Exactly," said the Badger; "that is my point. The weasels will trust entirely to their excellent sentinels. And that is where the passage comes in. That very useful tunnel leads right up under the butler's pantry, next to the dining-hall!"

"Aha! that squeaky board in the butler's pantry!" said Toad. "Now I understand it!"

"We shall creep out quietly into the butler's pantry—" cried the Mole.

"—with our pistols and swords and sticks—" shouted the Rat.

20. *"He discovered that passage—he didn't make it, of course; that was done hundreds of years before he ever came to live there."* In Grahame's letters, Toad's father built the passage rather than having found it: "He [Toad's father] made that passage, in case of danger, + when he had made it he showed it to me. 'Don't tell my son' said he. 'He's a good fellow, but he has a light character + can't hold his tongue'" (Letter from Kenneth Grahame, August 21, 1907).

21. *"I've been told I ought to have a salon."* In Toad's case the salon would be a large and lofty apartment within Toad Hall used principally to receive guests. People of social or intellectual distinction were the typical guests at such social gatherings, and it was exactly that kind of company Kenneth Grahame kept during his London years when he was a bachelor. According to Peter Green, Grahame was a regular guest at Verray's restaurant for a weekly gathering of poets and writers who contributed to W. E. Henley's *National Observer* and its successor, *The New Review*. (Crippled by tuberculosis, and having had a leg amputated due to the disease, Henley is also famous for being Robert Louis Stevenson's model for Long John Silver in *Treasure Island*.) Verray's was one of the more exclusive salons in London between 1890 and 1896. Grahame went to Henley's home on Sunday evenings for even more select gatherings. Poet W. B. Yeats describes them as follows: "We gathered . . . in two rooms with folding doors between, and hung, I think, with photographs from Dutch masters, and in one room there was always, I think, a table with cold meat. . . . [H]e [Henley] made us feel always our importance, and no man among us could do good work, or show the promise of it, and lack his praise." Grahame also was in attendance for meetings revolving around the publication of *The Yellow Book* from

"—and rush in upon them," said the Badger.

"—and whack 'em, and whack 'em, and whack 'em!" cried the Toad in ecstasy, running round and round the room, and jumping over the chairs.

"Very well, then," said the Badger, resuming his usual dry manner, "our plan is settled, and there's nothing more for you to argue and squabble about. So, as it's getting very late, all of you go right off to bed at once. We will make all the necessary arrangements in the course of the morning to-morrow."

Toad, of course, went off to bed dutifully with the rest—he knew better than to refuse—though he was feeling much too excited to sleep. But he had had a long day, with many events crowded into it; and sheets and blankets were very friendly and comforting things, after plain straw, and not too much of it, spread on the stone floor of a draughty cell; and his head had not been many seconds on his pillow before he was snoring happily. Naturally, he dreamt a good deal; about roads that ran away from him just when he wanted them, and canals that chased him and caught him, and a barge that sailed into the banqueting-hall with his week's washing, just as he was giving a dinner-party; and he was alone in the secret passage, pushing onwards, but it twisted and turned round and shook itself, and sat up on its end; yet somehow, at the last, he found himself back in Toad Hall, safe and triumphant, with all his friends gathered round about him, earnestly assuring him that he really was a clever Toad.

He slept till a late hour next morning, and by the time he got down he found that the other animals had finished their breakfast some time before. The Mole had slipped off somewhere by himself, without telling any one where he was going to. The Badger sat in the arm-chair, reading the paper, and not concerning himself in the slightest about what was going to happen that very evening. The Rat, on the other hand, was running round the room busily, with his arms full of weapons of every kind, distributing them in four little heaps on the

1894 to 1897 (Green, *Kenneth Grahame: A Biography*, 114).

22. *"I got Otter to disguise himself as a sweep and call at the back-door with brushes over his shoulder, asking for a job."* Variant, e. 247: "I got Otter to disguise himself as a sweep and call at the back-door with brushes over his shoulder, ~~looking~~ asking for a job."

Otter, like Kenneth Grahame's contemporary adventurers, is able to blend in with any stratum of the classes in any society.

floor, and saying excitedly under his breath, as he ran, "Here's-a-sword-for-the-Rat, here's-a-sword-for-the-Mole, here's-a-sword-for-the-Toad, here's-a-sword-for-the-Badger! Here's-a-pistol-for-the-Rat, here's-a-pistol-for-the-Mole, here's-a-pistol-for-the-Toad, here's-a-pistol-for-the-Badger!" And so on, in a regular, rhythmical way, while the four little heaps gradually grew and grew.[23]

"That's all very well, Rat," said the Badger presently, looking at the busy little animal over the edge of his newspaper; "I'm not blaming you. But just let us once get past the stoats, with those detestable guns of theirs, and I assure you we shan't want any swords or pistols. We four, with our sticks, once we're inside the dining-hall, why, we shall clear the floor of all the lot of them in five minutes. I'd have done the whole thing by myself, only I didn't want to deprive you fellows of the fun!"

"It's as well to be on the safe side," said the Rat reflectively, polishing a pistol-barrel on his sleeve and looking along it.

The Toad, having finished his breakfast, picked up a stout stick and swung it vigorously, belabouring imaginary animals. "I'll learn 'em to steal my house!" he cried. "I'll learn 'em, I'll learn 'em!"

"Don't say 'learn 'em,' Toad," said the Rat, greatly shocked. "It's not good English."

"What are you always nagging at Toad for?" inquired the Badger, rather peevishly. "What's the matter with his English? It's the same what I use myself, and if it's good enough for me, it ought to be good enough for you!"

"I'm very sorry," said the Rat humbly. "Only I *think* it ought to be 'teach 'em,' not 'learn 'em.' "[24]

"But we don't *want* to teach 'em," replied the Badger. "We want to *learn* 'em—learn 'em, learn 'em! And what's more, we're going to *do* it, too!"

"Oh, very well, have it your own way," said the Rat. He was getting rather muddled about it himself, and presently he retired into a corner, where he could be heard muttering,

23. *And so on, in a regular, rhythmical way, while the four little heaps gradually grew and grew.* This scene is an imitation of a Homeric arming ceremony. See chapter XII, note 1.

24. *"I'm very sorry," said the Rat humbly. "Only I* think *it ought to be 'teach 'em,' not 'learn 'em.'"* *Learn* means to acquire knowledge and has more punitive implications than the word *teach*. Learn implies committing to memory, or the rote memorization used in overcrowded schools common to the underprivileged, where pupils are taught to "learn by heart, memorize by rote." The phrase "I'll learn you" is a warning of impending punishment. When used ironically, it means: "I'll teach you never to do that again!" In his biography of Kenneth Grahame, Patrick Chalmers writes the following about the linguistic differences:

> [I]n 1930, The Times was to make a palinode. A leader, on the decline in the price and in the modishness of moleskin, entitled "The Gentleman in Velvet," mentions that the mole furnishes Hamlet with a title for his father's ghost and goes on to say, "but, if moles could read, they would think William Shakespeare no great shakes compared with . . . Mr. Kenneth Grahame." There may, of course, be sparkish youngsters down below there ready to assert that moles are higher in the social scale and in intellectual attainments than Mr. Kenneth Grahame makes them out (at least they know the modern and arbitrary distinction between "learn" and "teach"). (*Kenneth Grahame*, 127)

"Learn 'em, teach 'em, teach 'em, learn 'em!" till the Badger told him rather sharply to leave off.

Presently the Mole came tumbling into the room, evidently very pleased with himself. "I've been having such fun!" he began at once; "I've been getting a rise out of the stoats!"

"I hope you've been very careful, Mole?" said the Rat anxiously.

"I should hope so, too," said the Mole confidently. "I got the idea when I went into the kitchen, to see about Toad's breakfast being kept hot for him. I found that old washerwoman-dress that he came home in yesterday, hanging on a towel-horse before the fire. So I put it on, and the bonnet as well, and the shawl, and off I went to Toad Hall,[25] as bold as you please. The sentries were on the look-out, of course, with their guns and their 'Who comes there?' and all the rest of their nonsense. 'Good morning, gentlemen!' says I, very respectful. 'Want any washing done to-day?'

"They looked at me very proud and stiff and haughty, and said, 'Go away, washerwoman! We don't do any washing on duty.' 'Or any other time?' says I. Ho, ho, ho! Wasn't I *funny*, Toad?"

"Poor, frivolous animal!" said Toad, very loftily. The fact is, he felt exceedingly jealous of Mole for what he had just done. It was exactly what he would have liked to have done himself, if only he had thought of it first, and hadn't gone and overslept himself.

"Some of the stoats turned quite pink," continued the Mole, "and the Sergeant in charge, he said to me, very short, he said, 'Now run away, my good woman, run away! Don't keep my men idling and talking on their posts.' 'Run away?' says I; 'it won't be me that'll be running away, in a very short time from now!'"

"O *Moly*, how could you?" said the Rat, dismayed.

The Badger laid down his paper.

"I could see them pricking up their ears and looking at each other," went on the Mole; "and the Sergeant said to them, 'Never mind *her;* she doesn't know what she's talking about.'"

25. *"I found that old washerwoman-dress that he came home in yesterday, hanging on a towel-horse before the fire. So I put it on, and the bonnet as well, and the shawl, and off I went to Toad Hall."* Peter Hunt writes:

> Women are so potent a threat that they are excluded from the book as much as possible. Where they do intrude, they disturb its structure, language, and balance. Even their appearance is powerful: when Toad escapes from the gaol, "The washerwoman's squat figure . . . seemed a passport for every barred door and grim gateway." . . . And what puts the sentries at Toad Hall into disarray? Mole in the very same costume. (*The Wind in the Willows: A Fragmented Arcadia*, 88)

A towel-horse is a wooden frame or stand on which towels are hung.

"'O! don't I?'" said I. 'Well, let me tell you this. My daughter, she washes for Mr. Badger, and that'll show you whether I know what I'm talking about; and *you'll* know pretty soon, too! A hundred bloodthirsty badgers, armed with rifles, are going to attack Toad Hall this very night, by way of the paddock.[26] Six boatloads of Rats, with pistols and cutlasses,[27] will come up the river and effect a landing in the garden; while a picked body of Toads, known at the Die-hards, or the Death-or-Glory Toads, will storm the orchard and carry everything before them, yelling for vengeance. There won't be much left of you to wash, by the time they've done with you, unless you clear out while you have the chance!' Then I ran away, and when I was out of sight I hid; and presently I came creeping back along the ditch and took a peep at them through the hedge. They were all as nervous and flustered as could be, running all ways at once, and falling over each other, and every one giving orders to everybody else and not listening; and the Sergeant kept sending off parties of stoats to distant parts of the grounds, and then sending other fellows to fetch 'em back again; and I heard them saying to each other, 'That's just like the weasels; they're to stop comfortably in the banqueting-hall, and have feasting and toasts and songs and all sorts of fun, while we must stay on guard in the cold and the dark, and in the end be cut to pieces by bloodthirsty Badgers!' "

"Oh, you silly ass, Mole!" cried Toad, "You've been and spoilt everything!"

"Mole," said the Badger, in his dry, quiet way, "I perceive you have more sense in your little finger than some other animals have in the whole of their fat bodies. You have managed excellently, and I begin to have great hopes of you. Good Mole! Clever Mole!"

The Toad was simply wild with jealousy, more especially as he couldn't make out for the life of him what the Mole had done that was so particularly clever; but, fortunately for him, before he could show temper or expose himself to the Badger's sarcasm, the bell rang for luncheon.

26. *paddock.* A small field or enclosure, usually adjoining a house or farm building; a piece of pasture used for grazing animals. Mayfield, Grahame's house in Cookham Dean, was equipped with a paddock that was used every day. Naomi Stott refers to it numerous times in her correspondence with the Grahames in early 1908: "We have been having good times with the foot-ball. The paddock makes a fine play ground," she writes on March 9. "All afternoon we had a play in the paddock + garden" (March 13). "The paddock is very pretty now that the buttercups are out, + there is such a lovely Spring feel in the air. As the grass cutter goes up the lawn, there is Mouse kicking the ball at {King} ~~him~~, or running alongside. This natural sort of life is very good for him" (Harry Ransom Humanities Research Center, The University of Texas at Austin; see "The Letters").

27. " *'Six boatloads of Rats, with pistols and cutlasses.'* " The battle between the riverbankers and the Wild Wooders resembles the *Batrachomyomachia*, or the Battle of the Frogs and Mice, a comic epic or parody of the *Iliad* that was attributed to Homer by the Romans. *Batrachomyomachia* means "a silly altercation." Synopsis:

> A mouse drinking water from a lake meets the Frog King, who invites him to his house. As they swim across the lake, with the mouse seated on his back, the Frog King encounters a frightening watersnake. The Frog dives under the water, forgetting about the Mouse, who drowns while the Frog escapes. Another Mouse witnesses the scene from the shoreline, and runs to tell his friends. The Mice arm themselves for battle thinking that the Frog King intentionally drowned the mouse. The Mice declare war on the Frogs, and the Frogs in turn blame their King, who denies

It was a simple but sustaining meal[28]—bacon and broad beans, and a macaroni pudding; and when they had quite done, the Badger settled himself into an arm-chair, and said, "Well, we've got our work cut out for us to-night, and it will probably be pretty late before we're quite through with it; so I'm just going to take forty winks, while I can.' And he drew a handkerchief over his face and was soon snoring.[29]

The anxious and laborious Rat at once resumed his preparations, and started running between his four little heaps, muttering, "Here's-a-belt-for-the-Rat, here's-a-belt-for-the Mole, here's-a-belt-for-the-Toad, here's-a-belt-for-the-Badger!" and so on, with every fresh accoutrement he produced, to which there seemed really no end; so the Mole drew his arm through Toad's, led him out into the open air, shoved him into a wicker chair, and made him tell him all his adventures from beginning to end, which Toad was only too willing to do. The Mole was a good listener, and Toad, with no one to check his statements or to criticise in an unfriendly spirit, rather let himself go. Indeed, much that he related belonged more properly to the category of what-might-have-happened-had-I-only-thought-of-it-in-time-instead-of-ten-minutes-afterwards. Those are always the best and the raciest adventures; and why should they not be truly ours, as much as the somewhat inadequate things that really come off?[30]

Tailpiece by Nancy Barnhart.
Mole in silhouette, dressed as the washerwoman.

the incident. Meanwhile, Zeus, who sees both sides preparing for war proposes that the Gods take sides, ordering Athena to assist the Mice. Athena, who is squeamish around Mice, refuses. The Gods eventually decide to watch rather than get involved, and sit behind as the battle ensues. When the Mice win, Zeus decides to intervene, summoning an army of Crabs to prevent complete destruction of the Frogs. Powerless against the armored crabs, the Mice retreat, and the one-day war ends at sundown. (Green, *Kenneth Grahame: A Biography*, 261)

28. *It was a simple but sustaining meal.* This is the fourth major meal within this chapter.

29. *And he drew a handkerchief over his face and was soon snoring.* Badger naps after the midday meal in chapter IV. See Shepard's illustration of Badger sleeping with the handkerchief over his head.

30. *really come off?* Variant e. 247 continues with the following five lines. Grahame must have started another page and later discarded it; the paragraph ends mid-sentence, and the lines are hatched out:

> When it began to grow dark the Rat called them back into the parlour, stood each of them by his own little heap, + proceeded to dress them up for the expedition. He was very earnest about it, + the affair took quite a long time. First there was a belt to go round each animal, + then a sword to be stuck into

See "The Letters" for the complete text of Grahame's letters for chapter XI.

XII

The Return of Ulysses

Though many readers have suspected it all along, the title of chapter XII confirms the fact that Grahame intended *The Wind in the Willows* to mirror the plot of *The Odyssey*. Toad finally returns home to find weasels and stoats occupying Toad Hall.

The Wind in the Willows has half the number of chapters as *The Odyssey*, which takes its own number of chapters (24) from the number of letters in the Greek alphabet. In book 22, "Death in the Great Hall," Odysseus vanquishes the suitors much in the same manner Toad ousts the weasels and stoats.

When it began to grow dark, the Rat, with an air of excitement and mystery, summoned them back into the parlour, stood each of them up alongside of his little heap, and proceeded to dress them up for the coming expedition. He was very earnest and thorough-going about it, and the affair took quite a long time. First, there was a belt to go round each animal, and then a sword to be stuck into each belt, and then a cutlass on the other side to balance it. Then a pair of pistols, a policeman's truncheon, several sets of handcuffs, some ban-

Ernest H. Shepard's illustration of the book's climax captures the Homeric moment.

dages and sticking-plaster, and a flask and a sandwich-case.[1] The Badger laughed good-humouredly and said, "All right, Ratty! It amuses you and it doesn't hurt me. I'm going to do all I've got to do with this here stick."[2] But the Rat only said, "*Please*, Badger. You know I shouldn't like you to blame me afterwards and say I had forgotten *anything!*"

When all was quite ready, the Badger took a dark lantern in one paw, grasped his great stick with the other, and said, "Now

Bransom's last illustration of Badger leading the way in the tunnel, 1913.

1. ***and then a cutlass on the other side to balance it. Then a pair of pistols, a policeman's truncheon, several sets of handcuffs, some bandages and sticking-plaster, and a flask and a sandwich-case.*** Cutlass: a short sword with which sailors are armed. The cutlass has a flat, wide, curved blade, made for cutting rather than stabbing. Policeman's truncheon: slang: a "billy club." A short, thick staff with which a police constable is armed.

This scene is what Peter Green refers to as "an irreverent take-off of the stock Homeric arming ceremony" (*Kenneth Grahame: A Biography*, 260). Below is an example of an arming scene that occurs in book 22 of *The Odyssey*:

> "But come, let me bring you armour from the inner chamber, that ye may be clad in hauberks, for, methinks, within that room and not elsewhere did Odysseus and his renowned son lay by the arms." Therewith Melanthius, the goatherd, climbed up by the clerestory of the hall to the inner chambers of Odysseus, whence he took twelve shields and as many spears, and as many helmets of bronze with thick plumes of horse hair, and he came forth and brought them speedily, and gave them to the wooers. Then the knees of Odysseus were loosened and his heart melted within him, when he saw them girding on the armour and brandishing the long spears in their hands, and great, he saw, was the adventure. (Homer, *The Odyssey*, trans. by S. H. Butcher and A. Lang [New York: P. F. Collier & Son, 1909–1914], 311)

2. ***"All right, Ratty! It amuses you and it doesn't hurt me. I'm going to do all I've got to do with this here stick."*** Peter Hunt writes about the disparity between Badger's sticks and Ratty's weapons:

> Toad Hall is regained, most improbably, by basic, manly means: Just as in

then, follow me![3] Mole first, 'cos I'm very pleased with him; Rat next; Toad last. And look here, Toady! Don't you chatter so much as usual, or you'll be sent back, as sure as fate!"

The Toad was so anxious not to be left out that he took up the inferior position assigned to him without a murmur, and the animals set off. The Badger led them along by the river for a little way, and then suddenly swung himself over the edge into a hole in the river-bank, a little above the water. The Mole and the Rat followed silently, swinging themselves successfully into the hole as they had seen the Badger do; but when it came to Toad's turn, of course he managed to slip and fall into the water with a loud splash and a squeal of alarm. He was hauled out by his friends, rubbed down and wrung out hastily, comforted, and set on his legs; but the Badger was seriously angry, and told him that the very next time he made a fool of himself he would most certainly be left behind.

So at last they were in the secret passage, and the cutting-out expedition had really begun![4]

It was cold, and dark, and damp, and low, and narrow, and poor Toad began to shiver, partly from dread of what might be before him, partly because he was wet through. The lantern was far ahead, and he could not help lagging behind a little in the darkness. Then he heard the Rat call out warningly, "*Come* on, Toad!" and a terror seized him of being left behind, alone in the darkness, and he 'came on' with such a rush that he upset the Rat into the Mole and the Mole into the Badger, and for a moment all was confusion. The Badger thought they were being attacked from behind, and, as there was no room to use a stick or a cutlass, drew a pistol, and was on the point of putting a bullet into Toad. When he found out what had really happened he was very angry indeed, and said, "Now this time that tiresome Toad *shall* be left behind!"

But Toad whimpered, and the other two promised that they would be answerable for his good conduct, and at last the Badger was pacified, and the procession moved on; only this time

the popular literature of Grahame's childhood one Englishman was worth ten foreigners, so the Englishman would fight with his fists, not with weapons. (In *The Flying Inn* [1914] and in his "Father Brown" stories, G. K. Chesterton makes great play of the straightness of the play of the Englishman's sword against the scimitars of the heathen.) . . . Once they have cleared Toad Hall of the vulgar masses, they retire to bed, "safe in Toad's ancestral home, won back by matchless valour . . . and a proper handling of sticks." (*The Wind in the Willows: A Fragmented Arcadia*, 80)

3. *When all was quite ready, the Badger took a dark lantern in one paw, grasped his great stick with the other, and said, "Now then, follow me!"* It is possible that the inspiration for Badger's "great stick" came from Theodore Roosevelt, president of the United States from 1901 to 1909. On September 2, 1901, at the Minnesota State Fair, Roosevelt gave a speech on foreign affairs, saying his policy was to "speak softly and carry a big stick." The speech was widely quoted, even in England, and may have had an influence on Grahame. A big fan of Kenneth Grahame's books, including *The Wind in the Willows*, Roosevelt invited the Grahames to come stay in the White House, but they never did. Instead, Grahame and Roosevelt met at Oxford in 1910.

4. *So at last they were in the secret passage, and the cutting-out expedition had really begun!* A cutting-out expedition is a maritime expression for swift action in capturing one's enemies at sea.

the Rat brought up the rear, with a firm grip on the shoulder of Toad.

So they groped and shuffled along, with their ears pricked up and their paws on their pistols, till at last the Badger said, "We ought by now to be pretty nearly under the Hall."

Then suddenly they heard, far away as it might be, and yet apparently nearly over their heads, a confused murmur of sound, as if people were shouting and cheering and stamping on the floor and hammering on tables. The Toad's nervous terrors all returned, but the Badger only remarked placidly, "They *are* going it, the Weasels!"

The passage now began to slope upwards; they groped onward a little further, and then the noise broke out again, quite distinct this time, and very close above them. "Ooo-ray-oo-ray-oo-ray-ooray!" they heard, and the stamping of little feet on the floor, and the clinking of glasses as little fists pounded on the table. "*What* a time they're having!" said the Badger. "Come on!" They hurried along the passage till it came to a full stop, and they found themselves standing under the trap-door that led up into the butler's pantry.

Such a tremendous noise was going on in the banqueting-hall that there was little danger of their being overheard. The Badger said, "Now, boys, all together!" and the four of them put their shoulders to the trap-door and heaved it back. Hoisting each other up, they found themselves standing in the pantry, with only a door between them and the banqueting-hall, where their unconscious enemies were carousing.

The noise, as they emerged from the passage, was simply deafening. At last, as the cheering and hammering slowly subsided, a voice could be made out saying, "Well, I do not propose to detain you much longer"—(great applause)—"but before I resume my seat"—(renewed cheering)—"I should like to say one word about our kind host, Mr. Toad. We all know Toad!"—(great laughter)—"*Good* Toad, *modest* Toad, *honest* Toad!" (shrieks of merriment).

"Only just let me get at him!" muttered Toad, grinding his teeth.

"Hold hard a minute!" said the Badger, restraining him with difficulty. "Get ready, all of you!"

"—Let me sing you a little song," went on the voice, "which I have composed on the subject of Toad"—(prolonged applause).

Then the Chief Weasel—for it was he—began in a high, squeaky voice—

Toad he went a-pleasuring
Gaily down the street————

The Badger drew himself up, took a firm grip of his stick with both paws, glanced round at his comrades, and cried—

"The hour is come! Follow me!"

And flung the door open wide.

My!

What a squealing and a squeaking and a screeching filled the air!

Well might the terrified weasels dive under the tables and spring madly up at the windows! Well might the ferrets rush wildly for the fireplace and get hopelessly jammed in the chimney! Well might tables and chairs be upset, and glass and china be sent crashing on the floor, in the panic of that terrible moment when the four Heroes strode wrathfully into the room! The mighty Badger, his whiskers bristling, his great cudgel whistling through the air; Mole, black and grim, brandishing his stick and shouting his awful war-cry, "A Mole! A Mole!"[5] Rat, desperate and determined, his belt bulging with weapons of every age and every variety; Toad, frenzied with excitement and injured pride, swollen to twice his ordinary size, leaping into the air and emitting Toad-whoops that chilled them to the marrow! "Toad he went a-pleasuring!" he yelled. "*I'll* pleasure 'em!" and he went straight for the Chief

5. *Mole, black and grim, brandishing his stick and shouting his awful war-cry, "A Mole! A Mole!"* This odd war cry resembles one of the most famous lines in Shakespeare's *Richard III* (act 5, scene 4): "A horse! a horse! my kingdom for a horse!"

Weasel. They were but four in all, but to the panic-stricken weasels the hall seemed full of monstrous animals, grey, black, brown and yellow, whooping and flourishing enormous cudgels; and they broke and fled with squeals of terror and dismay, this way and that, through the windows, up the chimney, anywhere to get out of reach of those terrible sticks.

The affair was soon over. Up and down, the whole length of the hall, strode the four Friends, whacking with their sticks at every head that showed itself; and in five minutes the room was cleared. Through the broken windows the shrieks of terrified weasels escaping across the lawn were borne faintly to their ears; on the floor lay prostrate some dozen or so of the enemy, on whom the Mole was busily engaged in fitting handcuffs. The Badger, resting from his labours, leant on his stick and wiped his honest brow.

"Mole," he said, "you're the best of fellows! Just cut along outside and look after those stoat-sentries of yours, and see what they're doing. I've an idea that, thanks to you, we shan't have much trouble from *them* to-night!"

The Mole vanished promptly through a window; and the Badger bade the other two set a table on its legs again, pick up knives and forks and plates and glasses from the *débris* on the floor, and see if they could find materials for a supper. "I want some grub, I do," he said, in that rather common way he had of speaking. "Stir your stumps, Toad, and look lively! We've got your house back for you, and you don't offer us so much as a sandwich."

Toad felt rather hurt that the Badger didn't say pleasant things to him, as he had to the Mole, and tell him what a fine fellow he was, and how splendidly he had fought; for he was rather particularly pleased with himself and the way he had gone for the Chief Weasel and sent him flying across the table with one blow of his stick. But he bustled about, and so did the Rat, and soon they found some guava jelly[6] in a glass dish, and a cold chicken, a tongue that had hardly been touched,

6. *guava jelly.* Made from the tart yet sweet fruit of a guava. Guava trees are native to the tropical regions of the Americas, and guava jelly was a typical export of colonies in a warm climate.

some trifle,[7] and quite a lot of lobster salad;[8] and in the pantry they came upon a basketful of French rolls and any quantity of cheese, butter, and celery. They were just about to sit down when the Mole clambered in through the window, chuckling, with an armful of rifles.

"It's all over," he reported. "From what I can make out, as soon as the stoats, who were very nervous and jumpy already, heard the shrieks and the yells and the uproar inside the hall, some of them threw down their rifles and fled. The others stood fast for a bit, but when the weasels came rushing out upon them they thought they were betrayed; and the stoats grappled with the weasels, and the weasels fought to get away, and they wrestled and wriggled and punched each other, and rolled over and over, till most of 'em rolled into the river! They've all disappeared by now, one way or another; and I've got their rifles. So *that's* all right!"

"Excellent and deserving animal!" said the Badger, his mouth full of chicken and trifle. "Now, there's just one more thing I want you to do, Mole, before you sit down to your supper along of us; and I wouldn't trouble you only I know I can trust you to see a thing done, and I wish I could say the same of every one I know. I'd send Rat, if he wasn't a poet. I want you to take those fellows on the floor there upstairs with you, and have some bedrooms cleaned out and tidied up and made really comfortable. See that they sweep *under* the beds, and put clean sheets and pillow-cases on, and turn down one corner of the bed-clothes, just as you know it ought to be done; and have a can of hot water, and clean towels, and fresh cakes of soap, put in each room. And then you can give them a licking a-piece, if it's any satisfaction to you, and put them out by the back-door, and we shan't see any more of *them,* I fancy. And then come along and have some of this cold tongue. It's first rate. I'm very pleased with you, Mole!"

The goodnatured Mole picked up a stick, formed his prisoners up in a line on the floor, gave them the order "Quick

7. *trifle.* An English dessert served in a deep bowl or dish consisting of layers of cake, cream, sliced bananas, strawberries (or any berries in season), pudding, gelatin, sherry, jam, ice cream, and custard, and topped with whipped cream.

8. *lobster salad.* See previous notes on shellfish and Grahame's preference for seafood.

march!" and led his squad off to the upper floor. After a time, he appeared again, smiling, and said that every room was ready, and as clean as a new pin. "And I didn't have to lick them, either," he added. "I thought, on the whole, they had had licking enough for one night, and the weasels, when I put the point to them, quite agreed with me, and said they wouldn't think of troubling me. They were very penitent, and said they were extremely sorry for what they had done, but it was all the fault of the Chief Weasel and the stoats, and if ever they could do anything for us at any time to make up, we had only got to mention it. So I gave them a roll a-piece, and let them out at the back, and off they ran, as hard as they could!"

Then the Mole pulled his chair up to the table, and pitched into the cold tongue; and Toad, like the gentleman he was, put all his jealousy from him, and said heartily, "Thank you kindly, dear Mole, for all your pains and trouble tonight, and especially for your cleverness this morning!" The Badger was pleased at that, and said, "There spoke my brave Toad!" So they finished their supper in great joy and contentment, and presently retired to rest between clean sheets, safe in Toad's ancestral home, won back by matchless valour, consummate strategy, and a proper handling of sticks.

The following morning, Toad, who had overslept himself as usual, came down to breakfast disgracefully late, and found on the table a certain quantity of egg-shells, some fragments of cold and leathery toast, a coffee-pot three-fourths empty,[9] and really very little else; which did not tend to improve his temper, considering that, after all, it was his own house. Through the French windows of the breakfast-room he could see the Mole and the Water Rat sitting in wicker-chairs out on the lawn, evidently telling each other stories; roaring with laughter and kicking their short legs up in the air. The Badger, who was in an arm-chair and deep in the morning paper, merely looked up and nodded when Toad entered the room. But Toad knew his man, so he sat down and made the best breakfast he

9. *a coffee-pot three-fourths empty.* Variant e. 247: a coffee-pot ~~half~~ three-fourths empty.

Kenneth Grahame was fond of coffee, preferring to drink it when he was at home in Cookham Dean—an unusual preference in a nation full of tea drinkers. Grahame went back and corrected the *Wind in the Willows* manuscript, changing the more optimistic half-empty pot to the almost empty pot, which means the servants would need to be summoned to go through the elaborate process of making the coffee to his specifications.

This very tattered recipe was followed by the cook whenever Grahame was in residence.

Mr Grahame's Coffee

Put a freshly-ground full *desert* spoonful into a perfectly *dry*. clean *fire-proof china saucepan*—leave it to warm gently—while in the other china saucepan (these 2 are kept *only* for coffee) Bring a full pint of milk *nearly* to the boil, and when just on the point of boiling, pour into the saucepan containing the warmed dry coffee—do this very carefully—& gently as it bubbles & splashes up—Let it boil for 4 minutes, and then strain through *muslin* & pour into *warm dry* pot. (Harry Ransom Humanities Research Center, The University of Texas at Austin)

could, merely observing to himself that he would get square with the others sooner or later. When he had nearly finished, the Badger looked up and remarked rather shortly: "I'm sorry, Toad, but I'm afraid there's a heavy morning's work in front of you. You see, we really ought to have a Banquet at once, to celebrate this affair. It's expected of you—in fact, it's the rule."

"O, all right!" said the Toad, readily. "Anything to oblige. Though why on earth you should want to have a Banquet in

Nancy Barnhart's illustration (1922) used as the frontispiece to her edition. Caption abridged from text: OUT ON THE LAWN ROARING WITH LAUGHTER.

the morning I cannot understand. But you know I do not live to please myself, but merely to find out what my friends want, and then try and arrange it for 'em, you dear old Badger!"

"Don't pretend to be stupider than you really are," replied the Badger, crossly; "and don't chuckle and splutter in your coffee while you're talking; it's not manners. What I mean is, the Banquet will be at night, of course, but the invitations will have to be written and got off at once, and you've got to write 'em. Now, sit down at that table—there's stacks of letter-paper on it, with 'Toad Hall' at the top in blue and gold—and write invitations to all our friends, and if you stick to it we shall get them out before luncheon. And *I'll* bear a hand, too; and take my share of the burden. *I'll* order the Banquet."

"What!" cried Toad, dismayed. "Me stop indoors and write a lot of rotten letters on a jolly morning like this, when I want to go around my property, and set everything and everybody to rights, and swagger about and enjoy myself! Certainly not! I'll be—I'll see you———Stop a minute, though! Why, of course, dear Badger! What is my pleasure or convenience compared with that of others! You wish it done, and it shall be done. Go, Badger, order the Banquet, order what you like; then join our young friends outside in their innocent mirth, oblivious of me and my cares and toils. I sacrifice this fair morning on the altar of duty and friendship!"[10]

The Badger looked at him very suspiciously, but Toad's frank, open countenance made it difficult to suggest any unworthy motive in this change of attitude. He quitted the room, accordingly, in the direction of the kitchen, and as soon as the door had closed behind him, Toad hurried to the writing-table. A fine idea had occurred to him while he was talking. He *would* write the invitations; and he would take care to mention the leading part he had taken in the fight, and how he had laid the Chief Weasel flat; and he would hint at his adventures, and what a career of triumph he had to tell about; and on the fly-leaf he would set out a sort of a pro-

10. *"I sacrifice this fair morning on the altar of duty and friendship!"* Sacrificing on the altar of a particular idea or entity (or announcing a planned sacrifice) was a common way of indicating your adherence to that idea or entity. The Altar of Duty (Ara Pietatis) in Rome was begun under Emperor Tiberius (reigned AD 14–37) and finished under Emperor Claudius (reigned AD 41–51). During the reign of Tiberius, the Roman Senate also erected the Altar of Friendship (Ara Amicitiae) in response to the wars on the border with Germany.

—J. J.

gramme of entertainment for the evening—something like this, as he sketched it out in his head:—

SPEECH. . . . . BY TOAD

(There will be other speeches by TOAD during the evening.)

ADDRESS. . . . . BY TOAD

SYNOPSIS—Our Prison System—the Waterways of Old England—Horse-dealing, and how to deal—Property, its rights and its duties—Back to the Land[11]—A Typical Englilsh Squire.[12]

SONG . . . . BY TOAD

(Composed by Himself.)

OTHER COMPOSITIONS. . . . . BY TOAD

will be sung in the course of the evening by the . . . COMPOSER.

The idea pleased him mightly, and he worked very hard and got all the letters finished by noon, at which hour it was reported to him that there was a small and rather bedraggled weasel at the door, inquiring timidly whether he could be of any service to the gentlemen. Toad swaggered out and found it was one of the prisoners of the previous evening, very respectful and anxious to please. He patted him on the head, shoved the bundle of invitations into his paw, and told him to cut along quick and deliver them as fast as he could, and if he liked to come back again in the evening, perhaps there might be a shilling for him, or, again, perhaps there mightn't; and the poor weasel seemed really quite grateful, and hurried off eagerly to do his mission.

When the other animals came back to luncheon, very boisterous and breezy after a morning on the river, the Mole, whose conscience had been pricking him, looked doubtfully at Toad, expecting to find him sulky or depressed. Instead, he was so

11. ***Property, its rights and its duties—Back to the Land.*** See chapter XI, note 6.

According to the *OED*, "back to the land" is a catchphrase for converting the unemployed and underutilized citizens of urban areas into rural settlers. In particular, David Lloyd George thought unemployed miners, millers, and laborers should be resettled on the land. He wrote: "It is a crime, which after-generations will find almost incredible, that we should have millions of able-bodied men pinned in unwilling idleness while our land cries out to be tilled." George is also famous for saying: "Who ordained that the few should have the land (of Britain) as a prerequisite; who made 10,000 people owners of the soil and the rest of us trespassers in the land of our birth?"

12. ***A Typical English Squire.*** The title of a country gentleman or landed proprietor. In this case, Toad is the squire because he is the principal landowner in the village and district called Riverbank.

uppish and inflated that the Mole began to suspect something; while the Rat and the Badger exchanged significant glances.

As soon as the meal was over, Toad thrust his paws deep into his trouser-pockets, remarked casually, "Well, look after yourselves, you fellows! Ask for anything you want!" and was swaggering off in the direction of the garden, where he wanted to think out an idea or two for his coming speeches, when the Rat caught him by the arm.

Toad rather suspected what he was after, and did his best to get away; but when the Badger took him firmly by the other arm he began to see that the game was up. The two animals conducted him between them into the small smoking-room that opened out of the entrance-hall, shut the door, and put him into a chair. Then they both stood in front of him, while Toad sat silent and regarded them with much suspicion and ill-humour.

"Now, look here, Toad," said the Rat. "It's about this Banquet, and very sorry I am to have to speak to you like this. But we want you to understand clearly, once and for all, that there are going to be no speeches and no songs. Try and grasp the fact that on this occasion we're not arguing with you; we're just telling you."

Toad saw that he was trapped. They understood him, they saw through him, they had got ahead of him. His pleasant dream was shattered.

"Mayn't I sing them just one *little* song?" he pleaded piteously.

"No, not *one* little song," replied the Rat firmly, though his heart bled as he noticed the trembling lip of the poor disappointed Toad. "It's no good, Toady; you know well that your songs are all conceit and boasting and vanity; and your speeches are all self-praise and—and—well, and gross exaggeration and—and———"

"And gas," put in the Badger, in his common way.

"It's for your own good, Toady," went on the Rat. "You

13. *blue* boudoir. A small, elegantly furnished room where a woman may retire to be alone or to receive her intimate friends; formerly sometimes applied to a man's private apartment (*OED*).

know you *must* turn over a new leaf sooner or later, and now seems a splendid time to begin; a sort of turning-point in your career. Please don't think that saying all this doesn't hurt me more than it hurts you."

Toad remained a long while plunged in thought. At last he raised his head, and the traces of strong emotion were visible on his features. "You have conquered, my friends," he said in broken accents. "It was, to be sure, but a small thing that I asked—merely leave to blossom and expand for yet one more evening, to let myself go and hear the tumultuous applause that always seems to me—somehow—to bring out my best qualities. However, you are right, I know, and I am wrong. Henceforth I will be a very different Toad. My friends, you shall never have occasion to blush for me again. But, O dear, O dear, this is a hard world!"

And, pressing his handkerchief to his face, he left the room, with faltering footsteps.

"Badger," said the Rat, "*I* feel like a brute; I wonder what *you* feel like?"

"O, I know, I know," said the Badger gloomily. "But the thing had to be done. This good fellow has got to live here, and hold his own, and be respected. Would you have him a common laughing-stock, mocked and jeered at by stoats and weasels?"

"Of course not," said the Rat. "And, talking of weasels, it's lucky we came upon that little weasel, just as he was setting out with Toad's invitations. I suspected something from what you told me, and had a look at one or two; they were simply disgraceful. I confiscated the lot, and the good Mole is now sitting in the blue *boudoir*,[13] filling up plain, simple invitation cards."

At last the hour for the banquet began to draw near, and Toad, who on leaving the others had retired to his bedroom, was still sitting there, melancholy and thoughtful. His brow resting on his paw, he pondered long and deeply. Gradually his countenance cleared, and he began to smile long, slow smiles. Then he took to giggling in a shy, self-conscious manner. At last he got up, locked the door, drew the curtains across the windows, collected all the chairs in the room and arranged them in a semicircle, and took up his position in front of them, swelling visibly.[14] Then he bowed, coughed twice, and, letting himself go, with uplifted voice he sang, to the enraptured audience that his imagination so clearly saw,

TOAD'S LAST LITTLE SONG![15]

The Toad———came———home!
There was panic in the parlours and howling in the halls,
There was crying in the cow-sheds and shrieking in the stalls,
When the Toad———came———home!
When the Toad———came———home!
There was smashing in of window and crashing in of door,
There was chivvying of weasels that fainted on the floor,
When the Toad———came———home!
Bang! go the drums!
The trumpeters are tooting and the soldiers are saluting,
And the cannon they are shooting and the motor-cars are hooting,
As the———Hero———comes!
Shout———Hoo-ray!
And let each one of the crowd try and shout it very loud,
In honour of an animal of whom you're justly proud,
For it's Toad's———great———day!

He sang this very loud, with great unction and expression; and when he had done, he sang it all over again.

Then he heaved a deep sigh; a long, long, long sigh.

Then he dipped his hairbrush in the water-jug, parted his hair in the middle, and plastered it down very straight and sleek on each side of his face;[16] and, unlocking the door, went quietly down the stairs to greet his guests, who he knew must be assembling in the drawing-room.

14. *collected all the chairs in the room and arranged them in a semicircle, and took up his position in front of them, swelling visibly.* This arrangement of chairs resembles the earlier scene in chapter VI when Toad makes a motorcar out of his bedroom chairs.

15. *TOAD'S LAST LITTLE SONG!* Humphrey Carpenter points out, in *Secret Gardens*:

> Toad is a poet too, but his odes are hymns of self-love; not without merit, perhaps, and a little resembling the boasts of great heroes in ancient literature, but ultimately the poetry of excess and self indulgence. . . . Yet Toad, too, grows in wisdom, and by the end of the book has learnt to keep his boastful poems to himself. He recites "TOAD'S LAST LITTLE SONG!" in the privacy of his bedroom, and then, descending to the banquet celebrating his return to Toad Hall, maintains a discreet silence. (159–60)

Shepard made this small drawing of Toad in formal wear singing at the top of his lungs like the braggart he truly is. Unlike Wyndham Payne, Shepard left out any contextual details of Toad Hall. Consequently, this drawing was occasionally misplaced in later editions.

16. *Then he dipped his hairbrush in the water-jug, parted his hair in the middle, and plastered it down very straight and sleek on each side of his face.* Toads do not have hair. See letter by Beatrix Potter quoted in chapter X, note 5.

Shepard. Medallion of fat, swaggering Toad, 1931.

All the animals cheered when he entered, and crowded round to congratulate him and say nice things about his courage, and his cleverness, and his fighting qualities; but Toad only smiled faintly, and murmured, "Not at all!" Or, sometimes, for a change, "On the contrary!" Otter, who was standing on the hearthrug, describing to an admiring circle of friends exactly how he would have managed things had he been there, came forward with a shout,[17] threw his arm round Toad's neck, and tried to take him round the room in triumphal progress; but Toad, in a mild way, was rather snubby to him, remarking gently, as he disengaged himself, "Badger's was the mastermind; the Mole and the Water Rat bore the brunt of the fighting; I merely served in the ranks and did little or nothing.' The animals were evidently puzzled and taken aback by this unexpected attitude of his; and Toad felt, as he moved from one guest to the other, making his modest responses, that he was an object of absorbing interest to every one.

The Badger had ordered everything of the best, and the banquet was a great success. There was much talking and

17. *Otter, who was standing on the hearthrug, describing to an admiring circle of friends exactly how he would have managed things had he been there, came forward with a shout.* This is the first time we have seen Otter since he was reunited with Portly in chapter VII.

Wyndham Payne did not illustrate the preparation for battle and the ousting of weasels and stoats, instead cutting to the celebration when the riverbankers regain Toad Hall. The riverbankers—in their white ties and sipping champagne—look more like dapper and athletic young men at a formal dinner rather than woodland animals. Grahame never mentions that there is a fireplace in the scene—only that Otter stands on the hearthrug.

Payne's riverbankers congregate in front of a lit fireplace—the second fireplace in his edition. The first appears on the frontispiece and comes from a scene when Mole and Rat arrive at Toad Hall. The mantles on both fireplaces vary, which means the latter is in a different part of Toad Hall. Grahame makes no textual references to either location—the fact that they are illustrated at all is an embellishment on the part of the artist.

laughter and chaff among the animals, but through it all Toad, who of course was in the chair, looked down his nose and murmured pleasant nothings to the animals on either side of him. At intervals he stole a glance at the Badger and the Rat, and always when he looked they were staring at each other with their mouths open; and this gave him the greatest satisfaction. Some of the younger and livelier animals, as the evening wore on, got whispering to each other that things were not so amusing as they used to be in the good old days; and there were some knockings on the table and cries of

Payne's dapper riverbankers in formal dress, 1927.

"Toad! Speech! Speech from Toad! Song! Mr. Toad's song!" But Toad only shook his head gently, raised one paw in mild protest, and, by pressing delicacies on his guests, by topical small-talk, and by earnest inquiries after members of their families not yet old enough to appear at social functions, managed to convey to them that this dinner was being run on strictly conventional lines.

He was indeed an altered Toad!

After this climax, the four animals continued to lead their lives, so rudely broken in upon by civil war, in great joy and contentment, undisturbed by further risings or invasions. Toad, after due consultation with his friends, selected a handsome gold chain and locket set with pearls, which he dispatched to the gaoler's daughter with a letter that even the Badger admitted to be modest, grateful, and appreciative; and the engine-driver, in his turn, was properly thanked and compensated for all his pains and trouble. Under severe compulsion from the Badger, even the barge-woman was, with some trouble, sought out and the value of her horse discreetly made good to her;[18] though Toad kicked terribly at this, holding himself to be an instrument of Fate, sent to punish fat women with mottled arms who couldn't tell a real gentleman when they saw one. The amount involved, it was true, was not very burdensome, the gipsy's valuation being admitted by local assessors to be approximately correct.

Sometimes, in the course of long summer evenings, the friends would take a stroll together in the Wild Wood,[19] now successfully tamed so far as they were concerned; and it was pleasing to see how respectfully they were greeted by the inhabitants, and how the mother-weasels would bring their young ones to the mouths of their holes, and say, pointing, "Look, baby! There goes the great Mr. Toad![20] And that's the gallant Water Rat, a terrible fighter, walking along o' him!

18. *even the barge-woman was, with some trouble, sought out and the value of her horse discreetly made good to her.* The bargewoman would be difficult to locate because she herself is a Gypsy of sorts, wandering through the English canal system.

19. *Sometimes, in the course of long summer evenings, the friends would take a stroll together in the Wild Wood.* Tailpiece illustration by Wyndham Payne of the five riverbankers, each uniquely dressed, walking arm in arm and tipping their hats to the reader. One of the earliest reviews of *The Wind in the Willows* appeared in *The Saturday Review of Literature*: "[Payne's] rat, toad, and mole are very human in their behavior and remind us of undergraduates of sporting proclivities." This is the drawing that best evokes that sentiment.

20. *how the mother-weasels would bring their young ones to the mouths of their holes, and say, pointing, "Look, baby! There goes the great Mr. Toad!"* The riverbankers always live out of the way of the commoners. Each of their houses requires a significant walk to approach, whereas the weasels, along with most inhabitants of the Wild Wood, live right on the main roads. The weasels' homes are holes, not "bijoux riverside residence[s]," or passages that lead to garden-seated forecourts, with a front door. Nevertheless, though the weasels are economically unequal to the riverbankers, they respect them for having ousted the more dangerous faction of weasels and stoats who had inhabited Toad Hall. By ousting the Wild Wooders, the riverbankers broke up the gangs, restored peace to the Wild Wood, and made it a safe place to live again.

Tailpiece by Wyndham Payne.

And yonder comes the famous Mr. Mole, of whom you so often have heard your father tell!" But when their infants were fractious and quite beyond control, they would quiet them by telling how, if they didn't hush them and not fret them, the terrible grey Badger would up and get them. This was a base libel on Badger, who, though he cared little about Society, was rather fond of children; but it never failed to have its full effect.

Tailpiece by Nancy Barnhart. Toad making his toast.

The Letters

MY DEAREST MOUSE: LETTERS FROM KENNETH GRAHAME TO ALASTAIR GRAHAME, MAY 1907–SEPTEMBER 1907

From May through September of 1907, Kenneth Grahame composed a series of letters to his son, Alastair, that he would later expand and develop into *The Wind in the Willows*. What follows is the complete text of those letters, presented by chapter in the order that they eventually appeared in the story.

Chapter VI

The complete text to the letter that inspired chapter VI is included in the annotations on page 153.

Chapter VIII

The Fowey Hotel
Fowey, Cornwall, 31st May 1907.

My dearest Mouse

I hope you are quite well. I am very glad to hear that you have been having some boating, and sea-trips to America + other distant lands.

Now you may like to hear something further about poor toad. When Toad heard that they were being pursued by an engine full of policemen with revolvers, he fell on his knees among the coals + cried out "O kind Mr. Engine-driver, save me, save me, + I will confess everything! I am not the washerwoman I seem to be! I am a toad—the well-known Mr. Toad, of Toad Hall—+ I have escaped from prison, + those policemen are coming to recapture me!" Then the engine driver looked very grave, + said "What were you in prison for, Toad?" And the toad blushed deeply + said "I only borrowed a motor-car while the people were having lunch. I didn't mean to steal it really."

"Well", said the engine-driver, "you have evidently been a bad toad. But I will save you if I can." So he piled more coals on the fire, + the engine flew over the rails; but the engine behind kept gaining + gaining, + presently the engine-driver said with a sigh "I'm afraid it's no use. They must catch us up soon, + then they will climb along our train till they get to our engine, + if we attempt to resist they will shoot us dead with their revolvers." Then the toad said "O dear kind Mr. Engine-driver, do think of something to save me!". And the engine-driver thought a bit + then he said "There's just one thing I can do, + it's your only chance. We are coming to a long tunnel, + on the other side of the tunnel is a thick wood. I will put on all speed while we are running through the tunnel, + as soon as we are through I will 'slow up' for a few seconds, + you must jump off + run into the wood + hide yourself before the other engine gets through the tunnel, + then I will go on at full speed + they will continue to chase me, thinking you are still on the train."

Next moment they shot into the tunnel, + the engine-driver piled on more coals, + the sparks flew, + the train rushed + roared + rattled through the tunnel, + at last they shot out into the moonlight on the other side, + then the engine-driver put on his brakes hard + the train slowed down to almost a walking pace + the toad got down on the step + the engine driver said "Now jump!" And the toad jumped + rolled down the embankment + scrambled into the wood + hid himself. Then he peeped out + saw the train get up speed again + go off very fast. And presently the other engine came roaring + whistling out of the tunnel, in hot pursuit, with the policeman waving their revolvers + shouting

"Stop, Stop Stop!!! Then the toad had a good laugh—for the first time since he was put into prison.

But it was now very late, + dark, + cold + here he was in a wild wood, with no money + no friends. And little animals peeped out of their holes + pointed at him + made fun of him; + a fox came slinking by, + said "Hullo washerwoman! how's the washing business doing?" and sniggered. And the Toad looked for a stone to throw at him, + couldn't find one, which made him sad. Presently he came to a hollow tree, full of dry leaves; + there he curled himself up as comfortably as he could, + slept till the morning.

In my next letter I will try to tell you the Adventures of the Toad + the Bargee; + about the Gipsy, + how the Toad went into Horse-dealing.

Ever your affectionate
Daddy

Chapter X

The Fowey Hotel
Fowey, Cornwall, 7th June 1907.

My Dearest Mouse

I hope you are having better weather than we are getting here. It is so wet + windy here that we cannot go out rowing in boats, or fly kites, or sail, or anything.

You may be wishing to hear what further things happened to the Toad on his way home, after his escape from the policemen who were pursuing him to take him back to prison. Well, next morning the sun shone brightly into the hollow tree, + woke up Mr. Toad, who was sleeping soundly after his fatiguing exertions of the previous day. He got up, shook himself, combed the dead leaves out of his hair with his fingers; + set off walking briskly, for he was very cold + rather hungry. Well, he walked + he walked, till he came to a canal, + he thought that must lead to a town, so he walked along the tow-path, + presently he met a horse, with a long rope attached to it, towing a barge; + he waited for the barge to come up, + there was a man steering it, + he nodded, + said "Good morning, washerwoman! What are you doing here?" Then the toad made a pitifull face, + said "Please, kind sir, I am going to pay a visit to my married daughter, who lives near a fine house called "Toad Hall"; but I've lost my way, + spent all my money, + I'm very tired." Then the man said "Toad Hall? Why, I'm going that way myself. Jump in, + I'll give you a lift." So he steered the barge close to the bank, + the toad stepped on board + sat down, very pleased with himself. Presently the man said "I don't see why I should give you a lift for nothing, so you take that tub of water standing over there, + that bit of yellow soap, + here are some shirts , + you can be washing them as we go along". Then the toad was rather frightened, for he had never washed a shirt in his life; but he dabbed the shirt into the water, + he dabbed some soap on it, but it never seemed to get any cleaner, + his fingers got very cold + he began to get very ~~eee~~ cross. Presently the man came to see how he was getting on, + burst out laughing at him, + said "Call yourself a washer-woman? That's not the way to wash a shirt, you very silly old woman!" Then the Toad lost his temper, + quite forgot himself, + said "Don't you dare to speak to your betters like that! And don't call me a silly old woman! I'm no more an old woman than you are yourself, you common, Low, vulgar bargee!" Then the bargee looked closely at him, + cried out "Why no, I can see you're not really a washerwoman at all! You're nothing but an old toad!" Then he grabbed the toad by one hind-leg + one fore-leg, + swung him round + sent him flying through the air

Like that—Splosh!! [illustration]

He found himself head-over-ears in the water!

When the toad came to the surface he wiped the water out of his eyes + struck out for the shore; but the woman's dress he was wearing got round his legs, + made it very hard work. When at last he was safely on the tow-path again, he saw the barge disappearing in the distance, + the man looking back + laughing at him. This made Mr. Toad mad with rage. He tucked the wet skirt up well under his arms. + ran as hard as he could along the path, + passed the barge, + ran on till he overtook the horse that was towing it, and unfastened the tow-rope, + jumped on the horse's back, + dug his heels into its sides, + off they went at a gallop! He took one look back as they went, + he saw that the barge had run ~~a~~ into the opposite bank of the canal, + stuck, + the bargee was shaking his fist at him + calling out "Stop, stop, stop!! ["] But the toad never stopped, but only laughed + galloped on + on + on, across country, over fields + hedges, until he had left the canal, + the barge, + the bargee, miles + miles behind him.

I am afraid the Gipsy will have to wait till the next letter.

Your affectionate
Daddy

I am so glad to hear you have been out in a motor boat.

16, Durham Villas, Campden Hill. W.
21 June 1907

My Dearest Mouse

No doubt you will be interested to hear the further adventures of Mr. Toad, after he galloped away across counrty on the bargee's horse, with the bargee shouting after him in vain. Well presently the horse got tired of galloping so fast, and broke from a gallop into a trot, and then from a trot into a walk, + then he stopped altogether + began to nibble grass. And the Toad looked round about him + found he was on a large common. On the common stood a gipsy tent, and a gipsy man was sitting beside it, on a bucket turned upside down, smoking. In front of the tent a fire of sticks was burning, + over the fire hung an iron pot, and out of the pot came steam, + bubblings, and the most beautiful good smell that ever you smelt.

Then the Toad felt very hungry indeed, for he had had no breakfast that morning, + no supper the night before; so he sniffed + sniffed, + looked at the pot, + the gipsy; + the gipsy sat + smoked, + looked back at him.

Presently the gipsy took his pipe out of his mouth + said "Like to sell that there horse of yours? (Now you must understand that gipsies are very fond of buying + selling horses, + never miss an opportunity.)

This was an entirely new idea to Toad. He had never thought of trying to sell the horse; but now he saw a way of getting a little money, which he wanted so badly. So he said, "What, sell this beautiful young animal o'mine? No, I can't say I had thought of selling this beautiful young animal o'mine. You see its such a beautiful young animal—half an Arab + half a Race Horse + half a Prize Hackney[.] However, how much might you feel disposed to give me for this very beautiful young animal o'mine?"

The gipsy looked at the horse, + he looked at the Toad, + he looked at the horse again, + then he said "Shillin' a leg", + turned away + went on smoking.

"A shilling a leg"? said Mr. Toad—"please I shall want a little time to work that out, + add it up, see what it comes to." So he climbed down off the horse + left it to graze, + sat down by the gipsy, + counted on his fingers, + did sums in his head, + presently he said "A shilling a leg? Why that comes to exactly four shillings. O no. I could not think of selling this beautiful young animal for four shillings."

"Well," said the giypsy, "I'll tell you what I'll do. I'll make it five shillings, + that's a shilling more than he's worth; + that's my last word."

Then the Toad pondered deeply. For he was penniless, + five shillings seemed a very large sum of money. On the other hand, it did not seem very much to get for a horse. But then the horse hadn't cost him anything, so it was all clear profit. At last he said, "Look here, gipsy. You shall give me six shillings + sixpence, cash + as much breakfast as I can eat, out of that iron pot of yours that keeps sending forth such delicious smells. And I will give you my fine young horse + all the beautiful harness that is on him." Well the gipsy grumbled a bit, but at last he agreed. And he counted out six shillings + sixpence into Toad's paw; + then he fetched plates out of the tent: + poured hot stew into them out of the pot; + it was the most beautiful stew, made of partridges + pheasants + chickens + hares + rabbits + pea-hens + guinea fowls And the Toad stuffed + stuffed, + kept asking for more, + thought that he had never eaten so good a breakfast in all his life.

Your affectionate
Daddy

16, Durham Villas, Campden Hill.W.
17 July, 1907

My dear Robinson,

WELL!

So when the Toad had stuffed as much breakfast inside of him as he could possibly hold, he stood up, and shook hands with the Gipsy and said goodbye to him, + said goodbye to the horse, + set off in the direction of Toad Hall. And by this time he was feeling very happy, for the sun was shining brightly, + his wet clothes were quite dry again, + he had had a first-rate breakfast, + he had got money in his pocket, + he was getting near his home. And he thought of his adventures, + all the dangers he had escaped, + he began to be very proud + stuck-up, and "Ho ho," he said to himself as he tramped along, "What a clever animal I am! There is no one like me in the whole world! My enemies shut me up in prison; I escape with the greatest ease. They pursue me with engines + policemen + revolvers; I simply laugh at them + disappear. I am thrown into canals; I swim to land, seize a horse, sell it for a pocketful of money, get breakfasts given me + am made welcome wherever I go! Ho ho! I am The Toad, the handsome, the popular, the glorious Toad! Then he got so puffed up with pride + conceit that he made up a song in praise of himself, + it was a conceited song! Here are some of the verses:—

The world has held great Heroes,
As history-books have showed,
never a name, to go down to fame
But ~~none so divine, or half so fine~~
compared with that of
~~As the famous Mr.~~ Toad!

The clever men at Oxford
Know all that there is to be knowed:
But they none of them know half as much
As intelligent Mr. Toad!

The animals sat in the ark + cried,
Their tears in torrents flowed:
Who was it said "There's Land ahead"?
Encouraging Mr. Toad!

The Army all saluted
As they marched along the road.
—Was it the King?—or Kitchener?
No: it was Mr. Toad.

The Queen and her ladies-in-waiting
Sat at the window and sewed.

She cried "Look! who's that handsome man?"
They answered: "Mr. Toad!"

This was the sort of stuff that he sang, the conceited animal. But his pride was soon to have a fall. Let it be a lesson to us, not to be so ~~far~~ puffed up + conceited as the proud Toad.

Presently he came to the high-road which ran past the common: and as he glanced up it, he saw, very far away, a dark speck, which gradually grew larger + larger + larger: + then he heard a faint humming noise, which gradually grew louder + louder + louder: + then he heard a very well known sound, + that was

Poop! poop!

" 'Ho ho!' said the Toad, "this is life, this is what I like! I will stop them + ask them to give me a lift, + so I will drive up to Toad Hall in triumph on a motor-car! And perhaps I shall be able to—borrow that motor-car." He did not say "steal", but I fear the wicked animal thought it. He stepped out into the road to hail the car, when suddenly his face turned very pale, his knees trembled + shook, + he had a bad pain in his tummy. Why was this? Because he had suddenly recognized the car as the very one he had stolen out of the yard of the Red Lion Hotel! And the people sitting inside were the very people who had gone into the Hotel for refreshments on that fatal day!

(To be continued) Dy

16, Durham Villas, Campden Hill. W.
7th August, 1907.

My Dear Michael Robinson

When Toad saw that his enemies were close upon him, his heart turned to water, his muscles failed, + he sank down in a shabby miserable heap in the road, murmuring to himself "It's all up! It's all over now! Prison again! Dry bread + water again! Chains + policemen again! O what a fool I have been! What did I want to go strutting about the country for, singing conceited songs, instead of going quietly home by back ways + hiding, until it all blew over! O unhappy Toad! O miserable animal!" And his head sank down in the dust.

The terrible motor car drew nearer + nearer + nearer. Then it stopped. Some gentlemen got out. They walked round the trembling heap of misery lying in the road, + one of them said—"O dear! Here is a poor old washer woman who has fainted in the road! Perhaps she is overcome by the heat, poor thing, or perhaps she has not had enough food! Anyhow, let us lift her into the motor-car + take her to the nearest villiage."

So they tenderly lifted the toad into the motor-car + propped him up on the cushions, + started off. When the toad heard them talk in that kind way; + knew that he was not recognized, his courage began to revive, + he opened one of his eyes. Then one of the gentlemen said: "See, she is better already! The fresh air is doing her good! How do you feel now, washer woman?"

The toad answered in a feeble voice "Thank you kindly, Sir, I'm feeling rather better. I think if I might sit on the front seat, beside the chauffeur, where I could get more air, I should soon be quite right again."

"That's a very sensible woman" said the gentleman. So they helped ~~her~~ him into the front seat, beside the chauffeur, + on went the car. The toad began to sit up, + look about him, + presently he said to the chauffeur "Please Mr. chauffeur, I wish you would let me try to drive the car for a little; it looks so easy; I'm sure I could ~~s~~ do it quite well!"

The chauffeur laughed, heartily. But one of the gentlemen said "Bravo, washerwoman, I like your spirit! Let her try. She won't do any harm."

So the chauffeur gave up his seat to the toad, + he took the steering wheel in his hands, + set the car going, + off they went, very slowly + carefully at first, for the toad was prudent. The gentlemen clapped their hands, + cried "Bravo, washerwoman! How well she does it! Fancy a washerwoman driving a motor car! Bravo!

Then the toad went a little faster.

The gentlemen applauded. The toad went faster still.

Then, ~~when the~~ when he felt the air singing past his ears, + the car throbbing under him, the toad began to lose his head. He went faster + faster still. The gentlemen called out warningly "Be careful, washerwoman! Then the toad lost his head entirely. He stood up in his seat + shouted "Ho ho! Who are you calling washerwoman! I am the Toad!

The famous Mr. Toad! The motor-car-driver, the toad who always escapes, who baffles his enemies, who dodges policemen, who breaks out of prison, the always-victorious, the triumphant Toad!"

Thus the gentlemen + the chauffeur arose + flung themselves upon him. "Seize him! they cried, "seize the toad, the wicked animal who stole our motor-car! Bind him, chain him, drag him to the police-station! Down with the Toad!

Alas! They ought to have remembered to stop the motor-car before playing any pranks of that sort. With a half-turn of the wheel the Toad sent the car crashing through the hedge. Then it gave an enormous bound, and splooosh! It landed in a horse pond!

2.

The Toad found himself flying through the air like a swallow. He was just beginning to wonder whether he would ever come down again or whether he had somehow got a pair of wings + turned into a toad-bird, when bump! He landed on his back. He jumped up at once, + found himself in a meadow. Looking back, he saw the car, almost entirely covered by the water, while the gentlemen + the chauffeur were floundering about in their long thick motor coats in the pond. He did not stay to help them. No! He set off running at once, + ran + ran + ran, across country, till he was quite pumped out. Then he settled down into a walk, + as he walked along presently he began to giggle, + from giggling he took to laughing, + he laughed + laughed until he had to sit down under a hedge. "Ho ho!" he roared "The Toad again! Always Mr. Toad! Who got them to give him a lift? Who wanted to sit on the front seat to get fresh air? Who got the chauffeur to let him drive? Who upset them all into the horse pond? who escaped, free + unhurt, while they were floundering about in the water? Toad, clever Toad, <u>great</u> Toad, <u>good</u> Toad! Then he burst into song again, + sang

"The motor-car went poop-poop-poop
As it whizzed along the road;
Who was it steered it into the pond?
Ingenious Mr. Toad!

O how clever I am! How clever, how clever, how clev———"

He heard a slight noise behind him. He looked back. O horror! O misery! O despair! O my!

About two fields behind him, a chauffeur and two large policemen were running towards him as hard as they could!

The toad sprang to his feet + set off running again, his heart in his mouth. "O my!" he gasped as he panted along, "What an ass I am! What a conceited ass! O my! O my! O my!" He looked back and saw they were gaining on him. He kept looking back as he ran, + saw that they still gained. He struggled on, but he was a fat animal, + his legs were short, + as he looked back he saw that they still gained. They were near him now! He never looked where he was going, but ran on wildly, looking over his shoulder at the approaching enemy, when suddenly

[illustration]

Splosh!

The toad found himself head over ears in deep water, in a rapid stream. He had run straight into the river! He rose to the surface, + tried to grasp the reeds + the rushes that grew along the bank, but the stream was so fast that it tore them out of his hands. "O my!" said the poor toad. "If ever I steal a motor-car again——" Then down he went, + came up spluttering. Presently he saw a big dark hole in the bank, above his head, + as the stream bore him fast he reached out a paw + caught hold of the edge. Then he slowly drew himself up out of the water, till he was able to rest his elbows on the edge of the hole. There he remained for some minutes, puffing + panting, for he was quite exhausted.

Presently, as he gazed into the big dark hole, he saw a tiny speck of light, that looked like a glow worm, or a distant star. As he looked, it winked + glittered, + got more + more like a tiny eye! He looked + looked, + saw the outline of a tiny face round it!

A dark little face———

and whiskers!———

It

was

the Water-rat!

(To be continued)

Chapter XI

16, Durham Villas, Campden Hill. W.
12th August, 1907

Dear Robinson

The Water-Rat put out a neat little brown paw, + gave Toady a big hoist + a pull, over the edge of the hole, + there was Mr. Toad at last, standing safe + sound in the hall, covered with mud, + with the water streaming off him, but pleased + happy at being in a friend's house at last after so many perilous adventures. "O Ratty!" he cried, "I've been having such times, you can't think! Such dangers, such escapes, and all through my own cleverness! Been in prison—got out of it! Been thrown into a canal—swam ashore! Stole a horse—sold him for a pocketful of money! O I am a smart Toad + no mistake! Tell you what I did, only just now———"

"Toad":—said the Water-Rat firmly: "You go off up-stairs at once, + take off that old cotton rag that looks as if it had once belonged to a washerwoman, + clean yourself, + put on some of my clothes + try + look like a gentleman if you can; for a more shabby be-draggled disreputable-looking object than you are I never saw in my life! Now stop swaggering + be off!" ~~I'll talk to you later~~

So the Toad went very humbly upstairs to the rat's dressing-room, + changed his clothes, + brushed his hair, + by the time he came down again dinner was ready, + very glad the Toad was to see it, for he was very ~~quite~~ hungry again by this time, in spite of his good breakfast. There was roast veal, stuffed, + vegetable marrow; + a cherry tart.

While they {ate} ~~sat~~ their Dinner the Toad told the Rat all his adventures, not forgetting all his own cleverness, + presence of mind, + cunning; but the Rat looked very grave. When the Toad had done, the Rat said "Now Toady, seriously, don't you see what an old ass you are? You've been beaten, kicked, imprisoned, ~~starved~~ chased, ~~beaten~~ thrown into water; ~~insulted~~ there's no fun in that. And all because you tried to steal a motor-car. There's no need for you to steal motor-cars; you've got lots of money; you can buy a beauty if you like. When are you going to be sensible, + a credit to your friends?"

Now the Toad was really a very good-hearted animal, + never minded being jawed: so although, while the rat was talking, he kept saying to himself "But it was fun, though!" + making strange suppressed noises inside him, k.i.i.c.k, + poop.p.p + other sounds like snorts, or the opening of soda-water-bottles, yet when the rat had done he said very nicely + humbly "Quite right, Ratty! I have been a conceited old ass, I can see; but I'm going to be a good Toad, + not do it any more. As soon as we've had our coffee, and a smoke, I'm going to stroll down to Toad Hall, + I'm going to lead a respectable life there, + have a bit of dinner for my friends when they come to see me, + have a pony-chaise to jog about the country in, just as I used to in the old days."

"Stroll down to Toad Hall?" cried the Rat. "What are you talking about? Haven't you heard?"

"Heard what?" said the Toad, turning rather pale. "Go on Ratty! What haven't I heard?"

"Do you mean to tell me" said the Rat, thumping with his little fist upon the table, "that you haven't heard———"

(To be cont!)

16, Durham Villas, Campden Hill. W.
16th August, 1907

Dear Robinson,

"Do you mean to tell me" shouted the Water-Rat, thumping with his little fist upon the table, "that you've never heard about the animals?" ~~Stoats + weasels?~~

"N—n—no" murmured the Toad. trembling in every limb

"—and how they've been + taken Toad Hall?" went on the Rat.

Toad leaned his elbows on the table, + his chin on his hands; + a large tear welled up in each of his eyes, overflowed, + splashed on the table, plop! plop!

"Go on,~~"~~ Ratty" he murmured: "tell me all; I can bear it."

"When you—got into that trouble of yours" said the Rat, slowly and impressively: I mean when you—disappeared, you know, over that you-know-what———"

The Toad nodded.

"Well, it was a good deal talked about here, naturally," said the Rat. "Not only ~~along the riverside even~~ in the village, but in the wild-wood. And the animals went about saying that this time you would never come back, never, never!" ~~You were done for this time."~~

The Toad nodded.

~~That's the sort of little beasts they are~~

"—But the Mole + the Badger" continued the Water Rat, "They held out that you would come back somehow; they didn't know how, but somehow."

The Toad sat up in his chair, + began to smirk a little.

"So the Mole + the Badger" went on the Rat [. . .] "determined they would move their things in to Toad Hall, + sleep there, to look after it for you. The fact is, they didn't trust the animals!"

"I should think not indeed!" said Toad.

"One dark night" said the Rat, lowering his voice, "One <u>very</u> dark night,—and it was blowing hard too, + raining cats-+-dogs—a band of weasels, armed to the teeth, crept silently up the carriage-drive. At the same time a band of desperate ferrets advanced through the kitchen-garden; + a number of stoats who stuck at nothing surrounded the back-door.

The mole + the badger were sitting by the fire, smoking + telling each other stories, when these bloodthirsty villains broke down the doors + rushed in upon them. They made the best fight they could, but what are two people against hundreds? They took + beat them severely with sticks, the two poor faithful creatures, + turned them out into the cold + the wet".

Here the Toad sniggered a little, + then pulled himself up + tried to look very solemn.

"—And they've been living ~~there~~ {in Toad Hall} ever since" continued the Rat, "and going on anyhow! Lying in bed half the day, + breakfast at all hours, + the place in such a mess its not fit to be seen! Eating your grub, + drinking your drink, + making jokes about you, + singing vulgar songs about you + about—prisons + magistrates + all that; + they tell every body they've come to stay for good!

"O have they?" said Toad, getting up + seizing his stick.—I'll jolly soon see about that!"

"It's no good, Toad!" called the Rat after him. "You'd better come back! You'll only get into trouble!"

But the Toad was off, + there was no holding him. He marched valiantly down the road, his stick over his shoulder, till he got near the front gate, when suddenly behind the palings there popped up a long yellow ferret with a gun.

"Who comes there?" cried the ferret.

"Stuff + nonsense" said the Toad angrily. "What do you mean by talking like that to me? What do you———"

The ferret said never a word, but he brought his gun up to his shoulder. The Toad dropped flat in the road. Bang! a bullet whistled over his head. The Toad scrambled to his feet, + scampered off down the road; + as he ran he heard the ferret laughing.

He went back + told the Water-rat. "What did I tell you?" said Rat.

Still, the Toad would not give in at once. He got a boat, + set off rowing up the river to the back of Toad Hall, to where the garden came down to the river side. All seemed very peaceful and deserted. As he ~~ca~~ rested on his oars he could see Toad Hall quiet in the sunshine, with the pigeons cooing on the roof, + the garden, + the creek that led to the boat-house, + the little wooden bridge that crossed it. He paddled up very cautiously + turned to go under the bridge, + was just passing it when

Crash!

A great stone, flung from the bridge, smashed through the bottom of the boat, + Toad found himself struggling in deep water. He looked up, + saw the stoats leaning over the bridge watching him. "It'll be your head next time, Toady!" said they. And as Toad swam to shore, the stoats laughed + laughed + laughed, till they nearly had two fits—that is, one fit each, of course.

The Toad went back and told the Water-Rat. "What did I tell you?" said Ratty crossly: "+ look here! Now you've been + ruined my {nice} clothes that I lent you!"

Then the Toad was very humble, + apologized to the Rat for getting his clothes wet, + said "Ratty, I have been a headstrong + a wilful Toad. Henceforward I will be humble + submissive, + will do nothing without your kind advice + approval."

"If that is really so," said the Rat, "then my advice is, to sit down + have your supper + be patient. For I am sure that we can do nothing until we have seen the Mole + the Badger, + heard their news, + taken their advice in the matter."

"Oho, the Mole + the Badger!" said the Toad lightly: "Why, what's become of them? I had forgotten all about them."

"Well may you ask" replied the Rat reproachfully. "while you were riding about in motor-cars, those two faithful animals have been hiding in the wild-wood, ~~living~~ living very rough and sleeping very hard, spying + planning + contriving, how to get back Toad Hall again for you. See what it is to have true friends! Some day you'll be sorry you didn't value them more while you had got them."

So the Toad was humble + contrite again, of course, + they sat down to supper.

When they were about half-way through, there came a knock at the door. The Rat nodded mysteriously to the Toad, + went to the door + opened it: + in walked the badger. His shoes were covered with mud, + he looked very rough + touzled; but then he was never a very smart man, the Badger, at the best of times. He shook Toad by the hand + said "Welcome home Toad! Ah, what am I saying? Home indeed! This is a sad meeting. Alas, Poor, poor Toad!" Then he sat down at the table + helped himself to a large slice of cold pie.

The Toad was rather alarmed at this sort of greeting; but the Rat nudged him + whispered "Don't say anything. He takes it very much to heart. And he's always rather low when he's wanting his victuals.

Presently there was another knock. ~~at~~ The Rat nodded to the Toad, + went to the door + ushered in the Mole, very shabby + unwashed, with bits of hay + straw sticking in his fur.

(To be continued).

16, Durham Villas, Campden Hill. W.
21st Aug: 1907

Dear Robinson,

"Why, it's Toad!" cried the Mole, his face brightening up. "Fancy seeing you here!" And he began to dance round him. "Thought you were locked up in prison for the rest of your days! Why, you must have managed to escape, you clever Toad!"

The Rat pulled him by the arm, but it was too late. The Toad was puffing + swelling already.

"Clever? Well, I'm cleverer than you fellows seem to think me" said he. "Of course I escaped. What's a prison to me? But that's nothing to what I've done since. Just let me tell you!"

"Well, well, said the Mole, moving towards the table, "you can talk while I eat. Not a bite since breakfast! O my, O my!" And he sat down + helped himself liberally to cold beef + pickles.

The Toad ~~straggled~~ straddled on the hearth-rug, ~~th~~ thrust his hands into his pockets, + pulled out a handful of silver. "Look at that!" he said. "That's not bad, for a few minutes' work. And how do you think I done it? Horse-dealing! That's how I done it!"

"<u>Go</u> on, Toad!" said the Mole, immensely interested.

"Toad, do be quiet, please," said ~~that~~ {the} Rat: "and don't you egg him on, Mole, but please tell us what the position is, + what's best to be done."

"There isn't anything to be done, that I can see" replied the Mole, grumpily. "It's like the old riddle "Who goes round + round the house + never inside the house?" The Badger + I have been round + round the house, night + day; always the same thing. Sentries everywhere, guns poked out at us, stones thrown at us; always an animal on the look-out, and my! how they do laugh! That's what annoys me most."

"It's very difficult" said the Rat, reflecting deeply: "But I think I see ~~in the depths of my mind~~ what ~~the~~ Toad ought to do. He thought to———"

"No, he oughtn't!" shouted the Mole, with his mouth full. "Nothing of the sort. He ought to———"

"Well, I shan't do it, any way" cried the Toad, getting excited. I'm not going to be ordered about by you fellows. I'm going to———"

By this time they were all three talking at once, at the top of their voices, + the noise was simply deafening, when a small dry voice said "Be quiet, all of you!" and instantly everyone was silent.

It was the Badger, who had finished his pie + turned round in his chair. When he saw that they were all evidently waiting for him to address them, he turned to the table again + reached out for the cheese. And so great was the respect commanded by the solid qualities of that admirable animal, that not another word was uttered till he had quite finished his supper + brushed the crumbs from his legs. The Toad fidgetted a bit, but the Rat held him firmly down.

When the Badger had quite done, he got up + stood before the fire, reflecting. "Toad!" he said severely, "You're a bad little animal! What would your father have said, if he had been here tonight?"

The Toad began to shed tears, at once

"There, there!" said the Badger, more kindly, "never mind. We're going to let by-gones be by-gones. ~~and turn over a new leaf~~ But what the Mole says is quite true. The Stoats are on guard, + they're the best sentinels in the world. ~~No~~. It's no good our attacking the place. They're too strong for us."

"Then it's all over" sobbed the Toad, crying into the sofa-cushions. "I shall go + enlist for a soldier, + never see my dear Toad-Hall any more!"

"Cheer up, Toady", said the Badger; "Now I'm going to tell you a secret."

The Toad sat up at once + dried his eyes. He liked to be told secrets, + then to go + tell them to some other animal, after he had promised not to.

"There-is-a-secret-passage" said the Badger impressively, "leading right into the middle of Toad Hall!"

"O nonsense, Badger" said the Toad rather airily; "I know every inch of Toad Hall, inside + out. Nothing of the sort, I do assure you!"

"My young friend" said the Badger severely, "Your father, who was a very worthy animal—much worthier than some others I know—was a great friend of mine ~~+ told me a deal he wouldn't have thought of telling you~~. He made that passage, in case of danger, + when he had made it he showed it to me. "Don't tell my son" said he. "He's a good fellow, but he has a light character + can't hold his tongue. If he is ever in a real fix you may tell him, but not before!"

The other animals looked hard at Toad, to see how he would take it. Toad was inclined to be sulky at first. Then he brightened up, being a good fellow.

"Well, well" said he, perhaps I am rather a talker. A popular fellow like ~~such as I am~~ me—my friends get round me—& then I talk. Go on, Badger! How's this going to help us?"

"Tomorrow night," continued the Badger, as I have found out by calling at the back-door in ~~the~~ disguise {of a sweep}, there is going to be a great banquet. It's somebody's birthday—the Head Weasel's, I believe. And the animals ~~weasels~~ will be gathered in the dining-hall, feasting + laughing + carrying on, + suspecting nothing. No guns, no swords, no sticks, no arms of any sort."

"But the sentries will be posted, as usual" remarked the Rat.

"Exactly" said the Badger. "~~That is my point. The weasels~~ They will trust entirely to ~~their excellent~~ the sentries. And that's where our passage comes in. This blessed old passage ~~tunnel~~ leads right up under the butler's pantry, next to the dining hall!"

"Aha, that squeaky board in the butler's pantry!" cried the Toad. "Now I understand it".

"—We shall creep out quietly into the butler's pantry—" cried the Mole—

"—with our swords + our sticks + ~~our~~ things!" shouted the Rat—

"—And rush in upon 'em!—" said the Badger—

"And whack 'em, + whack 'em, and whack 'em!—" cried the Toad in extasy, running round + round the room + jumping over the chairs.

"Very well then" said the Badger, becoming suddenly grave + severe once more. Now that's settled, all of you go off to bed, at once, + we'll make our arrangements ~~in the course of~~ tomorrow ~~morning.~~

The Toad felt a great deal too excited to sleep. But he had had a long + tiring day, + his head had not been long on the pillow before he was snoring. Of course he dreamt a great deal—such a jumble of gipsies, motor-cars + policemen, fallings into water + fishings out again, as never was; + the secret passage twisted + turned, + shook itself, + sat up on its end; but somehow he as in Toad Hall at the last, + his friends sat round him, saying what a clever Toad he was.

He slept till a very late hour next morning, + when he got down the other animals had finished their breakfast a long time. The Mole had gone out by himself, without saying where he was going to. The Badger sat in the arm-chair, reading the paper, + not troubling himself in the slightest about what was going to happen that evening. The Rat ~~on the other hand~~ was running round excitedly with his arms full of weapons, distributing them in four little heaps, + saying rapidly under his breath, as he ran, "Here's-a-sword-for-the-Rat, here's-a-sword for-the-Mole, here's-a-sword for-the-Toad, here's-a-sword for-the-Badger! Here's-a-pistol for the-Rat, here's-a-pistol for the-Mole" + so on.

(To be continued)

16, Durham Villas, Campden Hill. W.
26th August, 1907

Dear Robinson,

"That's all very well, Rat", said the Badger, looking at him over the edge of his newspaper. "I'm not blaming you. But {first} let us ~~just~~ once get past those stoats, with their horrid guns, + I assure you we shan't want any swords or pistols. We four, with our sticks, once we're inside the dining-hall—why, we shall clear the floor of 'em, in five minutes. I'd have done the thing by myself, but I didn't want to deprive you fellows of the fun!"

"It's as well to be on the safe side" said the Rat, polishing a pistol-barrel on his sleeve + looking along it.

The Toad picked up a stout stick + swung it vigorously, thrashing imaginary animals with it. "I'll learn 'em to steal my house"! he cried. "I'll learn 'em, I'll learn 'em!"

"Don't say 'learn 'em' Toad", said the Rat, greatly shocked: "its not good English!"

"What are you always nagging at Toad for?" enquired the Badger. "What's the matter with his English? It's the same what I use myself, + what's good enough for me ought to be good enough for you!"

"I'm sorry", said the Rat humbly: "Only I think it ought to be 'teach 'em', not 'learn 'em".

"But we don't want to teach 'em" said the Badger. "We want to learn 'em,—learn 'em, learn 'em! + what's more, we're going to!"

"O all right, have it your own way" said the Rat. He was getting rather muddled about it himself, + presently retired into a corner, where he was heard muttering "learn 'em, teach 'em, teach 'em, learn 'em"—till the Badger told him rather sharply to leave off.

Presently the Mole tumbled into the room, evidently very pleased with himself. "I've been humbugging the Stoats", he began. "It was great fun. I put on that old washerwoman-dress that Toad came home in—found it hanging before the kitchen fire—and the bonnet, + went off to Toad Hall, + found the Stoat-sentries with their guns at the gate. "Good morning, gentlemen"! I says. "Want any washing done today"? They looked at me ~~very~~ proud + ~~still~~ haughty, + said "Go away" washer-woman! We don't do any washing on duty!" "Or any other time?" says I! "Haw, haw, haw! Wasn't I funny Toad!"

"Poor, frivolous animal!" said the Toad very loftily. The fact is, he was jealous of Mole, for what he had done. It was just what he would have liked to do himself, if he had only thought of it.

"Some of the Stoats turned quite pink" continued the Mole: "and the Sergeant said to me, very stiffly, "Now run away, my good woman, run away!" "Run away?" I said, "It won't be me that'll be running away, in a very short time from now!"

"O Moly!" said the Rat, dismayed.

The Badger laid down his paper.

"I could see them pricking up their ears" went on Mole. "My daughter" I said "washes for Mr. Badger, so I know what I'm talking about. A hundred bloodthirsty badgers, armed with rifles, are going to attack tonight by way of the paddock. Six boat-loads of rats, with pistols + cutlasses, will come up the river + effect a landing in the kitchen-garden; + a picked body of Toads, known as the Die-hards, or the Death—or-Glory Toads, will storm the orchard ~~yelling for vengeance. They seemed stuck all of a heap~~." Then I ran away. + hid; + presently I came creeping back through the bushes. They were all as nervous + excited as could be; running ~~xxxx~~ all ways at once, + everyone giving different orders, + the Sergeant sending off bodies of stoats to distant parts of the grounds in different directions; and I heard one stoat say "That's just like the weasels; they're to stop comfortably at home, + have feasting + all sorts of fun, + we're to stay out in the cold + the dark + be cut to pieces by bloodthirsty badgers!"

"You silly ass, Mole," cried the Toad, "You've been + spoilt everything!"

"Mole", said the Badger, in his dry quiet way, "You have more sense in your little finger than some other animals have in the whole of their fat bodies. I begin to have great hopes of you. Good Mole! Clever Mole!"

The Toad was simply wild with jealousy, especially as he couldn't see what the Mole had done that was particularly clever; but before he could say more the dinner-bell rang. It was bacon + broad beans, + a macaroni pudding; + when they had quite done, the badger settled himself into an arm-chair + said "Well, we've got our work cut out for us tonight, + we shall be up rather late, so I'm going to have forty winks". And he drew a handkerchief over his face + was soon snoring.

The Rat was still taken up with his arrangements, + ~~began~~ continued running between his four little heaps, muttering "Here's-a-belt-for-the-Rat, here's-a-belt for-the-Mole, here's-a-belt-for-the-Toad, here's-a-belt-for-the-Badger", + so on, so the Mole put his arm through the Toad's + drew him into the garden, where he put him into a wicker-chair + made him tell him all his adventures from beginning to end, which the Toad was very willing to do. Indeed, he not only told him everything, but I'm afraid he also told him several things that had not actually occurred; but they were all things that the Toad had intended to do, if he had had time; so perhaps he had almost persuaded himself that he had really done them.

When it grew dark, the Rat called them into the parlour, + stood each of them by his little heap, + proceeded to draw them up. He was very earnest about it + it took quite a long time. First there was a belt to go on each animal, + then a sword to be stuck into each belt, + then a cutlass on the other side to balance it, + then a pair of pistols, + a policeman's truncheon, + a pair of handcuffs, + some bandages + sticking-plaster, + a sandwich-case. The Badger laughed good-humouredly, + said "All right, Rat; it amuses you + it doesn't hurt me. But I'm going to do all I've got to do with this here stick!" But the Rat said "Please, Badger! You know I shouldn't like you to blame me afterward + say I had forgotten anything!" When all was ready, the Badger ~~said~~ took a dark lantern in his hand + said "Now then, follow me! Mole first, 'cos I'm very pleased with him: Rat next; Toad last. And look here, Toady! don't you chatter quite so much.

The Toad was so anxious to begin the attack that he took up the inferior position assigned to him without a murmur, + the animals set off. The Badger led them along by the river for some way, + then suddenly swung himself over the edge into a hole in the river-bank. The others followed silently one by one; of course when it came to the Toad's turn he managed to slip + fall into the water with a loud splash. He was hauled out by the others, + rubbed down, + comforted; but the Badger was seriously angry + told him that the next time he made a fool of himself he would be left be hind.

(To be cont!)

Chapter XII

16, Durham Villas, Campden Hill. W.
7 Sept ~~July~~ 1907

Dear Robinson

So at last they were in the secret passage!

It was cold, + dark, + damp, + muddy, + low; + the Toad began to shiver with dread, + partly also because he was wet through; + he lagged behind, + the others called out impatiently "*come* on, Toad!" Then he 'came on' with such a rush that he upset the Rat into the Mole + the Mole into the Badger. And the Badger thought they were attacked from behind, + drew a pistol, as there wasn't room to use a stick; + he nearly put a bullet through Mr. Toad. When he found out what had really happened he was *very* angry, + said "Now Toad *shall* be left behind this time!" But Toad whimpered, + the other two promised they would be answerable for him, + at last the Badger was pacified + the Toad was allowed to proceed, only this time the Rat brought up the rear, with a firm grip on the shoulder of Toad.

So they groped along + shuffled along, with their paws on their pistols, + presently the Badger said "We must be getting very near the Hall now!" Then they heard; far away + over their heads, a confused murmur of sound, as if people were shouting + cheering + stamping + hammering on tables; + ~~tho~~ Toad got nervous, but the Badger only said "Well, they *are* going it, those weasels!"

They groped along a bit further, + presently the noise broke out again, quite distinct this time, + close above them, "OOray-oo-ray-oo-ray-oo-ray!" they heard, + the stamping of little feet on the floor, + the clinking of glasses as little paws hammered on the table. "They are going it!" said the Badger: "Come on!" And they hurried along the passage till they found themselves standing under the trap-door that led into the butler's pantry!

There was such a noise going on in the Hall that there was little danger of their being overheard. The Badger said "Now, all together!" And the four of them put their shoulders to the trap-door + heaved it back. In another second they all stood in the pantry, with only a door between them + the dining-hall!

For a moment the noise was simply deafening, as the cheering + hammering slowly subsided, a voice was heard, saying "Well, I will not detain you longer (much applause) But before I sit down" (great cheering). "I should like to say one word about our host Mr. Toad! We all know Toad! (laughter) Good Toad, honest Toad, modest Toad!" (Shrieks of merriment).

"Only let me get at him!" muttered Toad, grinding his teeth.

"Hold hard a minute" said the Badger, restraining him with difficulty.

"—Let me sing you a little song" went on the voice: "which I have composed on the subject of Toad!" (much applause).

Then the head-weasel—for it was he—began in a high squeaky voice

"Toad he went a pleasuring
Gaily down the street—"

~~The~~ Badger drew himself up, took a firm grip of his stick in both hands, + cried

"The hour is come! Follow me!" and flung the door open wide.

My!

What a squealing + a squeaking + a screeching filled the air!

Well might the terrified weasels dive under the tables + spring at the windows! Well might the ferrets rush for the fire-place + get jammed in the chimney! Well might tables + chairs be upset + glass + china sent smashing on the floor, in the panic of that terrible moment when the Four Heroes Strode wrathfully into the room! The mighty Badger, his whiskers bristling, his great cudgel whistling through the air! Mole, black + grim + terrible, brandishing his stick + shouting his awful war-cry "A Mole, A Mole!" Rat, desperate + determined, his belt bulging with weapons of every age + every variety; Toad, frenzied with excitement + injured pride, swollen to twice his ordinary size, leaping into the air + emiting Toad-whoops that chilled ~~through~~ the marrow! "Toad he went a-pleasuring!" he yelled. "I'll pleasure ~~+ he went straight for the chief weasel~~ 'em!" They were but four, yet to the panic-stricken weasels the hall seemed full of monstrous animals, grey, black, brown, + yellow, whooping + flourishing enormous sticks; + they broke + fled with squeals of terror, this way + that, through the windows, up the chimney, any where to get out of reach of those terrible cudgels

The affair was soon over. Up + down, the length of the Hall, strode the four animals, whacking with their sticks at every head that showed itself. In five minutes the room was cleared. Through the broken windows ~~by which they had escaped~~ the shrieks of Terrified weasels ~~tearing~~ {escaping} across the lawn were borne faintly to their ears; on the floor lay some dozen or so of the enemy, on whom the Mole was busily engaged in fitting hand cuffs. The Badger, resting from his labours, leaned on his stick + wiped his honest brow. "Mole!" he said, "You're the best of fellows! Cut along outside + look after those stoats of yours! I've an idea we shan't have much trouble from them tonight!"

The Mole vanished through a window; + then the Badger bade the other two set a table on its legs, + pick up some plates + glasses, + see if they could find materials for a supper. "I want some grub, I do," he said, in the rather common way he had of speaking: "Stir your stumps, Toad, + look lively. We're doing all this for you, + you don't trouble to produce so much as a sandwich!"

The Toad felt rather hurt that the Badger didn't say pleasant things to him, as he had to the Mole, + tell him what a fine fellow he was, + how splendidly he had fought; for he was rather particularly pleased with himself, + the way he had gone for the head weasel + sent him flying across the table with one blow of his stick; but he bustled about, + so did the others ~~Rat~~, + presently they found some guava jelly in a glass dish, a cold chicken, a tongue that had hardly been touched, some trifle, + quite a lot of lobster salad; + in the pantry was a basket-full of French rolls, + a quantity of celery + cheese. They were just sitting down when the Mole clambered in through the window chuckling, his arms full of rifles.

"It's all over" he said, "When the stoats heard the shrieks + the yells + the uproar inside the hall, most of them threw down their rifles + fled. The rest stood fast, but when the weasels rushed out upon them they thought they were betrayed, + the stoats grappled with the weasels, + the weasels fought to get away, + they wrestled + wiggled + rolled till they fell into the river! And I've got all their rifles, so that's all right."

"Excellent animal" said the Badger, his mouth full of chicken + trifle: "Now there's just one more thing I want you to do for us, Mole, before you sit down to your supper along of us: because I can trust you {to see a thing done,} + I wish I could say the same of everybody I know".

(To be contd.)

16. Durham Villas
Kensington
Sept 1907

Dear Robinson

"What I want you to do, Mole", said the Badger, "is to take those fellows on the floor there, upstairs with you, + have some bedrooms cleaned out, + tidied, + made really comfortable. Make them put clean linen on all the beds, + turn down one corner of the bed clothes, just as you know it ought to be done; + have a can of hot water + clean towels put in each room; + then you can give them a licking apiece, if you've a mind to, + put them outside the door—they won't trouble us any further, I'll lay. And then come in and have some of this cold tongue. It's real good. I'm very pleased with you, Mole!"

So the goodnatured Mole formed his prisoners up in a line on the floor, + said "Quick, March!" + marched them off to the bedrooms: + presently he came down smiling, + said every room was ready, + as clean as a new pin. "And I didn't have to lick them, either," he added. "I thought they had had licking enough for one night, + the weasels, when I put it to them, quite agreed with me. And they were very sorry + very penitent, + said it was all the fault of the head-weasel + the stoats, + if ever they could do anything for us at any time—+ so on. So I gave them a roll apiece + let them out at the back door, + off they ran!"

Then the Mole pulled his chair to the table + pitched into the cold tongue: + the Toad with an effort put aside all his jealousy, + said heartily "Mole, you're a brick, + a clever brick! ~~done for me today~~ I wish I had your headpiece!" The Badger was pleased at that, + said "Good old Toad!" So they finished their supper in great joy + contentment, + presently retired to rest, between clean sheets, in the ancestral home of Toad, which they had won back for him by their valour {their strategy} + their sticks.

Next morning the Toad, who had overslept himself, came down to breakfast disgracefully late, + found a certain quantity of eggshells on the tables, some fragments of cold toast, a coffee pot two-thirds empty, + really very little else: which did not tend to improve his temper, considering that after all it was his own house. The Mole + the Water-Rat were sitting in wicker-chairs out on the lawn, telling each other stories; roaring with laughter + kicking their short legs up in the air. The Badger, who was deep in the morning paper, merely looked up + nodded when the Toad came in. But the Toad knew his man, so he sat down + made the best breakfast he could, observing to himself that he would get square with the others, sooner or later.

When he had {nearly} finished the Badger remarked rather shortly: "I'm afraid there's a heavy morning's work in front of you, Toad; you see we ought to have a Banquet, to celebrate this affair!"

"O, all right," said the Toad readily. "Anything to oblige, ~~friends~~ ! {Though} Why on earth you should want to have a Banquet in the morning I cannot understand. Did you know I do not live to please myself, but only to give ~~pleasure~~ {satisfaction} to my friends, + do everything they want, you dear Badger!"

"Don't pretend to be stupider than you are" said the Badger crossly; + don't chuckle + splutter in your coffee when you are talking. It's rude. What I mean is, the Banquet will be at night, of course, but the invitations have got to go out at once, and you've got to write 'em! Now sit down at that table—there's stacks of paper on it, with "Toad Hall" at the top in blue + gold—+ write to all your friends, + perhaps if you stick to it you'll have done by lunch time. And I'll help you, too. I'll order the Banquet!"

"What!" cried the Toad, dismayed: "Me write a lot of rotten letters on a jolly morning like this, when I want to go round my property, + set everything + everybody to rights, + enjoy myself!

I'll be—I'll see you—stop a minute though! Why, certainly, Dear Badger! What is my pleasure or convenience to that of others? You wish it done + it shall be done. Go my dear Badger, join our young friends outside in their innocent amusements. I sacrifice this fair morning on the alter of duty + friendship!"

The Badger looked at him very suspiciously, but Toad's frank open countenance made it difficult to suggest any unworthy motive in this change of attitude. As soon as the door had closed behind the Badger, the Toad hurried to the writing-table. He had had a fine idea while he was talking. He would write the invitations, to the otter, + all the hedgehogs, + the squirrels, + all the rest of them; + he would work in, somehow, what he had done during the fight, + how he had laid the head weasel flat; + the invitation-cards should have a note at the foot, something like this:

SPEECH. . . . . BY TOAD

(There will be other speeches by TOAD
during the evening.)

SONG . . . . BY TOAD

(composed by himself.)

Other Compositions. . . . . by Toad

will be sung at intervals . . . by the Composer.

The idea pleased him mightily, + he worked hard + got the letters finished by lunch-time, when it was reported ~~at~~ that there was a small + rather bedraggled weasel at the door, enquiring timidly whether he could be of any service to the gentlemen. The Toad went out, + found it was one of the hand cuffed ones of the previous evening, very timid + very respectful. Toad patted him on the head, shoved the invitations into his paw, + told him to deliver them all at once + if he would come back the next day perhaps there might be a shilling for him + perhaps there mightn't; + the poor weasel seemed really quite grateful, + hurried off eagerly to do his mission.

The other animals came in to lunch very boisterous + happy, after a mornings boating on the river, + expecting to find Toad somewhat sulky + depressed. Instead, he was so uppish + inflated that of course they began to suspect something; + the Rat + the Badger exchanged significant glances. After the meal was over the Toad thrust his hands deep into his trouser pockets, + was swaggering off into the garden, where he wanted to think out a few ideas for his speeches, when the Rat caught him by the arm

(to be continued)

16 Durham Villas, Kensington
Sept 1907

Dear Robinson

The Toad rather suspected what he was after, + did his best to get away; but the Badger taking him firmly by the other arm, he saw that the game was up. The animals conducted him between them into the small smoking-room that opened out of the entrance-hall, shut the door + put him down into a chair, Then they stood in ~~to~~ front of him, while the Toad sat silent and looked at them with much suspicion + ill-humour. "Now look here, Toad," said the Rat: "about this Banquet. We want you to understand, once + for all: there must be no speeches, and no songs. We're not arguing with you; we're just telling you." The Toad saw he was trapped. They understood him, they saw through him, they got ahead of him. His pleasant dream was shattered.

"Mayn't I sing them just one little song?" he said piteously.

"No, not one little song," said the Rat firmly, though his heart bled as he noticed the trembling lip of the poor disappointed Toad. "It's no good, Toady; you know your songs are all conceit + boasting, + vanity; + your speeches are all self-praise and—and—gross exaggeration and—and—"

"And gas," put in the Badger, in his common way. "It's for your own good, Toady", went on the Rat. "You must turn over a new leaf, + now seems a splendid time to begin. don't think that saying this doesn't hurt me more than it hurts you!"

The Toad remained a long while plunged in thought; At last he raised his head, + the traces of strong emotion were visible on his features. "You have conquered, my friends," he said. "It was but a small thing that I asked—merely leave to "blow" for yet one more evening, to let myself go + hear the tumultuous applause which always seems to me-somehow—to bring out my best qualities! But you are right, I know, + I am wrong. Hence forth I will be an altered toad. My friends, you shall never have occasion to blush for me again. But, O dear O dear, this is a hard world!"

And, pressing his handkerchief to his face, he left the room with faltering footsteps.

"Badger", said the Rat, "*I* feel like a brute; what do you feel like?"

"O I know, I know," said Badger: but the thing's got to be done. This dear good fellow has got to live here. Do you want him to be mocked, + ~~jeered~~ scorned, + laughed at, by stoats + weasels?"

[3 lines obscured]

"Talking of weasels" said the Rat, "It's lucky we came upon that little weasel just as he was setting out with ~~hi~~ Toad's invitations. I confiscated the lot, and the good Mole is now sitting in the blue boudoir, filling up plain, simple invitation-cards." . . . When at last the hour for the banquet began to draw near, Toad, slipped away from the others + went upstairs to his own bedroom very melancholy + thoughtful. Sitting down in an armchair he rested his brow upon his hand, + pondered long. Gradually his countenance cleared, + he began to smile long, slow smiles.; then he took to giggling in a shy, self-conscious manner. Then he got up, locked the door, drew the curtains across the windows, took all the chairs in the room + arranged them in a semi-circle, and took up his position in front of them, swelling visibly. Then he lifted his voice + letting himself go, sang loudly:

Toad's Last Little Song!

"The Toad—came—home!
"There was panic in the parlours and
howling in the halls,
"There was crying in the cowsheds +
shrieking in the stalls,
"When the Toad—came—home!

"When the Toad—came—home!
"There was smashing in of windows and
crashing in of doors,
"There was chivvying of weasels that
fainted on the floor,
"When the Toad—came—home!

"Bang! go the drums!
"The trumpeters are tooting and the soldiers
are saluting,
"And the cannon they are shooting and
the—motor-cars are hooting,

"As the Hero comes!

"Shout—Hoo-ray!

"And let each one of the crowd try +
do his very best to shout it loud,
"In honour of an animal of whom
you're ~~justly~~ rightly proud,
"For it's Toad's great day!"

He sang it, as has been said, very loud; also, he sang it over twice. Then he heaved a deep sigh; a long, long, long sigh. Then he dipped his hair-brush in the water-jug, parted his hair in the middle, and plastered it down very straight + sleek on each side; and, unlocking the door, went quietly down the stairs to greet his guests, who were assembling in the drawing-room.

Everyone ~~cheered~~ shouted when he entered, + crowded round to congratulate him + say nice things about his courage, + his cleverness, + his fighting qualities; but Toad only smiled faintly + murmured "not at all, not at all!" or sometimes "On the contrary!" The animals were evidently quite puzzled + taken aback by this new attitude of his; + Toad felt, as he moved from one guest to another, making his modest responses, that he was an object of absorbing interest to everyone.

The Badger had ordered everything of the best, + the banquet was a great success. There was much talking, + laughter, + chaff, but through it all Toad, who was in the chair, looked down his nose + murmured pleasant nothings to the animals on each side of him. At intervals he stole a glance at the Badger + the Rat, + saw them looking at each other with their mouths open; + this gave him the greatest satisfaction.

LIFE AT MAYFIELD WITH ALASTAIR: FIFTY-SEVEN LETTERS FROM NAOMI STOTT, ALASTAIR'S GOVERNESS, TO ELSPETH GRAHAME, APRIL 1907–MAY 1908

By including these letters, I hope to provide a vivid portrait of what Cookham Dean and the surrounding towns were like during that crucial year when Kenneth Grahame wrote *The Wind in the Willows*. Stott's descriptions of the town and country echo the community invoked in Grahame's masterpiece and in the letters he wrote at that time. More significantly, Stott gives firsthand perspective of what young Alastair Grahame and their day-to-day lives were like. Because of space limitations, readers will be redirected to wherever a letter has already appeared in either the preface or annotations. Where lacking in narrative, Naomi Stott's letters have occasionally been abridged. All of the letters are topped with "At / Mayfield, Cookham Dean, Berks" and signed "Yours Sincerely, Naomi Stott."

{1}
{April 7, 1907}
7.4.07

Dear Mrs: Grahame,

Today this was a song I heard—"The Suffragettes have no votes today So they are sulky & in dismay Because they have not won the day."

A.G. {Alaistair Grahame}

Mouse has had a quiet happy time with Kenneth {a relation of Naomi Stott's and a playmate of Alastair's}. He asked me if he were really going to the wedding on Thursday, & I told him that I should be pleased to take him but that it would not be wise because of draughts in this draughty month. I think that it would not be worth the risk of a cold. Quite cheerful he said "I shall have my dear Louise then, & can hear all about it, & Winnie & Eva must come to tea." Last night he dreamt that he was having tea with the servants & the table was decorated with tiny palms & currant bread & butter was lying about & pretending to be tigers in a wood. In another dream the hero was an enormous red beetle & he & the beetle took it in turns to eat oranges. Peter is a successful companion, & the new ball is liked.

{2}
Feb: 26th 1908

Dear Mrs: Grahame,

We hope to get into Maidenhead this morning to get Miss Jordan's present. It was too cold & showery yesterday for us to get out. She came to tea, & she & Miss Passey got on well together. After tea Mouse told us each our fortunes. He informed Miss Jordan that at her new home she was going to have a handy man to keep the shop clean, then he told Miss Passey that it would be in her lot to marry this handy man, so we all had a laugh, & Miss Jordan suggested that she might not want to give up her man, & so would not invite Miss Passey to see her. Life at present goes on quite peacefully here, & "The King of the House" lives his life contentedly enough. Just now he is busy with his daily paper. Hoping that you are better.

{4}
See chapter X, note 6.

{5}
March 3rd 1908

Dear Mr: Grahame,

I am very glad that Mrs Grahame is more comfortable. I told Mouse about Peter {one of Alastair's pet rabbits}, & he wonders when he will see him again. We had Mitey in to Tea to day. She was so very quiet & subdued. It was snowing fast when she had to go, & somebody has great hope that there will be a white world for tomorrow, & plenty of people to snow {b}all. We kept up shrove Tuesday. A special pancake was prepared. in a small frying pan, & at 12:30 Mouse tossed it over a swinging bar in the kitchen, & Miss Passy & I scrambled for it. He soon dropped the frying pan, & had a mouthful, which delighted him immensely. She & I in his interests ate far the greater part. He has talked of the fun over & over again, & when he was in bed, he told Rose {an employee of the Grahames'} how much he enjoyed the sport. A table cloth & white paper had been arranged as a carpet.

{6}

See "Alastair Grahame and *The Merry Thought*," page xli.

{7}

March 6th 1908

Dear Mrs: Grahame,

We shall be on the lookout for you on Sunday. I have given Miss Passey your message. Now our nursery fire behaves as it should, & once more indoor life is as comfortable as it can be, when the weather is bad. We had a good outing this morning, & the old man at Quarry Wood gate told us how his hut was broken into on Tuesday night, & his clock was stolen. We were on our way to him with a bag of bones for the dog, & I met Mrs Young, & her boys out on their donkeys. There was such a lovely clear view from Winter Hill today. The Park Farm dog accompanied us. As soon as he sees Mouse, he comes up as a comrade & makes such a good playfellow. He will wait in the garden until we are ready to go out again after dinner He looks in at the window in such an understanding sort of way, & puckers up his brow when he tries to understand what is said to him. Mouse is just off for a canter on Firefly. He is keen to have a fight with a young calf, & will probably request you to give him the opportunity.

{8}

March 9th 1908

. . . Mouse says he is sorry you could not come down to see the New Merry Thought. We have been having good times with the foot-ball. The paddock makes a fine play ground. Mouse had such a lot to tell his father, yet he said he had not time to finish. He meant to tell him about two men who went climbing in bathing costume. Mitey has not been to see us lately, probably because I asked her not to let Neb [her dog] come indoors.

{See chapter X, note 14, and chapter XI, note 26.}

{9}
March 11th 1908

Mouse is . . . singing "We'll I'm blowed if it aint old Toad Pom Pom Pom Pom" & he is getting on his boots. The weather looks doubtful. So it did yesterday, but we had a good outing in the morning. In the afternoon Miss Sullivan came, & she seemed in better spirits. Mouse enjoys having her very much, & drags her out of herself. He has spent a lot of his own time in painting lately, & has designed a cover picture for the April Merry Thought. Miss Thompson's card decorates the March number. The birds sing in such chorus every morning now.

{10}
March 12th 1908

. . . In the morning we spent most of our time in the sunny lane by High Wood Farm, near Quarry wood. The boy had a long play on the edge of the wood, & said that he felt as gay as a lark. In the afternoon Miss Passey accompanied us, & we took her to see Mrs: Haycock, who beamed with pleasure. Mouse had his hoop out for a run. On our way back through Mr: Darby's plantation we met Jim & Bill out with their dogs. An old servant was out with them, & she had enough to do to keep up with the 'trains.' I heard Jim say to her, "You are more like a woman than a truck."

{11}
March 13th 1908

Dear Mr: Grahame,

I hope that we shall soon have good news of Mrs: Grahame, & that you will be able to come for Sunday. We are making the most of this lovely weather. Yesterday we had a delightful drive to Maidenhead. Mouse was very interested in watching a harpist in the street, who had a gramophone to take part in his entertainment. We stood watching him while Miss Passey was in a shop. All afternoon we had a play in the paddock & garden, & just as we were coming in about 4, rather untidy, there was a caller awaiting us—Mrs Carter She stopped for a talk, & Mouse entertained her well.

{12}
March 15th 1908

Dear Mrs: Grahame,

It has been a lovely weather day to day. Mouse has been active enough in mind & body, & had two outings with his father. {Alastair includes a drawing of himself and his father at this meeting together in *The Merry Thought*.} He likes to have discussions with Miss Passey. Their latest "bone" is a political sort. She upholds the conservative party, & he denounces that party, & borrows the word "cursed" from Spenser to describe his foes & their doings. I heard her say. "Conservatives are not to be trusted any more than Chapel people, & Gladstone was a wicked old man."

Mouse rolled up his sleeves & suggested a fight with fists. Then she said "Liberals always want to take umbrellas in case it rains"; Conservatives have more pluck, she implied. Monday. "Firefly" is out for a canter, & his rider is singing pretty lustily.

{13}
March 17th 1908

Dear Mrs: Grahame,

Yesterday afternoon when we were playing at shuttlecock under the verandah outside the Dining Room, we saw a carriage & pair drive up, & found out it was Mrs. Luke & her new companion Miss Wait. We went down to them at the gate, & when she told Mouse about the mischief a rabbit did in her garden, he said that he could come & catch it for her in a sack, & would give it to her for dinner.[1] He told her that you were rather run down, & just as the elm trees stopped the railway accident at Wembley Park[2] from being extra bad, so the doctors had stopped you. Hoping that you will soon be able to get up.

1. Shades of Beatrix Potter's *Peter Rabbit*, 1904.

2. On March 14, 1908, a train consisting of an engine and five coaches derailed near Wembley Park Station. Though the sleeper cars were smashed beyond repair, branches of trees held the cars upright, preventing more serious injury to the passengers.

[14]
March 18th 1908

Dear Mrs: Grahame,

The weather is most changeable. We had a lovely day of sun yesterday. In the morning we had a drive to Maidenhead. The gorse on Pinkney's Green is not out much yet. In the afternoon we walked down to cockmarsh to look for tadpoles. It's too early, I think. It was so pretty down there in the sunshine. On our way back we saw a poor dead robin impaled on a hawthorn bush. Probably a shrike had made his larder there. Mouse enjoyed the walk, & scrambled about in bramble bushes. It is a mercy that his coat is of tough material, & stands the treatment. He so much revels in the freedom of the out door life here, & takes peculiar pleasure in creeping through bushes. It has been snowing fast this morning. The boy says that he feels springy, & very jolly. Mitey came to tea yesterday. Their cottage will be vacant on June 24th.

[15]
March 19th 1908

When we were out yesterday morning we met Mrs. Sullivan, & were walking homewards with her, when I heard Mouse talking, & looking back I saw that Dr: Shepard had overtaken him on bicycle, & the two were walking & talking together. At the foot of the hill they halted, & Mouse shewed no intention of coming on, nor did the Dr., so I parted company with Mrs. Sullivan & went back to capture Mouse. . . . . Just after tea, one of the Miss Carters came to call, & . . . read out of the magazine's Serial story of "The Whistle in the Pie", & he sat & listened with much beaming & smiling, & then introduced her to the gallant charger Firefly. She asked me to bring him to lunch with them to day.

[16]
March 20th 1908

Dear Mrs: Grahame,

So far Mouse is the worse for these cold winds. So many people have colds. He paid his call on Mrs Carter yesterday morning. They were out gardening. The boy told Miss Carter about his wish to be an astronomer,

& she took him indoors to shew him a map of the stars. Then Mrs Carter made the cuckoo clock go ½ hr. ahead in order that he might see the cuckoo announce the hour of 12. To get a good view Mouse stood on a chair, & was pleased. He brought back as a loan "the Children's Book of Stars" by G. E. Mitton, & has had two chapters read to him. Mrs Carter was sorry that we could not stay to lunch, & hopes that some day you will be able to allow it. After dinner, we were playing football,& some snow came on, & we came to the verandah to play at shuttlecock. In a few minutes, the sun shone out again, & we had a walk to the logs, where we went with Mr. Grahame last Sunday[.] Mouse sends "his love to you dearest, & hopes that you will soon come down."

{17}
March 21st 1908
See chapter VIII, note 40.

On our way back, Mouse discovered the first celandines, & also on a tub of water he smashed into ice that was nearly 1 inch thick. We called on Mrs Luke, & found her sitting out on her sunny terrace. Mouse asked her if she had the brains to write something for his magazine. I softened matters down by saying how often his friend (Miss Passey) at home says "Oh, but I have not the brains, you see they escaped when I was a child." He will learn one day that however much brain he has, he has not the monopoly. He has been talking big[3] lately. I wish that there were regular boy companions for him. We played football, & Miss Passey joined us for a time, in the afternoon.

{18}
March 23rd 1908

{19}
March 25th 1908

Dear Mrs: Grahame,

Mouse enjoyed good outings yesterday. We had a drive through Cookham in the afternoon, & it was such lovely spring weather. Mouse

3. As does Toad in chapter II.

was very interested in a certain policeman who was sitting on some railings, near the main road that goes from Cookham to Maidenhead, & he was on the watch for unwary motorists. The very name of police trap fascinated him, & he would have liked to sit on the railing near him, & watch for motors. . . . He keeps well, & his appetite is ravenous. You will see that he has grown taller. Each week it seems to me that there is more of him to rub down at bath time.

[20]
March 27th 1908

In spite of gloomy weather we had two outings yesterday. As we came along by "The Chequers" [local seventeenth-century inn] in the morning we saw Mr: Sullivan. He has done a picture of a bit in that region, & we are invited to call & see the picture on Saturday or Sunday.

. . . The April Merry Thought cover is to be designed by him [Mr. Sullivan]. He [Mouse] is still keen about his magazine. He has also asked to have a patch of ground for a garden, so I asked King about it, & he thinks of giving him a patch in the paddock, beyond the tennis lawn.

[21]
March 28th 1908

Yesterday it cleared up during the morning, & we had an outing on Winter Hill. After dinner we drove to Cookham & home by Cookham Dean. We came by The Mount.[4]

[22]
March 30th, 1908

Dear Mrs: Grahame,

We were glad to hear that you are going on well, & Mouse was pleased to think that you might be here for Easter. He goes on happily. Yesterday Mabel Kenyon came to call, & he shewed great pleasure, & frisked about with joy, chatted to her about "The Merry Thought" & asked her

4. The house Kenneth Grahame lived in as a small boy with his brothers and sister. See preface, page xix.

to send a contribution. Mitey is rather a disappointment to him because she does not seem keen to add a page or two to the magazine. I think that the artistic temperament in her, makes her dislike to do what she is asked to do . . . Mouse has improved in painting. He is busy now doing a picture for the Xmas number of the magazine.

[23]
March 31st 1908

Dear Mrs: Grahame,

Mouse is looking forward to tomorrow, because on what he calls "All Sillie's Day", he intends to play a trick on Miss Passey. She usually visits him before bed time for a play. To day we hope to plant some seeds in our new gardens.[5] Mouse wants to have a holly bush in the middle of his, & rose trees & geraniums round about. So often, he is disappointed when in answer to a question, King says, "It is not the time of year for that sir." A stray horse walked in the garden yesterday, & very much relished a few mouthfuls from the lawn. Mouse sat on Firefly to see the fun, when Miss Passey in white apron, armed with a stick followed in one direction, & Rose with a brush & shovel came to help drive the creature out into the road. King was out on "Kitty", & had left the doors open.

[24]
April 3rd 1908

Dear Mrs: Grahame,

It is very kind of you to say that I may ask Carrie & Kenneth[6] to stay here a day or two. As soon as I read the note from Mr. Grahame, I wrote off to tell her. We did some more gardening yesterday, after our morning walk. When it is so mild Mouse is warm enough in his little blue coat. I take his cape with me, so that sometimes he rests on a gate, & then the cape is of use. We have favourite gates here & there where we rest. We met Mr: Bishop yesterday in a field behind that inn. (it may be called The Hare & Hounds) on the common at the top of the chalk pit. We got to it by following a path through Mr: Darby's plantation, & it is

5. Alastair drew Stott in the garden. See page xlix in "Alastair Grahame and *The Merry Thought*."

6. Carrie is Naomi Stott's sister, and Kenneth her nephew.

a lovely walk, & takes one over stiles, just the sort of walk a boy enjoys, & you get a fine view of Mayfield district.

[25]

April 6th 1908

We are hoping that Kenneth & his Mother will come this morning. Mouse is so keen to go & meet them. The weather is very uncertain at present. If Mr Grahame had come yesterday he would have had to be indoors. The afternoon was shocking.[7] Just before dinner, a carriage stopped at the gate, & Miss Evelyn Lidderdale[8] came to call on you. She had a talk with Mouse, while her Mother drove on to make another call. They came to the cottage for the week end, & hope to come in residence there soon after Easter. . . . Mouse is very well, & is looking forward to Easter . . .

[26]

April 7th 1908

Kenneth & his Mother arrived safely, & have settled down very happily. Mouse seems very pleased to have them, & finds Kenneth very entertaining. All that Kenneth knows he may not do, he suggests that Mouse shall do. During a meal he says "Mouse, you jump down before you finish." "You open wide your mouth while you eat." "You eat [a] lot, too much & get ill," & various other directions he gives him. We ~~go~~ are just getting ready to go out. The little bachelor's room in conveniently near the bath room, & my sister finds it very comfortable. Mouse much enjoyed getting those flowers to send you, & gleefully carried the box, & posted it before I had time to get in at the shop door.

7. Alastair includes a drawing called "April weather" in *The Merry Thought*. It consists of heavy strikes through the sun, as if it had been stormy.

8. Her father, William Lidderdale, was responsible for getting Kenneth Grahame his first post at the Bank of England. Evelyn Lidderdale published an obscure children's book called *The Forget-me-not Clock* (no date available).

[28]
April 8th 1908

Mouse & Rose had a game with Miss Passey which much delighted him. A brush was hidden in her bed, & it was supposed that she would imagine that it was a hedgehog, & that she screamed at bed time, & spent the night in the passage. "Wait until I catch him with the poker," was a message sent. He crept down the front stairs to breakfast, & it would have made you smile to see the caution, & how he tried to tiptoe silently. He hid under the table, & Miss Passey walked round the room armed with the butcher poker, & poked everywhere but under the table—Just now she peeped in at the window, & Mouse hustled under the table.

[29]
April 8th 1908

Dear Mrs: Grahame,

It has been a lovely day. We had a walk on Winter Hill, & spent the rest of the time in the paddock & garden. The boys played with balls on the lawn, & Mouse is most generous to Kenneth. He encourages him to play with his toys, & Kenneth is a very happy little person. Today "Peter Rabbit" has been the favourite, yesterday it was the motor car. . . .

April 9th. This morning Kenneth refuses to walk, & wants a new leg. He is not used to kicking a football, & had a fine time with it yesterday. Mouse & I had a walk after tea. This morning, he looks very well. We shall lose our visitors tomorrow.

[30]
April 9th 1908

Dear Mrs: Grahame,

This letter is being written out under the verandah. Mouse is near at hand, engaged in talking with Miss Passey, & planning to play more tricks on her. . . . Yesterday my Plymouth brother, who is spending a few days in London came to call. The weather was dull. We shewed him Winter Hill, & round the garden, & Mouse introduced him to the rabbits & to the foot ball, & we had a game before coming in. I received Mr.

Grahame's note yesterday, & told Miss Passey that he would be here for lunch on Sunday.

{31}
April 10th 1908

Dear Mrs: Grahame,

It was a fine day yesterday, & after a stroll in Quarry Wood, & a play near some logs, we spent all our outdoor time in the garden. The boys had great fun playing with the cut grass which King collected when he was mowing. They got armfuls out of the wheelbarrow & threw it at him, & he was most patient. After tea Mouse & I generally attend to our gardens. I got him a small water can, & it gives him much pleasure to water his garden. Lately he has had a great fancy for mud pies, & they are baked in the sun near his den. That is a very popular haunt of his in the paddock. Kenneth had one bad night with his leg, he was very lame yesterday. It is much better to day, & last night he slept well. He has so much enjoyed himself here . . .

{32}
April 11th 1908

Dear Mr: Grahame,

I have let Miss Passey know that you may be here on Sunday. Mouse hopes that he will meet you, & introduce you to the new Merry Thought. He has shown a blinking tendency again. The hair is not quite long enough to need tying back, but it is a worry to him indoors. Out of doors his cap helps to keep it out of his eyes. [See chapter I, note 9.]

Our visitors left yesterday. The little boy was most reluctant to go, & expressed a wish to take several of Mouse's toys to his daddy. Mouse bestowed on him the toy motor car, which he used to pull about a great deal. He had very happy times, & King was very patient with him. When armed with trowel he went about to help clean the garden. He was just stopped in time, or he would have got {into} trouble among the [bee] hives. He intended to open the little houses. Mouse is well. I have forgotten to say that the rabbits Miss Flower knows of, may be ready by Easter. Mouse does not know. Perhaps you may mean them to be an Easter surprise[.]

[33]
April 13th 1908

[34]
April 14th 1908

. . . Mouse] looks well, & is very pleased that Mr: Grahame is coming down for a long week end. I believe that in his garden there is the first green shoot of seed to be seen. He will be very glad when King can let him have some geraniums, because then the garden will look inhabited. Mouse says that he sends you his very best love, & is very sorry that you cannot come down for Easter, that he holds on to the faint hope that you will be down Sunday after.

[35]
April 15th 1908

Dear Mrs: Grahame,

Yesterday morning it was too cold for the garden, & Mouse likes a walk to have an object, & it is not always easy to arrange a set purpose for a walk. We managed to get a brisk walk yesterday, & had a call on Mrs Carter, & took back her book about the stars. The two daughters & Dick were all busy in the Dining Room. Some were busy about a boat covering, & one was paring beeswax into a jar & stirring in turpentine with a stick. We stayed a few minutes, & Mouse had off his coat, & he undertook the stirring, & much enjoyed his call. We brought back with us two books, "The Little Duke" by Miss Yonge, & "The Dingo Boys" by Manville Fenn.[9] Mouse has 'love' for Mrs Carter. She is most kind in her ways, & evidently loves small boys. After dinner, our object was to call on Mrs. Haycock, & Mouse was glad that dear Jim was at home. He is looking forward to the coming of Peter Rabbit & Benjamin Bunny & King is busy about the hutch.

9. Charlotte Yonge, *The Little Duke, Richard the Fearless* (London: Macmillan and Co., 1906): about Richard I, Duke of Normandy; Manville Fenn, *The Dingo Boys—or, The Squatters of Wallaby Range* (London: Chambers, 1892): boys' adventure novel set in Australia, typical of the books Alastair Grahame liked to read and imitate.

[36]
April 16th 1908

We wended our way during the walk yesterday morning to Mrs Luke's She was out gardening, & Mouse & I helped to collect stones for her to put on a new path. Then we had an explore in her little wood & picked primroses & anemones. She too is very fond of small boys & knows how to interest them. She showed us an alpine rose pink primula in flower in a rockery, & Mouse told her that you had been to the Alps.

Mouse hopes that Mr[.] Grahame will be here by 1.

[37]
April 18, 1908

Dear Mrs: Grahame,

I have received safely the Easter present for Mouse, & found ~~the~~ the little ornament, & think it very pretty. He shall wear a new overall on Sunday, & probably his new brown suit with silver buttons. When Mr. Grahame came yesterday, we were just about to begin a magic lantern entertainment for Geoffrey's benefit. So often he has wanted it. I found it easy to darken the dining room, & there was a fire there & I planned to have it during the afternoon. The visitors were late, so the show had to be after ~~after~~ tea, & Mouse was all the more pleased to have his father to see it.

I am enclosing some snapshots for you to see.[10] If you will kindly let me have these back to send my sister, I shall be glad to print for you later on any particular ones you would like. Kenneth was perfectly happy here, & I believe that he will remember his visit. He loved Mouse, & wanted to step where he stepped, & sit where he sat, & eat what he ate. Mr: Grahame will soon be having Mouse for a walk.

[38]
April 20th 1908.

Dear Mrs: Grahame,

Mr: Grahame & Mouse had a walk together yesterday morning. The boy played a lot with the toy you sent him, & was very pleased with the

10. These are probably the photos of Mouse with his cricket bat and hoop, included in *The Merry Thought*.

chocolates. The rabbits have not come yet. Perhaps Miss flower does not get out much during this sort of weather. There are bright intervals, & it is good weather for brisk walking. Mr: Bishop says that 'Things are very backward.' Some fruit blossom is to be seen, & the cherry tree outside will soon be in flower. We went anemone picking on Saturday. Mr. Grahame was the quickest to spy them, & Mouse & I did the picking, & when we got back, we arranged them in moss in a soup plate for Easter decoration. Thank you for the return of the snapshots.

{39}
April 22nd 1908

We had a long active outing yesterday morning. On our homeward way, Mouse wanted to go & see "Uncle Tom's Cabin," because he plans when he is older to have his cottage built just opposite that inn.

{40}
April 24th 1908.

Dear Mrs: Grahame,

Yesterday we had to have a day indoors, but our mutual friend enjoyed that. We had Miss Passey to tea, & he acted as a clown to amuse her. & to enjoy himself after tea, & we had some singing. There was a white world this morning, & the view from the windows is very pretty, such a blue sky, & bright sunshine & the snow glistening. Mouse was keen on snow balling, but the rapid thaw makes the world too damp for him to play about on the ground.

It is his pocket money day, & he is quite jubilant over that fact. The rabbits have not come yet, they will be here as soon as they can leave the mother. I hope that the weather will be warm enough for Mr: Grahame to enjoy the weekend here. I am/ Yours Sincerely/ Naomi Stott.

{41}
April 24th 1908

Dear Mrs: Grahame,

When people enquire for you, Mouse says, "I think that she is rather better, & will soon be coming to Mayfield." Mrs Haycock said to him & "you'll be glad of that, won't you dear?," & he replied "Shan't I." You could not have enjoyed this sort of weather. It is cold & damp. We walked to Cookham yesterday morning, & had a look over the bridge. Only one boat was to be seen out. Mouse walks well now, & when he & I are out, he skips about like a small dog, & is to & fro, & likes to hover round rubbish heaps. He often says how much he likes living in the country, & except to see his friends he does not want to return to London.

{42}
April 25th 1908.

Dear Mrs: Grahame,

There is a very wintry outlook here today. Snow is falling steadily, & the trees & bushes are laden. Mouse is riding Firefly, & singing. The two little rabbits arrived yesterday, & are in their hutch in the stable. As soon as it clears up, we shall get out to visit them. While the weather is bad, King will feed them. I expect that it will be doubtful whether Mr. Grahame will visit tomorrow.

{43}

April 27th 1908

Mouse enjoyed . . . that there was snow about. That Park Farm dog was a very good tempered target. Whenever he sees Mouse he greets him with much joy. One night about 10 P.M. he came to call, & to content him Rose gave him a bone, & he enjoyed it in the moonlight on the lawn, & then took his departure.

{45}
April 29th 1908

It rained all day yesterday, but we had a very happy day indoors. A real live hedgehog gave us much pleasure by coming to call. I saw him on the mat outside our front door, & brought him in, & he spent the afternoon in an open dress box, where he roamed about, & feasted with relish on minced beef & brown bread. Miss Passey amused Mouse by being scared of it. After tea we put it out in the garden, & Mouse gave

Miss Passey a lesson in dancing. For fun she fell several times, & he shrieked with laughter.

{46}

April 30th 1908

Dear Mrs: Grahame,

It was such a lovely day yesterday, such whiffs of spring greeted us, & there was a lovely view of floods from Winter Hill. When we got to Geoffrey's we were told that his party was to happen that afternoon, so after the boys had had a happy play together, we returned on the understanding that we were to come again. Mouse made a collection of beetles & worms which he put in a match box & gave to Miss Passey to shock her. Mouse looked very well in his brown outfit in the afternoon, & made the acquaintance of Tristram & Delphine Gibbs. Bill young was the only other guest, & we played on the lawn at Nuts & May, & Mulberry Bush, & Blindman's Bluff, & the boy thoroughly enjoyed himself.

{48}

May 1st 1908

Dear Mrs: Grahame,

We have had a very enjoyable first of the month. We went to Maidenhead by train, for Mouse had his shilling to spend, & wanted to get his birthday present. He bought some soldiers, & very much enjoyed an explore round the toy shop.

When we got back to Cookham, King met us at the station with the 'pram', & pushed the boy home for me. I invited him to have his baby photographed, & Mrs. King brought her this afternoon, & I hope that I have got a good snapshot. It was so hot, that Mouse & I sat on chairs in the paddock, sheltered by the sun shade, & watched the gambols of the rabbits. Benjamin often came to the boy's {lap} for a cuddle, & Peter would go under his chair.[11] We had tea out of doors. Mrs King & Baby, & also Miss Passey & Rose, & Mouse was very gay indeed & happy. After tea Miss Passey joined in a foot ball game, & Mouse watered his garden, & then I

11. May 1 is probably the date that Stott took the photo titled "Mouse and Peggy." See "Alastair Grahame and *The Merry Thought*," page xlvi.

read some stories to him out of the Children's Encyclopedia. Do you ~~not~~ think that his bed time might be shifted later than 6 P.M. now? Might it be 6.30? I know that he wants a long night, & it takes us an hour to retire. I should like him to have the extra half hour now if you approve.

{49}
May 4th 1908

Dear Mrs: Grahame,

Mouse is as usual busy at drawing, when I am letter writing. He manages his dressing now in the mornings, & the process is always accompanied by singing & dancing. He had a picnic in the woods on Saturday. We were accompanied by Miss Passey, & pushed the tea out in the "pram". The woods were looking most lovely with the sun glinting through on to the new beech leaves. We have not found many nests. Mouse has not much patience at present, so I say nothing until I find one, & then get him to come & make the discovery. The rabbits have grown a lot, & often enjoy a free gambol in the paddock. "Peggy" the hedgehog has not been seen again.

{50}
May 5th 1908.

Dear Mrs: Grahame,

Yesterday morning we went up to Dealman's to get some Mignonette seeds & in there buying stamps was Mr: Hunt & one of his sons. Mouse greeted him, & he asked after you. In the afternoon the boy went to let the rabbits out for a run on the lawn, & presently he returned to me saying "The Wickedness of those rabbits, while I left Peter on the grass, & went to fetch Benjamin, Peter went off. "He soon came back, then while we were discussing gardens off he went again. We hunted the hedges, & I went up the road to look, & then got King. Mouse found him in the ivy by the tennis 'pavilion', & he dodged us with great agility. It was too wet at present for us to call yet on the ~~the~~ rabbits. Firefly is being exercised, & there is loud singing to be heard. {Mouse} ~~He~~ has been drawing a new airship, which contains all the conveniences of a modern mansion. He is very interested in the appearance of the Irish Leprechaun, & hopes soon to see one in Quarry Wood.

[51]
May 6th 1908

Dear Mrs: Grahame,

Mouse sends you his love, & wishes that you were down here, & would like to know if you are coming for the 12th of May.[12] Miss Passey asked me if she is to make the birthday cake. She knows how to make a fascinating 3 decker cake of sponge cake with a layer of plain chocolate cake. I told her that last year you ordered a cake from Barker's, & perhaps that had been done this year.

[52]
May 7th 1908

Dear Mrs: Grahame,

We had tea out on the lawn, & then a stroll through the woods. We had the rabbits out this afternoon in the paddock, & "Peter" gave us a fine chase. He looks wicked enough when he is caught & he is teaching "Benjamin" the trick of making off. I am enclosing a snapshot for you. Hoping that you are better.

[53]
May 11th 1908

Dear Mrs: Grahame,

Mouse is just having a fine laugh, because King gave a kick to the foot ball, & kicked off the toe of his boot. Grass cutting is going on, & gossipping, for Mouse has much to say. Mr. Grahame asked me yesterday if there were many of my possessions at Durham Vill as.[13] If Louise would kindly put together the books I left in the nursery cupboard, & the contents of the nursery table drawers, I think that would include my belongings there. It is good news to hear that you will soon be down. The paddock is very pretty now that the buttercups are out, & there is such a lovely Spring feel in the air. As the grass cutter goes up the lawn,

12. Alastair Grahame's birthday.

13. The Grahames' London house. They eventually sold it and relocated permanently to Cookham Dean. Naomi Stott started her employment with the Grahames at Durham Villas.

there is Mouse kicking the ball at {King} ~~him~~, or running alongside. This natural sort of life is very good for him.

{54}
May 13th 1908

Dear Mrs: Grahame,

Mouse had a very happy birthday. He thanks you for your letter, & hopes that you will be down for the opening of the White Rabbit Club, as he forgot to do it yesterday. We had a prettily arranged tea, & Mouse presided, & cut his cake, & the big white rabbit looked on, & drank to the health of everybody. Louise sent a kite, & Mrs Blunt, a silver napkin ring, & Edith & Agnes, a book each, & Mouse sends his thanks to them all, & he liked all his presents very much. . . . The flowers came safely this morning. All the visitors admired the birthday cake.

{57}
May 16 1908

Dear Mrs: Grahame,

The weather has again improved, & after two indoor days we have now an out door day. Mouse is busy drawing, & wondering how long it will be before his father is down. I hope that we shall go to Maidenhead this morning, & get the hair cut. It has been fidgeting the boy very much. Some children have arrived at the Campbell's & we hear loud chattering going on over the hedge. Yellow wall flowers make the garden borders here look very gay. You will enjoy the change I expect when you can come here & be out of doors. Progress will be all the quicker when you can live in fresh air, & the time passes quicker. Mouse is well, & is happy in his own way. He will be pleased to see you again.

A TREASURE HUNT

In a rarely seen letter to Alastair, Kenneth Grahame writes this story of a treasure hunt. Alastair was twelve years old at the time, and like the preceding summers, father and son were separate again. Kenneth probably wrote this story as a compensation for the extended holiday he and

Elspeth took without him, a holiday that would have overlapped with Alastair's term at Rugby School.

BOHAM'S,
BLEWBURY, DIDCOT.
BERKSHIRE.
23rd July, 1912.

My dear Sir,

The intelligence which you transmit to us, in your obliging communication of Sunday last, concerning the discovery of a cave, is evidently of

VAST AND FAR-REACHING IMPORTANCE.

You have clearly discovered, by sheer good luck, one of the secret hiding-places of that abandoned ruffian + pirate

CAPTAIN KIDD,

who is known to have pursued his lawless calling in those parts. It now only remains for you two Gentlemen Adventurers, D. Lawless + R.O. Hentzau Esqs., to discover the

HIDDEN TREASURE

which is doubtless concealed there. It was the practice of the wily Captain, whenever he buried any treasure, to take only one member of his crew with him, to assist in the work. When the treasure was safely buried, he

KILLED THE UNHAPPY SAILOR

by whacking him over the head with a spade. Kidd was a man who did not take any needless risks. He then buried the body over or near to the treasure. The first thing therefore that you have got to find is a

SKELETON

Which will be only an inch or so below the surface,

If the arms are close to the side, the

TREASURE IS BENEATH.

If one arm is extended, follow carefully the direction to the end of the fore-finger, measure off fifteen inches in the same line, +

THEN DIG!

If both arms are extended, or if one arm is bent with the thumb touching the point of the nose, then

IT'S ALL A SELL

+ there isn't any treasure there at all. Kidd was fond of doing things of that sort. He thought he was funny; but that's where he

MADE THE MISTAKE!

(there are lots of people like Kidd going about). If, however, it is not a sell, then you ought to find something like the following list:—

A. Box containing Gold Ingots

B. " " Spanish Moidores

C. " " Best Everton Toffee, of which Kidd, in his leisure moments, was said to be extremely fond.

D. Box containing ladies rings, most of them with fingers still inside them. Kidd when collecting rings, was generally in a hurry.

E. Post Office Savings Bank Book, in name of J. Kidd, Esq.

F. Box containing more Gold Ingots

G. " " Portuguese Moidores

H. " " Sailor's Tobacco Boxes, all full of Spade Guineas.

I. Box containing Specimens of Old Church Plate,—Chalices, Pattens, Candlesticks, re., all solid gold. This should be offered first to the South Kensington Museum.

J. Album containing photos of Mrs. Kidd + all the little Kidds. K. in private life was a devoted family man.

K. Large chest containing Watches, Chains, Seals, Rings, snuffboxes, Purses, Breast-pins, + other objects of interest to collectors.

Of course you may find other things as well, but all Kidd-Treasure-Hunters tell me that the above list is what is generally found.

The chief danger is, that parties of Kidd's descendants are often scouring the coast, in search of their ancestor's hidden treasure. They are desperate villains, + armed to the teeth. So a sentry should always be posted. He had better be registered as well (Extra fee 2^{d}). This is all I have to say at present.

From

Yours truly Daddy.

APPENDIX 1

Alastair Grahame's Bookshelf

The following is a list of Alastair Grahame's books in Alastair's handwriting in the order in which he catalogued them. Spelling errors are not corrected. The approximate date of the list—1911—was determined by the publication date of numerous titles. Additions in brackets and boldface type are the editor's.

TITLE OF WORKS

Flowering Plants of Great Britain (3 vols:), Anne Pratt.
Pilgrims Progress, Bunyan.
Child's Garden of Verses R. L. Stevenson.
Twenty Tears After, Dumas.
Introductory History of England (3 vols:), Fletcher.
Every Boy's Book of Hobbies. C Bullivant.
[Cecil H. Bullivant, illustrated by John Hassall, 1911]
Legends and stories of Italy. Katherine Cameron
[Amy Steedman, illustrated by Katharine Cameron, 1909]
King Arthur's Knights, Henry Gilbert.
[Henry Gilbert, illustrated by Walter Crane, 1911]
52. Sketches of Germans, Rev. F. Close.
Tumblies, Edward Lear.
World of Animal Life, Edited by F. Smith.
Two little savages, E. Thompson Seton
[Ernest Thompson Seton, 1903]

Treasure Island, Stevenson.
Pickwick Papers, Dickens.
Stories and Fairy Tales, Hans Anderson.
Princeess of Hearts, Sheila Braine.
Honey Bee, Anatole France.
Fairy Tales, Madame D'aulnoy.
Child's Book of Warriors, William Canton.

Jungle Book, Kipling.
Book of Knight and Barbara, Jordon.
Grim's Goblins, Grim.
Jungle Book, (Duplicate), Kipling.
Indian Fairy Tales, Joseph Jacobs.

English Fairy Tales, Joseph Jacobs.
Five Days Entertainment at Wentworth Grange, F. T. Palgrave.
[Francis Turner Palgrave, 1868]
Six Aylmer's Heir, Everett Green. [1890]
Tom Sawyer Abroad, Mark Twain.
Bell's Standard Elocution, Bell.
Pontiac Chief of the Ottawas, E. S. Ellis.
Hunt of the White Elephant, E. S. Ellis.
Hyms for Children, Mrs. Alexander.
Paleface and Redskin, F. Antstey.
Prester [Pastor?] John, John Buchan.
Nine unlikely Tales. E. Nesbitt

Bed-time Stories, Mr & Mrs. C Kirnakan.
John Halifax, Gentleman, Dr. Mr. Inulock.
Three Midshipmen. W.H.Y. Kingston.
Innocents' Day Addresses, Dean Bradley.
Don Quixote, de Cervantes.
Celtic Fairy Tales, Joseph Jacobs.
Robinson Crusoe, Defoe.
52. Nature Ramble, W. P. Westell.
Spain of Today, I. T. Shaw.
True Tilda, Quiller-Couch.
Peter the Whaler, W.H.Y. Kingston.

Parables from Nature, Mrs. Scott Gatty.
Soldiers Three, ETC. Kipling.
Gulliver's Travels, Dean Swift.
Arabian Knights Entertainment, Andrew Lang.
The Other Side of the Sun. Evlyn Sharp.
David and Jonathan, Julia Hock.
Tales of Jack and Jane, Charles Young.
Poison Island, Quiller-Couch.
The Dog Corusoe, Ballantyne.

Mr. Dormouse & Other Poems, Geraldine Seymour.
I Go A-Walking, Rev: C. A. Johns.

All the way to FairyLand (2 copies) Evelyn Sharp.
Wymps, Evelyn Sharp.
Masterman Ready, Marriot. Peterkins, Translated by Mrs. lane.
Wizards of Rye Town, Smedley & Talbot.
Well-Spent Lives, Herbert Edmonds.
With Lord Methuen in South Africa, H. S. Gaskell.

What Katy did at Schook[1], Susan Coolidge.
All Sorts of Stories Book, Andrew Lang.
Baboo Jabberjee B. A., F. Anstey
[Illustrated by J. Bernard Partridge, 1897]
Minnows and Tritons, B. A. Clarke.
Teddy's Button, Amy Le Feuvre **[ca. 1890]**.
One of Rupert's Horse **[A story of the reign of Charles the First]**, Strong and Stoad. **[Herbert Strang and Richard Stead]**
Alice's Adventures in Wonderland, and through the Looking Glass, Lewis Carroll.
The King's pistols, Plant.
Left on the Prairie, Mr. B. Cox.
[M. B. Cox, (Noel West), illustrated by A. Pearce, 1896]
The Gorilla Hunters, Ballantyne.
[The Gorilla Hunters: A Tale of The Wilds of Africa, 1861]

The Captured Cruiser, Cutliffe-Ayne [1893].
The Story of a Happy Home, Mary Howith.
The Coral Island, Ballantyne.
The Concise Oxford Dictionary.
The Wind in the Willows, K. Grahame.
The Olive Fairy Book, Andrew Lang.
The Holly Tree Inn, Dickens.
Chronicles of Martin Hewitt, A. Morrison.
Bofin's Heritage, Amy Le Feuvre.

Feats on the Fjord, Harriot Mortimor.
Quentin Dunword, Scott.

Tom Sawyer, Mark Twain.
Household Stories, Grimm.
Drake, Parker.
The Prisoner of Zenda, Anthony Hope,
Three Men in a Boat, Jerome K. Jerome.
Adventures of Huckleberry Finn, Mark Twain.
A Mariner of England, Herbert Strang and Richard Stead.

Swiss Family Robinson, Kingston.
Tales of Ancient Greece, Cox.
Horatic Opera, Horace.
Hereward the Wake, C. Kingsley.
Masterman Ready, Marriot.
Tom Brown's School Days, T. Hughs.
Treasure Island & Kidnapped, Stevenson.
Children of the New Forest, Marriot.
Parent's Assistant, Maria Edgeworth.
Holiday House, Katherine Sinclaire.
Thrilling Stories of the Railway, Victor 1.
Whilech[obscured]. Australasia, Philip H. Gibbs.
India, Our Eastern Empire, Philip H. Gibbs.
Peoples at [obscured] Lands; Italy, J. Finnimore.
Strange Adventures in Dicky-Bird Land, R, Kestton.
Heraldry Explained, Fox-Davies.
Old Christmas Dinner, Washington Irving.
Dispensations of God with Adam, Wardle.
Signalking [*sic*]

APPENDIX 2

Critical Reception

Following are excerpts from the reviews that appeared at the time of the initial publication of *The Wind in the Willows.*

Our chief complaint is that our review copy is defiled with a mark like a dairyman's egg stamp. No reviewer in his senses would want to sell so nice a little book as this. All the same we cannot help thinking it a false, as it is an undoubtedly ugly, economy on the part of the publishers (quoted in Chalmers, *Kenneth Grahame*, 127).

The author of "The Golden Age" and "Dream Days," the historian of the immortal Harold, has disappointed us. There is no getting away from the melancholy fact. He has written THE WIND IN THE WILLOWS (Methuen 6g), a book with hardly a smile in it, through which we wander in a haze of perplexity uninterested by the story itself and at a loss to understand its deeper purpose. The chief character is a mole whom the reader plumps upon on the first page whitewashing his house. Here is an initial nut to crack. A mole whitewashing. No doubt, Moles like their abodes to be clean; but whitewashing? Are we very stupid? Or is this joke really inferior? However, let it pass. Then enters a water-rat on his way to a river picnic, in a skiff, with a hamper of provisions, including cold tongue, cold ham, French roles and soda water. Nut number two; for obviously a water rat is of all animals the one that would never use a boat with which to navigate a stream. Again, are we very stupid, or is this nonsense of poor quality? Later we meet a wealthy toad, who, after a tour of England in a caravan drawn by a horse, becomes a rabid motorist. He is also an inveterate public speaker. We meet also a variety of animals whose foibles doubtless are borrowed from mankind, and so the book goes on until the end. Beneath the allegory ordinary life is depicted more or less closely, but certainly not very amusingly or searchingly. While as a contribution to natural history the work is negligible. There are neat and fanciful passages; but they do not convince. The puzzle is, for whom is the book intended? Grown up readers will find it monstrous and elusive, children will hope, in vain for more fun. The materials for an English "Uncle Remus" are here, but without the animating spirit. For ourselves we lay *The Wind in the Willows* reverently aside and again, for the hundredth time, take up *The Golden Age*. Perhaps that is the real inner purpose of the new work—to send readers to its deathless forerunners. To "The Golden Age" and "Dream Days," so be it (Edward Verrall Lucas, *The Times* [London]).

But the book for me is notable for its intimate sympathy with Nature and for its delicate expression of emotions which I, probably in common with most people, had previously believed to be my exclusive property. When all is said the boastful, unstable Toad, the hospitable Water-Rat, the shy, wise, childlike Badger, and the Mole with his pleasant habit of brave boyish impulse, are neither animals nor men, but are types of that deeper humanity that sways us all. To be wise, an allegory must admit of a wide application, and the man has read his *Pilgrim's Progress* in vain who does not realize that not merely Christian but Ignorance, Talkative and Justice Hategood himself, are crying for the mastery in the hearts of us all. And if I may venture to describe as an allegory a work which critics, who ought to have known better, have dismissed as a fairy story, it is certain that *The Wind in the Willows* is a wise book. It is wise, moreover, with that simplicity which has its appeal to children as well as to grown-up folk. Just as young people read *Gulliver's Travels* for the story, so I fancy they will find Mr. Grahame's book a history of exciting adventures, and value it in this aspect no less than we, who find it a storehouse of glowing prose, gracious observation, delicate fantasy, and life-like and even humorous dialogue.

It will be apparent to the reader, accustomed to the tepid outpouring of anonymous reviewers, that in writing this notice of Mr. Grahame's book I have been appreciative rather than critical. It may not occur to him that it is rarely possible to be both when the love is new. Time will often show us blemishes in the objects of our admiration, whether they be books or women, but I confess, though it is some ten years since I first read them, that I still find Mr. Grahame's Dream Days and The Golden Age as perfect as when they first taught me what my boyhood meant. *The Wind in the Willows* is a wider, fuller book than these, and yet I believe that Mr. Grahame has accomplished the harder task with no less sureness of touch, with no less qualified a success. And I think it will be time to lay down my pen, when I shall be able to review soberly a book that gives me such unalloyed pleasure at the first reading (Richard Middleton, *Vanity Fair*, quoted in Chalmers, *Kenenth Grahame*, 128).

His rat, toad and mole are very human in their behaviour, and remind us of undergraduates of sporting proclivities (*Saturday Review of Literature*).

All the animals had a stirring time, and but for their peculiar shapes they would well pass for first rate human boys (H .W. Nevinson, *The Nation*).

The Wind in the Willows is an attempt to write for children instead of about them. But Mr. Grahame's past has been too strong for him. Instead of writing about children for grown up people, he has written about animals for children. The difference is only in the names. He writes of the animals with the same wistfulness with which he wrote of children, and, in his attitude towards his audience, he is quite unable to resist that appeal from dreamland to a knowledge of the world that makes the charm of all his books, and separates them from children's literature. The poems in the book are the only things really written for the nursery, and the poems are very bad.

If we judge the book by its aim, it is a failure, like a speech to Hottentots made in Chinese. And yet, for the Chinese, if by any accident there should happen to be one or two of them among the audience, the speech might be quite a success (Arthur Ransome, *The Bookman*).

But the book is fairly certain to be misunderstood of [*sic*] the people. The publishers' own announcement describes it as "perhaps chiefly for youth," a description with which I disagree. The obtuse are capable of seeing in it nothing save a bread-and-butter imitation of The Jungle Book. . . . The author may call his chief characters the Rat, the Mole, the Toad,—they are human beings, and they are meant to be nothing but human beings. . . . The book is an urbane exercise in irony at the expense of the English character and of mankind. It is entirely successful (Arnold Bennett, *The New Age*).

It is a very long time since Mr. KENNETH GRAHAME gave us a book, and now that he has done so in *The Wind in the Willows* (Methuen) it proves to be on entirely different lines from those of *Dream Days* and *The Golden Age*, though it has many pages which could have been written only by their author. I should describe it myself as a sort of irresponsible holiday story in which the chief characters are woodland animals, who are represented as enjoying most of the advantages of civilization—shopping, caravanning, motoring, traveling by train, and so on—apparently on terms more or less equality with the human world. . . . Some grown up readers may cavil at this, others may find in the story a satirical purpose which its author would probably exclaim. But children will, I think, accept Mr. Grahame's Rat, Mole and Badger as personal friends, and enjoy Toad's adventures and mishaps with a heartiness untroubled by any such curious considerations (*Punch*).

[Kenneth Grahame's *The Wind in the Willows* is] thoroughly delightful from beginning to end. There is something of everything in the book from broad farce to beautiful poetry. There are exquisite bits of nature, cheerful glimpses of England, quaint and wise reflections, and adventures exciting and comical (*New York Sun*).

Some may call it nature faking of the baldest sort, but such pedantry carries its own punishment. The book is not easily classified—it is simply destined to be one of those dog-eared volumes which one laughs over and loves. Which should be quite enough for any book to achieve (*New York Times*).

APPENDIX 3

Kenneth Grahame on Abridgment by Eleanor Graham

excerpted from her book, *Kenneth Grahame: A Walck Monograph*
(New York: Henry Z. Walck, 1963)

Something should be said here about the special edition which went to elementary schools so widely in the 1920's and 1930's, when times were so hard in London's East End—and in many other places as well. It seemed then that there was hardly a child there who did not know and love the book. The only boats those children knew were the barges moored at the wharves, and the cargo boats coming and going in the docks. Few could ever have seen a badger, probably not a mole: and they knew rats in only a very different connection. Yet the story took hold of them too.

The first suggestion from the publishers had been for a shortened version which, being incomplete, would not interfere with the sales of more expensive editions. They asked Kenneth Grahame if he would do the necessary cutting.

He replied gravely, after careful consideration, that he did not care for the idea. Such drastic cutting entailed either omitting four complete chapters, or cutting piecemeal to an equivalent extent: and he was not moved by the plea about other sales.

"I do not care," he wrote finally, "to have a form or version of the story in print which has been cut down—not for literary reasons, such as redundancy or verbosity or parts being not quite suited to children, or too much over their heads, and so on, but for the purely arbitrary and 'trade' reason of getting it within 192 pages. I can't abridge satisfactorily without a loss of quality, and that's the long and the short of it."

His views were accepted. The school edition contained the complete text. It sold in the thousands, a neat, well-produced book which sent roots down very deeply into homes where otherwise it might never have been known, for the Public Libraries had not then developed their present level of service (58–60).

APPENDIX 4

The Rural Pan, An April Essay

Grahame first wrote about Pan early in 1891. Though he was firmly entrenched in life in London at the time—working in the Secretary's office in the Bank of England, and beginning his literary career—Grahame's writing reflects his longing for a more rural and elemental life. "The Rural Pan: An April Essay" was first published anonymously in the *National Observer* on April 25, 1891. The essay was later included in Grahame's first book, *Pagan Papers* (1893), which received lukewarm reviews. With the publication of a quarterly called *The Yellow Book* in 1894—to which Grahame became a regular contributor—and his collection *The Golden Age* (1895), Grahame rapidly became a best-selling author.

From Grahame, *Pagan Papers* (1893)

Through shady Throgmorton Street and about the vale of Cheapside the restless Mercury is flitting, with furtive eye and voice a little hoarse from bidding in the market. Further west, down classic Piccadilly, moves the young Apollo, the lord of the unerring (satin) bow; and nothing meaner than a frock-coat shall in these latter years float round his perfect limbs. But remote in other haunts than these the rural Pan is hiding, and piping the low, sweet strain that reaches only the ears of a chosen few. And now that the year wearily turns and stretches herself before the perfect waking, the god emboldened begins to blow a clearer note.

When the waking comes at last, and Summer is abroad, these deities will abroad too, each as his several attributes move him. Who is this that flieth up the reaches of the Thames in steam-launch hired for the day? Mercury is out—some dozen or fifteen strong. The flower-gemmed banks crumble and slide down under the wash of his rampant screw; his wake is marked by a line of lobster-claws, gold-necked bottles, and fragments of veal-pie. Resplendent in blazer, he may even be seen to embrace the slim-waisted nymph, haunter of green (room) shades, in the full gaze of the shocked and scandalised sun. Apollo meantime reposeth, passively beautiful, on the lawn of the Guards' Club at Maidenhead. Here, O Apollo, are haunts meet for thee. A deity subjectively inclined, he is neither objective nor, it must be said for him, at all objectionable, like them of Mercury.

Meanwhile, nor launches nor lawns tempt him that pursueth the rural Pan. In the hushed recesses of Hurley backwater where the canoe may be paddled almost under the tumbling comb of the weir, he is to be looked for; there the god pipes with freest abandonment. Or under the great shadow of Streatley Hill, "annihilating all that's made to a green thought in a green shade"; or better yet, pushing an explorer's prow up the remote untravelled Thame, till Dorchester's stately roof broods over the quiet fields. In solitudes such as these Pan sits and dabbles, and all the air is full of the music of his piping. Southwards, again, on the pleasant Surrey downs there is shouting and jostling; dust that is drouthy and language that is sultry. Thither comes the young Apollo, calmly confident as ever; and he meeteth certain Mercuries of the baser sort, who do him obeisance, call him captain and lord, and then proceed to skin him from head to foot as thoroughly as the god himself flayed Marsyas in days of yore, at a certain Spring Meeting in Phrygia: a good instance of Time's revenges. And yet Apollo returns to town and swears he has had a grand day. He does so every year. Out of hearing of all the clamour, the rural Pan may be found stretched on Ranmore Common, loitering under Abinger pines, or prone by the secluded stream of the sinuous Mole, abounding in friendly greetings for his foster-brothers the dab-chick and water-rat.

For a holiday, Mercury loveth the Pullman Express, and a short hour with a society paper; anon, brown boots on the pier, and the pleasant combination of Métropole and Monopole. Apollo for his part will urge the horses of the Sun: and, if he leaveth the society weekly to Mercury, yet he loveth well the Magazine. From which *omphalos* or hub of the universe he will direct his shining team even to the far Hesperides of Richmond or of Windsor. Both iron road and level highway are shunned by the rural Pan, who chooses rather to foot it along the sheep track on the limitless downs or the thwart-leading footpath through copse and spinney, not without pleasant fellowship with feather and fir. Nor does it follow from all this that the god is unsocial. Albeit shy of the company of his more showy brother-deities, he loveth the more unpretentious humankind, especially them that are *adscripti glebæ,* addicted to the kindly soil and to the working thereof: perfect in no way, only simple, cheery sinners. For he is only half a god after all, and the red earth in him is strong. When the pelting storm drives the wayfarers to the sheltering inn, among the little group on bench and settle Pan has been known to appear at times, in homely guise of hedger-and-ditcher or weather-beaten shepherd from the downs. Strange lore and quaint fancy he will then impart, in the musical Wessex or Mercian he has learned to speak so naturally; though it may not be till many a mile away that you begin to suspect that you have unwittingly talked with him who chased the flying Syrinx in Arcady and turned the tide of fight at Marathon.

Yes: to-day the iron horse has searched the country through—east and west, north and south—bringing with it Commercialism, whose god is Jerry, and who studs the hills with stucco and garrotes the streams with the girder. Bringing, too, into every nook and corner fashion and chatter, the tailor-made gown and the eyeglass. Happily a great part is still spared—how great these others fortunately do not know—in which the rural Pan and his following may hide their heads for yet a little longer, until the growing tyranny has invaded the last common, spinney, and sheep-down, and driven the kindly god, the well-wisher to man—whither?

Acknowledgments

The making of an annotated edition of *The Wind in the Willows* has been an extraordinary process that has taken a decade, and involved an extended and ever-widening village of collaborators. It began as an exploration of Grahame's papers and manuscripts at the Bodleian Library in 1997 when I was at Oxford. During my time in England I couldn't get enough of the rivers surrounding that great academic cake of a city. My mornings were spent with Grahame in the Department of Western Manuscripts and my afternoons punting with friends. All of it was a great escape from a modern North American life inundated with daily commutes and highways dotted with corporate shopping malls and the kind of subdivisions that Grahame in his day referred to as "the dormitories to the city." My venture became a college honors thesis, and then a graduate thesis, and, mostly, became the means to the end of prolonging the time spent at Trinity College, Oxford, as a guest of the University of Massachusetts, Boston.

When I approached the children's literature historian Peter Hunt about the possibility of working on an annotated edition of *The Wind in the Willows* as a doctoral thesis at the University of Wales, Cardiff, his daunting reply was:

> You realise, of course, that doing an annotated "Willows" is roughly the literary equivalent of building the space shuttle single-handed. So,

> let me see the annotations you have thus far for chapters one and two or whatever, and I'll give you a fair estimate of your chances of not being demolished by the local scholars.

Luckily, I was not meant to return to the UK to study. England came to me in the form of Christopher Ricks and Geoffrey Hill's Editorial Institute at Boston University. I will be forever grateful that they took me on, letting me explore the topic of early illustrators and the history of Grahame's book itself. I also thank Julia Prewitt Brown for her beyond-excellent seminars on Charles Dickens and Jane Austen, and her devotion to Trilling's "explication of the text."

My time with Christopher Ricks led to strokes of luck in finding original sources. I am especially indebted to David J. Holmes, who has been generous with his collection of Grahame's papers. I thank the Holmes family: Sarah Holmes, Barbara Ware Holmes, and Steven Margulis. Roger Oakes has been generous in his advice on Grahame's manuscripts and editions, and he allowed us to print his photo of Graham Robertson with his Old English Sheepdog, Richard. The photos of Folly Bridge and the old sawmill in Golant are reprinted courtesy of Nigel McMorris and the Kenneth Grahame Society. Thanks go to David Paroissien for always offering a feast in information on Dickens; and devotion beyond all devotion goes to Elizabeth Mavor, who took me to Cookham Dean and all over southern England and who fed me, bought me books, and has remained a faithful pen pal for all these years. I thank Peter Hunt for supporting the idea of an annotated *Wind in the Willows*, and Peter Green, Grahame's biographer, who turned out to have retired in my hometown of Iowa City, Iowa. Ernest Hofer, at the University of Massachusetts, Amherst, for dreaming up the U. Mass. Seminar and keeping it running all these years. Fiona Robertson, Anthony Mellors, and Cora Mellors-Robertson for their warmth and support over the years, especially to Cora for her uncanny depth of knowledge on the nature of rodents. Clare Hopkins and the President and Fellows of Trinity College, Oxford, for permission to quote from their Quiller-Couch/Kenneth Grahame letters. Secretary of the University Chest Office at Oxford University for permission to quote from Kenneth Grahame's letters and manuscripts. And Trinity College, herself, for her incredible sanctuary. The Arthur Rackham illustrations are reproduced with the kind permission of his family and the Bridgeman Art Library.

The Harry Ransom Humanities Research Center at The University of Texas, Austin, where all of Peter Green's papers have been archived. Michael Patrick Hearn for his encouragement and depth of knowledge. Maria Tatar for her work on fairy tales. Michael Purves for sharing family stories about the Grahames and the Purveses in Fowey and Blewbury; and Edmund Spenser Purves for pointing out that his father and my grandfather were architectural colleagues over sixty years ago. Janie Yates for starting a junior repertory theater and once upon a time casting me as Mr. Toad. Thanks also to Betty Rosse and Helen Finken. From my Minneapolis Children's Theater era: Truda Stockenstrom and Adam Shankman—come find me: tag, you're it.

From the bottom of my heart I thank the English Department of the University of Massachusetts, Boston, which saw fit to send me to Oxford. Professor Mary Shaner, who steered the initial thesis when I fell under the spell of England. Without Mary, this project would never have begun. The following professors helped me greatly: Alan Helms, George and Loretta Slover, Monica McAlpine, Robert Crossley, Lloyd Schwartz (even though I still think poetry anthologies should include pop-up illustrations of Kubla Khan). Louise Smith, Taylor Stoehr, John Tobin, Duncan Nelson, Linda Dittmar, Pam Annas, Libby Fay, Paul Hayes Tucker, and Martha Collins for forever being an Iowan. James Higgins, Janet Michevich, and Joyce Morrissey, patron saints of the English major. Finally, I thank Jennie Butler and the family of Peter Brooks Butler. John Keller and Charlotte Sheedy, whose initial support helped me get to Oxford.

I thank my boating companions for my best afternoons of squandered time: Noemi Hollander, Julia Wahnsiedler, Allyson Casey, and, most recently, Jean Marie Connors.

I thank Patricia Davidson, dean of the School of Arts and Sciences at the University of Massachussetts. The Boston University Department of Arts and Humanities and the Children's Literature Association for their support with the Hannah Beiter Scholarship for graduate research. All three above-mentioned parties enabled me to return to Oxford in 2001. Librarians and libraries: Mary Margaret Pitt, Boston Public Library; Patricia Fox, Harry Ransom Humanities Research Center, Austin, Texas; Clive Hurst, Bodleian Library, Oxford; Houghton Library, Harvard; AnnaLee Pauls & Margaret M. Sherry, Rare Books & Special Collections, Princeton University Library;

research assistant Betsy Norris, University of Indiana, for combing through the fragile Methuen ledgers to determine the quantity of the first printing and those thereafter; Sue Presnell, reference associate; The Lilly Library, Bloomington, Indiana; the New York Public Library; and the local Turner Free Library of Randolph, Massachusetts. Other people who have helped along the way: Frances Whistler, Leslie S. Klinger. And Bill Behr, University of Massachusetts librarian extraordinaire. Thanks also to Kera Yonker at Oxford University Press. Professor Ian Hancock at The University of Texas, Austin, for advising me on Romani history, and Iona Opie for being Iona Opie. And Rachel Earnshaw, for putting me up in London and putting up with my enthusiasm.

Special kudos go to my editors, Robert Weil and especially Tom Mayer for his persistence and his excellent editorial sensibilities. His goodwill and patience with such a big project has made all the difference. I am indebted to Janet Byrne for her careful reading, rereading, and attention to detail, and also to Norton editorial assistant Denise Scarfi, for her help with the illustrations. This book would not have been possible without the heroic labors of the Norton team: Julia Druskin, Andy Marasia, Don Rifkin, Nancy Palmquist, Eleen Cheung, Sue Carlson, and Joe Lops. Ellen Geiger, my agent, for going the distance. I thank my family: William, Carole, David, and Mark Gauger, and Ann Goodenberger and Beth Roberts Gauger. I even thank the dogs, Lovey and Durga, for their insistence on daily jaunts in the local Wild Wood. And I thank my village, Phyllis and Gerry Pirkot, for the endless supply of Guinness and all beers English. Brad and Kari Metz for their deep pots and room at their table. The house of Finnell for sending lawn boys and a credentialed babysitter.

I recently had the good fortune to visit Fowey down in Cornwall. Special thanks go to Nigel McMorris, who not only started the Kenneth Grahame Society when there was none yet that he could join but then rented a bijou riverside residence in Fowey and invited us all to come stay. E. H. Shepard could not have drawn a more perfect place.

Thanks go to Lynn and Bernard Goold, who led us around their beloved Fowey, letting us in on her secrets and pleasures. The Daphne du Maurier Literary Centre, the Fowey Hotel, and further up the hill, the Fowey Hall Hotel—Toad Hall if ever there was one. Emily Williams, who joined us, and the one and only Peter Hunt, who has corresponded and advised me all these years. What ever would I do without you? Thanks to Ruth Taylor and Dennis Smith of Sawmills Studio, and Joan and Gordon Coombs, who made me feel welcome at the Royal Fowey Yacht Club. It was amazing to watch the boats race and capsize, the racers quickly uprighting themselves again as though they could walk on water, knowing full well Kenneth Grahame had stood there doing the same a century ago.

Mostly, I dedicate this work to my wife, Cynthia, and our daughter, Mackenzie Remarkable August Gauger, who have been my northern stars. Cynthia took on a second job as a security guard so that I could go to Oxford in 1997. Her dedication to the opportunity involved working seven days a week, taking in exchange students, and wearing a polyester uniform for two days out of seven. For our daughter—I take it as an auspicious sign that at the ripe age of one year, Mackenzie Remarkable's favorite song is "Row, Row, Row Your Boat." It is my deepest wish that we will explore England's rivers together when she is old enough.

An invitation to readers of *The Wind in the Willows* and devotees of Kenneth Grahame:

Peter Hunt was correct in observing that to annotate *The Wind in the Willows* would be like building a space shuttle with one hand, especially for a North American. I have done my best sorting through papers, texts, original sources, and the accretion of scholarship on Kenneth Grahame and his writing. Any omissions or errors are purely unintentional. Undoubtedly there is more to be added to (or perhaps deleted from) the notes. I'd like to open the door for more discussion. Certainly there are more sources out in the Wide World—more letters, photographs, and papers—waiting to come to light. After more information built up in his files, Martin Gardner published *More Annotated Alice* in 1992, thirty years after publishing the initial *Annotated Alice*. I invite readers to correspond with me, care of W. W. Norton, with the idea that an emended edition will be published some day. Perhaps I am incapable of letting go of a ten-year-old project, or maybe what I really want to do is to daily ponder that brown god—that sleek, sinuous, full-bodied animal. The river.

ANNIE GAUGER

Provincetown, August 2007

Bibliography

WORKS BY KENNETH GRAHAME

Christmas Trees. Compiled by Roger A. Oakes. North Newbald, York, England: Parrot Press, 1998.

Dream Days. London: John Lane, The Bodley Head, 1898.

The Golden Age. London: John Lane, The Bodley Head, 1895.

The Golden Age. Illustrated by R. J. Enraght-Moony. London: John Lane, The Bodley Head, 1915.

The Headswoman. 1898. Illustrated by Marcia Lane Foster. London: John Lane, The Bodley Head, 1921.

My Dearest Mouse. London: Pavilion Books, 1988.

Pagan Papers. Aubrey Beardsley illust. title page. London: John Lane, The Bodley Head, 1894.

The Wind in the Willows. London: Methuen & Co., 1908 and 1934.

The Wind in the Willows. Illustrated by Paul Bransom. New York: Charles Scribner's Sons, 1913.

The Wind in the Willows. Illustrated by Nancy Barnhart, 1922. New York: Charles Scribner's Sons, 1940.

The Wind in the Willows. Illustrated by Nancy Barnhart. London: Methuen, 1922.

The Wind in the Willows. Illustrated by Wyndham Payne, 1927. London: Methuen & Co, 1930.

The Wind in the Willows. Illustrated by Ernest H. Shepard. New York: Charles Scribner's Sons, 1933, 1953, and 1983.

The Wind in the Willows. Illustrated by Arthur Rackham. Introduction by A. A. Milne. New York: Heritage Press, 1940.

The Wind in the Willows. Illustrated by Michael Hague. New York: Holt, Rinehart & Winston, 1980.

The Wind in the Willows. Vol. I, The Wild Wood. Illustrated & Adapted by Michel Plessix. New York: Nantier, Beall, Minoustchine, 1997.

Grahame, Kenneth, ed. *Cambridge Book of Poetry for Children.* 1916. Illustrated by Gwen Raverat. Cambridge: Cambridge University Press, 1946.

OTHER SOURCES

Andrew, Martin: *Collins Rambler's Guide to the Chilterns & Ridgeway.* London: HarperCollins, 2001.

Archard, Charles. *The Portland Peerage Romance*. London: Greening & Co., Ltd, 1907.

Baum, L. Frank. *The Annotated Wizard of Oz.* Edited, with an introduction, by Michael Patrick Hearn. New York: Norton, 2000.

Beaumont, Cyril W. *The Mysterious Toyshop.* Illustrated by Wyndham Payne, 1924. New York: The Metropolitan Museum of Art / Holt, Rinehart & Winston, 1984.

———. *Sea Magic.* Illustrated by Wyndham Payne. London: John Lane, The Bodley Head Ltd., 1928.

Blackwood, Algernon. *Pan's Garden.* 1912. Illustrated by W. Graham Robertson. London: Macmillan & Co., 1914.

Blatchford, Robert: *Merrie England*. London: Clarion Newspaper Co., 1894.

Borrow, George. *Lavengro.* 1851. Boston: Houghton Mifflin Company, 1926.

———. *Romany Rye.* New York: Harper & Brothers, 1857.

Brown, Curtis. *Contacts.* New York: Charles Scribner's Sons, 1934.

Butcher, S. H., and A. Lang, trans. *The Odyssey*. New York: P. F. Collier and Son, 1900–1914.

Byrne, Eleanor, and Martin McQuillan. *Deconstructing Disney.* London and Sterling, Virginia: Pluto Press, 2000.

Carpenter, Humphrey. *Secret Gardens.* Boston: Houghton Mifflin, 1985.

Carpenter, Humphrey, and Marie Pritchard. *Oxford Companion to Children's Literature.* Oxford and New York: Oxford University Press, 1983.

Chalmers, Patrick R. *Kenneth Grahame.* First edition, signed by author. Frontispiece by W. Graham Robertson. London: Methuen, 1933.

Cook, Theodore Andrea. *The Fourth Olympiad, Being the Official Report, The Olympic Games of 1908, Celebrated in London.* London: The British Olympic Association, 1909.

Coombs, Joan. *The History of the Royal Fowey Yacht Club*. Fowey, UK: R.F.Y.C. Books, 2000.

Corvo, Frederic Baron. *In His Own Image*. London: John Lane, 1901.

———. *Stories Toto Told Me*. London: John Lane, 1898.

Deforest, Mary. "The Wind in the Willows: A Tale for Two Readers." *Classical and Modern Literature* 10, no. 1 (1989): 303–23.

Dickens, Charles. *Bleak House*. 1852. Edited by George Ford & Sylvère Monod. New York: Norton Critical Editions, 1977.

———. *A Christmas Carol*. London: Chapman & Hall, 1843. Doubleday, Doran & Co, 1928.

———. *David Copperfield.* 1851. Edited by Jerome Buckley. New York: Norton Critical Editions, 1990.

———. *Oliver Twist; or the Parish Boy's Progress.* Illustrated by George Cruikshank. London, 1846.

Doyle, Arthur Conan. *The Complete Adventures and Memoirs of Sherlock Holmes: A Facsimile of the original* STRAND MAGAZINE *stories, 1891–1893.* Illustrated by Sidney Paget. New York: Bramhall House, 1975.

Duffy, Maureen. *A Thousand Capricious Chances: 100 Years of the Methuen List, 1889–1989.* London: Methuen, 1989.

Dyer, Christopher C. *Everyday Life in Medieval England.* London: Hambledon & London, 2000.

Fielding, Henry. *An Enquiry into the Causes of the Late Increase of Robbers and Related Writings.* Edited by Malvin R. Zirker. Middletown, CT: Wesleyan University Press, 1988.

Foreman-Peck, James, Sue Bowden, and Alan McKinlay. *The British Motor Industry*. Manchester: Manchester University Press, 1995.

Forster, E. M. *The Celestial Omnibus, and Other Stories.* London: Sidgwick & Jackson, 1911.

Frost, Robert. *A Boy's Will.* New York: Henry Holt & Co., 1915.

Fussell, Paul. *Class: A Guide Through the American Status System.* New York: Simon & Schuster, 1983.

Gasper, Giles G. M. "Kenneth Grahame's *Wind in the Willows* and William Morris's Old Norse Translations." *Oxford Journals, Notes and Queries* (50: 323–24).

Gillin, Richard. "Romantic Echoes in the Willows." *Children's Literature* 16 (1988): 169–74.

Gladwin, D. D. *A Pictorial History of Canals*. London: B. T. Batsford, 1977.

Graham, Eleanor. *Kenneth Grahame: A Walck Monograph.* New York: Henry Z. Walck, 1963.

Grahame, Elspeth. *First Whispers of "The Wind in the Willows."* Philadelphia: Lippincott, 1944.

Grahame, Georgina. *In a Tuscan Garden.* 1902. London: John Lane, The Bodley Head, 1911.

Grahame, Kenneth. *First Whisper of "The Wind in the Willows."* Edited, with an introduction, by Elspeth Grahame. Philadelphia and New York: J. B. Lippincott Co., 1945.

Green, Peter. *Beyond the Wild Wood: The World of Kenneth Grahame*. New York: Webb & Bower, 1982.

———. *Kenneth Grahame: A Biography.* Cleveland: World Publishing, 1959.

Grossmith, George, and Weedon Grossmith. *The Diary of a Nobody.* Bristol: J. W. Arrowsmith, 1892.

Haining, Peter. *Paths to the Riverbank*. London: Souvenir Press, 1983.

Hancock, Ian. *We Are the Romani People.* Hatfield, UK: University of Hertfordshire Press, 2002.

Hanson, Harry. *The Canal Boatmen, 1760–1914*. Manchester: Manchester University Press, 1975

Harris, Joel Chandler. *The Complete Tales of Uncle Remus.* 1888. Boston: Houghton Mifflin & Co., 2002.

Harvey, John. *Victorian Novelists and Their Illustrators.* New York: New York University Press, 1971.

Head, F. B. *Stokers and Pokers; or, the London and North-Western Railway*: New York: Augustus M. Kelley, 1969.

Hearn, Michael Patrick. "Arthur Rackham's Adventures in Wonderland," from *Lewis Carroll Observed*, ed. Edward Guliano. New York: Clarkson Potter, 1976.

Heath, Jeffrey M. *The Picturesque Prison: Evelyn Waugh and His Writing.* McGill-Queen's University Press, 1982.

Hibbert, Christopher. *Garibaldi and His Enemies*. New York: Signet Classics, 1970.

Higgins, Patrick, Maura Kate Kilgore, and Paul Hertlein. *The Homebrewer's Recipe Guide.* New York: Fireside / Simon & Schuster, 1996.

Hollander, Anne. *Sex and Suits: The Evolution of Modern Dress.* New York: Kodansha International, 1994.

Homer. *The Odyssey*. Translated by S. H. Butcher and A. Lang. New York: P. F. Collier, 1909–1914.

———. *The Odyssey.* Translated by Robert Fitzgerald. Garden City, NY: Doubleday & Co., 1961.

Horn, Maurice. *World Encyclopedia of Cartoons.* New York: Chelsea House, 1980.

Houfe, Simon. *The Dictionary of British Book Illustration & Caricaturists, 1800–1914*. Suffolk, UK: Baron Publishing, 1978.

Hudson, Derek. *Arthur Rackham: His Life and Work.* New York: Charles Scribner's Sons, 1960.

Hughes, Thomas. *The Scouring of the White Horse; or, The Long Vacation Ramble of a London Clerk.* Illustrated by Richard Doyle. Cambridge: Macmillan & Co., 1859.

Hunt, Peter. *Children's Literature: An Illustrated History.* Oxford and New York: Oxford University Press, 1995.

———. "Dialogue and Dialectic: Language and Class in the Wind in the Willows." *Children's Literature* 16 (1988): 159–68.

———. *The Wind in the Willows: A Fragmented Arcadia.* New York: Twayne Publishers, 1994.

Hyman, Alan. *The Rise and Fall of Horatio Bottomley: The Biography of a Swindler*. London: Cassell and Co., Ltd, 1972.

Jeffries, Richard. *Amaryllis at the Fair.* 1887. London: Duckworth & Co, 1908.

———. *Bevis: the Story of a Boy.* 1882. Illustrated by Ernest H. Shepard. London: Jonathan Cape, 1932.

———. *Nature Near London.* New York: Thomas Y. Crowell & Co., 1907.

———. *The Open Air.* London: J. M. Dent & Sons, n.d.

———. *The Story of My Heart—My Autobiography.* London: Longmans, 1883.

———. *Wood Magic: A Fable.* 1881. London: Longmans Green and Co. 1934.

Jerome, Jerome K. *Idle Thoughts of an Idle Fellow.* New York and Boston: H. M. Caldwell Co., 1890.

———. *Three Men in a Boat; To Say Nothing of the Dog.* Bristol: J. W. Arrowsmith, 1889.

Johnson, Clifton. *Among English Hedgerows.* 1899. New York: Macmillan & Co., 1925.

Kipling, Rudyard. *Many Inventions.* 1893. Garden City, NY: Doubleday, Page & Co., 1923.

Klinefelter, Walter. *Sherlock Holmes in Portrait and Profile.* Syracuse, NY: Syracuse University Press, 1963.

Knox, Rawle. *The Works of E. H. Shepard.* New York: Schocken Books, 1980.

Kuznets, Lois R. *Kenneth Grahame.* Boston: Twayne Publishers, 1987.

———. "Toad Hall Revisited." *Children's Literature* 7 (1978): 115–28.

Lewis, C. S. "On Three Ways of Writing for Children," in *Only Connect: Readings on Children's Literature.* Edited by S. Egoff et al. Toronto: Oxford University Press, 1980.

Linder, Leslie. A History of the Writings of Beatrix Potter. London: Frederick Warne & Co., Ltd, 1971, 175. London: Longmans, Green and Co. 1911.

London, Jack. *The Call of the Wild.* 1903. Illustrated by Paul Bransom, 1912. New York: Macmillan, 1931.

Lowes, John Livingston. *The Road to Xanadu: A Study in the Ways of the Imagination.* Boston: Houghton Mifflin, 1927.

Mahony, Bertha. *Illustrators of Children's Books, 1744–1945*. Boston: The Horn Book, Inc., 1947.

Marolles, Michel de. *Tableaux du Temple des Muses.* Paris: 1655.

McCracken, Harold. *The Last of the Sea Otters.* Illustrated by Paul Bransom. Philadelphia: Frederick A. Stokes Company, 1942.

McGuckin, Mildred. *Little Cabbages.* Illustrated by Nancy Barnhart. Garden City, NY: Doubleday, Doran & Co., 1928.

Meyer, Susan. *A Treasury of the Great Children's Book Illustrators.* New York: Harry N. Abrams, Inc., 1983.

Michelin Guide to the British Isles. London, 1911.

Milne, A. A. *Toad of Toad Hall.* London: Methuen, 1929.

———. *The World of Pooh: The Complete Winnie the Pooh and The House at Pooh Corner.* Illustrated by E. H. Shepard, 1926. New York: Dutton Children's Books, 2003.

Munro, H. H. *The Complete Works of Saki.* 1912. Garden City, NY: Doubleday & Co., 1976.

Murphy, Thos. D. *British Highways and Byways from a Motor Car.* Boston: L. C. Page & Co., 1908

———. *In Unfamiliar England with a Motor Car.* Boston: L. C. Page & Co., 1910.

Opie, Iona, Robert Opie, and Brian Alderson. *The Treasures of Childhood: Books, Toys, and Games from the Opie Collection.* New York: Little, Brown & Company, 1989.

Onions, C. T. *A Shakespeare Glossary*. Oxford: Clarendon Press, 1911.

Paternoster, Sidney G. *The Cruise of the Motor-Boat Conqueror, Being the Further Adventures of the Motor Pirate*. Boston: L. C. Page & Company, 1906.

———. *The Lady of the Blue Motor.* New York: Grosset & Dunlap, 1907.

———. *The Motor Pirate.* New York: A. Wessels Company, 1906.

Patey, Douglas Lane. *The Life of Evelyn Waugh: A Critical Biography.* Oxford: Blackwell Publishing, 1998.

Philpotts, Trey. *The Dickens Companions. Vol. 9: Companion to Little Dorrit.* East Sussex: Helm Information Ltd., 2003.

Pitz, Henry. *Illustrating Children's Books.* New York: Watson-Guptill Publications, 1963.

Poss, Geraldine. "An Epic in Arcadia: The Pastoral World of the *Wind in the Willows.*" *Children's Literature* 4 (1975): 80–90.

Potter, Beatrix. *The Complete Tales.* 1902–1930. London: Penguin, 2002.

Prince, Alison. *Kenneth Grahame: An Innocent in the Wild Wood.* London: Allison & Busby, 1994.

Quayle, Eric. *The Collector's Book of Children's Books.* New York: Clarkson N. Potter, 1982.

Quiller-Couch, Arthur. *From a Cornish Window.* Bristol, UK: Arrowsmith, 1906.

Ramsey, L. G. G., ed. *The Complete Color Encyclopedia of Antiques.* London. New York: Hawthorn Books, 1962.

Richards, Jeffrey, and John Mackenzie. *The Railway Station: A Social History.* Oxford: Oxford University Press, 1986.

Richardson, Kenneth: *The British Motor Industry, 1986–1939*. London: Macmillan, 1977.

Robertson, W. Graham. *The baby's day book for a woman of four.* London: John Lane, The Bodley Head, 1908.

———. *Letters from Graham Robertson.* Edited by Kerrison Preston. London: Hamish Hamilton, 1953.

———. *Pinkie and the Fairies.* London: William Heinemann, 1909.

———. *Time Was.* London: Hamish Hamilton, 1931.

———. *A Year of Songs for a Baby in a Garden.* London: John Lane, The Bodley Head, 1906.

Roth, Cecil. *History of the Jews in England.* Oxford: Oxford University Press, 1941.

Rowling, J. K. *Harry Potter and the Prisoner of Azkaban*. New York: Arthur A. Levine Books, 1999.

Sackville-West, Vita. *English Country Houses.* London: Collins, 1947.

Sanger, George. *Seventy Years a Showman.* Introduction by Kenneth Grahame. London: J. M. Dent and Sons, 1926.

Schlobin, Roger C. "Danger and Compulsion in *The Wind in the Willows:* Or, Toad and Hyde Together At Last." *Journal of the Fantastic in the Arts* 8, no. 1 (1997): 34–41.

Scott-Moncrief, D. *Veteran and Edwardian Motor Cars.* London: B. T. Batsford Ltd, 1955.

Shepard, Ernest H. *Drawn from Memory.* London: Methuen, 1957.

Simpson, William Kelly, ed. *The Literature of Ancient Egypt: An Anthology of Stories, Instructions, Stelae, Autobiographies, and Poetry*. New Haven: Yale University Press, 1972.

Sims, George. *More of the Rare Book Game.* Philadelphia: Holmes Publishing, 1988.

Skene-Melvin, David. "A Study in Literary Influence." *Sherlock Holmes Journal* 6, no. 1 (Winter 1962): 16–17.

Smally, George Washburn, and Thomas Haysweet Escott. *Society in the New Reign*. London: T. F. Unwin, 1904.

Smedley, Constance. *An April Princess.* New York: Dodd, Mead & Company, 1903.

———. *Crusaders: Reminiscences of Constance Smedley.* London: Duckworth, 1929.

———. *Magnolia Lady.* London: Hurst & Blackett, Ltd, n.d.

Smedley, Constance, contributor. *The Case for Women's Suffrage*. Edited by Brougham Villiers. London: T. Fisher Unwin, 1907.

Snell, K. D. M. *Annals of the Labouring Poor: Social Change and Agrarian England, 1660–1900.* Cambridge: Cambridge University Press, 1995.

Steig, Michael. "At the Back of the Wind in the Willows: An Experiment in Biographical and Autobiographical Interpretation." *Victorian Studies* 24, no. 3 (Spring 1981): 322 n. 27).

Stevenson, Robert Louis. *An Inland Voyage*. London: C. Kegan Paul & Co., 1874.

Sturluson, Snorri. *Heimskringla; or, The Chronicle of the Kings of Norway.* "Saga of Sigurd the Crusader and His Brothers Eystein and Olaf." Translated by Samuel Laing. London, 1844.

Trevelyan, George Macaulay. *Garibaldi and the Making of Italy, June–November 1860.* London: Longmans, Green and Co., 1911.

Tucker, Paul Hayes. *Monet in the 20th Century.* New Haven and London: Yale University Press, 1998.

———. *Claude Monet: Life and Art.* New Haven and London: Yale University Press, 1995.

Thwaite, Ann. *A. A. Milne: The Man Behind Winnie-the-Pooh.* New York: Random House, 1990.

Vine, P. A. L. *London's Lost Route to the Sea.* London: David & Charles, 1965.

Ward-Jackson, C. H., and Denis E. Harvey, *The English Gypsy Caravan*. New York: Drake Publishers, Inc., 1973.

Wells, Robert. *The Bread and Biscuit Baker's and Sugar-Boiler's Assistant*. London: Crosby Lockwood and Son, 1890.

Wilde, Oscar. *The Ballad of Reading Gaol, and Other Poems.* London: Heron Books, n.d.

———. *De Profundis.* Preface by Richard Ellmann and W. H. Auden. New York: Random House, 2000.

———. *The Happy Prince*. London: David Nutt, 1888.

Williamson, C. N., and A. M. *My Friend the Chauffeur.* New York: A. L. Burt & Co., 1905.

Willis, Lesley. "A Sadder and a Wiser Rat/He Rose the Morrow Morn: Echoes of the Romantics in Kenneth Grahame's *The Wind in the Willows.*" *Children's Literature* 13 (1988): 108–111.

Willis, Mrs. F. M. *Colonel John Whitehead Peard: "Garibaldi's Englishman."* Pendeen, Par Green, Par, Cornwall, UK, 1957.

Wordsworth, William. *The Complete Poetical Works*. London: Macmillan, 1888.

Wright, David, trans. *Beowulf.* New York: Penguin Books, 1957.

Wullschlager, Jackie. *Inventing Wonderland.* New York: Free Press, 1995.